The Mystery of Matter

CONTRIBUTORS:

Theodore A. Ashford	Antony Van Leeuwenhoek
Isaac Asimov	Lucretius
Francis Bacon	Brian Mason
Carl L. Becker	Gregor Mendel
Henri Bergson	Dmitri Mendeléeff
Jacob Bronowski	Walter M. Miller, Jr.
Robert M. Coates	Ruth Moore
Arthur H. Compton	Hans J. Morgenthau
James Conant	Philip Morrison
Marie Curie	H. J. Muller
John Dalton	Guy Murchie
Farrington Daniels	Ogden Nash
Tobias Dantzig	A. I. Oparin
René Dubos	Michael Ovenden
Albert Einstein	Linus Pauling
Loren Eiseley	Henri Poincaré
Earl A. Evans, Jr.	Alexander Pope
Thomas F. Farrell	Eugene Rabinowitch
George Gamow	Alfred Romer
George W. Gray	Erwin Schrödinger
John Scott Haldane	George Gaylord Simpson
Garrett Hardin	Phylis Singer
Selig Hecht	Edmund W. Sinnott
Werner Heisenberg	Huston Smith
Alan Holden	Steven M. Spencer
Gerald Holton	Edward Teller
Julian Huxley	George Wald
Leopold Infeld	Victor Weisskopf
James Jeans	G. P. Wells
Joseph Wood Krutch	H. G. Wells
Albert Latter	Hermann Weyl

THE
MYSTERY
OF MATTER

Prepared by AMERICAN FOUNDATION
FOR CONTINUING EDUCATION

Edited by LOUISE B. YOUNG

New York
OXFORD UNIVERSITY PRESS   1965

The Mystery of Matter is designed to provide a background for under-standing the problems and implications of the atomic age. Through the original writings of many famous scientists it traces the development of the physical concepts which led to the discovery of atomic energy and the structure of living matter. By combining these two aspects of scientific research into one volume it emphasizes the unity of the living and non-living aspects of the physical world. A sense of this unity is important in considering the human implications of the use of atomic energy and in discussing such vital current issues as the effect of atomic testing on the genetic constitution of man.

This volume is the outgrowth of several years of research and experi-mentation by the American Foundation for Continuing Education. Work was started in 1960 under a grant from the National Science Foundation on the design and testing of a study-discussion program in science to assist the concerned adult to develop a deeper understanding of science as the basis for sound judgments on public policy.

The years of work which we have devoted to the preparation of our science program have deepened our concern about citizen understanding of science. The lack of scientific literacy among otherwise well-informed laymen is one of the most critical problems confronting education in the United States today.

Our concern is a concern for democracy itself because the lack of understanding of science raises in dramatic form a number of unsettling questions. It poses the issue of the proper relationship between laymen and experts; it compels us to consider the adequacy of the decision-making process in a free society; and it challenges us to justify, in terms that meet the demands of the modern world, the basic right of the people to govern themselves. In the past this right has been made operative by the conviction that well-informed and thoughtful men are competent to do so; that the citizen can in fact understand issues, evaluate con-flicting opinions, and make intelligent decisions on matters of public policy. In our time, when public policy has become increasingly inter-meshed with science and hurtled forward by the accelerating rate of scientific discovery, unless the lay citizen develops an adequate under-standing of the nature of science and of the limits of scientific expertise, he becomes less able to understand a growing number of the most sig-nificant public policy issues and less competent to make sound judgments about them. In the most fundamental sense this science program is an attempt to ensure that the thoughtful citizen will not become an anachro-nism, that his thoughtfulness will be relevant to the demands of the modern world.

The long-range program which has grown out of these years of research consists of several collections of readings covering different areas of sci-ence. The first book, *Exploring the Universe,* published in 1962, was de-signed to provide the layman with a background of understanding of the principles on which the Space Age has been built, to give him a glimpse of the mystery and the majesty of the universe which man has begun to explore and, above all, to suggest the methods and nature of the search itself. *Exploring the Universe* was used as the basis for a series of shows by the same name prepared by National Educational Television and shown over the educational channels during 1962.

The readings in this second book, *The Mystery of Matter,* deal with the very smallest features of our physical world and show how scientific con-cepts were developed to account for the nature of both living and non-living matter. In addition to providing a background for the atomic age, it examines some of the philosophical implications of man's investigation of the nature of matter, such as the rise of materialism and new non-mechanical aspects of reality which are beginning to emerge from modern physics.

A third book of readings is now in preparation. *The Evolution of Man* will focus on the nature of man and his role in the evolutionary process. Its special emphasis will be on the issue of human control in eugenics, population growth, and ecology.

These various books are planned to complement each other and can most profitably be read together. However, each individual book is also designed to stand alone. In several important ways these books represent an unusual approach to the problem of appreciating and understanding science. First, by showing historically how scientific ideas develop rather than by simply explaining the present state of scientific knowledge, these selections assist the reader to gain insight into how science works, under what conditions important advances are made, and why scientific theories change from time to time. Second, from the original writings of many different scientists, the reader learns, in the scientists' own words, the ways in which they pursue their visions and the attitudes they have toward science. It is our hope that by following the scientist into his realm the reader will learn not only something scientific, but something of science and will sense the qualities that give science its place in today's world. Third, unlike the usual textbooks or expositions of science, there are many questions asked in these readings which are not answered. In several, different points of view are presented with no editorial decision made about which is the right point of view. The reader is never told what to think. The aim of these readings is to stimulate thought about some of the basic issues raised and to examine the different arguments about these issues. Confronted by differences in views, the reader will be encouraged to think through his own ideas and to deepen his understanding of the part science plays in his world.

The readings in each book are divided into eleven parts. Generally, the first articles in each part are descriptive and expository of a scientific concept. The articles toward the end of a part turn to an exploration of the human response or the religious, philosophical, and social aspects of the science material. As the articles in each part are selected to complement one another and are arranged to bring into focus a fundamental aspect of science, they should be read in the order in which they appear. Many of the selections have been excerpted. Titles have sometimes been changed to indicate more clearly the nature of the selection's function in this book. In some cases footnotes and illustrations have been omitted because in this context they do not contribute to the central issue; editorial notes and illustrations have been added where they were deemed useful. References to illustrations are enclosed either by parentheses or by brackets. References enclosed in parentheses indicate figures based on illustrational concepts of the author of the article; square brackets are used for references to illustrations in other articles and for illustrations that have been added by the editors for clarification. We have included an index of subjects and authors and a glossary of scientific terms that appear in the readings. This glossary contains definitions and equations, as well as additional information on some of the terms that appear in the text. At the end of each group of readings, questions are suggested for consideration, and a list of appropriate readings will help the layman to continue his own education in this very important field of human endeavor. You will see that a few of the books are mentioned frequently throughout the reading lists. You may wish to purchase these books, for they will serve as valuable supplementary material. The titles listed are just a sample of the many fine science books available for the layman, and more are being published each month. Consult your local librarian and bookstore for other suggestions of good books on these subjects.

As with other programs which the AFCE has prepared and published, we do not represent or support any particular viewpoint with respect to the public policy questions or the philosophical, religious, or social issues contained in these readings. The AFCE is a not-for-profit educational organization devoted to the development of study programs in the liberal disciplines for adults concerned with their own continuing education.

We are grateful to the many scientists and educators throughout the country who assisted us in developing the idea of a study-discussion program in science. Whereas final responsibility for the selections in this volume rests with the editor, we should especially like to thank Dr. Earl Evans, Professor of Biochemistry, University of Chicago; Dr. Joseph Kaplan, Professor of Physics, University of California at Los Angeles; and Dr. Irving Klotz, Professor of Chemistry, Northwestern University.

TABLE OF CONTENTS

1

Can Matter Be Measured?

The great simplifying assumption that there is a fundamental substance, a matter, underlying the apparent
variety of nature led to the search to identify, measure,
and define this matter in precise scientific terms. The
nature of matter still eludes us but the search for it has
revealed many of its properties and has led to a realization of the limitations inherent in the process of measurement itself.

Can Matter Be Measured?

The Editor

Introduction

EVERYONE FEELS that he knows intuitively what matter is. It is the "stuff" of the world, the common denominator in all the things we can see and feel in our natural environment. And yet this idea which we think we perceive intuitively is actually quite a sophisticated concept, developed over centuries of thought, study, and experimentation. The natural world of our experience is made up of an almost infinite variety of forms, shapes, colors, and textures. Matter can be as massive and enduring as the rock formations of the earth.

Figure 1–1. Monolith—The Face of "Half Dome." (Photograph by Ansel Adams. From The Eloquent Light *by Nancy Newhall. Copyright 1963, Sierra Club, San Francisco. Reprinted by permission.)*

3

It can be as fragile and evanescent as raindrops.

Figure 1–2. "Raindrops." (Photograph by Edward Steichen. Collection of The Museum of Modern Art, New York. Reprinted by permission.)

Or it can be as intricately patterned as a living plant.

Figure 1–3. "Frost on Rambler Roses." (Photograph by Edward Steichen. Collection of The Museum of Modern Art, New York. Reprinted by permission.)

The assumption that external forms are transitory, that there is a common substratum beneath the incredible variety of physical things, this assumption requires an enormous leap of the imagination.

Figure 1–4. "Walden Pond." (Photograph by Edward Steichen. Collection of The Museum of Modern Art, New York. Reprinted by permission.)

The idea that air and sand, water and stone could be different forms of the same fundamental substance was first suggested by Thales of Miletus six centuries before Christ. "All things are made of water," he said, thus expressing the belief in an underlying unity and simplicity in nature.

Since that time the search has gone on to identify and define the mother substance, the matter, from *mater* meaning *mother* in Latin. The search has taken scientists into fantastically small worlds which cannot be seen even with the most refined modern instruments but can only be imagined and calculated.

Instead of simplicity, scientists have found complexity; instead of a single fundamental substance, they have found a large number of fundamental forms; and yet the faith that there is some kind of common denominator in the apparent variety of nature has not wavered. In the course of the search, a vast amount of information has been gathered about the nature of matter. Scientists have taken it apart, piece by piece, and have learned to put it together again into entirely new arrangements. They have discovered many unexpected and useful properties. They have tapped some of its energy. Nevertheless, the exact nature of matter itself still eludes us. As the frontiers of knowledge are pushed back, there is an ever receding horizon and the central concept remains to this day a vague, speculative idea which is difficult to define in any precise terms.

If you go to a dictionary or an encyclopedia you will find definitions like this: "Matter is the substance out of which a physical object is composed . . ." [1] or "Matter is the substance comprising bodies perceptible to the senses . . ." [2] Do these definitions define in the sense of distinguishing clearly between what is matter and what is not matter? Sunlight can be seen and felt. Is it made of matter? Is music a thing, or something that happens to things? We can see an electric spark and feel an electric shock. Is electricity a material thing? How about a magnetic field? How about gravitation?

Scientific definitions are usually expressed in terms of some property which can be measured. In this way, scientists avoid confusion about the meaning of words. Measurement is an objective procedure which can be repeated and checked by other scientists. Measurement is also a means of establishing mathematical relationships between phenomena and these relationships can be used to formulate physical laws.

"When you can measure a thing and express it by a number, then you know something of your subject." This observation, attributed to Lord Kelvin, expresses the belief in the value of measurement which is fundamental to all the physical sciences. Over the years, measurement has proven to be one of the most powerful means for gaining knowledge about the physical world. Kepler anticipated the success of this method when he said: "To measure is to know."

Using the principle of measurement, physics defines matter in terms of the property called *mass*. Mass is measured by weighing the object or by finding the amount of effort required to produce a given change in its motion.[3] Matter is defined as *that which has mass when it is at rest.*

1. *Webster's Third New International Dictionary*, G. & C. Merriam Co., 1961.
2. *McGraw-Hill Encyclopedia of Science and Technology*, McGraw-Hill Book Co., Inc., New York, 1960.
3. See Glossary for a discussion of *gravitational* and *inertial mass*. Ed.

This definition does not explain what matter is but it does give us a way of measuring how much of it there is. It also draws a clear distinction between matter and non-matter. Perhaps this is what Bertrand Russell meant when he said that matter is merely "what satisfies the equations of physics."

Traditionally, the physical sciences have been largely concerned with the aspects of nature which can be measured. In the biological sciences, the subject matter has been less amenable to measurement. However, this distinction is becoming decreasingly true as new advances are made in the chemistry and physics of living things. The questions we are going to consider in these readings cut across the physical and biological sciences to inquire into the very smallest units of both living and non-living matter. In these ultramicroscopic realms the limitations of the process of measurement become significant and many of the questions that are raised have to do with the nature of measurement itself.

What is the fundamental process involved in any measuring operation?

Suppose you mark two points on this page and measure the distance between them with a ruler. You are measuring the separation between two objects by comparing this distance with a fixed standard length.

Early standards of measurement which were devised were not very precise. In Egypt a mouthful was used as a unit of liquid measure. In England the yard was defined by royal decree as the distance from Henry I's nose to the end of his thumb. But as civilization became more complex, the need for accuracy increased, and more reliable measuring devices were invented.

Today standard lengths and weights have been precisely established by mutual agreement and are maintained under accurately controlled conditions of temperature and pressure. However, it is worth bearing in mind that no matter how much the degree of accuracy is improved, all measurement is still just a way of comparing an unknown relationship with a known standard relationship. If we say that A is twice as long as B it is obvious that we have made a comparative statement; but when we say A is 62.544 inches long, have we made an absolute statement or a comparative one?

On the subject of accuracy, it is important to understand that most measurements cannot be made with perfect precision—the degree of inaccuracy (or margin of error, as it is sometimes called) is determined by a number of factors such as the nature of the material to be measured and the limitations of the measuring and recording devices. The only exception to this statement is the case in which identical, indivisible units are concerned and simple counting techniques can be used. For instance, we can determine with absolute accuracy the number of pennies in a child's bank but we can never know with absolute accuracy the size of the bank that contains them.

The relationship between the size of the measure used and the size of the object to be measured is an important factor in the accuracy that can be obtained. It would be difficult, as well as time consuming, to obtain a reasonably accurate measure of a mile with a six-inch ruler and it would be impossible to use that same ruler to measure the thickness of this piece of paper. To measure effectively, a ruler must have divisions much smaller than the distance to be determined. As we shall see later, this requirement imposes a lower limit on our powers of measurement. How can a measuring stick be made that will measure the smallest, ultimate particles of matter?

There is a well-known story about Galileo, which, as George Gamow tells us, may be more colorful than true: "It all started one day when young Galileo was attending a Mass in the Cathedral of Pisa, and absent-mindedly watched a candelabrum swinging to and fro after an attendant had pulled it to the side to light the candles (Figure 1–5). Galileo noticed that although the successive swings became smaller and smaller as the candelabrum came to rest, the time of each swing (oscillation period) remained the same. Returning home, he decided to check this casual observation by using a stone suspended on a string and measuring the swing period by counting his own pulse. Yes, he was right; the period remained almost the same while the swings became shorter and shorter. . . ." [4]

A sceptic might point out here that Galileo had only shown that the periods timed out equally with the beats of his pulse. If he had become more and more excited and his pulse had beat faster as the periods were actually becoming progressively shorter, the result would have been the same. However, since Galileo's time this measurement has been checked against many other pulses and timing devices and it seems highly improbable that they would all be varying in exactly the same manner. Therefore it is generally accepted that Galileo's pulse was regular in making this experiment, that the period of swings was constant, and it is on this theory that our clocks are based. Today we have clocks that are controlled by the frequency of an alternating electric current, stabilized by the natural vibration rate of quartz crystals and are accurate to three parts in a billion; but the principle involved is the same as Galileo's pulse. Notice that here again we are making a comparative observation between the phenomena to be studied and a standard relationship. Einstein says, "We understand

---

4. From George Gamow, *Gravity*. Copyright © 1962 by Educational Services, Inc. (Science Study Series). Reprinted by permission of Doubleday & Co., Inc.

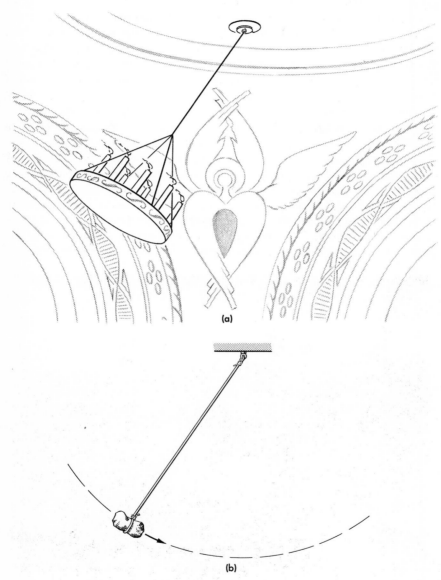

(a)

(b)

Figure 1–5. (After George Gamow, Gravity, Doubleday & Co., Inc., Garden City, New York. Copyright © 1962 by Educational Services, Inc., Science Study Series. Reprinted by permission.)

by a clock something which provides a series of events which can be counted." Aristotle almost two thousand years earlier had said much the same thing: "Time is the number of motion."

It was Einstein who injected the first serious doubts into our concepts of measurement. He did this by asking essentially the same question that we asked in connection with Galileo's pulse—how do we know that our fixed standards really do remain the same? Does the spacing of a ruler always stay constant? Does time slow down on a rapidly moving body? Does the mass of a standard gram always remain the same? Some of the answers to these questions have made our traditional concepts of space and time seem as flabby and unreliable as Salvador Dali's watches (Figure 1–6). If measurement is comparison with a fixed standard and if the standard itself does not remain fixed, then what does measurement mean?

It is true, of course, that the deviations from regularity are predictable and only occur (as far as we know) under conditions which can be regulated (like changes in temperature and pressure) or under extreme conditions (like speeds approaching the speed of light). Scientific measurements are being made every day with astonishing precision. Nevertheless, the problems inherent in the process of measurement remain and as scientists

Figure 1–6. "The Persistence of Memory" (1931), by Salvador Dali. (Oil on canvas, 9½" x 13". Collection of The Museum of Modern Art, New York. Reprinted by permission.)

explore more and more extreme realms of speed and size these problems become increasingly significant.

Furthermore, in their search for the ultimate substance of the physical world, scientists are beginning to feel somewhat like Winnie-the-Pooh looking for his friend Piglet—the more they looked, the more it wasn't there. Ironically, scientists are beginning to believe that form may be more fundamental than substance, after all, and that the common denominator of all things is not "that which has mass when it is at rest." The new idea, as Schrödinger puts it, is that what is permanent in the ultimate particles of matter is their shape and organization. They appear to be pure shape without any material substratum.[5] These discoveries pose new questions: Can anything as abstract as shape or organization be weighed or measured? Can it be compared with any known standard? Is there still a meaning to the concept of a fundamental substance? In the selections which follow, we will see how scientists are grappling with these questions in their continuing effort to identify and define a common denominator in the things we see and feel in the world about us, and to reveal an underlying order and unity in nature.

5. These ideas are explained in more detail in the Schrödinger selection beginning on p. 121. Ed.

Questions To Consider

How does measurement help to define a concept?

What is meant by the relativity of measurement?

If measurement is relative can it also be objective?

Why do all measurements (except counting) contain a margin of error?

Can matter be measured?

Suggestions for Further Reading

Bitter, Francis: *Mathematical Aspects of Physics: An Introduction,* Anchor Books, Doubleday & Co., Inc., 1963. This book introduces the reader to the methods used in the physical sciences to uncover the mathematical patterns of nature. This Science Study Series book requires a knowledge of high school mathematics.

Matter and *Mathematics,* Life Nature Library, Time, Inc., New York, 1963. Written for the general public and very well illustrated. These books will add to your understanding of the nature of matter and the mathematical interpretation of nature.

The following books are suggested as supplementary reading on scientific method and the nature of the scientific process:

American Foundation for Continuing Education, Louise B. Young, Editor: *Exploring the Universe,* McGraw-Hill, 1963. This earlier volume of readings on science by the American Foundation devotes the first seven parts to the nature of the scientific process. Parts 2, 5, and 7 are especially recommended for an understanding of the role of observation, theory, and experiment in scientific method.

* Beveridge, W. I. B.: *The Art of Scientific Investigation,* Modern Library, 1957. Written as a general guide to the research scientist. This book provides an unusual insight into the methods actually used by the working scientist.

* Conant, James: *Science and Common Sense,* Yale University Press, 1961. An excellent interpretation of the nature of science. Conant uses historical examples to show the importance of experimentation, intuition, doubt, accident, and observation in the development of scientific concepts.

* Poincaré, Henri: *Science and Hypothesis,* Dover Publications, Inc., 1952. An investigation of the nature and role of hypothesis in scientific method. Poincaré discusses the nature of mathematical reasoning and shows how the basic concepts of size, space, and force have been developed.

* Paperback edition

2

Is Matter Infinitely Divisible?

Starting with the assumption of ultimate indivisible particles, the readings in this part trace the early development of atomic theory and show how this concept helped to unravel some of the mysteries of the behavior of matter. Does the success of the theory prove the validity of the assumption? And what are the philosophical implications of discontinuity as opposed to the more intuitive concept of continuity?

Is Matter Infinitely Divisible?

Introduction

W HATEVER CAN be done once can always be repeated." This assumption seems at first glance to be irrefutable. It is the assumption on which the various concepts of infinity are based. The atomic idea as originally conceived by Leucippus was a denial of the validity of this assumption as it applied to the realm of matter. An object can be divided once and then those halves can be divided and those halves and so on, but this process cannot be repeated indefinitely. Somewhere in the process of division we come upon particles that are indivisible. Even though the number may be incredibly great there must be a finite number of pieces in each lump of matter. Thus the atomic theory banished the concept of infinite divisibility from the realm of matter. But the idea of infinity remained as part of our framework of thought in such abstractions as time, space, motion, and numbers.

As the atomic idea was developed by Democritus and later put into a literary form by Lucretius, the atoms of any one element were believed to be identical. Groups of discrete, identical objects lend themselves well to certain types of measurement. If the size of each individual object is known then the size of the assembly can be accurately determined by counting the number of individuals. Even if nothing is known of the size of each atom, some facts can be learned about them by observing the proportions by weight (or volume) in which changes occur. For instance, if there are five identical objects in a container and some of them are removed, the weight of the remaining objects will differ from the original total by $\frac{1}{5}$th, $\frac{2}{5}$ths, $\frac{3}{5}$ths, or $\frac{4}{5}$ths. If we did not know how many objects were originally present, experiments yielding the above ratios of change would be a pretty clear indication that five identical objects had been present.

The selections in this part show how the nineteenth-century scientists used reasoning of this type to explain why constant ratios turned up during chemical changes. The idea that matter consists of small parts which are identical at least for any one element gave early science a conceptual scheme which could be used as a means of establishing various relationships and which led to our present understanding of the nature of matter.

Figure 2–1. "Entrance to the Harbor, Port-en-Bessin" (1888), by Georges-Pierre Seurat. (Oil on canvas, 21⅝″ x 25⅝″. Lillie P. Bliss Collection, The Museum of Modern Art, New York. Reprinted by permission.)

The atomic theory has been a very successful scientific theory. It has explained the known facts and has led to further deductions which can be tested by experiment. Although it has been modified during the course of its development so that we no longer think of atoms as being the ultimate indivisible particles, the basic assumption of the discontinuity of nature does remain. The unit of indivisibility has just been shifted down the size scale. The assumption of discontinuity has also been extended to include the discontinuity of charge and energy. In Part 3 we will see how the discoveries of Heisenberg, Bohr, and Einstein were to suggest that energy must come in minimum packets or "quanta."

The success of this discontinuous view of nature leads to speculations about whether this view represents the best approach to all aspects of nature. As David Hilbert says:

Our first naïve impression of nature and matter is that of continuity. Be it a piece of metal or a volume of liquid, we invariably conceive it as divisible into infinity, and ever so small a part of it appears to us to possess the same properties as the whole.[1]

But modern science sees nature as being composed of small indivisible quanta like a pointillist painting. (See Figure 2–1.) The painting appears to be continuous if we stand far enough away from it so that the dots blend together. Is continuity a naïve concept due to our comparatively large size in the scale of things? Is the concept of infinity a lazy man's way of reaching the last number? Or are there some aspects of nature which may be infinitely extended and infinitely divisible, like time and space?

1. As quoted by Tobias Dantzig in *Number, the Language of Science*, 4th edition. Copyright 1954 by The Macmillan Company.

The Atomic Idea

The Atom Is Conceived [*]

by Guy Murchie (1961)

Before going deeper into the mysterious inner nature of our world, it may help to step back into the well-worn sandals of Leucippus, who lived in Abdera in Thrace in the fifth century before Christ, and consider his meditations while strolling upon a gray Aegean strand. He is said to have wondered aloud to his young pupil Democritus whether the water of the sea, which appears continuous in structure, could really be composed of separate, extremely tiny grains like the beach, which, at first glance, likewise appears continuous.

"I can divide it into drops," he observed, "and then I can divide each drop into smaller drops. Is there any reason why this process of sub-division cannot continue forever?" If it continues without end, of course, there will be no end of drops or smaller things—but at some degree of smallness the things must pass from the known into the unknown, then from the knowable into the unknowable or, depending on definition, from the tangible into the intangible, mayhap even from the concrete into the abstract, yet not—heaven preserve our reason—not quite from the something into the nothing. (Figure 2–2.)

In any case, it was the kind of question Greek philosophers liked to discuss, for they were strangely drawn to the fundamental mysteries. But no one knew of any experiment by which to test it. Instead, by deep intuition alone, Leucippus, and later Democritus, concluded that there must be a limit to the subdivision of any material—that somewhere there must be "parts which are partless" and that the world is therefore made of ultimately indivisible or "a-tomic" grains that are nothing but themselves in a state of constant motion and which, by being at various times and places packed densely together or spread thinly apart, compose and decompose the four classic elements of fire, air, water and earth, besides all the compound materials of the world.

Figure 2–2.

Leucippus assumed that the forms of such atoms were infinite in number since there was "no reason why they should be of one kind rather than another" and because he observed an "unceasing becoming and change in things." Democritus more specifically defined them as identical in substance though different in shape, order and position—three differences which he attributed to rhythm, interconnection and spin respectively. This amazingly modern hypothesis included also the principle of conservation of matter, since the atoms themselves were considered hard to the point of being absolutely indestructible, and all chemical changes in all minerals, vegetables and animals were therefore due to the unceasing aggregation and disaggregation of these constituent grains in their limitless combinations.

The Character of Atoms *

by Lucretius (58 B.C.)

Bodies again are partly first-beginnings of things, partly those which are formed of a union of first-beginnings. But those which are first-beginnings of things no force can quench: they are sure to have the better by their solid body. Although it seems difficult to believe that aught can be found among things with a solid body. For the lightning of heaven

* From Lucretius, *On the Nature of Things*, Book I (483) and Book II (308), translated by H. A. J. Munro.

passes through the walls of houses, as well as noise and voices; iron grows red-hot in the fire and stones burn with fierce heat and burst asunder; the hardness of gold is broken up and dissolved by heat; the ice of brass melts vanquished by the flame; warmth and piercing cold ooze through silver, since we have felt both, as we held cups with the hand in due fashion and the water was poured down into them. So universally there is found to be nothing solid in things. But yet because true reason and the nature of things constrains, . . . there are such things as consist of solid and everlasting body, which we teach are seeds of things and first-beginnings, out of which the whole sum of things which now exists has been produced. . . .

And herein you need not wonder at this, that though the first-beginnings of things are all in motion, yet the sum is seen to rest in supreme repose, unless where a thing exhibits motions with its individual body. For all the nature of first things lies far away from our senses beneath their ken; and therefore since they are themselves beyond what you can see, they must withdraw from sight their motion as well; and the more so that the things which we can see, do yet often conceal their motions when a great distance off. Thus often the woolly flocks as they crop the glad pastures on a hill, creep on whither the grass jewelled with fresh dew summons and invites each, and the lambs fed to the full gambol and playfully butt; all which objects appear to us from a distance to be blended together and to rest like a white spot on a green hill. Again when mighty legions fill with their movements all parts of the plains waging the mimicry of war, the glitter then lifts itself up to the sky and the whole earth round gleams with brass and beneath a noise is raised by the mighty trampling of men and the mountains stricken by the shouting re-echo the voices to the stars of heaven, and horsemen fly about and suddenly wheeling scour across the middle of the plains, shaking them with the vehemence of their charge. And yet there is some spot on the high hills, seen from which they appear to stand still and to rest on the plains as a bright spot.

Early Atomic Theory

Atoms and Molecules *

by Selig Hecht (1947)

WHY ATOMS?

Why do we speak of atoms? Why do we say that matter is made up of a host of atoms? Objects like the table and the chair, and substances like iron and sugar, appear to be continuous. Water looks as if it were continuous, and so does the glass that contains it; otherwise the water would come through the glass.

Nevertheless, even Democritus in 400 B.C. suspected that the continuous appearance of objects and substances is not a revelation of their true structure, and he suggested that matter is basically discontinuous. He supposed it to be made up of exceedingly small parts, so small that they cannot be made any smaller. These he called atoms. Why did Democritus conceive such a curious idea?

Simple and common experience can give the answer. Ordinary table salt dissolves and disappears when put into water. So does sugar in coffee, and so do hundreds of common substances when placed in water or other liquids. If water were as continuous as it appears to be, there would be no room for the salt and sugar to disappear into. There must be holes in water; many, many holes. Moreover, salt and sugar must be made up of very tiny particles that can get into these holes and disappear.

Another experience shows this even more strikingly. Take a glass of water and put a crystal of any colored dye on the bottom. Very slowly, even without stirring, the dye dissolves and gradually spreads throughout the water. To hasten the process we stir the water and the dye, and end with an evenly colored solution in the glass. Surely both the water and the dye must be made up of microscopic particles that can mingle, so that the particles of the dye come to occupy spaces between the particles of water.

Take another common observation. A quart of water when mixed with a quart of alcohol produces less than two quarts of mixture. Part of the alcohol works its way into the spaces between the water particles, and part of the water works its way between the alcohol particles.

These things happen not only in water and other liquids. They occur in air and even in solids. Our neighbor's bacon frying in the morning liberates something that can diffuse into the air and finally reach our nostrils. Clearly there must be holes in the air, spaces where there are no air particles, so that the odoriferous fragments from the bacon can push through and reach us yards away.

If a bar of gold with a sharp clean edge is put in close contact with the similarly clean edge of a bar of silver, and the two bars are pressed together for several months and then separated, some gold can be found inside the silver bar and some silver inside the gold bar. Particles of gold and silver have migrated across the boundary. Solids can diffuse into other solids, just as gases diffuse into other gases, and solids dissolve in liquids.

All this tells us that appearance is not reality; that what we can see is only a superficial continuity of matter; that fundamentally there are innumerable holes in all substances, even the most solid. We explain these holes by supposing them to be the spaces between the ultimate small particles, the atoms, that compose matter.

ATOMS AND MOLECULES

The phenomena of diffusion and interpenetration are excellent reasons for assuming the existence of atoms. However, there are even better ones, and these better ones give further insight into the nature of atoms. To understand these reasons we must learn something more about the properties of matter.

It is well to start with common things like wood, bread, beans, cheese, sugar, and hair. When these materials are burned or charred they yield charcoal or carbon. Examination shows that this carbon when cleaned and purified is the same regardless of its origin. The question as to whether the carbon was in the wood and sugar all the time, or whether it was produced by the process of burning was settled long ago. We know that the carbon was there originally. Later it will be clear why.

If we now try to change the carbon by boiling it with acids, or with ammonia and other alkalis, with benzine, or with dozens of other agents, nothing happens to the carbon. It always comes back as carbon. There is almost nothing that can be done with carbon to change its appearance and properties; it remains carbon. Even if it is heated in air, and slowly disappears as a gas, the gas can be caught, and carbon can be got back from it.

Carbon is thus a substance that enters in the composition of a variety of more complex materials ranging from butter to marble; it can always be pulled out of these materials to assume its typical carbon appearance and properties; and it cannot be transformed into any simpler material. Carbon, therefore, is an irreducible, an elementary substance.

In the same way that carbon emerges from a variety of complex materials, other elementary substances such as zinc, copper, gold, sulfur, hydrogen, helium, iron, and mercury can be derived from the innumerable materials in the world. Each possesses unique properties, each differs from the other elementary substances, and each retains its individuality. No chemical procedures can transform one of these elementary substances into another. The most violent chemical actions cannot change carbon into gold, or sulfur into mercury, or lead into silver. They are irreducible elementary substances. By 1940 there were ninety-two of these substances known. They are called the chemical elements, or more briefly, elements. As one result of the atomic-bomb development, eleven more have been developed—man-made chemical elements that do not occur in nature.

All the infinite variety of materials in the world is made up of combinations of these elements, by twos, threes, fours, and even fives. Thus sugar is made of carbon, hydrogen, and oxygen; marble of calcium, carbon, and oxygen; sand of silicon and oxygen; and so on forever with the rest of the 103 elements.

Since each of these elementary substances is irreducible and unique, and we have already assumed that all matter is made up of atoms, it seems sensible to suppose that the atoms that compose each element are themselves unique. In this way we can think of atoms of copper, carbon, gold, silver, hydrogen, and aluminum as special, each to its own kind. Indeed, we must assume 103 different species of atoms corresponding to the 103 chemical elements. The justification and the consequences of this assumption form the burden of our story, and will emerge as we develop it.

All the things in the world are made up of combinations of the chemical elements. Objects such as rocks, chairs, lampshades, and rugs are built of materials like marble, wood, iron, parchment, cotton, and wool. Some of these materials have a complicated structure of their own. Wood, for example, is not the same all through. It has grain, formed by the alternation of hard and soft fibers, and the varieties of wood depend on this visible organization. Wood is therefore an inhomogeneous substance; it cannot be purified and rendered completely homogeneous. However, the essential ingredient of wood is cellulose, which can be purified and prepared so as to be uniform throughout. Such purified, reproducible, and homogeneous materials are called pure substances, and there are hundreds of thousands of them. Sugar is one; table salt another. Aluminum, iron, calomel, bicarbonate of soda, lime, penicillin, diamond, alcohol, and DDT are examples of substances that can be prepared in pure form, so that any small fragment is like any other fragment.

When this vast array of pure substances is examined chemically, it can be divided into two kinds. First there is the small group of 103 elementary substances like iron, aluminum, and carbon, which we already know about. They cannot be decomposed by any chemical treatment. And second, there is the remaining, enormous group, containing substances that can be decomposed chemically to yield some of the 103 elements. These pure but decomposable substances are compounded from the elements and are known as chemical compounds.

The nature of these compounds and their formation may be illustrated by the behavior of iron and sulfur. Both iron and sulfur are elements, and both are solids. If we grind them into fine powders and mix them thoroughly, they are still iron and sulfur. With a microscope the particles of sulfur and the particles of iron can be seen as separate and differently colored. If now the mixture is heated, the recurring miracle of chemistry takes place. The heated mass becomes transformed. The two separate substances disappear, and a new substance appears, made up of both iron and sulfur. This is iron sulfide, which looks, behaves, and dissolves differently from either iron or sulfur. It can be cleaned and purified, and is a compound substance uniform throughout. Iron sulfide occurs in nature as crystals, and is known as fool's gold because of its superficial resemblance to gold.

What is the ultimate structure of such compounds? They too must be built up of extremely small particles, because they too can dissolve and diffuse in liquids. In fact, our first examples of this behavior were compounds like sugar and salt. The supposition is that in compounds the ultimate particles are built up of atoms of the elements that form the compounds. In this way an atom of sulfur and an atom of iron unite to form a new unit, a molecule of iron sulfide. The smallest unit of a compound is a molecule.

Molecules are made up of atoms of one or more of the 103 elements. Because it is easy to break up compounds into their constituent elements, it must be that the atoms in the molecule maintain most of their individuality. No matter how complex the compound, no matter how large its molecule, one can always get back the constituent elements. In other words, molecules can be separated into their constituent atoms.

Until recently it could be asserted that all this talk about atoms and molecules is theory; that no one has seen an atom or a molecule, even with the highest power of the microscope. This is still true of the ordinary "light microscope"; but the electron microscope,[1] in which light rays are replaced by a stream of electrons, provides clear pictures of at least the largest molecules, such as those of the proteins, which contain thousands of atoms, and quite recently a new and very simple device was invented that made it possible for the first time to see the shape of a comparatively simple molecule—that of a dye called phthalocyanin, containing less than one hundred atoms.

However, long before these first direct glimpses into the world of molecules became possible, scientists had ceased to argue as to whether these particles really existed. Atoms and molecules originated as concepts of the human mind, because they appeared useful in explaining the behavior of ordinary substances in bulk. The idea was that if we assume matter to be composed of invisible atoms or molecules, then a lot of events that are visible become understandable. The more we have learned about the properties of matter and the behavior of different substances, the more illuminating and the more reasonable appeared this relatively simple notion—that substances are made up of atoms and molecules—until it became a certainty, long before anyone saw a molecule under an electron microscope.

The procedure is something like this. We observe phenomena like diffusion, like the nontransformation of elementary substances, like the homogeneity of compounds and the ease of their decomposition into elementary substances. In order to explain these observations we assume the existence of atoms and molecules. Then we say that if atoms and molecules are what we think they are, ordinary substances should have certain definite properties that we can predict. If the predicted properties turn out to be correct, we have strengthened the reasons for believing in the reality of atoms and molecules. This reciprocal development of information and explanation is the essence of science; . . . When scientists finally saw direct photographs of molecules, they were thrilled, but hardly astonished, to find that, in size and shape, these particles looked exactly as they had assumed them to be.

1. See Glossary for description of this instrument. Ed.

THE WEIGHTS OF ATOMS

The differences between elements and compounds became clear toward the end of the eighteenth century; and in 1780 Antoine Lavoisier, the great chemist who died in the French Revolution, was able to list nearly fifty known elements. In working with elements and compounds, Lavoisier established the fundamental fact that during all the transformations of one substance into another, and of compounds into elements and the reverse, there is no loss in total weight of material involved. This is the principle of the conservation of matter. Regardless of what you do to substances, no matter how their properties change as they react with each other, no matter how different they look afterward, you end with the same total weight of matter with which you started.

As an example actually studied by Lavoisier, we can consider a burning candle. When a candle burns, it disappears and in its place gases are formed. In addition, the air surrounding the candle becomes changed so that it is no longer fit to breathe. Lavoisier knew that the hot wax of the candle combined with the oxygen of the surrounding air (which he called "free" air) to form water vapor and carbon dioxide (which he called "fixed" air). We can write this in the form of an equation as

$$\text{Candle} + \text{free air} = \text{fixed air} + \text{water vapor}$$

Lavoisier measured the weight of the candle that disappeared and the weight of the oxygen that combined with it, and found their sum to equal the weight of the carbon dioxide and the water vapor or moisture that were formed.

In the conservation of matter during chemical reactions it makes no difference whether the beginning substances are gas or solid or liquid, and it makes no difference whether the end products are gas or solid or liquid. The important thing is to measure everything that enters into the reaction and to catch everything that forms during the reaction. If you do that, you find that there is no loss of matter. The equation balances.

The observed conservation of matter is easily translated in terms of the theoretical atoms and molecules. It says that atoms contain all the mass of any substance, and that regardless of the ways in which the atoms join to form molecules, they carry their individual masses with them. This is a revealing generalization; but the experiments that followed its formulation were even more revealing of the nature of matter. It turned out that when elements combine to form compounds they always do so in definite proportions.

For example, when you burn coal or carbon you find that by weight

3 parts of carbon always combine with 8 parts of oxygen. Thus 3 ounces of carbon as it burns take out 8 ounces of oxygen from the surrounding air. Similarly, when hydrogen in air is transformed into water vapor, the weight of oxygen consumed in the process is always eight times the weight of the hydrogen. By the same token, if you examine any pure chemical compound such as sugar, water, carbon dioxide, marble, or sulfadiazine, you always find that the elements in it exist in definite proportions by weight. From 11 pounds of carbon dioxide you can always get 3 pounds of carbon and 8 pounds of oxygen; and from 9 pounds of water you can always collect 1 pound of hydrogen and 8 pounds of oxygen.

The idea of definite proportions in the combination of elements or in the composition of compounds seems natural to us now. But it is important to put ourselves back one hundred and fifty years. At that time all that Lavoisier and the other chemists knew was that air in which a candle could burn and which was fit for breathing was rendered unfit for either job after several candles had been burned in it. The "free" air had become "fixed" air; and the chemist's problem was to find out how "fixing" air rendered it useless for burning candles and for animal breathing. It was a revelation to find that the burning candle abstracted a definite amount of material—oxygen—from the air and produced in the process a given quantity of a new substance—carbon dioxide.

The recognition of the fact that when substances combine with each other they do so in definite proportions by weight marked the emergence of chemistry as a science. It made possible the next giant step forward in understanding the nature of matter. This step was taken in 1808 by John Dalton, who formulated the modern atomic theory. The original atomic idea of Democritus was philosophically basic, but practically vague. He had suggested that matter is discontinuous and composed of indivisible atoms. Dalton started from here and built a clearly formulated, scientific, working hypothesis.

Editor's Note. The process of converting a vague philosophical concept into a scientific theory may seem in retrospect to be obvious and straightforward. The need to simplify the story in explaining the development of a scientific concept to non-scientists sometimes leads to a false impression that science moves triumphantly forward, building each step unerringly on the step before. However, science does not usually advance in this triumphant manner but in a more tentative and halting manner, often taking several steps backward before the significant breakthrough is made. In the selection that follows James Conant describes some of the difficulties besetting the nineteenth-century scientists who attempted to use the philosophical concept of the discontinuity of matter to explain certain experimental facts and how they eventually succeeded in converting it into a fruitful scienitfic theory.

The Development of the Chemist's Atomic Theory *

by James Conant (1951)

The historical fact that it required fifty years of experimentation and discussion to develop an atomic theory that would accommodate the experimental observations of the chemists is perhaps not surprising. But to one unfamiliar with this fact of scientific history it is amazing to discover that all the relevant ideas and all the basic data were at hand almost from the outset. An analysis of the rival views and the arguments pro and con shows clearly that certain preconceived ideas then current among scientists blocked the development. I hope to indicate in the next few pages the nature of these ideas and how the prejudices arising from them were finally overcome.

Before the reader becomes involved in the somewhat intricate mass of facts and hypotheses which will shortly follow, I venture to point up the moral of this story by a quotation from a modern writer who believes there is *a* scientific method. "The scientific way of thinking requires the habit of facing reality quite unprejudiced by any earlier conceptions." This is a fair sample of one set of views about science that is popular in many quarters, one of those half-truths with which it is most difficult to deal. If the writer means merely that science requires intellectual honesty we must all agree; if he had in mind that the scientist honestly seeks a clear-cut answer from his experiments planned within the framework of the conceptual fabric of his day and in terms of the hypotheses to be tested, then again there can be no dissent. But the statement seems to say much more than this. It implies that the mind of a scientist must be a blank when a new problem arises. Actually, . . . the effective investigator must be armed with a whole series of "earlier conceptions." These are the concepts and conceptual schemes of his science, and the real pioneers must have a new idea as well. But it might be put forward in rebuttal that all these ideas are explicit; prejudices are nonlogical emotional reactions. To this I would agree and still maintain that every scientist must carry with him the scientific prejudices of his day—the many vague half-formulated assumptions which to him seem "scientific common sense." And no better illustration of the role of such factors in science can be found than in the story of the attempts of nineteenth-century chemists to formulate an atomic theory.

* From James Conant, *Science and Common Sense*, Yale University Press. Copyright 1951 by Yale University Press. Reprinted by permission.

The discovery of the role of oxygen in combustion and the composition of water set the stage for the new chemistry. Lavoisier's *Elements of Chemistry* expounded the new ideas and impressed upon the scientific world the significance of the "principle of the balance sheet." According to the new conceptual scheme, there were two very important classes of materials: elements and compounds, the latter resulting from the combination of two or more elements in definite amounts. One could thus define water as a compound of the elements hydrogen and oxygen in the ratio by weight of 1 to 8; such a statement was the summation of difficult quantitative experimentation.

Dalton about 1805 sought to bring into the new chemistry the ancient doctrine of atoms. The idea of matter being composed of atoms was one of those general speculative ideas in the background of the thinking of most scientists of the eighteenth century; Newton had made use of the concept of atoms in some of his writings about the physical properties of gases. To Dalton goes the credit, however, of suggesting that the atoms would provide a simple explanation of why the elements always combine in the same proportion by weight to form a definite compound. If one assumes that all the atoms of a given element, say hydrogen, have the same weight and that the combination of, say, hydrogen and oxygen always involves the union of the same number of atoms, then the experimental facts are adequately accommodated. To illustrate, let us make the simplifying assumption (as did Dalton) that the smallest water particle is composed of one atom of hydrogen and one of oxygen. (According to our present conceptual scheme this is incorrect.) Then since we know by experiment that 1 part by weight of hydrogen combines with 8 parts by weight of oxygen, the *relative* weights of the hydrogen and oxygen atoms are 1 to 8. Though atoms were far too small to weigh individually, Dalton argued one could determine their relative weights from the experimental facts by the type of reasoning we have just employed.

There was one difficulty apparent at the start and this difficulty remained to plague the chemists for half a century. How is one to know how many atoms unite to form the smallest unit of a compound? Dalton said we cannot know but had best *assume* the simplest relationship which will fit the experimental facts. One may note that here is an example of invoking the general principle which has sometimes been called the "rule of greatest simplicity." Dalton said the water molecule (our name for the smallest particle of a compound) was composed of an atom of oxygen and one of hydrogen; in modern symbols his formula for water was HO. This assumption made, *then* it follows from the weights of hydrogen and oxygen which combine that an atomic-weight scale can be constructed in which, if hydrogen is taken as unity (arbitrarily), oxygen must be 8.

Briefly, the scientists in the first half of the nineteenth century were wrestling with a threefold relationship of which only *one* point was fixed by experiment, namely the combining weight ratios of the elements. If one assumed a formula for a few compounds such as water, then an atomic-weight scale could be constructed from the experimental facts; or, conversely, if one assumed an atomic-weight scale, then the formulas of the compounds followed from the weight relationships of the elements. But what was needed was new evidence as to either the relative weights of the elementary atoms or the number of atoms in such simple compounds as water.

Both the evidence and new concepts for interpreting the evidence were presented to the scientific world in the second decade of the nineteenth century. *But this fruitful combination was ignored.* Avogadro, an Italian physicist, saw how another set of quantitative data could be used to establish the formula of water. But it was not until 1860 that, under the leadership of another Italian, Cannizzaro, the scientific fraternity returned to the ideas of Avogadro and built on them an atomic and molecular theory that could be widely accepted. Yet this is the theory which has served so well as a foundation for all subsequent developments about the structure of matter.

To understand the prejudices which prevented Avogadro's ideas being accepted in his own day we must examine both the experimental evidence and his concepts. Avogadro (and some of his contemporaries) were impressed by the quantitative relationship that had been found to hold when *gaseous* elements combine. Here we are considering not weight but volumes of gases, let it be carefully noted. One illustration will suffice. If a mixture of hydrogen gas and oxygen gas is exploded by a spark, the following relationship is found to hold:

1 volume of oxygen + 2 volumes of hydrogen → 2 volumes of water vapor.

(Any units of volume, for example cubic feet, may be used to express this relation.) The relation between volumes is very simple: 1 to 2 to 2. Other gaseous elements were likewise found to combine in a volume relationship expressed by *small whole numbers*.

Avogadro made two assumptions to account for the whole-number relationship between the *volumes* of gaseous elements which combine to form compounds. The first was that *equal volumes of gases under the same conditions of temperature and pressure contain the same number of particles*. The second was the particles [molecules] of hydrogen and oxygen are each composed of *two* atoms united together.

With the aid of these assumptions Avogadro accounted for all the known facts about chemical reactions between gases and was led to the conclusion that the water molecule was composed of two atoms of hydrogen and one of oxygen, that is, it is to be represented by H_2O. Thus, by bringing in as new evidence the measurement of the *volume* relationship between *gaseous* elements which combine and his own chain of reasoning, Avogadro established the formula of a few compounds. He thus solved the threefold relationship referred to earlier; the atomic-weight scale could then be constructed from the proportions by weight in which the elements combined. To be specific, the formula of water as H_2O followed from the *volume* relationship between water vapor, hydrogen, and oxygen in the synthesis of water from the elements; the atomic weight of oxygen must then be 16 if hydrogen is 1, since the weight relations of oxygen and hydrogen in water are as 8 is to 1 or 16 is to 2. The combination of oxygen and hydrogen Avogadro pictures as shown in Figure 2–3 (and this is the way we picture it today).

Dalton would have none of this; neither would the vast majority of chemists for nearly fifty years. Why? Because Avogadro's conceptual scheme involved the assumption that either the particles of hydrogen gas were divisible, which was contrary to the definition of an atom, or else the particles were composed of two *like* atoms held together. But what could hold two identical atoms together?

Berzelius, the great Swedish chemist of the first half of the nineteenth century, was particularly insistent that identical atoms would not unite, for he had developed a concept of chemical combination that depended on the assumption of an electrical attraction between different kinds of atoms. This was a conceptual scheme which reflected the recent discovery of the decomposition of some compounds such as water by an electric current (electrolysis). According to Berzelius' electrochemical ideas, identical atoms could not combine.

Berzelius, however, accepted half of the Italian physicist's postulates. He said that the fact that one volume of oxygen combines with two

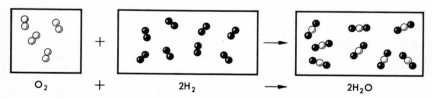

O_2 $+$ $2H_2$ $\longrightarrow$ $2H_2O$

Figure 2–3. Diagram illustrating Avogadro's view of gaseous combination; the square represents one volume, each oblong two.

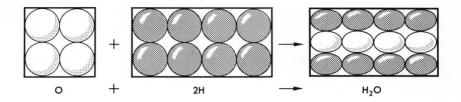

Figure 2–4. Diagram illustrating Berzelius' view of gaseous combination.

volumes of hydrogen is of the utmost significance and that for *gaseous elements* Avogadro's premise is undoubtedly correct (i.e., equal volumes of gaseous elements contained an equal number of atoms). Therefore Berzelius formulated the combination of oxygen and hydrogen as shown in Figure 2–4.

In this diagram I have represented the atoms as touching each other, for Berzelius and his contemporaries thought of the particles in a gas as contiguous. In Avogadro's conceptual scheme we think of the molecules as occupying but a small portion of the space. Berzelius did not account for the fact that exactly two volumes of steam were formed. In his picture the atoms in the water molecule were squeezed together, but why the volume of the product was related so simply to that of the components he did not say. Perhaps it was "just one of those things we cannot yet explain." In spite of its inadequacies this conceptual scheme was very fruitful. With his assumptions Berzelius developed a system of chemistry of great value, but before long it ran into difficulties and was discarded.

In retrospect, we see that there were at least three prejudices current in 1815 unfavorable to Avogadro's ideas. The first was the notion that the particles of a gas were in contact with each other; the second, that identical atoms could not unite; a third was Berzelius' electrochemical theory. The latter was so explicit an idea, however, that it is perhaps wrong to call it a prejudice; rather it was a conceptual scheme which served to block another's acceptance.

One attempt to obtain experimental evidence to support Avogadro's ideas was made by a French chemist in the 1820's, but the result of these studies was almost to destroy all faith in the atomic theory. This is indeed a curious chapter in the history of nineteenth-century science. In a few words, what occurred was this: a way was discovered of measuring the relative weights of the vapors of such elements as mercury and sulfur, which are gases only at high temperatures. If Avogadro's first postulate [that equal volumes contain an equal number of molecules] is sound, the relative weights of equal volumes of gases should be a measure of the relative weights of the particles which compose these gases. The followers of Berzelius accepted this idea provided one considered only the elements. Now came the disconcerting discoveries. The relative weights of vapors of most of the elements could not be reconciled with the data used for constructing the atomic-weight scale. In modern terms one would say that if hydrogen gas were to be represented as H_2 (two atoms per molecule), in gaseous mercury the atoms were single, while gaseous sulfur had to have no less than six atoms united together.

Such conclusions [which were subsequently confirmed] seemed pre-posterous to the chemists of the 1830's. The simple gaseous elements, hydrogen, oxygen, nitrogen, chlorine, all behaved in a uniform manner (they could be regarded as having either one atom per particle according to Berzelius or two per particle according to Avogadro). Who could imagine that nature was so contrary as to have other elements with one or six particles per molecule? Often, unconsciously, scientists operate on the principle of assuming the greatest simplicity in nature. The applica-tion of this principle to the elements in the first few decades of the nineteenth century certainly led to the idea that the number of atoms per particle in the gaseous state should be the same for the elements. Therefore, confronted with the alternative of throwing over the prin-ciple of uniformity among the elements or abandoning Avogadro's postulate, most scientists took the latter course. With the postulate like-wise went most of Berzelius' system (which was in trouble on other counts as well). Therefore the 1840's saw a period of reaction against the whole atomic theory. Any attempt to find a basis for determining the number of elementary atoms united in a compound molecule seemed hopeless. Chemists retreated to a position similar to that taken by Dalton. They arbitrarily assumed the law of the greatest simplicity and wrote the formula of water HO and a corresponding atomic-weight scale.

It would be interesting, if space permitted and if the necessary factual information were not so great, to trace the ebb and flow of the faith of the scientific world in the "reality" of atoms. The 1840's and 1850's would represent a very low point indeed. But as a consequence of the develop-ment of the kinetic theory of gases [1] to account for physical phenomena, Avogadro's first postulate came to seem more and more plausible. Furthermore, without an adequate atomic theory further progress in

---

1. The kinetic theory of gases is based on the assumption that gases consist of very small molecules in rapid motion. This theory is consistent with Avogadro's picture (see Figure 2–3) and not with Berzelius' (see Figure 2–4) where the molecules occupy the entire space. The kinetic theory of gases will be discussed in greater detail in later readings. Ed.

chemistry was blocked. The complicated facts of the chemistry of organic compounds (carbon compounds) could not be handled without some agreement as to the number of atoms in a molecule of at least the simple substances. A generation of chemists and physicists produced a mass of converging evidence. Then in almost a rush everyone turned back to Avogadro. The earlier doubts were overcome: a great many facts revealed by the workers of the forties and the fifties were seen to fit into Avogadro's conceptual scheme. . . . Therefore in 1860, largely as the result of a beautiful exposition by Cannizzaro of Avogadro's ideas, the atomic-molecular theory was accepted in the form in which it is taught to elementary students of chemistry today. Immediately there followed rapid progress in chemistry in many directions. This illustrates again the revolutionary effects of concepts or conceptual schemes which like new instruments often open up wide fields for exploration.

A New System of Chemical Philosophy *
by John Dalton (1808)

ON THE CONSTITUTION OF BODIES

There are three distinctions in the kinds of bodies, or three states, which have more especially claimed the attention of philosophical chemists; namely, those which are marked by the terms *elastic fluids*,[1] *liquids*, and *solids*. A very famous instance is exhibited to us in water, of a body, which in certain circumstances, is capable of assuming all the three states. In steam we recognize a perfectly elastic fluid, in water a perfect liquid, and in ice a complete solid. These observations have tacitly led to the conclusion, which seems universally adopted, that all bodies of sensible magnitude, whether liquid or solid, are constituted of a vast number of extremely small particles or atoms of matter bound together by a force of attraction, which is more or less powerful according to circumstances. . . .

Whether the ultimate particles of a body, such as water, are all alike, that is, of the same figure, weight, et cetera, is a question of some importance. From what is known, we have no reason to apprehend a diversity in these particulars: if it does exist in water it must equally

* From John Dalton, *A New System of Chemical Philosophy*, Manchester, 1808.
1. Gases, in modern terminology. Ed.

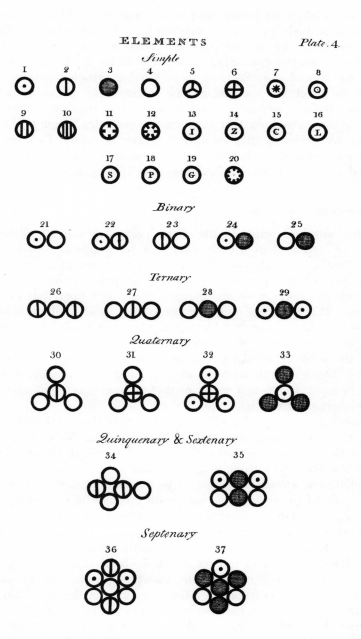

Figure 2–5. (From John Dalton, A New System of Chemical Philosophy, *Manchester, 1808. Courtesy of the John Crerar Library.)*

exist in the elements constituting water, namely, hydrogen and oxygen. Now it is scarcely possible to conceive how the aggregates of dissimilar particles should be so uniformly the same. If some of the particles of water were heavier than others, if a parcel of the liquid on any occasion were constituted principally of these heavier particles, it must be supposed to affect the specific gravity of the mass, a circumstance not known. Similar observations may be made on other substances. Therefore we may conclude that *the ultimate particles of all homogeneous bodies are perfectly alike in weight, figure, et cetera.* In other words, every particle of water is like every other particle of water; every particle of hydrogen is like every other particle of hydrogen, et cetera.

ON CHEMICAL SYNTHESIS

When any body exists in the elastic [gaseous] state its ultimate particles are separated from each other to a much greater distance than in any other state; each particle occupies the center of a comparatively large sphere and supports its dignity by keeping all the rest which, by their gravity or otherwise, are disposed to encroach upon it at a respectful distance. When we attempt to conceive the *number* of particles in an atmosphere it is somewhat like attempting to conceive the number of stars in the universe: we are confounded with the thought. But if we limit the subject by taking a given volume of any gas, we seem persuaded that, let the divisions be ever so minute, the number of particles must be finite; just as in a given space of the universe the number of stars and planets cannot be infinite.

Chemical analysis and synthesis go no farther than to the separation of particles one from another, and to their reunion. No new creation or destruction of matter is within the reach of chemical agency. We might as well attempt to introduce a new planet into the solar system, or to annihilate one already in existence, as to create or destroy a particle of hydrogen. All the changes we can produce consist in separating particles that are in a state of cohesion or combination, and joining those that were previously at a distance.

In all chemical investigations it has justly been considered an important object to ascertain the relative *weights* of the simples [elements] which constitute a compound. But unfortunately the inquiry has terminated here; whereas from the relative weights in the mass the relative weights of the ultimate particles or atoms of the bodies might have been inferred, from which their number and weight in various other compounds would appear, in order to assist and to guide future investigations, and to correct their results.

The Atom as a Homogeneous Ball *
by Selig Hecht (1947)

Now let us set an arbitrary value of 16 units of mass as the weight of one oxygen atom. Then from [the combining] ratios it follows that the weight of a hydrogen atom is 1, and the weight of a carbon atom is 12. Notice (in Figure 2–6) that these relative weights of the atoms of hydrogen, carbon, and oxygen have been derived from the definite proportions by weight in which these elements in bulk combine to form carbon dioxide and water. This was part of Dalton's hypothesis. He suggested that the atoms of different elements differ in weight in the same relative way as do the combining weights of the elements when they form compounds. We have a fact and a theory. The fact is that when elements combine to form compounds they do so in definite proportions, known as their combining weights. The theory is that these relative weights are dependent on the relative weights of the atoms out of which the elements are composed.

In presenting these ideas I have used whole numbers for the combining weights. This is not merely because it is convenient but also because it is correct as a first approximation. But only as a first approximation; and this too is of interest.

* From Selig Hecht, *Explaining the Atom.*

	Reaction	Carbon	+	Oxygen	=	Carbon Dioxide
Fact	In Bulk (pounds)	3	+	8	=	11
	Combining Weights	3	+	8	=	11
Theory	Atoms	●		 ◯◯	=	 ◯●◯
	Equation	C	+	2 O	=	CO_2
	Relative Weights	3	+	2×4	=	11
	Atomic and Molecular Weights	12	+	2×16	=	44

Figure 2–6. The burning of coal or carbon. When carbon and oxygen combine during the burning of coal they do so in definite proportions, weight for weight. These proportions are accounted for by the atomic theory in terms of the constituent atoms and their weights. From the behavior of matter in bulk we deduce the properties of atoms.

In Dalton's day the combining weights of a number of elements had been worked out with fair accuracy . . . it is instructive to arrange the elements in the order of their atomic weights [based on oxygen as 16]. The first twelve that were then known are:

Hydrogen	H	1.01	Oxygen	O	16.00
Lithium	Li	6.94	Fluorine	F	19.00
Beryllium	Be	9.02	Sodium	Na	23.00
Boron	B	10.82	Magnesium	Mg	24.32
Carbon	C	12.01	Aluminum	Al	26.97
Nitrogen	N	14.01	Silicon	Si	28.06

Notice in this series that, except for magnesium and boron, the atomic weights are nearly but not all quite whole numbers. It is almost as if they were regular multiples of hydrogen, which has an atomic weight of practically 1. This fascination with integral multiples and whole numbers has never left the problem of atomic weights. In fact, it dominated the scene for a while when William Prout, a contemporary of Dalton, actually did suppose that all elements were made up of hydrogen. Prout's hypothesis had to be discarded because the facts persisted in showing that the atomic weights were rarely whole numbers and as a rule contained some values beyond the decimal point. We find as we go on with this story that the interest in whole numbers appears again and again as each new generalization and each new series of facts become available. Then, careful measurements show that the expected whole numbers do not materialize, and the differences between reality and expectation force us to look for new phenomena in the behavior and structure of atoms and molecules.

ATOMS IN SERIAL ORDER

Dalton's atomic theory was formulated at the beginning of the nineteenth century, and served as a powerful stimulus to hunt for as many elements as possible. By the middle of the century about seventy-five had been isolated and studied, and their properties had become common chemical knowledge. The first thing that became apparent was that the elements differed in atomic weight, and could be placed in serial order, much as we arranged the first twelve in the preceding section.

Another observation was that some elements were similar to others, and the similar elements seemed to occur in groups of three, called triads. The oldest and most familiar of these triads is copper, silver, and gold, whose similarities have been known for centuries. A less familiar group of three is lithium, sodium, and potassium. These are metals that are soft and shiny when freshly purified, but tarnish rapidly on exposure. In pure form all three react violently to water and therefore have to be kept immersed in kerosene. Moreover, they can be substituted for one another in compounds, and the resulting compounds are similar. Thus sodium chloride, or ordinary table salt, is white, crystalline, salty, and easily dissolved in water. So is lithium chloride, and so is potassium chloride.

Early in the nineteenth century groups of similar elements had been found only in threes, and some remnant of the medieval mystery of the number 3 hung over them. However, some of the triads were purely accidental, because all the elements were not known. As more elements were discovered and isolated, groups began to include not only three, but four, five, and sometimes six elements that behaved alike.

Such groups of similar elements were indeed tantalizing. Why should elements of such diverse atomic weights as 63.6, 107.9, and 197.2 be as similar as copper, silver, and gold? And why should two elements as similar in atomic weight as 32.1 and 35.5 be as different as sulfur and chlorine—a yellow solid and a green gas? Many were the speculations and guesses; many were the arrangements to which the elements were subjected—all to little avail until the year 1869. It was then that Dmitri I. Mendeléeff, the Russian chemist, arranged the elements in a pattern known as the Periodic Table, which not only unified all the chemical information about them but served as well to predict the properties of undiscovered elements. Since then the Periodic Table has been the central core around which all chemical and physical knowledge of the elements has grown. It has served as explanation and as inspiration, and in terms of it there has developed the beautiful edifice that is modern atomic physics and chemistry.

To construct a modern Periodic Table first write down on a continuous ribbon according to their atomic weights the 103 elements, beginning with hydrogen, and number them from 1 to 103. (Numbers 57 to 71 and 89 to 103 should be treated as two groups, each placed in a single box.) Next mark off with a heavy line successive segments of the ribbon so that the first segment contains two elements; the second and third segments contain eight elements each; the fourth and fifth segments contain eighteen elements each; the sixth segment contains thirty-two elements; and the seventh segment contains the remaining eighteen.

Now take the ribbon of elements and coil it in a descending helix so that each segment begins and ends in the same vertical line. Thus the first elements of the segments are one under the other, and the last elements of the segments are also one under the other. The result is the Periodic Table shown in Figure 2–7. The ribbon is drawn as viewed both from the left and from the right, so that it may be read continuously. The first segment, because it holds only two elements, has to be coiled

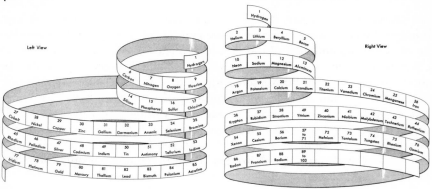

Figure 2–7. The Periodic Table. The chemical elements have been arranged in sequence on a ribbon and coiled in a helix. As a result, elements with similar properties fall one under the other vertically. Two views of the coiled ribbon are shown so that one can see it from both sides at the same time.

tightly. Even so, hydrogen and helium need to be separated somewhat; hydrogen is put in twice for reasons that become clear later. Note also that elements 57 to 71 have been jammed into one place, as suggested on page 39; actually they jut out in a secondary small coil of their own, which represents the so-called rare-earth series. (The heaviest elements, from 89 on, must be treated in the same way. This group, called the actinide series, begins with actinium, and includes thorium, protactinium, and uranium, as well as the "artificial" elements, 93 to 103, which are grouped.)

The segments of the Periodic Table contain two, eight, eighteen, or thirty-two elements. These numbers are not arbitrary; they are two times the squares of 1, 2, 3, and 4, respectively. The square of 1 is 1, which multiplied by 2 equals 2. The square of 2 is 4, which multiplied by 2 equals 8. The square of 3 is 9, which multiplied by 2 equals 18. The square of 4 is 16, which multiplied by 2 gives 32. This simple numerical series was not known to Mendeléeff; we learn more about it later.

A host of interesting relations becomes evident in the Periodic Table. The first segment-coil begins with hydrogen and ends with helium, which is an inert gas. The next segment-coil begins with lithium, the soft metal we have already discussed, and ends with neon, another inert gas, used in illuminated signs. The third coil begins with sodium, a metal like lithium, and ends with argon, another inert gas, also used in signs. The fourth coil begins with potassium, another of the soft metals, takes in more elements than the preceding coil, and ends with krypton, which is still another inert gas, much like helium, neon, and argon. The fifth segment begins with rubidium, which, like sodium and potassium, is a soft metal, and ends with xenon, a gas like neon and helium. In short, all the elements in the first vertical column are similar, and all the elements in the terminal column are similar.

Precisely the same is true of the other vertical columns, even the short ones. Note our old friends the triad of copper, silver, and gold under element 29. Or take the elements next to these: zinc, cadmium, and mercury, which form a triad of similar metals known from the days of the alchemists. Now skip to the column formed by the penultimate elements of each coil: fluorine, chlorine, bromine, and iodine. Even the most uninitiated knows that the first three are noxious gases and that iodine easily becomes a smelly gas at ordinary temperature.

Perhaps the most curious series of elements is in the vertical column under helium. All are gases, and all were unknown and even unsuspected at the time of Mendeléeff. They were discovered after 1890 by Lord Rayleigh and William Ramsay. With the exception of radon they occur normally in the air in very minute amounts. They are called "noble gases" [1] because with a few exceptions they do not combine with other elements; they act as if they are completely satisfied with themselves. Most other elements combine relatively easily with others. The noble gases stand alone. There they are at the end of each coil, one under another.

When Mendeléeff first arranged the Periodic Table only about seventy-five elements were known [Figure 2–8]. Therefore it was not so easy to see the regularities as it is now. Many empty spaces had to be put in, and it required an original feat of creative imagination to arrange the available elements in this regular and intelligible series. Mendeléeff, however, did more than this. He had the intellectual courage to predict not merely the existence of these missing elements but also their quantitative properties. In every instance his predictions were verified, with remarkable accuracy.

As an example of this prediction, consider spot 32 in the fourth horizontal coil of the Periodic Table. This element lies in the vertical column between silicon and tin, and is now called germanium. Mendeléeff in 1871 predicted its existence and called it eka-silicon. He said it would be grayish-white in color, and would give a white oxide when burned in air, and would not be affected by acids or by alkalis. Moreover, he gave definite values for its atomic weight, its density, its atomic volume, and even its boiling point. Fifteen years later, when Clemens Winkler discovered and isolated it, he found Mendeléeff's predictions almost perfectly fulfilled. Winkler called the element germanium for obvious national reasons, as is commonly done. [Figure 2–9.]

1. Also called "inert gases." Ed.

Series	Period	ZERO GROUP	GROUP I — R_2O	GROUP II — RO	GROUP III — R_2O_3	GROUP IV RH$_4$ RO$_2$
0						
1			Hydrogen H = 1.0078 No. 1			
2	1	Helium He = 4.002 No. 2	Lithium Li = 6.940 No. 3	Beryllium Be = 9.02 No. 4	Boron B = 10.82 No. 5	Carbon C = 12.00 No. 6
3	2	Neon Ne = 20.183 No. 10	Sodium Na = 22.997 No. 11	Magnesium Mg = 24.32 No. 12	Aluminum Al $\doteq$ 26.97 No. 13	Silicon Si = 28.06 No. 14
4	3	Argon A = 39.944 No. 18	Potassium K = 39.10 No. 19	Calcium Ca = 40.08 No. 20	Scandium Sc = 45.10 No. 21	Titanium Ti = 47.90 No. 22
5	3		Copper Cu = 63.57 No. 29	Zinc Zn = 65.38 No. 30	Gallium Ga = 69.72 No. 31	Germanium Ge = 72.60 No. 32
6	4	Krypton Kr = 82.9 No. 36	Rubidium Rb = 85.44 No. 37	Strontium Sr = 87.63 No. 38	Yttrium Y = 88.92 No. 39	Zirconium Zr = 91.22 No. 40
7	4		Silver Ag = 107.880 No. 47	Cadmium Cd = 112.41 No. 48	Indium In = 114.8 No. 49	Tin Sn = 118.70 No. 50
8	5	Xenon Xe = 130.2 No. 54	Caesium Cs = 132.81 No. 55	Barium Ba = 137.36 No. 56	Lanthanum La = 138.90 No. 57	Cerium Ce = 140.13 No. 58
9	5					
10	6					Hafnium Hf = 178.6 No. 72
11	6		Gold Au = 197.2 No. 79	Mercury Hg = 200.61 No. 80	Thallium Tl = 204.39 No. 81	Lead Pb = 207.22 No. 82
12	7	Radon Rn = 222 No. 86	No. 87	Radium Ra = 225.97 No. 88	No. 89	Thorium Th = 232.12 No. 90

Elements not classified in the table above:

Praseodymium Pr = 140.92 No. 59	Neodymium Nd = 144.27 No. 60	Illinium Il = 146(?) No. 61	Samarium Sm = 150.43 No. 62	Europium Eu = 152.0 No. 63
	Gadolinium Gd = 157.3 No. 64	Terbium Tb = 159.2 No. 65	Dysprosium Dy = 162.46 No. 66	

Figure 2–8. Mendeléeff's periodic arrangement of the elements.

GROUP V RH_3 R_2O_5	GROUP VI RH_2 RO_3	GROUP VII RH R_2O_7	GROUP VIII		
Nitrogen N = 14.008 No. 7	Oxygen O = 16.000 No. 8	Fluorine F = 19.00 No. 9			
Phosphorus P = 31.02 No. 15	Sulfur S = 32.06 No. 16	Chlorine Cl = 35.457 No. 17			
Vanadium V = 50.95 No. 23	Chromium Cr = 52.01 No. 24	Manganese Mn = 54.93 No. 25	Iron Fe = 55.84 No. 26	Cobalt Co = 58.94 No. 27	Nickel Ni = 58.69 No. 28
Arsenic As = 74.93 No. 33	Selenium Se = 79.2 No. 34	Bromine Br = 79.916 No. 35			
Columbium Cb = 93.3 No. 41	Molybdenum Mo = 96.0 No. 42	Masurium Ma = ? No. 43	Ruthenium Ru = 101.7 No. 44	Rhodium Rh = 102.91 No. 45	Palladium Pd = 106.7 No. 46
Antimony Sb = 121.76 No. 51	Tellurium Te = 127.5 No. 52	Iodine 1 = 126.932 No. 53			
Tantalum Ta = 181.4 No. 73	Tungsten W = 184.0 No. 74	Rhenium Re = 186.31 No. 75	Osmium Os = 190.8 No. 76	Iridium Ir = 193.1 No. 77	Platinum Pt = 195.23 No. 78
Bismuth Bi = 209.00 No. 83	No. 84				
No. 91	Uranium U = 238.14 No. 92	No. 93			

Holmium Ho = 163.5 No. 67	Erbium Er = 167.64 No. 68	Thulium Tm = 169.4 No. 69	Ytterbium Yb = 173.5 No. 70	Lutecium Lu = 175.0 No. 71

Mendeléeff's prediction for eka-silicon (Es) (1871)	*Winkler's data for germanium (Ge)* (*Discovered in* 1886)
Atomic weight will be about 72	Atomic weight is 72.6
Will be obtained from EsO_2 or K_2EsF_6 by reduction with Na	Was obtained from K_2GeF_6 by reduction with Na
Will be a dark gray metal with high melting point and density about 5.5	Is a gray metal with melting point 958°C and density 5.36
On heating, Es will form the oxide EsO_2 with high melting point and density 4.7	Reacts with oxygen forming GeO_2 with melting point 1,100°C and density 4.7
The sulfide EsS_2 will be insoluble in water but soluble in ammonium sulfide	GeS_2 is insoluble in water but readily soluble in ammonium sulfide

Figure 2–9. (*From George Gamow,* Matter, Earth, and Sky. © 1958 *by Prentice-Hall, Inc. Reprinted by permission.*)

Prediction always appears mysterious. But quantitative prediction of the properties of unknown things appears doubly mysterious. Sometimes the process is relatively easy and obvious; sometimes it involves a kind of inspired guessing that only a person of considerable scientific experience can do. In the present case it depends on the fact that the properties of the elements are periodic; similar properties occur at regular intervals when the elements are arranged in the order of atomic weights.

As a simple example, suppose that one of the elements in the vertical column under lithium were not known. One could say in advance that it must be a soft metal since all the others in that column are like that. One could also say that it must be an alkali metal, which does not exist free in the natural state, because it is easily changed in the air and reacts violently with water. These are the properties of lithium, sodium, potassium, rubidium, and cesium. Therefore, if one of these were missing, as francium was until recently, its obvious properties could be predicted.

The more detailed and quantitative predictions require closer study. Figure 2–10 shows the relation that various elements have to a property known as the atomic volume, which is the volume or space occupied by an element as a solid in an amount of grams (1/28 ounce) equal to its atomic weight. Thus the atomic volume is the volume taken up by 6.94 grams of lithium, 9.02 grams of beryllium, 12.01 grams of carbon, and so on. From the drawing it is apparent that this property goes through cycles as the elements increase in atomic weight. The maximal atomic volume in each cycle is attained by the metals of the column in the Periodic Table under lithium, and includes sodium, potassium, rubidium,

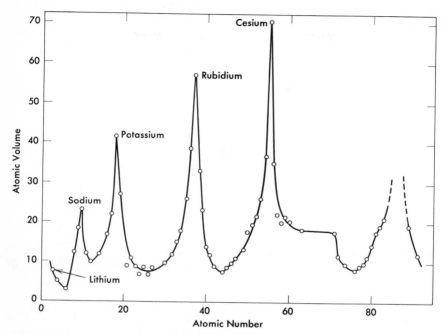

Figure 2–10. *Atomic volume and atomic numbers. Notice the regular way in which the atomic volume rises and falls as the elements grow heavier; notice also how the soft alkali metals all lie on the peaks, while the other elements fall in between.*

and cesium. The values for the other elements lie on the slopes and valleys between these peaks. Obviously, after the atomic weight of an unknown element has been estimated, it is easy to calculate its probable atomic volume merely by picking its position on the periodic graph (Figure 2–10).

When Mendeléeff made the Periodic Table there were many empty spaces in it. He was able to construct the table only by putting similar elements into the same vertical columns. All the empty spaces have now been filled, and the elements can be arranged in succession from 1 to 103 as we have done. This numbering of the elements in sequence has turned out to be a property even more useful than the atomic weight. Each element thus has an atomic number recording its location in the sequence from hydrogen to uranium. The Periodic Table then shows that elements with similar characteristics occur at regular intervals of two, eight, eighteen, or thirty-two elements apart.

It is tempting to ask what these numbers mean and what this periodicity tells us. They must surely be an expression of the internal structure of the atom. However, even at the end of the nineteenth century no one knew anything about the inside of atoms. When a chemist or a physicist thought of an atom he considered it a solid sphere like a billiard ball, relatively hard and uniform throughout.

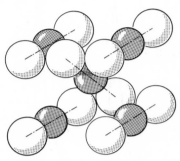

Figure 2–11. A crystal of solid carbon dioxide, or dry ice. Notice how each carbon atom (stippled) always has two oxygen atoms attached to it. A large crystal contains millions of such units arranged in this orderly geometrical way.

Even now this concept of an atom is useful for most work in chemistry. The organic chemist who builds complicated molecules like those of DDT or penicillin or rubber rarely thinks of the atom in any other way. The mineralogist still uses this concept whenever he wishes to describe the crystal structure of a compound. Figure 2–11 is an example of a kind of diagram that is repeatedly employed to make visual the make-up of chemical compounds. It is a diagram of solid carbon dioxide. The arrangement of the atoms in the molecule accounts for the properties of the compounds.

The Periodic Law of the Chemical Elements *

by Dmitri Mendeléeff (1889)

The periodic law has shown that our chemical individuals display a harmonic periodicity of properties dependent on their masses. Now natural science has long been accustomed to deal with periodicities observed in nature, to seize them with the vice of mathematical analysis, to submit them to the rasp of experiment. And these instruments of scientific

* From Dmitri Mendeléeff, *Faraday Lecture,* delivered before the Fellows of the Chemical Society, 1889.

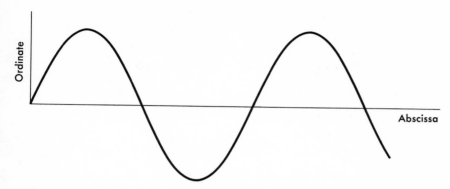

Figure 2–12. Plot of a sine curve showing a smooth periodic curve. Every point on this curve has a meaning since it is a plot of a continuous function. Compare this with Figure 2–10 in the last selection. Although the points are connected by lines to make it easier to follow there is no physical significance to the positions between the points representing the various elements. As Mendeléeff points out, the changes are sudden and discontinuous.

thought would surely, long since, have mastered the problem connected with the chemical elements, were it not for a new feature which was brought to light by the periodic law, and which gave a peculiar and original character to the periodic function.

If we mark on an axis of abscissae a series of lengths proportional to angles, and trace ordinates which are proportional to sines or other trigonometrical functions, we get periodic curves of a harmonic character. [Figure 2–12.] So it might seem, at first sight, that with the increase of atomic weights the function of the properties of the elements should also vary in the same harmonious way. But in this case there is no such continuous change as in the curves just referred to, because the periods do not contain the infinite number of points constituting a curve, but a *finite* number only of such points. An example will better illustrate this view. The atomic weights—

$$Ag = 108 \qquad Cd = 112 \qquad In = 113 \qquad Sn = 118 \qquad Sb = 120$$
$$Te = 125 \qquad I = 127$$

steadily increase, and their increase is accompanied by a modification of many properties which constitutes the essence of the periodic law. Thus, for example, the densities of the above elements decrease steadily, being respectively—

$$10.5 \qquad 8.6 \qquad 7.4 \qquad 7.2 \qquad 6.7 \qquad 6.4 \qquad 4.9$$

while their oxides contain an increasing quantity of oxygen—

$$Ag_2O \qquad Cd_2O_2 \qquad In_2O_3 \qquad Sn_2O_4 \qquad Sb_2O_5 \qquad Te_2O_6 \qquad I_2O_7$$

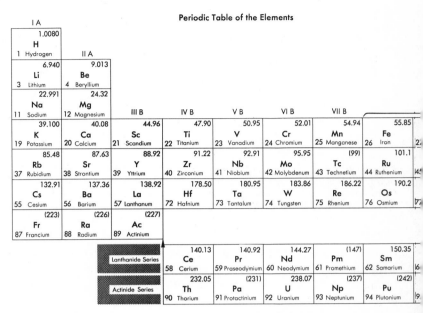

Figure 2–13. Periodic Table of the Elements. (Central Scientific Co., Chicago,

But to connect by a curve the summits of the ordinates expressing any of these properties would involve the rejection of Dalton's law of multiple proportions. Not only are there no intermediate elements between silver, which gives AgCl, and cadmium, which gives $CdCl_2$, but, according to the very essence of the periodic law, there can be none; in fact a uniform curve would be inapplicable in such a case, as it would lead us to expect elements possessed of special properties at any point of the curve. The periods of the elements have thus a character very different from those which are so simply represented by geometers. They correspond to points, to numbers, to sudden changes of the masses, and not to a continuous evolution. In these sudden changes destitute of intermediate steps or positions, in the absence of elements intermediate between, say, silver and cadmium, or aluminium and silicon, we must recognise a problem to which no direct application of the analysis of the infinitely small can be made. . . .

While connecting by new bonds the theory of the chemical elements with Dalton's theory of multiple proportions, or atomic structure of bodies, the periodic law opened for natural philosophy a new and wide

Periodic Table of the Elements

							Inert Gases
							4.003 **He** 2 Helium
	III A	IV A	V A	VI A	VII A		
	10.82 **B** 5 Boron	12.011 **C** 6 Carbon	14.008 **N** 7 Nitrogen	16.000 **O** 8 Oxygen	19.00 **F** 9 Fluorine	20.183 **Ne** 10 Neon	
	26.98 **Al** 13 Aluminum	28.09 **Si** 14 Silicon	30.975 **P** 15 Phosphorus	32.066 **S** 16 Sulfur	35.457 **Cl** 17 Chlorine	39.944 **Ar** 18 Argon	

	I B		II B	III A	IV A	V A	VI A	VII A	
3.71	63.54 **Cu** 29 Copper		65.38 **Zn** 30 Zinc	69.72 **Ga** 31 Gallium	72.60 **Ge** 32 Germanium	74.91 **As** 33 Arsenic	78.96 **Se** 34 Selenium	79.916 **Br** 35 Bromine	83.80 **Kr** 36 Krypton
6.4	107.880 **Ag** 47 Silver		112.41 **Cd** 48 Cadmium	114.82 **In** 49 Indium	118.70 **Sn** 50 Tin	121.76 **Sb** 51 Antimony	127.61 **Te** 52 Tellurium	126.91 **I** 53 Iodine	131.30 **Xe** 54 Xenon
.09	197.0 **Au** 79 Gold		200.61 **Hg** 80 Mercury	204.39 **Tl** 81 Thallium	207.21 **Pb** 82 Lead	209.00 **Bi** 83 Bismuth	(210) **Po** 84 Polonium	(210) **At** 85 Astatine	(222) **Rn** 86 Radon

26	158.93 **Tb** 65 Terbium	162.51 **Dy** 66 Dysprosium	164.94 **Ho** 67 Holmium	167.27 **Er** 68 Erbium	168.94 **Tm** 69 Thulium	173.04 **Yb** 70 Ytterbium	174.99 **Lu** 71 Lutetium
47)	(249) **Bk** 97 Berkelium	(251) **Cf** 98 Californium	(254) **Es** 99 Einsteinium	(253) **Fm** 100 Fermium	(256) **Md** 101 Mendelevium	**No** 102 Nobelium	103

Illinois. Copyright 1960. Reprinted by permission.)

field for speculation. Kant said that there are in the world "two things which never cease to call for the admiration and reverence of man: the moral law within ourselves, and the stellar sky above us." But when we turn our thoughts towards the nature of the elements and the periodic law, we must add a third subject, namely, "the nature of the elementary individuals which we discover everywhere around us." Without them the stellar sky itself is inconceivable; and in the atoms we see at once their peculiar individualities, the infinite multiplicity of the individuals, and the submission of their seeming freedom to the general harmony of Nature.

Having thus indicated a new mystery of Nature, which does not yet yield to rational conception, the periodic law, together with the revelations of spectrum analysis,[1] have contributed to again revive an old but remarkably long-lived hope—that of discovering, if not by experiment, at least by a mental effort, the *primary matter*—which had its genesis in the minds of the Grecian philosophers, and has been transmitted, together with many other ideas of the classic period, to the heirs of their civilisation.

1. Spectrum analysis will be discussed in Part 3. Ed.

The Atom Becomes Complex *
by Selig Hecht (1947)

Even before the end of the nineteenth century many chemists knew that the concept of the atom as a homogeneous elastic ball was merely a useful fiction. It explained a tremendous amount about the structure of matter, but it could not be true. There were several reasons for this, and the investigation of the reasons furnished new information that helped clarify and expand our ideas about atoms.

The most potent doubt about the complete homogeneity of atoms comes from the fact that atoms join with each other to form molecules. Billiard balls do not stick to each other, or enter into stable combinations by twos and threes. But atoms do; and because they combine, their surfaces must have special arrangements for holding on tightly to one another. Chemists called these holding devices bonds; and they soon found consistent regularities in the number and strength of the bonds that different elements possess.

An atomic bond can be defined as the capacity of an atom to hold a hydrogen atom or its equivalent. For example, an oxygen atom can hold two hydrogen atoms as in H_2O, water; therefore it has two bonds. A carbon atom can hold four hydrogen atoms as in methane, CH_4, and therefore it has four bonds. Moreover, since each oxygen atom has two bonds, carbon can hold two oxygen atoms, as in carbon dioxide, which is CO_2. A nitrogen atom can hold three hydrogen atoms as in ammonia, NH_3, and therefore has three bonds.

Elements in the same vertical column of the Periodic Table have the same number of atomic bonds. Often these bonds are spoken of as valences, especially when the elements rather than their atoms are referred to. In this way, hydrogen is single valent, or monovalent; oxygen is divalent; nitrogen, trivalent; and carbon, tetravalent.

All chemical reactions consist of the transformation of one molecular species into another, or several others. For example, when wood burns, the complex molecule of cellulose, which contains atoms of carbon, hydrogen, and oxygen, is transformed by combination with more oxygen atoms from the air into molecules of water and carbon dioxide. By means of their bonds the atoms in molecules can be rearranged into new combinations of atoms to produce different molecules. . . .

What are these surface structures, these bonds? Obviously a bond is not a hook that one atom sticks into another. If this were so, there would

* From Selig Hecht, *Explaining the Atom.*

be aggressive atoms and passive atoms, and there is no evidence for this. The behavior of the elements is such that, in water for example, it is just as correct to say that one oxygen atom holds two hydrogen atoms as that two hydrogen atoms hold one oxygen atom between them. Bonds represent reciprocal arrangements between atoms. When two atoms are joined, each atom undoubtedly contributes something to the bond holding them together.

But what is this that each atom contributes to make the bond that ties it to another atom? For years no one knew. Chemists generally were satisfied with the idea of bonds without caring much about its ultimate meaning. In fact, the answer to the question did not come from chemistry, but from electricity. And when the answer came it far transcended the original question, because it helped our understanding of many other phenomena beside atomic structure.

"ATOMS" OF ELECTRICITY

The ancient Greeks knew that when an amber rod is rubbed with cloth or fur, the amber becomes electrically charged, and is capable of picking up bits of straw and paper. Similarly, glass rods and many other objects when they are rubbed with cloth, silk, or fur become electrified. Some substances become positively charged, whereas others become negatively charged; this classification depends on whether in the charged state they are attracted or repelled by charged amber, which is arbitrarily considered negative. The Greek word for amber is *elektron*.

This kind of electrification of objects was called static or frictional electricity, and for many years it was considered different from flowing electricity, which had been discovered by Luigi Galvani and by Alessandro Volta in the eighteenth century. Flowing electricity is the form we know commonly; it is easily made chemically from batteries and flows along wires. However, one of the accomplishments of the nineteenth century was to show that the two sorts of electricity are really the same. The experiments for this purpose involved the discovery and isolation of the fundamental unit of electricity—the electron.

Let us take a glass tube sealed at each end, with a metal plate inside each end connected by a wire to an outside source of current. Such a system is shown in Figure 2–14. When the current is turned on, nothing happens in the tube. Normally the air in the tube offers such resistance to the passage of electricity that no current flows through it. If, however, the air has previously been sucked out of the tube so that the inside is almost a vacuum, the electricity can jump across the long gap in the tube, between the two terminal metal plates.

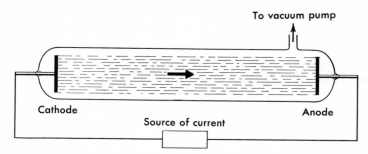

Figure 2–14. A Geissler tube. As the current is passed through the near vacuum in the tube, a stream of negative electrons passes from the negative cathode to the positive anode. The extremely dilute gas in the tube shows all sorts of pretty colors during the passage of the current.

When the current jumps from one metal plate to the other, something actually passes through the gas in the tube; something flows in a stream from one end to the other. If a small glass plate coated with zinc sulfide is placed in the path of the stream inside the tube, the zinc sulfide lights up the moment the current is turned on. If you look closely at the glowing plate of zinc sulfide, you can see that the glow is made up of tiny bursts of light all over it. It is as if now one particle of zinc sulfide is hit and bursts into a flash of light, then another particle of zinc sulfide is hit and bursts into light, then another, and another, and so on. The bursts of light are all the same size, a phenomenon that shows that the stream of electricity passing through the tube is composed of uniformly sized pieces, each of which when it hits a particle of zinc sulfide makes it give off a flash of light.

The stream that passes through the tube is made up not merely of units, but of negatively charged units. Their charge can be demonstrated by deflecting the stream with a magnet outside the tube. [Figure 2–15.] If the stream in the tube is narrow, it makes a glowing spot on the plate of zinc sulfide. As the magnet is brought near the tube the glowing spot shifts to the right or to the left depending on which way the magnet is held, and one can tell that the stream is negatively charged.

It was J. J. Thomson, the English physicist, who first showed that this stream is made up of charged unit particles, and he succeeded in weighing them. This sounds mysterious, but it is not. Just remember that it is easier to deflect a moving stream of ping-pong balls than a moving stream of freight cars. When a moving object is heavy it takes a lot of force to pull it out of its direct path, whereas if it is light, it can easily be pushed or pulled out of its motion in a straight line.

By measuring the magnetic force required to divert the stream of charged particles in the evacuated tube, J. J. Thomson was able to measure their mass. They turned out to be lighter by far than anything previously known. It will be recalled that the hydrogen atom was the lightest previously known material particle. Each of these charged units weighs only 1/1840 as much as a hydrogen atom.

As a result of this work we possess a new unit of matter, a particle that is 1840 times lighter than a hydrogen atom, and, unlike the hydrogen atom, carries a unit charge of electricity. In fact, Thomson was able to show that it *is* a unit charge of electricity. He called these new particles electrons, and demonstrated that they are the electric current. Electricity is electrons, and when the current flows, electrons move.

All electrons are alike. In Figure 2–14 the electrons come out of the metal plate on the left called the cathode, and travel to the metal plate on the right called the anode. It makes no difference what these metals are; the electrons that stream out from the negative cathode are all alike. They all weigh the same, and all have the same electrical charge.

Where are the electrons when the current does not flow through the evacuated tube? Where are the electrons in the battery when the wires are not connected? Where are the electrons when the generator is not

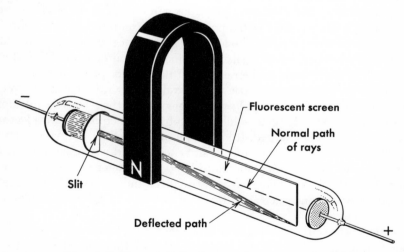

Figure 2–15. The deflection of cathode rays in a magnetic field. A moving charged body is deflected by a magnetic field. The direction of the deflection is perpendicular to the directions of both the magnetic field and the electron movement. (From Konrad Krauskopf and Arthur Beiser, The Physical Universe, *McGraw-Hill Book Co., Inc. Copyright 1960 by McGraw-Hill Book Co., Inc. Reprinted by permission.)*

turning in the powerhouse? These questions bring us right back to the structure of atoms. Clearly the electrons must be somewhere, since surely they are not created the moment the switch is closed in the lighting circuit. Where are they?

The electrons are in ordinary matter. Consider frictional electricity. The amber that has been rubbed with fur is negatively charged. This means that the amber has acquired electrons on its surface. These electrons can be led off the surface by a conducting wire and properly measured. They are the same electrons that form the stream in the evacuated tube and the current in the electric light. The amber acquired these electrons from the fur by rubbing them off the fur. As a result the amber became negative and the fur positive.

Evidently it is fairly easy to rub electrons off many materials. We do this every time we walk briskly on a carpet. The electrons are pulled off the carpet material and accumulate on the surface of the body. When we touch something metallic that can conduct the electrons from the surface of the body to the ever-receptive earth, they jump as a spark across the point of contact, and it is this concentration of electrons that causes the shock we feel on such occasions.

By various means electrons can be pulled out of all sorts of objects, no matter how innocent-looking. Fur, carpets, copper, gold, cheese, salt, and even water yield electrons. Electrons can be boiled off a wire merely by heating it in a vacuum, as happens in every vacuum tube in a radio set. Some of these electrons must be near the surface of the matter from which they can be rubbed off so easily. And since all matter is made of atoms, some of the electrons must be near or on the surface of the atoms.

Ordinarily, objects are electrically neutral, and so are their atoms. When their surface electrons are pulled off, objects and their constituent atoms become positively charged, while the substance acquiring the electrons becomes negatively charged. It looks as if atoms in their normal or neutral condition are made of something positive, combined with electrons, which are negative. Atoms cannot be considered any longer as uniform homogeneous elastic balls. They have a structure; and at least the surface of this structure is concerned with the way in which atoms stick together to form molecules.

In the last section we learned that when two atoms are joined, each contributes something to the bonds that hold them together. Without going into the details of the experiments, we can say at once that what each atom contributes to the bond is an electron. The chemical bond that keeps atoms together consists of a pair of electrons, one from each atom, which the participating atoms hold in common. In this way a one-bond atom (a monovalent atom) like hydrogen, or sodium, has one surface electron ready to be shared with another atom that is capable of reciprocal action.

The result is a two-electron tie that keeps the atoms together. Elements that are divalent have two surface electrons that can be shared, and these can be reciprocally taken up by another divalent atom or by two monovalent atoms. And so on with trivalent atoms.

Water has the capacity of breaking some of these bonds in such a way that one of the atoms gives up its electron and becomes positive, while the other atom takes up the electron and becames negative. Ordinary salt is sodium chloride and is written as NaCl, in which Na is the symbol for natrium or sodium. This is a neutral molecule, as we all know who have eaten it all our lives. When sodium chloride is dissolved in water, the sodium loses an electron and becomes Na^+, which is positively charged, while the chlorine gains this electron and becomes negatively charged, Cl^-. [Figure 2–16.]

If now a current of electricity is sent through such a salt solution, Na^+ picks up a negative charge at the cathode or negative pole, and becomes a neutral sodium atom (which reacts with water to form sodium hydroxide, NaOH). We can measure the number of electrons, that is, the amount

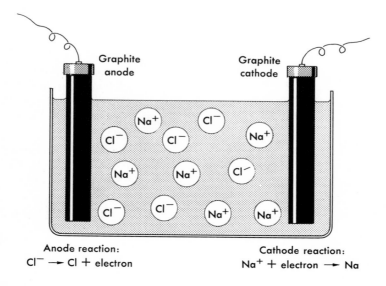

Anode reaction:
$$Cl^- \longrightarrow Cl + electron$$

Cathode reaction:
$$Na^+ + electron \longrightarrow Na$$

Figure 2–16. The electrolysis of molten sodium chloride. (From Krauskopf and Beiser, The Physical Universe.*)*

of current, required to discharge a certain large number of sodium atoms at the cathode. Let us call this amount a faraday of electricity. We can also measure the amount of current required to discharge that same number of copper atoms out of solution. The result is two faradays of electricity. Thus it takes twice as many electrons to form a neutral copper atom as it did to make a sodium atom. In other words, in solution copper was Cu^{++} while sodium was Na^+. Copper is divalent, and sodium is monovalent. And this holds not only here but in all the chemical transformations that sodium and copper undergo. In the same way we find that aluminum, which is trivalent, requires three electrons to be neutralized and deposited out of solution. In solution it is therefore Al^{+++}.

A substance in the charged condition such as Na^+ or Cu^{++} or Cl^- is often spoken of as ionized, and the individual charged atoms like Al^{+++} are called ions. The Greek word *ion* means wanderer, and these charged atoms are so called because they can wander in an electric field.

Gone now is the simple billiard-ball atom. In its place we have a sort of electrically neutral structure with easily detachable electrons on the surface. By the end of the nineteenth century this was all that was known for sure. However, during the last five years of the century there were ominous rumblings of future transformations in this simple structure that would eventually lead to the atomic bomb. These rumblings were the discoveries of X rays and radioactivity.

Two Ways of Looking at Nature

Figure 2–17. Stroboscopic photograph of a man swinging Indian clubs artificially divides a continuous motion into a series of instantaneous positions. (Photograph by Harold Edgerton of M.I.T. Reprinted by permission of Wide World Photos, New York.)

Figure 2–18. An eight-hour time exposure of the sky near Polaris blends the series of stellar positions which we observe into continuous circles. (Photograph by Lick Observatory. Reprinted by permission.)

Continuity and Discontinuity *
by Albert Einstein and Leopold Infeld (1938)

A map of New York City and the surrounding country is spread before us. We ask: which points on this map can be reached by train? After looking up these points in a railway timetable, we mark them on the map. We now change our question and ask: which points can be reached by car? If we draw lines on the map representing all the roads starting from

* From Albert Einstein and Leopold Infeld, *The Evolution of Physics*, Simon and Schuster, Inc., New York. Copyright 1938 Albert Einstein and Leopold Infeld. Reprinted by permission of the estate of Albert Einstein and Leopold Infeld.

New York, every point on these roads can, in fact, be reached by car. In both cases we have sets of points. In the first they are separated from each other and represent the different railway stations, and in the second they are the points along the lines representing the roads. Our next question is about the distance of each of these points from New York, or, to be more rigorous, from a certain spot in that city. In the first case, certain numbers correspond to the points on our map. These numbers change by irregular, but always finite, leaps and bounds. We say: the distances from New York of the places which can be reached by train change only in a *discontinuous* way. Those of the places which can be reached by car, however, may change by steps as small as we wish, they can vary in a *continuous* way. The changes in distance can be made arbitrarily small in the case of a car, but not in the case of a train.

The output of a coal mine can change in a continuous way. The amount of coal produced can be decreased or increased by arbitrarily small steps. But the number of miners employed can change only discontinuously. It would be pure nonsense to say: "Since yesterday, the number of employees has increased by 3.783."

Asked about the amount of money in his pocket, a man can give a number containing only two decimals. A sum of money can change only by jumps, in a discontinuous way. In America the smallest permissible change or, as we shall call it, the "elementary quantum" for American money, is one cent. The elementary quantum for English money is one farthing, worth only half the American elementary quantum. Here we have an example of two elementary quanta whose mutual values can be compared. The ratio of their values has a definite sense since one of them is worth twice as much as the other.

We can say: some quantities can change continuously and others can change only discontinuously, by steps which cannot be further decreased. These indivisible steps are called the *elementary quanta* of the particular quantity to which they refer.

We can weigh large quantities of sand and regard its mass as continuous even though its granular structure is evident. But if the sand were to become very precious and the scales used very sensitive, we should have to consider the fact that the mass always changes by a multiple number of one grain. The mass of this one grain would be our elementary quantum. From this example we see how the discontinuous character of a quantity, so far regarded as continuous, can be detected by increasing the precision of our measurements.

If we had to characterize the principal idea of the quantum theory in one sentence, we could say: *it must be assumed that some physical quantities so far regarded as continuous are composed of elementary quanta.*

Continuity and Discontinuity *

by Tobias Dantzig (1954)

The words *continuum, continuous, continuity* were used in the exact sciences from their very beginning. From time immemorial the term *continuous* has been applied to space, time and motion in the undetermined sense of something uninterrupted, something that is of the same nature in its smallest parts as it is in its entirety, something *singly connected*, in short *something continuous!* don't you know. It is one of those vague, loosely conceived notions of which intuition perceives the sense; and yet any attempt to formulate it in a precise definition invariably ends in an impatient: "Well, you know what I mean!" . . .

If, without venturing on a precise formulation of our intuitive idea of continuity, I should try to describe roughly what I mean by *continuous,* I should be thinking aloud as follows:

"Time is the essence of all things. Mother Nature *makes* no jumps, because Father Time *knows* no jumps. Time cannot be conceivably interrupted, that is why there is nothing spontaneous in nature. Time flows on and in its flow it carries all things conceivable."

And so when we attempt to describe the continuity of any phenomenon, we find ourselves invariably, even if unconsciously, invoking the continuity of time. The line appears to us as the prototype of all things continuous because we conceive it as generated by a continuous passage, because to our minds it is but a concrete representation of the Stream of Time, frozen as it were.

So too, is it with other phenomena. The mind shrinks before the spontaneous; that is why our scientific theories cling so desperately to evolution. Be it a cosmogony, a theory of life, or a sociological hypothesis, everywhere we find this horror of the cataclysm. At any cost we refuse to recognize that catastrophe and revolution, spontaneous generation and accidental discovery, may have been dominant factors in the history of the universe or of the race.

And just as evolution gives us a smooth picture of our past, the doctrine of causality, by linking all phenomena into one continuous chain, safeguards our future against all spontaneous disturbances and protects us against the horror of chaos. These vague ideas of continuity and causality are so closely associated that one is constantly invoked to support the other. And no wonder: our belief in the continuity of the

* From Tobias Dantzig, *Number, the Language of Science,* 4th edition. Copyright 1954 by The Macmillan Company. Reprinted by permission.

universe and our faith in the causal connection between its events are but two aspects of this primitive intuition that we call *time*. . . .

Your consciousness attests of the *now;* your mind recalls other *nows,* less distinct as they recede into the *past* until lost in the hazy dawn of memory. These temporal series, vague and overlapping, you attach to one individual, whom you call *I*. In the course of a few years, every cell of this individual's body has changed; his thoughts, judgments, emotions, and aspirations have undergone a similar metamorphosis. What is then this permanence which you designate as *I*? Surely not the mere name which differentiates this individual from his fellow men! Is it then this temporal series strung like beads on the filament of memory? [Figure 2–19.]

A discrete sequence of disjointed recollections which begins some time in infancy and abruptly terminates with the present, such is *time* as an immediate datum of consciousness. When, however, this raw material has undergone the mysterious refining process known as physical intuition, it emerges as something quite different. *Intuitive time is extrapolated time,* extrapolated beyond the dawn of consciousness, into the infinite recesses of the *past,* and beyond the present into the infinite *future,* this latter also being conceived as made up of *nows,* as the past has been. By an act of our mind we separate time into these two classes, the past and the future, which are mutually exclusive and together comprise *all* of time, *eternity.* The *now* to our mind is but a partition which separates the past from the future; and since any instant of the past was once a *now,* and since any instant of the future will be a *now* anon, we conceive any instant of the past or the future as such a partition.

Is this all? No, intuitive time is *interpolated* time: between any two instants of the past, however closely associated in our memory, we insert—again by an act of the mind—other instants, in number indefinite.

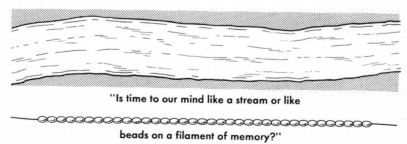

"Is time to our mind like a stream or like

beads on a filament of memory?"

Figure 2–19. "*Is time to our mind like a stream?*" "*Or like beads on a filament of memory?*"

This is what we mean by *continuity* of the past; and the same continuity we impose on the future. *Time, to our mind is a stream;* to be sure, of this stream our experience knows but disconnected elements; yet our intuition fills in the gaps left by experience; it converts time into a *continuum,* the prototype of all continua in nature.

What is, for instance, that perfect continuity which we ascribe to a geometrical line, if not the conviction that we can describe such a line by an *uninterrupted* motion of the hand? We transfer the streamlike character of duration to all physical phenomena: our first attempt to analyze any phenomenon, whether it be light or sound, heat or electricity, is to express it in terms of distance, mass, or energy, so that we may reduce it to a *function of time.*

The conflict between the discrete and the continuous is not a mere product of school dialectics: it may be traced to the very origin of thought, for it is but the reflection of the ever present discord between this conception of time as a stream and the discontinuous character of all experience. For, in the ultimate analysis, our number concept rests on *counting,* i.e., on enumerating the discrete, discontinuous, interrupted, while our time intuition paints all phenomena as flowing. . . .

Herein I see the genesis of the conflict between geometrical intuition, from which our physical concepts derive, and the logic of arithmetic. The harmony of the universe knows only one musical form—the *legato;* while the symphony of number knows only its opposite—the *staccato.* All attempts to reconcile this discrepancy are based on the hope that an accelerated *staccato* may appear to our senses as a *legato.* Yet our intellect will always brand such attempts as deceptions and reject such theories as an insult, as a metaphysics that purports to explain away a concept by resolving it into its opposite.

But these protests are in vain. To bridge the chasm between the continuity of our concept of time and the inherent discontinuity of the number structure, man had to invoke once more that power of his mind "which knows itself capable of conceiving the indefinite repetition of the same act when once this act is possible." This was the historic role of the infinite; this is why through the ages the problems of the continuum and of the infinite were but the two horns of a single dilemma.

PROBLEMS OF NUMBER AND INFINITY

Written numeration is probably as old as private property. There is little doubt that it originated in man's desire to keep a record of his flocks and other goods. Notches on a stick or tree, scratches on stones and rocks, marks in clay—these are the earliest forms of this endeavor to

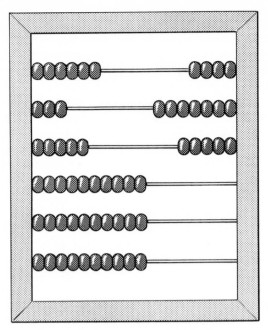

Figure 2–20. A schematic drawing of a counting board.

record numbers by written symbols. . . . Most of us have learned to count at a very tender age, and few of us have had occasion to reflect on the subject since. Let us refresh our memories.

It all begins as a sort of coordination between *fingers* and *lips*. The child learns to associate certain patterns formed by his fingers or blocks with certain words. He is told that these words are called numbers, and he is made to memorize them in an *ordered series*. By the time he has run short of fingers and blocks, he is taught to use a quaint *rhetorical* procedure which enables him to extend his counting scope without recourse to new tangible patterns. By now, counting has turned into a race with numbers or a game of words, a game which the child is only too eager to play, at first. Until one day he comes to realize that, after all, *what has been said or done once can always be repeated;* then stopping abruptly at some term in this number series, he dismisses the rest with an impatient "and so forth and so on." On that day his education in counting has been completed. There is planted, at the same time, in his mind the germ of an idea which many years later will rise to perplex him in the guise of the *concept of infinity.* . . .

The strength of arithmetic lies in its *absolute generality.* Its rules admit of no exceptions: they apply to *all numbers.*

All numbers! Everything hangs on this short but so tremendously important word *all*.

There is no mystery about this word, when it is applied to any *finite* class of things or circumstances. When, for instance, we say "all living men," we attach a very definite meaning to it. We can imagine all mankind arranged in an array of some sort: in this array there will be a *first* man, and there will be a *last* man. To be sure, to prove in all rigor a property true of all living men we should prove it for each individual. While we realize that the actual task would involve insurmountable difficulties, these difficulties, we feel, are of a purely *technical* and not of a *conceptual* character. And this is true of any *finite* collection, i.e., of any collection which has a *last* as well as a *first* member, for *any such collection can be exhausted by counting.*

Can we mean the same thing when we say *all numbers?* Here too, the collection can be conceived as an array, and this array will have a first member, the number *one.* But how about the last?

The answer is ready: *There is no last number!* The process of counting cannot conceivably be terminated. *Every number has a successor.* There is an *infinity* of numbers.

But if there be no last number, what do we mean by all numbers, and particularly, what do we mean by *the property of all numbers?* How can we prove such a property: certainly not by testing every individual case, since we know beforehand that we cannot possibly exhaust all cases.

At the very threshold of mathematics we find this *dilemma of infinity,* like the legendary dragon guarding the entrance to the enchanted garden.[1]

What is the source of this concept of infinity, this faith in the inexhaustibility of the counting process? Is it experience? Certainly not! Experience teaches us the finitude of all things, of all human processes. We know that any attempt on our part to exhaust number by counting would only end in our own exhaustion.

Nor can the existence of the infinite be established mathematically, because infinity, the inexhaustibility of the counting process, is a mathematical assumption, *the basic assumption of arithmetic,* on which all mathematics rests. Is it then a supernatural truth, one of those few gifts which the Creator bestowed upon man when he cast him into the

---

1. Around infinity have grown up various mathematical paradoxes, as for example, Zeno's famous paradox: If the tortoise has the start of Achilles, Achilles can never come up with the tortoise; for while Achilles traverses the distance from his starting point to the starting point of the tortoise, the tortoise advances a certain distance, and while Achilles traverses this distance, the tortoise makes a further advance, and so on ad infinitum. Consequently, Achilles may run ad infinitum without overtaking the tortoise. (Zeno's paradox, *Encyclopaedia Brittanica*, 1911.) Ed.

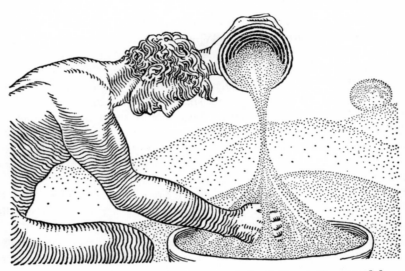

Figure 2–21. (From Guy Murchie, Music of the Spheres. *Reprinted by permission.)*

universe, naked and ignorant, but free to shift for himself? Or has the concept of infinity grown upon man, grown out, indeed, of his futile attempts to reach the last number? Is it but a confession of man's impotence to exhaust the universe by number?

"There is a last number, but it is not in the province of man to reach it, for it belongs to the gods." Such is the keynote of most ancient religions. The stars in the heavens, the grains of sand, the drops of the ocean exemplify this *ultra-ultimate* which is beyond the mind of man to reach. "He counted the stars and named them all," says the psalmist of Jehovah. And Moses in invoking the promise of God to his chosen people says: "He who can count the dust of the earth will also count your seed." [Figure 2–21.]

. . . It is a plausible hypothesis that the early conception of infinity was not the uncountable, but the yet uncounted. The last number meant *patience* and *perseverance*, and man seemed to be lacking in these qualities. It was of the same order of things as reaching heaven in the story of the Tower of Babel. The last number, like the heavens, belonged to God. In His jealous wrath He would confound the tongues of the ambitious builders.

Questions To Consider

How was the atomic idea used to account for the experimental fact that elements combine in definite proportions by weight?

How did the interest in whole numbers influence the development of atomic theory?

How does a scientific theory differ from a philosophical idea?

In Part 1 Aristotle was quoted as saying "Time is the number of motion" and in this part Dantzig describes time as "a series [of events] strung like beads on the filament of memory." Is it possible that our intuitive idea of a continuously flowing time is mistaken and that time is atomic like matter and electricity?

Suggestions for Further Reading

* Born, Max: *The Restless Universe,* Dover Publications, Inc., 1951. One of the most readable accounts of modern physics ever written. This book covers such subjects as atomic and molecular theory, the periodic table, ions, and electronic charge as well as many subjects which will be covered later.

* De Santillana, Giorgio: *The Origins of Scientific Thought,* Mentor Books, The New American Library, Inc., 1961. Chapter 9 is especially recommended for a discussion of the Greek atomic theory.

* Gamow, George: *The Atom and Its Nucleus,* Spectrum Books, Prentice-Hall, Inc., 1961. A popular introduction to atomic and nuclear physics. This book will be useful supplementary reading for Parts 2, 3, 4, and 5.

* Haber, Heinz: *Our Friend the Atom,* Dell Publishing Co., Inc., 1956. An elementary introduction to atomic science enlivened with Walt Disney illustrations. This popular little book will be good supplementary reading also for the next three parts.

* Heisenberg, Werner: *Physics and Philosophy: The Revolution in Modern Science,* Torchbooks, Harper & Row, 1962. The first part of this book is a presentation of the author's views on the historical basis of atomic science. The latter part discusses the quantum theory and will be pertinent to Part 3.

Russell, Bertrand: *Our Knowledge of the External World,* Mentor Books, The New American Library, Inc., 1956. A collection of lectures, discussing, among other things, the theory of continuity and the problem of infinity. Zeno's paradox is dealt with in some detail.

* Paperback edition

3

Is Matter Substance or Form?

The physics of the twentieth century has dematerialized matter. Beginning with the discovery of radioactivity, the selections in this part lead into a discussion of the strange duality of the quantum and wave nature of matter and leave a number of unanswered questions. Is matter not substance at all but just pure shape? How do these new developments affect the concept of matter and the materialistic interpretation of nature?

Is Matter Substance or Form?

Introduction

THE WORLD of our experience seems to consist of two unrelated types of phenomena. There are the material objects which occupy space and are relatively permanent. These objects have properties that can be measured and defined—weight, size, density, and so on. Taken together, they constitute the physical world and were the first objects of scientific study. In addition there exists a broad category of more ephemeral phenomena which, nevertheless, seem to be just as real and important: thought, emotion, spirit, and abstract ideas like courage, freedom, beauty, and harmony. These abstractions do not occupy space and time in the same sense that material objects do. In between there are a few phenomena that don't seem to fit clearly into either realm: air, fire, heat, color, sound, light and shadow, and forces like gravity and electricity and magnetism.

Several of the early philosophers such as Plato and Pythagoras suggested that the realm of the mind was more important than the material realm, that objects in the physical world were imperfect reflections of pure forms which existed outside of space and time.

Science, however, by turning its attention first to the physical world led to an acceptance of the opposite point of view. As scientific understanding of the objective world grew, more and more of the unclassified phenomena were found to belong to the physical realm. They were discovered to be either matter very thinly dispersed (like air) or matter that was undergoing change (like fire, sound, and heat). Light, gravity, and electromagnetic fields still resisted classification. But, by and large, it was assumed that it was just a question of time before all phenomena including those of mind and emotion could be fitted neatly into the material realm. This belief led to the view that all reality consisted essentially of brute matter operating according to immutable laws and that thoughts and ideals were only ephemeral and probably unimportant by-products of some physical process.

The first crack in the materialistic front appeared with the discovery of radioactivity where matter was seen to be disintegrating before our eyes into light and energy. This discovery was followed by Einstein's theory that matter and energy are different manifestations of the same thing. And, simultaneously, the unraveling of various aspects of atomic structure led to the strange conclusion that both matter and energy could be described as either particles or waves, depending on the circumstances under which they were studied. Finally, it was suggested that even particles can be presented as configurations of confined waves. Waves of what? Physics has not answered that question. Some scientists believe that they are not waves of anything but are just pure shapes.

These ideas can all be expressed best in terms of mathematical equations. There is no one set of physical concepts that will enable us to understand them in concrete terms and thus reality appears to be more closely related to abstract formulations than to any physical models. As James Jeans expresses it: "Today there is a wide measure of agreement which on the physical side of science approaches almost to unanimity, that the stream of knowledge is heading towards a non-mechanical reality; the universe begins to look more like a great thought than like a great machine." [1]

This interpretation implies that reality is simply a manifestation of thought and brings us back almost full circle to the ideas of Plato and Pythagoras who believed that relationships are more real than things.

Modern physics, however, does not support this extreme view. Rather it lends support to the view that both realms may be equally real. Niels Bohr suggested one solution to the wave-particle puzzle by saying that each of the two apparently contradictory concepts is valid within its own context. Although it may not ever be possible to resolve the two concepts because they represent different aspects of reality, taken together, they give a complete description of atomic events. This theory suggests to some writers a new resolution of the apparent contradiction between the physical and spiritual elements in human experience which could lead to a major revolution in man's view of reality.

1. From James Jeans, *The Mysterious Universe*, Cambridge University Press, New York, 1930.

Radioactivity

Penetrating Rays [*]
by Alfred Romer (1960)

Early in the new year of 1896, all over the world, people opened their newspapers to read a little story from Vienna. The report said that a German professor named Routgen had discovered a way of photographing hidden things, even to the bones within a living, human hand. It was a startling story, especially since it happened to be true. In a very few weeks laboratories in every country began to turn out pictures of bones: bones of hands and bones of feet, bones of arms and of legs and of anything else that could be managed in the human anatomy. Surgeons saw the usefulness of this strange photography, and (once the spelling of his name had been corrected) Professor Wilhelm Conrad Röntgen of the University of Würzburg became one of the most celebrated men of the day. . . .

How [Röntgen] first came upon his rays we do not know, but it was probably by accident when he was busy about something else. The apparatus he needed to produce them was common and likely to be found in any university laboratory. He used a spark coil to supply electricity at high voltage, a cathode-ray tube to discharge it through, and that was all. The "tube" was simply a bulb of glass, which might be round or sausage-shaped [1] or pear-shaped, pumped down to a good vacuum and provided with a pair of metal "electrodes" for the electric discharge to pass between. (Figure 3–1.)

It was at one of these electrodes, the "cathode," where negative electricity jumped off to the scanty gas remaining in the tube, that the cathode rays came into being, and they stretched away at right angles to its surface. If the walls of the tube were close enough for the cathode rays to reach them, then under the play of those rays the glass lit up with a

1. See also Geissler tube, p. 52. Ed.

Negative
electrode
or cathode

Positive
electrode
or anode

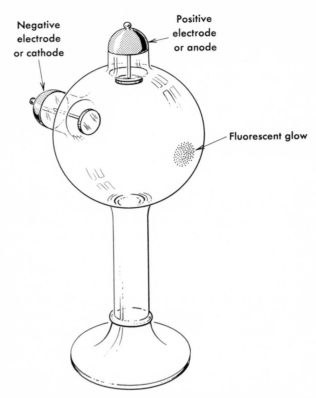

Fluorescent glow

Figure 3–1. Simple cathode-ray tube. The tube is an evacuated glass bulb with a negative electrode, or "cathode," and a positive electrode, or "anode," sealed through the glass wall. The location of the anode is not important. When a fairly high voltage is applied, the cathode rays, which are streams of electrons, come off the cathode at right angles to its surface. Where they strike the glass wall a fluorescent glow is excited.

fluorescent glow [2] which was green for tubes made of English lime glass and blue for the lead glass of the Germans. Here, in this fluorescent glow, Röntgen's X-rays were produced.

However Röntgen first happened to notice them, the important thing he did was to investigate. He found where they were produced; he found how they traveled in straight lines, how they could excite a fluorescent glow in a particular compound, called barium platinocyanide; how they

2. A fluorescent substance has the property of absorbing light of one wave length and in its place emitting light of another wave length. Ed.

would penetrate some materials and be stopped by others, so that familiar objects cast very strange shadows across the glow they excited. He found that they would expose a photographic plate (film had been invented then, but everyone preferred glass plates for serious work), and he photographed the shadows, making strange, new pictures of the insides of things. During the last two months of 1895 he worked at top speed, and by Christmas he felt ready to make an announcement.

It is understood in science that the first man to make his discovery public may claim the credit for it. He may claim no more than he announces, however, and once he has announced it, it stands over his name, right or wrong, forever. Röntgen now was sure of what he knew, and he chose the quickest of all possible ways of getting it into print. There was in Würzburg a scientific society which met for the reading of "papers" (as research reports are usually called) and published them later in its *Proceedings*. On the Saturday after Christmas, Röntgen called on the secretary of this society, who accepted his paper and sent it to the printer, to be set up in type and run off at once as a ten-page pamphlet. On New Year's Day, Röntgen mailed copies of this pamphlet to the leading physicists of Europe, and into each envelope he slipped a handful of the pictures he had taken, the first X-ray pictures in the world. It was from the pamphlet sent to Vienna that word reached the newspapers, and this is how it happened that this German discovery was first made known in Austria.

Our business, however, is with the copy of Röntgen's pamphlet that went to Paris, to the mathematical physicist Henri Poincaré. In Paris was the *Académie des Sciences,* whose seventy-eight members were the most distinguished scientists of France, and which stood at the center of all French science. It met on Mondays for the reading of papers (which it published within two weeks), and there, on the afternoon of January 20, 1896, the Academicians had the pleasure of seeing the first French X-ray of the bones of a hand, the work of two physicians named Oudin and Barthélemy. The pictures led to talk and the talk to questions, which Poincaré, of course, could answer.

Among the curious listeners was Henri Becquerel, an Academician as his father and grandfather had been and, like his father and grandfather also, Professor of Physics at the Museum of Natural History. What interested him was the report that the X-rays arose in the fluorescent spot on the wall of the cathode-ray tube. The fluorescence produced by light was one of the effects his father had investigated, and he himself had worked with it a little. If the fluoresence of the cathode rays contained X-rays, then X-rays might be produced in other varieties of the fluorescent glow.

So Röntgen's publication accomplished its work. To a total stranger it had given a new idea, and Becquerel went back to the Museum to put his idea to the test.

For a month he found nothing, and then for a new set of experiments he happened to choose as his fluorescent material some crystals of potassium uranyl sulfate. This is a complicated compound of potassium, uranium, oxygen, and sulfur, whose crystals (as he knew from personal experience) would glow under ultraviolet light. To detect the penetrating rays he still hoped for, he took a photographic plate, wrapping it in heavy black paper to screen it from ordinary light. For the ultraviolet light to excite the fluorescence of his crystals he chose sunshine, and he set the plates outside his window with the crystals lying above the paper wrappings. Hours later he took them in, and as he developed them under the red light of his darkroom, he was pleased to see the grayish smudges which slowly grew on their creamy surfaces wherever a crystal had lain.

He tried again, laying a coin or a bit of metal pierced with holes below each crystal, and now he saw those metal objects silhouetted in light patches on the darker gray around them. In a third trial, he set each crystal on a thin slip of glass to act as a barrier against any vapors which the sun's heat might have driven through the pores of the paper to blacken the plate by chemical action. Once more the plates darkened as though the glass were not there, and Becquerel was confident that he had found a penetrating ray which was produced by light. On February 24, at the next session of *Académie* he reported it.

Notice how neatly it all worked out. Becquerel had made an hypothesis that X-rays were a normal part of fluorescence. The hypothesis had suggested an experiment, and the experiment had given exactly the results he predicted. It was as pretty and as misleading a piece of scientific work as you could ask. Luckily, Becquerel went on with new experiments, and even before his announcement appeared in print, he had learned a good deal more about his rays and was a good deal more perplexed.

In the next three days the weather changed. Wednesday's plates were hardly ready when clouds came over the sun, and into a drawer went plates, black paper, crystals and all. There they lay in the dark until Sunday, and in the dark, as Becquerel knew, nothing could happen. Potassium uranyl sulfate would glow only while the ultraviolet light fell on it; when that light was shut off, the fluorescent glow ceased within a hundredth of a second. Even so, when Sunday came, Becquerel, with a kind of methodical impatience, pulled out the unused plates and developed them anyway. What leaped up before his eyes were patches far blacker than he yet had seen. Even without light the crystals seemed able to send out their rays, and when he ran through the experiments once more in the total blackness of his darkroom, he found that this was true.

It was true and inexplicable, and all he could do was investigate. Some of his crystals he laid away in darkness to see how long it might take their penetrating rays to fade. Whenever he tested them, in the hours and days and weeks that followed, there were always rays pouring out vigorously. He tried other fluorescent materials, and whenever they contained uranium, he found his rays, but when they were made with calcium or zinc he did not. He tried uranium compounds that were not fluorescent, and from them, oddly enough, the rays appeared again.

What was puzzling about all this was the energy [3] involved. It took energy to expose the photographic plates, energy which the crystals had somehow stored away. Becquerel would have liked to know how that energy entered a crystal, what he needed to do to start a crystal going, but none that he had seemed ready to run down. Shut away in his darkroom, he tried the trick of gently heating a crystal of uranyl nitrate until the water molecules which were built into its structure were set free by the warmth, and the crystal dissolved at last in its own "water of crystallization." That might have been expected to set free any stored-up energy, but when the test tube cooled and the uranyl nitrate recrystallized in the darkness, it regained its power to give out the rays. It was truer in fact to say that it kept it, for he presently found that rays came from the solution as freely as from the solid crystals.

The one constant thing in all his experiments was the presence of uranium. So long as his material contained uranium it did not matter whether it was fluorescent or not, whether it lay in light or darkness, whether it was solid or in solution. It seemed to Becquerel worth trying whether pure, metallic uranium might not give the rays also. Pure uranium did not exist, but, as it happened, Henri Moissan of the School of Pharmacy in Paris was busy at the moment on a new process for refining it. Becquerel waited, and when Moissan succeeded in early May, he tried out a disc of simple, uncombined, uranium metal. Its rays were more intense than any he had ever seen.

It was true, and yet altogether odd (as he pointed out) that a pure metal should have the power to give out rays from some unknown source of stored-up energy.

3. Energy is defined as the capacity for doing work. There are a number of different kinds of energy: kinetic, potential, electrical, etc. At the time of Becquerel's experiments it was believed that the energy of a closed system always remained constant. Although it could change its form (for instance from potential to kinetic) the total energy remained the same. Today this conservation law is recognized as part of the broader law of conservation of mass-energy. Ed.

THE CURIES AND THEIR TWO NEW ELEMENTS

Since they did not give pictures of bones, Becquerel's rays were not nearly as fascinating as Röntgen's, and no one else saw any profit in studying the mysterious penetrating rays from uranium. Perhaps this is why they attracted Marie Curie near the end of 1897 when they had lain neglected for nearly a year and a half.

Madame Curie had begun life as Marya Sklodowska, the daughter of a teacher of mathematics and physics in Warsaw, in what was then Russian Poland. A driving ambition to study those subjects had sent her to Paris, where she had taken her preliminary degrees at the Sorbonne, and where she had met and married Pierre Curie, Professor of Physics at a technical school which the city of Paris maintained, the Municipal School for Industrial Physics and Chemistry. Now, after the birth of her first daughter, she was anxious to go on. The next stage would be the doctor's degree, and in France that required a long and elaborate piece of private research. A topic in which no one else was interested would give her an ideal project, since there was little danger that an unknown competitor in some other laboratory might solve its problems first.

She did not plan to work by photography as Becquerel had done, but to detect the rays by another property he had discovered. This was their curious ability to discharge electrified bodies. It was as though they managed to convert the air through which they passed from an insulator to a conductor of electricity, and in this effect she saw the possibility also of gauging their intensity. To do it, she would have to measure exceedingly delicate currents, but she had an excellent instrument for just such work, an improved electrometer, which Pierre Curie and his brother Jacques had designed.[4]

She began with Moissan's uranium metal, and tried, like Becquerel, to find the source of its energy, but no heating of the disc, nor any exposure to light or X-rays managed to change the strength of its rays. At last, in February, she turned to something new. Becquerel had shown that the rays came from uranium in whatever state he had it. It occurred to her that the ray-giving might be a power other metals shared, and she began a hunt which went on and on with no particular success. Sometimes she tested pure metals, sometimes minerals just as they came from the mine, sometimes the carefully purified compounds of the chemical manufacturer. Again and again she found nothing, with the one very odd exception of pitchblende.

Pitchblende is an ore of uranium, but since its uranium had to share

4. See Glossary for description of this *electrometer*. Ed.

space inside the crystals with oxygen, not to mention a number of assorted impurities, it was most astonishing to find it giving out rays with considerably more intensity than the pure metal. She ran a long series of measurements with purified compounds of uranium and found only what might have been expected, that the more other elements diluted the uranium, the weaker were the rays. Yet quite regularly uranium minerals gave very strong rays. Just possibly the complex crystal structure of a mineral might somehow strengthen the ray-giving, but it was a lame argument, which she proceeded to demolish by cooking up an artificial chalcolite (copper uranyl phosphate) out of laboratory-pure reagents. The uranium it contained gave no stronger rays in the crystal form of the mineral than in the storage bottles on the shelves, and the imitation remained weaker than natural chalcolite.

This raised the possibility that an impurity in the minerals was contributing the extra rays, but when she searched the Periodic Table from end to end, she was able to find only two ray-giving elements, uranium and thorium—and there was no thorium to speak of in the minerals she was testing. Could the impurity be an undiscovered element?

Although Marie Curie did not spell out the argument in the paper reporting all this, which Professor Gabriel Lippmann of the Sorbonne read for her at the *Académie*, it was plain enough to anyone who looked at the Periodic Table. Gallium, scandium, and germanium had by no means filled up all the gaps. There was a particularly impressive set between bismuth near the bottom and uranium and thorium at the very end. Those two heavy metals, with the fantastic names of forgotten gods, were the only ray-givers of all the elements known. If an unknown, ray-giving element also existed, it might well fit one of the gaps in their neighborhood. (Figure 3–2.)

Tracking down a new element was a job for a chemist, for an experienced chemist who knew intimately all the varieties of behavior of all the known elements. Neither Marie nor Pierre Curie was a chemist at all, and Gustave Bémont, the man they turned to for advice, was only the laboratory instructor at the Municipal School. Yet the element they were looking for would be easy to find. It must be a ray-giver, and if it differed only from uranium and thorium, then it had to be new.

Pierre Curie had gradually been drawn into the electrometer measurements and all the puzzles they raised, and now he took his place as an equal partner in the hunt for the new element. Together the two Curies ground up some pitchblende, dissolved it in acid, and set to work. What they had to do was to sort out all the different elements that might be in the mineral, and the great device for this kind of sorting was the filter. Whenever they could produce a slushy mixture of a liquid with the

I	II	III	IV	V	VI	VII	VIII		
Li 7.03	Be 9.08	S 10.95	C 12.0	N 14.04	O 16.0	F 19.06			
Na 23.05	Mg 24.3	Al 27.1	Si 28.4	P 31.02	S 32.1	Cl 35.45			
K 39.11	Ca 40.1	Sc 44.1	Ti 48.2	V 51.4	Cr 52.14	Mn 55.0	Fe 56.0	Co 58.9	Ni 58.1
Cu 63.6	Zn 65.4	Ga 69.9	Ge 72.5	As 75.0	Se 79.0	Br 80.0			
Rb 85.4	Sr 87.6	Y 89.0	Zr 90.4	Nb 93.7	Mo 96.0	?	Ru 101.7	Rh 103.0	Pd 106.4
Ag 107.9	Cd 112.0	In 113.9	Sn 119.1	Sb 120.4	Te 127.5	I 126.9			
Cs 132.9	Ba 137.4	La 138.6	Ce 140.2						
		Yb 173.2		Ta 182.8	W 184.8		Os 191	Ir 193.1	Pt 194.9
Au 197.2	Hg 200.0	Tl 204.1	Pb 206.9	Bi 208.1					
			Th 232.6		U 239.6				

Figure 3–2. The Periodic Table. This is the Periodic Table in its 1898 version. Vacant spaces in the table led to the hypothesis that unknown elements of the appropriate characteristics must exist, and the search for these unknowns had a prominent part in the discovery of radioactivity.

undissolved grains of some stuff, they would pour this into a cone of paper set down in a glass funnel. Then the liquid would ooze through the pores of the paper and drip away while the undissolved grains were caught and held back. That gave them two different things in two different places, and they had begun to sort out the mixture.

When, for example, they bubbled the unpleasant but very useful gas called hydrogen sulfide into their solution, this reacted with a few, perhaps five, metals to form insoluble sulfides, and these "precipitated" [5] out in a slimy mass, which could be filtered off. Here there would be neither uranium nor thorium, but still there was an activity of ray-giving —a "radioactivity" they were beginning to call it—on the filter paper, and they knew that they were on the track. After that it was a matter of routine, to re-dissolve, re-precipitate, and re-filter until the five different metals had been got into five different dishes. In this way they discovered that the radioactive substance went along with the bismuth.

It could not be bismuth, for they knew (and made sure again) that bismuth was not radioactive. Then, after a little experimenting, they found a way to coax the bismuth and the radioactive substance apart.

5. Precipitation is the process by which a substance in solution separates out in the form of small particles. Ed.

If they formed them into sulfides again, sealed up the mixture in a vacuum in a hard glass tube, and heated it strongly, the radioactive material would evaporate; it left the bismuth sulfide behind and condensed in a dark stain at the cooler end of the tube.

This was little enough to go on, but it seemed clear that the radioactive substance was not uranium nor thorium nor bismuth. It might be proved an element yet, and in their report (which this time Becquerel read for them) they proposed to call it polonium.

Perhaps it was a foolish sentiment that prompted them to name an element for a vanished nation. Long before, the Kingdom of Poland had been divided among Austria, Russia, and Prussia, and there seemed no prospect that the three powerful empires ruling its fragments might ever disintegrate to set them free. Yet even in Marie Curie's lifetime, this same sort of stubborn and romantic patriotism did manage to bring a Polish nation back into being.

The "bismuth" activity of polonium was not the only radioactivity the Curies found in their pitchblende, however. There was another, which sorted out with barium, and this one yielded to a chemical process of separation. The trick was to form chlorides out of the barium and the new element, to dissolve in water as much of the mixed chlorides as possible, and then to pour alcohol into the saturated solution. This forced out some of the dissolved material as a white precipitate, which could be filtered off, and the clear "filtrate," which had dripped down below, could be evaporated to recover the rest. When they compared these two portions, there was always more radioactivity in the precipitate than in the material which had remained in solution.

It was only a partial separation, but by doing it over and over, they were able gradually to crowd more and more of the active material into a smaller and smaller sample, until at last they had hardly a pinch of white powder, and this precious pinch, weight for weight, was nine hundred times more radioactive than uranium metal.

If they were to prove that this new substance was an element, they must get an atomic weight for it, and that meant accumulating enough of it to weigh. The day when they could do that was still in the future, but in the meanwhile they might get some hint by taking its spectrum.

This "spectrum" is a kind of characteristic, atomic light. If you evaporate a substance with a hot flame or an electric spark, and if the atoms of the substance have enough energy to set themselves glowing, then the light they give out is colored, and colored in a unique way. When you disperse the light with a prism, you do not see a continuous band of blending tints running all across from red to violet, but a pattern of sharp, narrow, brilliantly colored lines, separated by wide spaces of absolute darkness. For each different element the pattern is different, and although in a mixture of elements the patterns become entangled, with care and patience an expert can distinguish one from another. [Figure 3–3.]

Figure 3–3. Arc spectrum of iron, under high dispersion.

In Paris there was such an expert, Eugène Demarçay, a chemist, from whom Marie Curie already had borrowed samples of some of the rarer elements to test for radioactivity. As their material had grown more concentrated, the Curies had kept taking it to Demarçay. In the spectrum of their last, most active specimen he found a single line in the ultraviolet range which did not belong to the pattern of the barium composing the bulk of the material, nor of the platinum of the wire by which he drew his sparks, nor indeed to the pattern of any known element.

On this evidence, on the basis of its radioactivity, of its partial separation from barium, and its single spectral line, the Curies announced their second new element at the very end of 1898, and for the great intensity of its rays they named it radium.

Then it was time to begin again. They could hardly afford to buy more pitchblende, but luckily they found a cheaper substitute. Through the Austrian government they got as a gift some hundreds of pounds of residues from the uranium refinery at Joachimsthal in Bohemia. (It is called Jáchymov now, and is in Czechoslovakia.) There was no uranium, of course, in that brownish powder mixed with pine needles, but then it was the radium that they wanted. Back they went to their chemistry, dissolving and precipitating and dissolving again. It was quite as well that they did not realize how the pounds of residues would grow to tons before they could scrape together a weighable amount of pure radium chloride.

Editor's Note. In 1922 Marie Curie came to America to accept a gift of a gram of radium from the women of America in gratitude for her organization of radiological service in hospitals during World War I. The following selection is from her single public address during her American tour. It was delivered in English to an impromptu gathering in the chapel at Vassar College.

The Discovery of Radium *

by Marie Curie (1922)

I could tell you many things about radium and radioactivity and it would take a long time. But as we cannot do that, I shall give you only a short account of my early work about radium. Radium is no more a baby; it is more than twenty years old, but the conditions of the discovery were somewhat peculiar, and so it is always of interest to remember them and to explain them.

We must go back to the year 1897. Professor Curie and I worked at that time in the laboratory of the School of Physics and Chemistry where Professor Curie held his lectures. I was engaged in some work on uranium rays which had been discovered two years before by Professor Becquerel. . . .

I spent some time in studying the way of making good measurements of the uranium rays, and then I wanted to know if there were other elements, giving out rays of the same kind. So I took up a work about all known elements and their compounds and found that uranium compounds are active and also all thorium compounds, but other elements were not found active, nor were their compounds. As for the uranium and thorium compounds, I found that they were active in proportion to their uranium or thorium content. The more uranium or thorium, the greater the activity, the activity being an atomic property of the elements, uranium and thorium.

Then I took up measurements of minerals and I found that several of those which contain uranium or thorium or both were active. But then the activity was not what I could expect; it was greater than for uranium or thorium compounds, like the oxides which are almost entirely composed of these elements. Then I thought that there should be in the minerals some unknown element having a much greater radioactivity than uranium or thorium. And I wanted to find and to separate that element, and I settled to that work with Professor Curie. We thought it

---

* Ellen S. Richards, Monograph No. 2, Bureau of Publications of Vassar College. Reprinted by permission.

would be done in several weeks or months, but it was not so. It took many years of hard work to finish that task. There was not *one* new element; there were several of them. But the most important is radium, which could be separated in a pure state. . . .

The difficulty was that there is not much radium in a mineral; this we did not know at the beginning. But we now know that there is not even one part of radium in a million parts of good ore. And, too, to get a small quantity of pure radium salt, one is obliged to work up a huge quantity of ore. And that was very hard in a laboratory.

We had not even a good laboratory at that time. We worked in a hangar where there were no improvements, no good chemical arrangements. We had no help, no money. And because of that, the work could not go on as it would have done under better conditions. I did myself the numerous crystallizations which were wanted to get the radium salt separated from the barium salt, with which it is obtained, out of the ore. And in 1902 I finally succeeded in getting pure radium chloride and determining the atomic weight of the new element, radium, which is 226, while that of barium is only 137.

Later I could also separate the metal radium, but that was a very difficult work; and, as it is not necessary for the use of radium to have it in this state, it is not generally prepared that way.

Now, the special interest of radium is in the intensity of its rays, which is several million times greater than the uranium rays. And the effects of the rays make the radium so important. If we take a practical point of view, then the most important property of the rays is the production of physiological effects on the cells of the human organism. These effects may be used for the cure of several diseases. Good results have been obtained in many cases. What is considered particularly important is the treatment of cancer. The medical utilization of radium makes it necessary to get that element in sufficient quantities. And so a factory of radium was started, to begin with, in France, and later in America, where a big quantity of ore named carnotite is available. America does produce many grams of radium every year but the price is still very high because the quantity of radium contained in the ore is so small. The radium is more than a hundred thousand times dearer than gold.

But we must not forget that when radium was discovered no one knew that it would prove useful in hospitals. The work was one of pure science. And this is proof that scientific work must not be considered from the point of view of the direct usefulness of it. It must be done for itself, for the beauty of science, and then there is always the chance that a scientific discovery may become, like the radium, a benefit for humanity.

But science is not rich; it does not dispose of important means; it does not generally meet recognition before the material usefulness of it has been proved. The factories produce many grams of radium every year, but the laboratories have very small quantities. It is the same for my laboratory, and I am very grateful to the American women who wish me to have more of radium, and give me the opportunity of doing more work with it.

The scientific history of radium is beautiful. The properties of the rays have been studied very closely. We know that particles are expelled from radium with a very great velocity, near to that of light. We know that the atoms of radium are destroyed by expulsion of these particles, some of which are atoms of helium. And in that way it has been proved that the radioactive elements are constantly disintegrating, and that they produce, at the end, ordinary elements, principally helium and lead. That is, as you see, a theory of transformation of atoms, which are not stable, as was believed before, but may undergo spontaneous changes.

Radium is not alone in having these properties. Many having other radioelements are known already: the polonium, the mesothorium, the radiothorium, the actinium. We know also radioactive gases, named emanations. There is a great variety of substances and effects in radio-activity. There is always a vast field left to experimentation and I hope that we may have some beautiful progress in the following years. It is my earnest desire that some of you should carry on this scientific work, and keep for your ambition the determination to make a permanent contribution to science.

The Structure of the Atom

Rutherford's Theory of the Nuclear Atom *
by Theodore A. Ashford (1960)

Considerable insight into the phenomenon of [radioactivity] was gained by the study of the emitted rays themselves. Three distinct types of rays were soon recognized, and were christened alpha (a), beta (β), and gamma (γ) rays, in the order of their discovery. All three rays affect the photographic plate, but they differ markedly in penetrating power. The alpha rays are easily stopped by a piece of paper or by a few centimeters of air. The beta rays go through the thickness of a book to darken a photographic plate on the other side. The penetrating power of the gamma rays is fantastic. They go through hundreds of feet of air, or several inches of solid lead, to darken a photographic plate beyond. . . . (Figure 3–4.)

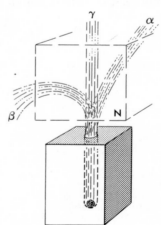

Figure 3–4. Rays from radioactivity. A magnetic field separates them into α, β, and γ rays.

Each type of ray has other individual characteristics. When the alpha rays impinge on a surface coated with zinc sulfide paint, they produce tiny sparks, which are visible as individual sparks under a good magnifying glass. Each spark is presumably produced by a single particle in the ray hitting the screen. In many early experiments a low-power microscope, called the spinthariscope, was used to count individual particles. On striking a zinc sulfide screen the beta rays produce a glow remarkably similar to that produced by cathode rays, and the gamma rays produce a fluorescence very similar to that produced by X-rays.

The nature of the rays was established by studying their behavior in strong magnetic fields. A beam of rays from a radioactive source can easily be produced by taking a block of lead several inches thick, drilling a hole in it, and placing some radioactive materials in it. The rays are absorbed by the lead, except those coming out in the direction of the hole. If a strong magnetic field is placed above the hole at right angles to the beam, the beam is resolved into the three types of rays. The alpha rays are bent moderately in one direction, the beta rays are bent strongly in the opposite direction, and the gamma rays continue undeflected. From the direction of the bending we conclude that the alpha rays are positively charged, the beta rays are negatively charged, and the gamma rays are uncharged.

The charged rays were definitely identified by measuring the amount of bending in strong magnetic fields, using exactly the same methods which were used to identify the rays in evacuated tubes. [See page 53.] . . . the alpha rays are helium atoms carrying a double positive charge, He^{++}. The only difference is that their speeds are very high, being of the order of one-twentieth that of the speed of light. The beta rays . . . are high-speed electrons, their speeds being of the order of 0.95 of the speed of light or higher. The gamma rays are identified as very penetrating X-rays—that is, X-rays of very short wavelength. . . .

To Rutherford, the significant aspect of the phenomenon was the implication of what happens to the atoms that emit these rays. The emission of material particles from the atom, and especially the emission of the heavy alpha particles, implies that the atom loses an appreciable part of its mass in the process. Consequently the atom must become lighter, and perhaps become an atom of a different and lighter element.

This conclusion was confirmed by investigating another group of phenomena associated with radioactivity. It was known by this time that all uranium minerals contain polonium, radium, lead, and perhaps other elements, in addition to the helium which they emit. All the atoms of these elements are lighter than the uranium atoms, the latter being the heaviest known at that time. Consequently, Rutherford conceived the idea that in the emission of these rays, the uranium atoms disintegrate into lighter atoms, which in turn disintegrate into still lighter atoms. The end product appeared to be lead, which is not radioactive and hence does not disintegrate. The net result of these successive and complex changes is the transformation of uranium into lead and helium.

This was a revolutionary idea. In all the hitherto observed phenomena of physical and chemical changes, the elements retained their identity. Apparently, in radioactivity, however, the changes are of a more drastic character, the elements being transmuted into other elements. This implies the breakdown of the atoms themselves. The old idea of the alchemists of transmuting base elements into gold, which was completely abandoned during the nineteenth century, was again revived. Not only can the elements be transmuted into other elements; it is happening spontaneously. . . .

Let us now summarize some of the important conclusions to which the phenomena of radioactivity point. The atoms of the radioactive elements are unstable, and decompose, giving off alpha particles, beta particles, and gamma rays, becoming lighter atoms in the process. They must contain these particles or at least the materials from which these particles are formed. Moreover, the structures of the atoms must be very complex. The emitted particles must be present in very powerful electric fields. To Rutherford, the simple picture of a smear of "jelly," fairly uniformly distributed, was too simple to account for these phenomena. There must be some sort of "bunching" of the matter and of the electric charge in the atom.

RUTHERFORD'S SCATTERING EXPERIMENTS

The concept of the atom as a minute solar system was suggested directly from a series of historic experiments on the penetrability of matter by alpha and beta particles. We have already mentioned, but dismissed without comment, that the rays from radioactivity go through considerable thicknesses of solid matter. The beta rays go through $\frac{1}{8}$ inch of solid aluminum without appreciable absorption. The alpha rays are completely stopped by a metal plate about 0.005 inch thick, but they do go through thinner foils of gold and silver.

This phenomenon becomes significant on closer examination. There is every reason to believe that in solids the atoms are virtually in contact with one another. Just as we conclude that there are large spaces between molecules of gases from the fact that gases are so highly compressible, so we conclude that there is very little "free" space between the atoms of solid metals from the fact that the metals are practically incompressible. In fact, on the assumption that the atoms in metals "touch" one another, it is possible to estimate their size, knowing Avogadro's number and the density of the metals. The sizes of the atoms thus obtained are in good agreement with those obtained by other methods. Realizing that even the thinnest foils contain hundreds of thousands of layers of atoms, we cannot escape the conclusion that the alpha and beta particles go right through the interiors of the atoms.

The German physicist Phillip Lenard was the first to investigate the penetration and absorption of thin metallic foils by beta rays. Quite unexpectedly he found that most of the rays go through the foils without suffering any appreciable slowing down or deflection. He did notice, however, that a small fraction of the rays *are* deflected, and some of them are deflected very sharply. On reading the reports of these experiments Rutherford had the insight to sense that these experiments provide a method for probing into the interior of the atom.

Rutherford repeated Lenard's experiments using alpha particles from polonium. He chose alpha particles for several reasons. In the first place, alpha particles are whole ions, having a mass of 7500 times that of the beta rays, and since they move at about 10,000 miles per second, they have enormous kinetic energies. Moreover, alpha particles are relatively easy to observe. Each alpha particle produces a tiny spark on hitting a zinc sulfide screen and, therefore, can be observed individually by the spinthariscope. Furthermore alpha particles go through very thin foils, but are stopped by thicker foils. Therefore it should be relatively easy to count the number of alpha particles that penetrate the foil, the number that are absorbed, the number that are slowed down by various amounts, and the number that are deflected by various angles. This information should give a good idea of the structure of the atom.

In a typical experiment, Rutherford directed at a gold leaf about 0.0005 inches thick a beam of alpha particles from polonium (Figure 3–5). He measured the kinetic energy of the particles and counted the number of particles in the beam. Then he proceeded to count the number of particles at various distances and angles, after they had hit the foil. To his surprise, even the heavy alpha particles behaved like Lenard's beta rays. The vast majority of the alpha particles went through undeflected and unretarded as though the leaf were not there. The leaf behaved like a ghost. Since the alpha particles go through several hundred thousand atoms, the atom appeared pretty empty. Where was the matter of the leaf? Where was the matter of the atom?

The key to this puzzle lay hidden in the small number of particles that *were* deflected. Considering only the particles that were deflected, he found a good fraction of them deflected by *very large* angles. In fact some

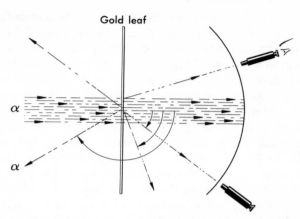

Figure 3–5. *Scattering of alpha rays on going through a thin gold leaf. The vast majority of the rays go through the leaf without deflection. A few suffer large deflections.*

particles were deflected by more than 90° and appeared on the same side of the foil as the incident beam. A few were even deflected by nearly 180°. Apparently these particles hit something hard and massive; for it takes a considerable mass to deflect such a heavy projectile moving at these high speeds. Here then was the elusive matter of the leaf. Apparently the mass of the leaf—and therefore the mass of *each atom* in the leaf —is concentrated in certain *centers* or *nuclei,* leaving the rest of the space quite empty.

The significance of these results may be appreciated by a simple analogy. If a contractor has 500 pounds of iron for the purpose of enclosing an open side of a room, he can make the wall in two distinct ways. He can hammer the iron into a thin sheet and cover the space with it, or he can cast the iron into a stout wire and make a fence to cover the same area. If the contractor covers the wall with wallpaper on both sides before anyone else sees it, would it be possible to find out which way the wall was made? (Figure 3–6.)

A very simple method would be to shoot some bullets straight at the wall and observe them on the other side. If the wall is a sheet of iron, all the bullets will be slowed down by the same moderate amount and none will be deflected. If, on the other hand, the wall is a wire fence, most of the bullets will go through the spaces between the wires, practically unaffected. In the latter case, however, a small percentage of the bullets will hit the wire and be deflected; and most of those deflected will be deflected sharply. Rutherford had the same situation with the alpha particles going through the gold leaf.

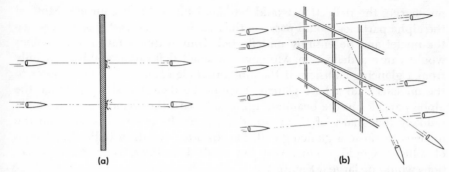

Figure 3–6. Two types of iron "fence." (a) All bullets are slowed down by moderate amounts; none is deflected. (b) Bullets deflect only on hitting the wire.

The analogy can be carried one step further. By counting the percentage of the bullets that are deflected it is possible to estimate the ratio of the area covered by the wire to the total area. If, for example, 6 per cent of the bullets are deflected, 6 per cent of the area is iron wire and the rest of it is empty space between the wires. Continuing the analogy, if the fence has two layers, one in front of the other with little or no overlapping of the wires, in each of the fence layers the area of the wire is about 3 per cent of the total area of the fence.

Reasoning in this manner Rutherford proceeded to estimate the size of the nucleus relative to the size of the atom. Knowing the thickness of the gold leaf, he could calculate rather accurately the number of layers of atoms (the number of fences in the analogy). Then, by actual counting he could estimate the percentage of alpha rays that were deflected, and thus calculate the ratio of the cross-sectional area of the nuclei relative to the total area of the layer, per single layer. This ratio must also be the ratio of the cross-sectional area of a single nucleus to that of the whole atom. On carrying out the counts and the calculations, Rutherford obtained a ratio of one to about 100 million. This makes the diameter of the nucleus about $\frac{1}{10,000}$ that of the atom, and the volume of the nucleus *one millionth of a millionth* of the volume of the atom. Yet this small nucleus contains nearly all the mass of the atom.

Rutherford then went on to investigate whether the nucleus was merely a minute ball of mass or whether it had an electric charge. The key to this problem lay in a finer analysis of the nature of the collisions causing the deflections. What was the nature of the collisions? Was the collision like a bullet hitting the wire (or a billiard ball hitting another billiard ball), or was the deflection due to electric forces? He knew, of course, that the alpha particle had a double positive charge. If the nucleus had no charge, the deflection would be like a billiard-ball collision. Most of the alpha particles would pass, on the average, in the vast spaces between the nuclei and be entirely undeflected. Only a direct hit on the nucleus would cause a deflection. Moreover, a small deflection could result only from a glancing collision. If the alpha particle came even a little closer to the nucleus than a bare glance, it would be deflected sharply. Since the alpha particles in the beam are quite far apart, the chances are extremely unlikely that many of them would come at the exact distance from the nucleus to cause a glancing collision. In other words, a billiard-ball type of collision would produce very few small deflections. Most of the deflections would be large. (Figure 3–7.)

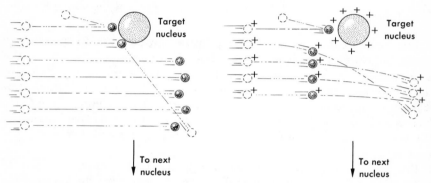

Figure 3–7. *Billiard-ball type of collision. Only a grazing collision would result in a small deflection. The next nucleus is 10,000 diameters away— about 300 feet on the scale of the diagram.*

Figure 3–8. *"Collision" by electric forces. Many small deflections due to electric forces acting at a distance. The next nucleus is 10,000 diameters away.*

If, on the other hand, the nucleus had a charge, say positive, then the deflecting forces would be effective at relatively larger distances from the center of the nucleus. (Figure 3–8.) Of course these forces would become weaker rapidly, decreasing as the square of the distance, but they would still be strong enough at several diameters from the nucleus to produce noticeable deflections. This would not alter the ratio of those deflected to those undeflected to any extent, since the distances between the nuclei are some 10,000 nuclear diameters. But it would alter radically the ratio of small to large deflections. A charged nucleus would result in many small deflections, fewer large deflections, and only occasionally a complete turning back of those alpha particles that happen to aim directly at a nucleus. If the nucleus happened to have a negative charge, exactly the same situation would exist, with one exception. The deflections would be due to attraction toward the nucleus, rather than repulsion away from the nucleus, but the percentage of deflections at various angles would be exactly the same.

Rutherford carried out the above argument, using rigorous mathematics, the laws of motion and of force between charged bodies. The problem is identical in form to the problem of comets coming toward the sun; for in both cases the force decreases as the square of the distance. From this analysis he calculated the number of deflections to be expected at the various angles. He then patiently counted the number of sparks at various angles and found them as predicted for a charged nucleus. He found a great number of small deflections and, more significantly, the predicted proportions for each angle. He therefore concluded that the nucleus had an electric charge. However, this experiment did not settle the question whether the charge was positive or negative.

Rutherford concluded that the charge in the nucleus is positive from other considerations. First, the electrons that have a negative charge are associated with negligible mass, while all positive rays are associated with practically the whole mass of the atom. The smallest particle carrying a positive charge is the proton, and this is 2000 times as heavy as the electron. The alpha particle itself, which has positive charge, has a mass 7500 times that of the electron. The alpha particle may very well be the nucleus of the helium atom. In fact these very experiments provide further support on this point. The experiments indicate not only that the mass of the target atom is concentrated, but also that the mass of the projectile (that is, the alpha particle) itself is concentrated. Rutherford obtained such an excellent agreement with experiment by assuming the alpha particles to be extremely small in size relative to an atom. This argues that all the atoms are built on the same plan and that the charge on all the nuclei is positive.

Further analysis of this experiment permitted Rutherford to obtain a rough estimate of the amount of charge on the target nucleus. . . . The charge on the nucleus of the gold atom is about 100 times that of the hydrogen atom or about 50 times that of the alpha particle. Repeating the experiments for other metals he found the nuclear charge to be about 50 for silver and about 30 for copper.

These numbers, although only approximate, are highly suggestive in that they are roughly half of the respective atomic weights. Thus gold, with the atomic weight 197, behaves as though it contains about 49 alpha particles. This would give it an atomic weight of 196 and a charge of +98. The situation is similar for silver, copper, and the other elements. The alpha particle itself has a weight of four times that of the hydrogen atom and a charge of only twice that of the hydrogen ion. Also significant is the fact that during radioactivity, alpha particles do come out from the atom. They can only come from the nucleus, since only the nucleus has so much mass; moreover, only the nucleus has a positive charge. All these considerations point to the conclusion that all the atoms are built on the same plan and Rutherford proceeded to uncover it.

THE RUTHERFORD THEORY

By synthesizing the evidence from scattering experiments and from radioactivity, by 1911 Rutherford had worked out the general pattern of the atom. From these phenomena he had firmly established that the atom consists of two parts: a very small, extremely dense nucleus containing nearly all the mass and all the positive charge; and a tenuous envelope making up the rest of the volume, and consisting of negatively charged electrons of negligible mass. He then proceeded to investigate further each of these parts.

The scattering experiments indicated that the nucleus has a charge roughly equal to half of the atomic weight. As a first approximation, the nucleus appeared to consist of alpha particles; or at least to contain the materials from which the alpha particles themselves are made, and in about the same proportions. The radioactivity experiments provided supplementary evidence consistent with this picture. A dozen or more radioactive elements emit alpha particles. The alpha particles can only come from the nuclei, since only the nucleus contains the bulk of the mass and the positive charge. Moreover, since the alpha particles are emitted with high energies, only a nucleus with considerable mass and a positive charge can propel them with these high speeds. Further, the decaying atom, after losing four units of mass and two units of charge, must result in an atom that again has a mass to charge ratio of about 2 to 1.

However, the idea that the nuclei consist only of alpha particles could not be the entire story. The charge on the nucleus was at best estimated only roughly. Also, several radioactive elements emit negatively charged beta particles, and since these particles emerge with stupendous speeds, they, too, in all probability, come out of the nucleus. An emission of a beta particle would leave the nucleus with a charge *greater by one positive unit*. Therefore, not all nuclei could have charges multiple of the alpha particle. Moreover, the atomic weights of most elements are not multiples of four, and hence could not contain only alpha particles.

Other considerations indicated that the nuclei contain protons, which are positively charged hydrogen ions. So many atomic weights are very nearly whole numbers, that is, whole number of times that of hydrogen.

The frequency of whole numbers in the atomic weights is far greater than would be expected by pure chance. More significantly, the smallest particle carrying a positive charge is the proton. All these considerations inevitably suggested that the heavy positive particles in the nucleus are protons and that the proton is itself a nucleus—*the nucleus of the hydrogen atom.*

The structure of the alpha particle itself provided the key to the further development of the theory. The alpha particle weighs four times as much as the hydrogen atom, but has a charge of only twice that of the proton. If the helium nucleus contained four protons, the mass could be accounted for, but not the charge. All efforts to find an alpha particle with a charge of +3 or +4 or to obtain a positive-ray beam from helium with more than two charges had failed. Furthermore, the size of the alpha particle is so small compared to the whole helium atom as to preclude the possibility that it has any extranuclear electrons. The only other reasonable alternative was to assume that the alpha particle is itself a nucleus, and that in this nucleus there are two electrons in *close association* with two of the protons. Thus, two of the charges are neutralized in the nucleus, leaving only *two* net positive charges. . . .

Outside the nucleus are the electrons. In a neutral atom the number of extra nuclear electrons is numerically equal to the number of nuclear protons or, what is the same thing, to the charge on the nucleus expressed in electronic units. . . .

The reader will recall that the periodic system was obtained by arranging the elements in the increasing order of their atomic weights. The atomic number was defined provisionally as the serial number of the element, from the lightest to the heaviest. The numerous and complex regularities excluded the possibility of the existence of unknown elements between *adjacent* columns of the periodic system. Therefore, the atomic numbers represented the "natural" order of the elements without any gaps.

Rutherford had the inspiration to postulate that the atomic number represents the positive charge on the nucleus of the element. The idea

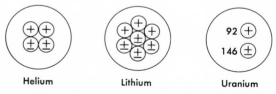

Helium   Lithium   Uranium

Figure 3–9. Sample atomic nuclei. The nuclei of three elements as they were pictured in the years before 1932. Each nucleus contains several protons (+) and several proton-electron combinations (±). (After Selig Hecht, Explaining the Atom.)

that each element had a nuclear charge one unit greater than the immediately preceding lighter element had a strong appeal. Thus helium, the
second lightest element, has twice the nuclear charge of hydrogen;
lithium, the third element, has three times the nuclear charge of hydrogen; uranium, the ninety-second element, has 92 positive charges on its
nucleus. [Figure 3–9.]

Wave or Particle?

Atomic Structure and Quantum Theory *
by Victor Weisskopf (1962)

THE GREAT PROBLEMS OF ATOMIC STRUCTURE

[The] reduction of the qualitative differences among ninety-two kinds of atoms to a quantitative one represented an enormous step forward. But every great scientific discovery creates new problems when it solves old ones. When we know more, we have more questions to ask. Our knowledge is an island in the infinite ocean of the unknown, and the larger this island grows, the more extended are its boundaries toward the unknown. The recognition of structure in the atom immediately poses a question. How can those quantitative differences of structure be the cause of the observed qualitative differences in the properties of the elements? How is it possible, for example, that bromine, with thirty-five electrons, is a brownish liquid forming many characteristic chemical compounds, while krypton, with thirty-six electrons, is a gas forming no compound at all, and rubidium, with thirty-seven electrons, is a metal? Why should one electron more or one electron less make such a great difference in the properties of the atom? This question was not answered until later, when the quantum nature of matter was understood. . . .

What motions do we expect in the atom? When Rutherford found out that the atom consists of a massive positive center surrounded by light negative electrons, it was obvious that the atom must be very similar to a planetary system. The electrons are attracted to the center by the electric attraction between opposite charges. This force is much stronger than the force of gravity between the nucleus and the electron, but it obeys the same law in its dependence on the distance—it decreases with the square of the distance. We therefore expect the electrons to move around the nucleus in much the same way the planets move around the sun. Electric attraction between nucleus and electron replaces the force of gravity. An atom should be a small planetary system, and each kind of atom would

* From Victor F. Weisskopf, *Knowledge and Wonder*, Doubleday & Company, Inc., Garden City, New York. © 1962 by Educational Services, Inc.

Figure 3–10. Arc spectrum of sodium. Institute

have a different number of planet electrons. We might expect to find in the small world of the atom a replica of the big world in the sky. . . .

But the planetary atomic model soon runs into great difficulties. If the atom were a true planetary system in which electric charges are constantly circling the nucleus, the revolving electrons should emit light all the time,[1] in ordinary cool hydrogen as well as in hydrogen incandescent under very high temperatures. This does not happen. There is another important shortcoming: The light of hydrogen gas, and of any other gas too, is emitted and also absorbed only at definite frequencies, which are characteristic of the element making up the gas. It is as if every atomic species is a radio station to which have been assigned certain specific frequencies for transmitting and receiving activities. The spectroscopists have studied these assignments over many decades. The frequencies provide an excellent tool for the identification of elements; it is as if one would identify a radio station by looking up its frequency in the lists of radio transmitters. It is the only way to get information about the chemical compositions of the stars.

Now it is very difficult to reconcile this situation with a planetary system structure. There are many possible orbits around the center. In some of these orbits around the nucleus, the electron circles faster and in others slower. The question arises why the electron should circle only in those orbits which have the assigned frequency. It is all the more incomprehensible since we know that in a gas the atoms collide with each other about 10^{12} times a second (that, on the average, is once in 10,000 hydrogen-atom years). The energy of these collisions can be deduced from the heat energy in a gas. The impacts are quite powerful and should change the orbits of the electrons completely in respect to their size, shape, and frequency. How then is it possible that they keep their assigned frequencies?

In order to illustrate this question more vividly, let us consider a sample of sodium gas. It absorbs only light that has the particular frequency assigned to the sodium atom. When heated up, sodium emits the well-known yellow sodium light, its assigned frequency. Let us now condense the gas to a solid piece of sodium metal by cooling or compressing. In the metal the atoms touch each other and therefore the planetary orbits inter-

1. According to *electromagnetic theory* (see Glossary), an electric charge changing its speed or direction of motion would generate electromagnetic waves. Ed.

of Physics and The Physical Society, London.

mesh. We shall not be astonished to find that the metal does not respond particularly to the frequency assigned to the free sodium atom. In fact, the metal does not seem to have any particular frequency of response, as one might expect of a complicated intermesh of electron orbits. Let us then transform the metal back into sodium gas by evaporation. The gas will have exactly the same properties as before: it will absorb and emit only the frequencies typical for the sodium atom. [Figure 3–10.]

This behavior is utterly at variance with, and completely incomprehensible on, the basis of a planetary atomic model. These are properties one would never expect of a planetary system. How could we imagine that the electrons will find their way into exactly the same orbits when the atoms are evaporated from the metal? There is not the slightest reason for it. In fact it would appear improbable to the highest degree that the orbits after evaporation will be similar at all to the orbits before evaporation, except in general shape and in approximate size. But what we do find is an equality of frequency and of many other features, to a degree that is accurate to the most minute details. It is as if the planet Venus, after having been knocked out of its orbit in some collision with another star, should obediently glide back into its previous orbit when the star has gone.

We are accustomed to find in nature substances with well-defined and reproducible properties. It is deeply ingrained in our way of thinking that nature is so, and we are not at all astonished that, for example, two atoms of gold, mined at different locations and processed in different ways, end up identical, indistinguishable from one another. All our lives are built upon the experience that substances have their characteristic properties; we are able to recognize metals, minerals, and chemicals and to distinguish between different kinds of substances on the basis of their characteristic and ever recurring properties. Gold always has the properties of gold, and the seed of a zinnia will produce zinnias every spring.

We must realize, however, that all this remains incomprehensible on the basis of the planetary model of the atom. Not only is it beyond explanation, but it is opposed to the most characteristic features of a planetary system. The structure of the orbits is bound to depend upon the initial conditions; there are many possible forms and shapes of the orbits, which depend on the previous history of the system. Only very rarely would two atoms of the same kind exhibit identical properties if they were ordinary planetary systems.

Let us summarize the situation: All about us nature exhibits characteristic and specific properties of various materials. In spite of the overwhelming variety of substances, each substance is reproducible and recurrent with all its characteristic properties. For this situation to exist, the atoms must have three properties:

√ 1. *Stability.* The atoms keep their specific properties in spite of heavy collisions and other perturbations to which they are subjected.

√ 2. *Identity.* All atoms of the same kind (same electron number) exhibit identical properties; they emit and absorb the same frequencies, they have exactly the same size, shape, and internal motion.

√ 3. *Regeneration.* If an atom is distorted and its electron orbits forced to change by high pressure or by close neighboring atoms, it regains its exact original shape and orbits when the cause of distortion is removed.

Experiments indicate, however, that the atom is a planetary system of electrons circling around the nucleus, a system which should never exhibit these three properties. Hence this picture of the atoms cannot explain at all the specificity of material qualities. We must find a new and essential trait in the structure of the atom that is not contained in the classical picture of the atom as a planetary system. This new insight into the nature of the atom was provided by the development of quantum theory. . . .

THE QUANTUM STATES OF THE ATOM

In 1913 James Franck and Gustav Hertz performed a series of experiments in which they attempted to change the planetary orbits of the electrons in the atom. They argued this way: The atom seems to resist changes of its electron orbits. Let us try to change these orbits by force and see how, and how much, the atom can resist. We would expect that the orbits of the planets would be changed if a star should pass close to our solar system. Franck and Hertz arranged an experiment in the atomic world that would correspond to such a solar cataclysm. In simple terms, their experiment was this: We have a container filled with a gas of atoms, perhaps sodium or hydrogen atoms (Figure 3–11). We pass a straight beam of electrons through the gas. Since electrons have a strong electric effect on each other, we expect that an electron of the beam, when passing near an atom, will influence the orbiting electrons in the atom and change their orbits, just as a nearby passing star would change the orbit of the Earth.

We cannot look directly at the electron orbits and see whether they have been changed, but we can find out indirectly what has happened.

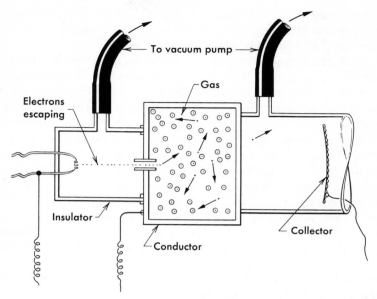

Figure 3–11. *The general idea of an experiment to measure the changes in the energy of electrons when they collide with gas atoms. The electrons pass through a sample of gas (mercury vapor) in the middle chamber. Electrons leave the gun with energy given by the accelerating voltage. Their energy remaining after collisions is measured in the right-hand chamber.*

We make sure that in the beam of electrons all electrons have exactly the same speed when they enter the gas. Any change the electrons may cause in the atom will be associated with a change of speed of the electrons. This prediction follows from the law of conservation of energy. Energy is needed to alter the orbit of an electron in an atom; [2] hence, if the orbit is changed by a beam electron passing by, this electron must lose some energy. Speed is energy; therefore the electron's speed will be reduced, and this reduction can be observed when the beam leaves the gas on the other side. The same would happen if a star passed by our solar system. Its passing would give a push to the Earth, thus increasing the Earth's energy and decreasing the energy of the star.

What should we expect on the basis of the planetary model? There should be all kinds of changes of orbits, small and large, depending upon how close the electron has passed by an atom. We should expect energy

2. Whenever something happens in nature, energy is exchanged: If I rap on the table with my finger, energy is transmitted from my body to the table, and the energy of my body is reduced by this amount. I shall have to eat again in order to replenish it.

losses (or sometimes gains) ranging over all values from zero up; the average loss should be less when the beam goes through a more dilute gas, since there then would be fewer close approaches.

The observations turned out to be completely different. No change of speed at all was observed if the initial energy of the electrons was less than a certain minimum. This minimum energy was quite high—more than a hundred times greater than the heat energy of electrons at ordinary temperatures. When the energy was higher than that minimum, the electrons lost either certain specific amounts of energy or none at all. These specific amounts, and also the minimum, are characteristic of the kind of atom in the gas; they do not depend on the density of gas or on any other external circumstances. What can this strange result mean? It tells us that one cannot change the electron orbits in the atom by any arbitrary amount. Either they do not change at all, or they change by specific, and rather large, amounts of energy. Here the concept of the quantum of energy comes in. Energy can be fed into an atom only in certain characteristic quanta—no more, or less.

It is as if the atom accepts energy only in predetermined lumps. It does not take a small bite, but only the full lump. Every atom has its own characteristic lumps of energy that it can accept. If less is offered, the atom does not budge at all. In fact it budges (changes its state) only if it is offered just the right amount.

This situation is certainly foreign to our picture of a planetary system. A passing star can feed any amount of energy into the Earth's orbit. The greater the distance of passing, the smaller the energy transferred. But the result of our experiment is not so startling in view of what we already know about the atom. It shows that the state of the atom has an intrinsic stability. Weak impacts cannot change it, only a large amount of energy. There must be something that keeps the atom in its normal characteristic state, and that something can be overcome only with large energies. May it not be the same phenomenon that gives rise to the specificity of the atoms, that always forces the electrons back into the configuration characteristic of the special type of atom?

We must be more quantitative now. What is the minimum energy necessary to change the state of an atom? . . .

The threshold energy of a sodium atom—the minimum energy it is able to take in and add to its energy content—was found to be 2.1 electron volts, in the hydrogen atom it is as high as 10 electron volts. These are much higher energies than the energy of heat motion at room temperature.[3] We immediately see a connection here with the fact that the atoms

3. The average kinetic energy of molecules at room temperature is 1/30 electron volt.

in a gas of room temperature maintain their identity and are not changed in spite of the many collisions they suffer. The energy of these collisions is 'way below the threshold energy, that is, below the smallest energy quantum that the atom can accept. Thus the Franck-Hertz experiments showed in their own way the surprising stability of atoms and gave it a quantitative aspect. The atom remains unchanged and stable so long as the impacts upon it are less energetic than a certain well-defined threshold energy, and this energy has a characteristic value for each element. Franck and Hertz "measured" the atomic stability.

The results of the Franck-Hertz experiments go farther than this. They tell us not only the minimum amount of energy which the atoms would accept; they tell us the whole series of specific energy values, from the minimum up, which the atom is willing to accept. Only these amounts of energy can be fed into the atom; it rejects anything in between. For example, the hydrogen atom accepts only the following amounts: 10 ev, 12 ev, 12.5 ev and 12.9 ev, and higher values at decreasing intervals. The sodium atom accepts only 2.1 ev, 3.18 ev, 3.6 ev, 3.75 ev, etc. Figure 3–12 shows a graphic representation of these energies. Each energy corresponds to a certain state of motion of the electron in the atom. Hence each line represents a selected state that the atom is allowed to assume. All other states lying in between are seemingly forbidden. The selected states are

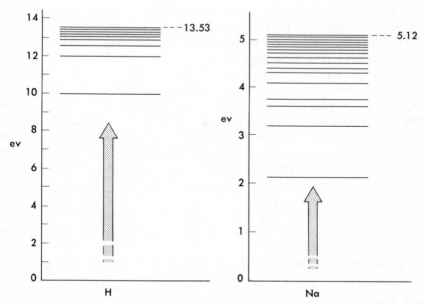

Figure 3–12. Energy of quantum states of hydrogen (H) and sodium (Na).

called quantum states. The state of lowest energy is the ground state in which the atom is found normally; the other ones are called excited states. The threshold energy is the difference between the energy of the first excited state and the ground state.

These facts contrast sharply with what we expect from the behavior of the planetary model. Why should the energy of the electrons be quantized within the atom? What prevents us from adding an arbitrarily small amount to the energy of an atom? If one compares the energy of an atom with the size of a bank account, it is as if the bank would allow only certain prescribed amounts of money to be withdrawn or deposited, to keep the value of the bank account at one of a series of predetermined numbers.

Let us now have a closer look at the different quantum states. One generally refers to the series of allowed energy values as the "spectrum" of the atom. The two spectra in Figure 3–12 reveal a very important general property of quantum states. The higher the energy lies above the ground state, the smaller the energy gap between quantum states becomes. It is a property observed in all atomic systems; for large excitation energies the quantum states become so close to one another that they almost merge. At high energies the quantum effects disappear. The atom then is affected by any amount of energy, as an ordinary planetary system would be. It is as if the strange rules regarding the bank account are waived for very large accounts, since the permitted deposits and withdrawals become smaller and smaller for bigger accounts.

This fact has turned out to be of fundamental importance and much more sweeping than it appears here. Today we know that if we pumped great energy into atoms, they would behave as planetary systems do. These conditions can be realized under extremely high temperatures, which one can produce with strong electrical discharges in gases. Under these conditions the gas forms a so-called "plasma," [4] and the atoms lose their characteristic properties. A plasma of neon gas, where there are ten electrons per atom, has the same properties as a plasma of sodium gas, with eleven electrons per atom. There is no selected electron orbit any more; no one atom behaves like another; there is no characteristic radiation. Chaos reigns in a plasma; it is a chaos of very high temperatures and is rarely found here on Earth except when produced in our laboratories. We find it, however, in cosmic space among the gases expelled by the Sun and other hot stars.

In the plasma all orderly features disappear, the features by which we

4. The name "plasma" has nothing to do with blood plasma, or the living matter in a cell. The first realizations of an atomic plasma in a discharge tube looked like the biological plasma; hence this terminology.

recognize one atom from the other. Order and differentiation occur only when the atoms are in their low-energy states, which are far apart on the energy scale. Then we find the stability that leads to specific shapes and orbits and, consequently, to specific chemical and physical properties. At high energy all these features are gone. Let us keep in mind, however, that it was the characteristic features at *low* energy that defied our understanding. The chaotic behavior of atoms at high energy is just what one would expect on the basis of a planetary model. It is just what one would expect of planetary systems colliding with one another at high speed.

THE WAVE NATURE OF ATOMIC PARTICLES

Particle and Light Beams. We now come to the most striking but most revealing group of observations. They deal with the nature of the atomic particles. Let us consider the simplest form in which atomic particles, say electrons, are found. This is when they are removed from atoms, and freely moving in empty space. If all the electrons in a stream are all moving in the same direction and with the same speed, we call it an electron beam. Such beams are produced in any radio tube, in particular in television tubes. They hit the television screen from the inside of the tube and form the picture. Electron beams must be produced in a vacuum, since in ordinary air the electrons would bump into the air molecules and quickly get out of alignment.

You might expect that such electron beams would have very simple properties. They represent a group of particles moving along parallel trajectories at the same speed. They would travel in straight lines in free space; if they hit an obstacle, the particles would be scattered in all directions. On the contrary, however, we find very strange and unexpected phenomena.

Before we describe these effects, let us consider another kind of beam, a beam of light—the well-focused beam of a searchlight, for example. We assume that the light is of one color.

Let us compare these two beams. We expect them to be fundamentally different things: The light beam is a bundle of electromagnetic waves propagating through space in a certain direction; no material is moving, only the state of the electromagnetic field in space is changing. In contrast, a beam of particles should consist of actual matter in small units moving straight forward. You would expect the two to be as different as the motion of waves on a lake from that of a school of fish swimming in the same direction.

Let us [perform two] experiments in which . . . an obstacle is put in the way of the beam, as indicated in Figure 3–13 for light and in Figure

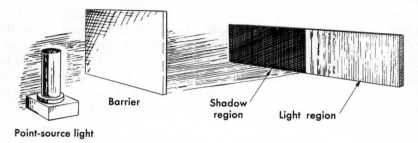

Point-source light

Figure 3–13. Light and barrier making interference pattern.

3–14 for an electron beam. This setup seems to be ideal to bring out the difference between a beam of waves and a beam of particles. If the obstacle is put in the way of a particle beam, the particles that hit it will not get to the screen; the ones missing it will reach the screen; the ones just passing by at the edge might be scattered and deviated from their

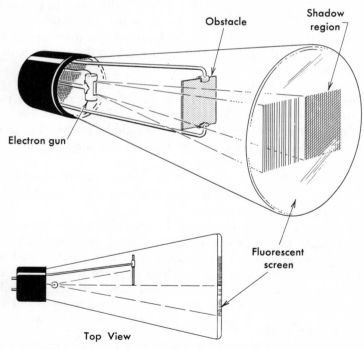

Figure 3–14. Electron-beam diffraction apparatus, analogous to light diffraction apparatus in Figure 3–13.

path. Hence, if we use a screen of the same material of which television screens are made, we should observe a region of shadow and a region of light, the transition being not quite sharp because of the scattering at the edge. No stripes are expected when no wave phenomenon is involved.

What a surprise for the physicists when they performed this and similar experiments and found electron beams exhibiting wave properties similar to those of light beams! Figure 3–15A shows the pattern an electron beam formed on a screen in the arrangement of Figure 3–14. The pattern is identical with the one of Figure 3–15B observed with light. This amazing

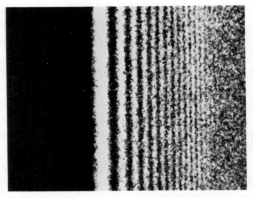

Figure 3–15A. An actual photograph of the interference pattern created by light passing a sharp-edged screen.

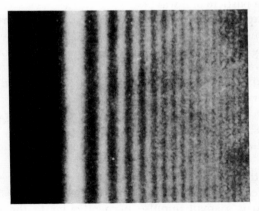

Figure 3–15B. Interference of electrons is demonstrated by this actual photograph which is analogous to the phenomenon of A. (Reprinted courtesy of Handbuch Physik, Volume 32, Professor H. Raether, "Elektroneninterferenzen," p. xxx.)

result is only one of many that have shown beyond doubt that electron beams must have some kind of wave nature; the propagation of a particle beam seems to have the character of a wave pattern. There must be a wave involved in the electron motion.

A quantitative study of these interference patterns allows one to measure the wave length of this mysterious "electron wave." The wave length depends upon the speed of the electron—the higher the speed, the smaller the wave length; for electrons with an energy of a few electron volts the wave length is of the size of the atoms. It is a very small wave length indeed, and this is why the wave nature of electron beams is not easy to detect. In most practical applications of electron beams, such as television tubes, the wave nature plays no role whatsoever.

Here a fundamental discovery was made—the wave nature of particles. The result is bewildering and highly unexpected. Many experiments had to be performed before the physicists were really convinced that the wave effects were not caused by some other phenomenon. All these experiments, however, only made it more and more clear that waves play a part in the motion of electrons and also of other atomic particles such as protons.

An obvious question poses itself: How can an electron be a particle and a wave at the same time? A wave is something that is spread over space in a continuous way, but a particle is strictly localized; at a given moment the particle is here and not there, whereas a wave is a state of "tension" of space that must spread over at least a few wave lengths in order to represent something that can be called a wave. Can we perform some decisive experiment to settle the question unambiguously? Is the electron really a particle or a wave?

This is perhaps the most interesting question of modern physics. But before we discuss this problem, we must be aware of the most exciting thing regarding the electron waves—the dual nature of electrons as particles and waves contains the clue to the riddle of atomic structure! The unexpected properties of the electrons circling around atomic nuclei are directly connected with their wave nature.

The Properties of Confined Waves. In order to understand the connections between electron waves and atomic properties, we must first study the peculiar behavior of waves when they are confined to a limited region.

Let us take the simplest example, of waves along an extended rope. If the rope is very long, we can produce a wave running along the rope by imparting to it a small impulse perpendicular to the rope, as every child playing with a skip rope knows well. If the rope is tied at its far end to a fixed object and held under tension, the impulse travels along the rope and sometimes returns to us after being reflected at the point where the rope is attached. With adroit manipulation we can impart to the rope any form of wave, with long or short wave length, just as we wish. The long wave lengths will perform slow oscillations, and in the short ones the rope will vibrate fast when the wave passes by. Now let us confine the rope between two nearby points. It is then better to think not of a rope but of a string, which is suspended under tension between two points, such as a string on a violin. The form of vibration of such a string is what is called a *standing wave*. We have no longer the choice of wave length and frequency. In fact only those vibrations can be set up whose (half-) wave length fits once or twice or any integral number of times into the space between the two points of attachment, as shown in Figure 3–16.

Not only the shapes of the vibrations are determined, but also the frequencies (the number of ups and downs per second), once the tension of the string is kept fixed. Each of the different vibrations which can be set up has its characteristic frequency, so the string can vibrate only with a set of given frequencies. The lowest of these frequencies, the easiest to set up, is the one whose half-wave length just fits the distance between the fixed ends of the string. It is the one the violinist plays when he sets the string in motion with his bow. But he can also set up higher vibrations, the so-called flageolet tones, where two or more half-wave lengths fit in the string.

Even when he plays a normal tone, the motion of the string is not purely the lowest vibration. The actual motion is a combination of several permitted forms of motion. In fact the ordinary musical tone of

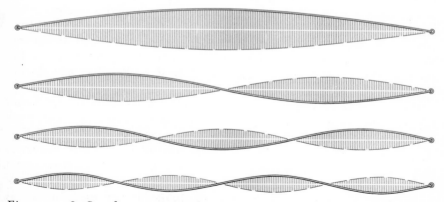

Figure 3–16. Standing waves. Vibrations of a string confined between the points of attachment. Only vibrations set up in which one, two, three, four, etc., half-wave lengths fit in the space between the attachments. White line is position of the string at rest.

a violin contains the higher modes to a certain degree; they are the harmonics, whose presence is important for the beauty of the sound. The difference between the tone of Pablo Casals and that of an ordinary cello player is the different admixture of higher modes. But whatever the combination is, it can contain only frequencies from the set assigned to the tuned string.

The lesson learned with the string is true generally of all kinds of waves. Whenever waves are confined to a finite space, we observe special wave forms and a set of assigned frequencies which are characteristic of the system. Most musical instruments are built on this principle. The string instruments make use of the series of discrete and characteristic frequencies of the string. A wind instrument is based upon the assigned frequencies of air waves enclosed in the pipe of the instrument, be it a trumpet or an organ pipe. . . .

Electron Waves and Quantum States. Let us now return to the electron waves. How can one confine electron waves and observe similar phenomena? Any situation that confines electrons will also confine electron waves. Such a situation exists when an electron is close to an atomic nucleus. The positive charge of the nucleus attracts the electron and prevents it from leaving the immediate neighborhood of the nucleus; the electron is confined to a space near the nucleus. What effect will this confinement have on the electron wave? This question was asked and answered first by Erwin Schrödinger in 1926.

He was able to calculate the shape and the frequencies of the characteristic patterns that develop when electron waves are confined by a nucleus. It is a straightforward problem of dynamics of confined waves, once the relation between the wave length of the electron wave and the velocity of the electron is known. The result is a series of distinct vibrations, each of them with a characteristic pattern and frequency. The wave nature of the electron immediately "explains" the fact that the electron can assume only certain well-defined states of motion in the atom.

This result is of fundamental significance. A connection was found between the wave nature of the electron and the existence of discrete states in the atom. Here we are touching the very nerve of nature. When an electron is confined to a limited region around the nucleus, the wave properties of the electron permit only certain special, predetermined states of motion. Therefore the atom cannot change its state continuously; it must change abruptly from one allowed state to the other. It will stay in the state of lowest energy until it gets enough energy to be lifted into the next state, as it was observed in the Franck-Hertz experiment.

The success of the electron-wave picture of the atom is all the more remarkable because of the way it fits all facts in every quantitative detail. Schrödinger first calculated the simplest problem, the hydrogen atom, in which one single electron is confined by the nucleus. He found a series of states of vibration which correspond in every respect to the observed quantum states of the hydrogen atom. In particular, the frequencies of the electron-wave vibrations correspond exactly to the energies of the observed quantum states when the famous formula of Planck is used, which connects frequencies with energies: The corresponding energy E is always equal to the frequency v (nu) multiplied by a fixed number called h: $E = hv$. The number h is the so-called constant of Planck.[5] This relation is almost incredible to contemplate: Schrödinger calculated the vibrations of an electron wave confined by the attraction of the center. He multiplied the frequencies by Planck's constant and obtained, exactly to the last decimal point, the energies of the quantum states of hydrogen, the allowed values of the energy bank account of the hydrogen atom.[6] Obviously the wave nature of the electron must be a decisive factor for the understanding of atomic properties.

The confinement of electron waves admits a series of possible states and furnishes a set of assigned frequencies. If we keep in mind the fundamental law connecting frequency with energy, we obtain a series of states with assigned energies. The one with the lowest frequency is the most important one, since it is the quantum state of lowest energy, the normal state of the atom. It is also the one that exhibits the wave nature most prominently.

The confined electron waves in atoms cannot be directly observed. We can measure their extension, their frequencies (to be exact, the differences between frequencies, which are observed as energy differences) and other indirect properties. But it is both constructive and impressive to look at pictures of these wave patterns. The pictures are not photographs; this would be impossible, as we shall see later in more detail. They are models made from the results of calculations. Figure 3–17 shows the electron-wave patterns, in the order of increasing frequency or energy, of successive quantum states of an electron confined by a nucleus. The lowest state, the ground state, is the simplest one; the higher the frequency, the more involved is the pattern. The ground state has spherical symmetry. The

5. h is a very small number; if one measures energies in electron volts, and frequencies in ups and downs per second, 4×10^{-15}. A vibration of 10^{15} times per second corresponds to four electron volts.

6. Everyone who contemplates this fantastic discovery sympathizes with the famous Italian physicist Enrico Fermi, who used to say when presenting this calculation in his lectures with his well-known Italian accent, "It has no business to fit so well!"

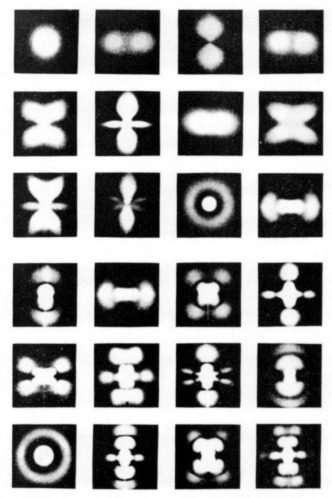

Figure 3–17. These are photographs not of real electrons but of models carefully constructed according to our observations and calculations.

next ones have a "figure-eight" form. The higher ones are usually more complex, although we also find simpler ones among them.

These patterns are of utmost importance in the make-up of nature. They are the fundamental forms on which matter is built. They are the shapes, and the *only* shapes, that the electron "motion" can assume under the conditions prevailing in atoms—that is, under the influence of a central force (the attraction of the nucleus) which keeps the electron confined.

Hence these patterns are the symbols of the way in which nature combines and forms everything we see around us.

The patterns of Figure 3–17 and their inherent symmetries determine the behavior of the atoms; they are the basis of the orderly arrangement in molecules and also of the symmetric arrangement of atoms or molecules in crystals. The simple beauty of a crystal reflects on a larger scale the fundamental shapes of the atomic patterns. Ultimately all the regularities of form and structure that we see in nature, ranging from the hexagonal shape of a snowflake to the intricate symmetries of living forms in flowers and animals, are based upon the symmetries of these atomic patterns.

Looking at the patterns, we see that the higher we go in frequency (or energy), the finer the pattern becomes, the smaller are the distances between the ups and downs. The wave length becomes shorter. If one goes to very high frequencies (energies), the pattern is so varied and fine-grained that it looks almost smooth and continuous. Hence the motion it describes will be nearly the one of an ordinary particle without wave properties. Here again we see that our wave picture exactly reproduces what we have found in atoms. When the energy is high, the quantum phenomena cease to be important and the atom behaves as if it were an ordinary planetary system. The transition to the "plasma" conditions at high energy is also contained in the wave nature of the electron.

The hydrogen atom in its ground state vibrates in the simplest possible pattern, the first one in Figure 3–17. Other atoms, however, exhibit the more complex patterns even in their ground states. This is explained by an important principle which was first discovered by Wolfgang Pauli in 1927. It says that when more than one electron is confined in an atom, each electron must assume a different pattern. Thus an added electron will have to assume the next higher pattern in the scale. The ground state of a complex atom is one of the excited states of a simpler atom.

Here we find the explanation of the fact that one electron added or removed makes so much difference in the atomic world. The pattern of the last electron added determines the configuration of the atom. This in turn determines the way the atoms fit together, whether they form a crystal, a liquid, or a gas. This pattern can change appreciably when going from one number of electrons to the next higher one, as we can see from the examples in Figure 3–17. Quantity becomes quality in the atomic world; one electron more may lead to a complete change of properties.

Schrödinger's discovery of the fundamental significance of the electron wave for the structure of the atom and the development of the theory by Heisenberg, Max Born, and Pauli mark a turning point in man's understanding of nature comparable to Newton's discovery of universal gravity, Maxwell's electromagnetic theory of light, and Einstein's relativity theory.

The properties of the atoms, which seemed so strange and incomprehensible on the basis of the planetary model, fall into place when considered in the light of a confined-wave phenomenon. A confined wave assumes certain well-defined shapes and frequencies such as the vibration of the air in an organ pipe, of the string on the violin, or the water surface in a vibrating glass. They all form a series of vibrating patterns, beginning with the simplest pattern, which vibrates with the lowest frequency, and including more complicated patterns of higher frequencies. So do the vibrations of electron waves in atoms.

With this new way of looking at nature, we now can understand the three remarkable properties of the atom which we enumerated on p. 98. The *stability* comes from the fact that considerable energy must be added to change the lowest pattern to the next higher one.[7] As long as the effects upon the atom are less energetic than this energy, the atom remains in its lowest pattern. The configuration which it represents, therefore, exhibits the typical stability. The *identity* of atoms comes from the fact that the wave patterns are always the same and are determined by the way the waves are confined. One sodium atom is identical with another because the electron wave is confined in all sodium atoms by the same conditions —that is, by the attraction of the nucleus and the electric effects of the other electrons in the atom. The identity of two gold atoms comes from the fact that the same number of electrons are confined by the same electric charge in the center and therefore produce the same wave vibrations. Finally, the ability to *regenerate* its original shape after distortion is exactly what one expects of a vibrational-wave phenomenon on the same grounds as the identity. When the original conditions are re-established, the electron vibration must assume again the same pattern as before, since the patterns are uniquely determined by the conditions in which the electron moves and are quite independent of what happened before. The patterns do not depend at all upon the previous history of the atom; we may destroy an atom by removing a few electrons or distort it by condensing the material into a solid, as we did in the example of sodium . . . but whenever we get the atom back into the original conditions, the electron waves will assume the same quantum states they had before. There exists only one wave pattern of lowest frequency or energy.

It is remarkable that we actually find in the world of atoms what Pythagoras and Kepler sought vainly to find in the motion of the planets. They believed that the Earth and other planets move in special orbits, each unique to the planet and determined by some ultimate principle that is independent of the particular fate and past history of our planetary

7. According to Planck's formula, this energy is equal to the frequency difference multiplied by Planck's constant.

Figure 3–18. *Harmony of Spheres (from* Harmonicus Mundi *by Johannes Kepler, 1619).*

system. There is no such principle in the motion of planets, but there is in the motion of electrons in atoms—the wave principle. We are reminded of the Pythagorean harmony of the world: The atomic quantum states have specific shapes and frequencies that are uniquely predetermined. Every hydrogen atom in the world strikes the same chord of vibrations, as given by its set of characteristic frequencies. Here we find the "harmony of the spheres" reappearing in the atomic world, but this time clearly

There is geometry in the humming
of the strings. There is music in the
spacings of the spheres.

PYTHAGORAS
5th century B.C.

Figure 3–19. *(After Guy Murchie,* Music of the Spheres.*)*

understood as a vibration phenomenon of confined electron waves.

THE LIGHT QUANTA

The Graininess of Light. We have learned that electrons and other atomic particles exhibit wave properties. Particle beams sometimes behave as if they were waves. This property was shown to be the basis of the quantum behavior of the atoms. It turned out in the course of research that this duality is not restricted to particles only. Light waves were found to behave sometimes as if they were particles.

All observations regarding the propagation of light indicate that a light beam is a continuous wave of oscillating electromagnetic fields. But when the effects of light upon matter were studied, some unexpected phenomena were observed that seemingly contradicted the picture of a continuous flow of light. What happens if light falls upon matter? If the object is transparent, such as a windowpane, light is partially reflected and partially transmitted. If the object is opaque, such as a piece of coal, or partially transparent, such as colored glass, a good part of the light is neither reflected nor transmitted. It disappears into the object. Since light is a form of energy, it can disappear only by giving its energy to matter in some way. This disappearance is called the absorption of light.

The energy of the absorbed light must show up in some other form. We feel the heat when sunlight is absorbed by our skin. When light is absorbed by some metals, its energy is often transferred to electrons, which then have acquired so much energy that they jump out of the metal. This jumping is called the photoelectric effect, which is of practical use when we want to transform light pulses into electrical pulses.

It is possible to measure with great accuracy the energy transferred to matter when light is absorbed. These measurements have had a most unexpected result: Light energy can be absorbed only in definite units of a certain amount; a fraction of these units can never be absorbed. If we compare energy with money, we might say that a light beam transmits its energy to matter only in full dollars but never in small change. The units are called light quanta, or photons. As far as the effect of light on matter is concerned, we can compare a light beam to a stream of bullets. Each bullet is filled with the same amount of explosive. Whenever a bullet hits an object, it causes an effect whose energy is determined by the amount of explosive. Stronger light means more explosions of the same size, but not stronger explosions.

In the photoelectric effect each light quantum hitting the metal forces an electron to jump out of the metal. The energy of the jumping electron is a measure of the size of the light quantum (it measures the amount of explosive in each bullet). The number of electrons jumping out measures the intensity of the light beam.

The amount of energy in the light quantum depends upon the kind of light we are dealing with. It is different for light of different wave lengths —longer wave lengths have smaller units; shorter wave lengths, larger ones (Figure 3–20). The energy quantum of visible light is small. It contains

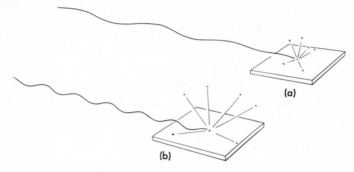

Figure 3–20. *Photoelectric effect.* (a) *Long wave length light impinging upon metal ejects slow electrons.* (b) *Short wave length light ejects fast electrons.*

an energy of only a few electron volts, about 10^{-12} (a millionth of a millionth) smaller than the energy necessary for a touch on your finger that you barely can feel. The quantum of radio waves (also a kind of light) is some billion times smaller, since their wave lengths are so much larger. Of course, the retinas in our eyes are much more sensitive to visible light than our finger tips. Still we would be unable to see single light quanta because they are too weak. If we could see them, a very weak light source would appear as an intermittent light, since we would see light only when a quantum arrived at the retina.

Although light is an electromagnetic wave, its effect on matter, on our eye, on the photoelectric cell, is quantized. It acts as if the light beam consisted of small grains, each of the same size. This phenomenon emphasizes the particle-wave duality in nature: Electrons are particles with wave properties; light is a wave with particle properties.

Let us be a little more quantitative. The size of the energy quantum of light is connected to the frequency of light by the formula of Planck. The energy E of a quantum is given by $E = h\nu$, where ν is the frequency of light [8] and h is again Planck's constant. A quantum of visible yellow

8. The frequency of a light wave is the number of vibrations of the electric field per second. Long wave lengths correspond to low frequencies; short wave lengths have high frequencies. Ordinary radio waves have frequencies of about 10^8 per second; visible light has frequencies of about 10^{16} per second.

light ($\nu = 5 \times 10^{14}$ vibrations per second) comes out to be about two electron volts.

Small as these quanta are, they are not small amounts of energy compared to the energies of atoms. They are of the same order of magnitude as the energy of the atomic quantum states. For example, the quantum of yellow light (two electron volts) is just equal to the energy necessary to lift the sodium atom from its ground state to its next higher state.

Atoms and Light Quanta. Strange as the idea of the light quantum is, it opens up a new aspect of the question how an atom limits and absorbs light, how light is produced by atoms, and how atoms are influenced by light. Let us combine the concept of the light quantum with the concept of the quantum states of the atom. We have learned that an atom can be found only in certain quantum states, with definite energies which are characteristic of the type of atom. Thus an atom can gain or lose energy only in amounts corresponding to the energy differences between its quantum states. If the atom absorbs light or emits light, the energy of this light must be equal to one of those differences. Hence the atom can emit or absorb only light whose quanta have the correct amount—namely, an amount equal to one of these differences.

This property explains immediately why atoms radiate and absorb only light with certain typical frequencies. For example, an atom in its ground state can accept only light whose quantum energy is just the right size to lift the atom into one of the higher quantum states. An atom can absorb only light of those frequencies which possess the corresponding quanta. The same is true of light emission. Light can be emitted by an atom only when the atom is in a state higher than the ground state, and then it can emit only light whose quanta correspond to the energy difference between that state and a lower state. The atom can give off or take in only such light quanta that the energy balance will leave it again in a quantum state. Hence any light absorbed or emitted by an atom must have a frequency corresponding to the difference of two characteristic energy values.

Let us take the sodium atom as an example. When sodium gas is cool, all atoms are in the ground state. No radiation is emitted. The gas is transparent to light, except for light whose quanta would lift it to an excited state. For example, according to Figure 3–12 the first excited state is 2.1 ev higher than the ground state; hence light whose frequency is

$$\nu = \frac{2.1 \text{ ev}}{h} = 5.2 \times 10^{14}$$ has just the right quantum and will be absorbed

by sodium gas. It is a special kind of yellow light. Let us now pour energy into the sodium gas either by heat or by an electric discharge, as is done in the yellow sodium street lights along some of our highways. Then a few sodium atoms will be put into higher quantum states. Those atoms are then able to emit light. The ones in the first excited state emit the same yellow light which the cool gas has absorbed. It is the color we see radiated by these street lights. When the temperature or the discharge energy is raised, higher and higher quantum states will be created and more colors will be radiated. [Figure 3–10.]

It is most remarkable how well the results of light-radiation experiments fitted the results of the Franck-Hertz experiments. Without exception, all frequencies emitted and absorbed by atoms correspond to a transition from one quantum state to another.

THE COMPLEMENTARITY BETWEEN THE PARTICLE AND WAVE PICTURES

Now we must return to our fundamental question: How can an electron be a particle and a wave at the same time? It is difficult to formulate the answer to this question in simple terms. The unexpected dual characteristic of matter has shown that our ordinary concepts of particle motion are not adequate for a description of what goes on in the atomic world. After all, these concepts are formed from human experience with visible objects which are larger than the atomic particles by factors of many billions. In order to understand what is going on at the atomic scale, we must be prepared to give up accustomed ways of thinking and replace them with new concepts that nature has forced upon us.

One of the features of classical physics that we must question is the "divisibility" of such phenomena. This is the idea that every physical process can be thought of as consisting of a succession of particular processes. According to this idea, theoretically at least, each process can be followed step by step in time and space. The orbit of an electron around the nucleus would be thought of as a succession of small displacements. Is this kind of description consistent with what one finds within the atoms?

In our ordinary way of looking at things, the electron must be either a particle or a wave. It cannot be both at the same time. After all, a careful tracing of the electron along its path must decide this question and put it in either one or the other category. Here the problem of the divisibility of atomic phenomena comes in. Can we really perform this tracing? There are technical problems in the way. If we want to "look" at the detailed structure of the orbit, we must use light waves with very small wave length, since one can see only things that are larger than the wave length of the light with which one observes. Such light, however, has a high frequency, hence a big energy quantum. In fact, light whose wave length is as small as an atomic orbit has quanta of an energy that would be far more than enough to tear away the electron from the atom. When it hits the electron, it will knock it out of its orbit and destroy the very object of our examination.

This reaction is not peculiar to experiments when light is used to trace the electron orbit. Quite generally, all measurements which could be used for a decision between the wave and the particle nature of the electron (or the proton, or any other entity) have the same property. If one performs these measurements, the object changes its state completely in the performance itself, and the result of the measurement applies not to the original state but to the state into which the object was put by the measurement. That latter state, however, is a state of very high energy which no longer shows any wave properties.

The quantum nature, the coarseness of light or of any other means of observation, makes it impossible to decide between wave and particle. It does not allow us to subdivide the atomic orbit into a succession of partial motions, be it particle displacements or wave oscillations. If we force a subdivision of the process and try to look more accurately at the wave in order to find out where the electron "really" is, we will find it there as a real particle, but we will have destroyed the subtle individuality of the quantum state. The wave nature will have disappeared, and with it all the characteristic properties of the atom. After all, it was the wave nature that gave rise to the typical properties of quantum states —the simple shape, the regeneration of the original form after perturbation, and all other specific qualities of the atom.

The wave nature of the electron is predicated upon the indivisibility of the quantum state. The great new insight of quantum physics is the recognition that the individual quantum states form an indivisible whole, which exists only as long as it is not attacked by penetrating means of observation. In the quantum state the electron is neither a particle nor a wave in the old senses. The quantum state is the form an electron assumes when it is left alone to adjust itself to the conditions at low energies. It forms a definite individual entity, whose pattern and shape correspond to a wave motion, with all the peculiar properties spreading out over a finite region of space. Any attempt to look at its detailed structure by direct observation would unavoidably destroy it, since the tools of observation would pour so much power into the system that the condition of low energy would no longer hold.

At this stage of our discussion it will appear quite natural that predictions of atomic phenomena sometimes must remain probability statements only. The prediction of the exact spot where the electron will be found after the quantum state has been destroyed with high-energy light is a case of this kind. If the quantum state is examined with pinpointing light, the electron will be found somewhere in the region of the wave, but the exact point cannot be predicted with accuracy. Only probability statements can be made—such, for example, as that the electron will be found most probably where the electron wave was most intense.

The impossibility of measuring certain quantities relating to atomic particles is the basis of the famous uncertainty principle of Heisenberg. It states, for example, that one cannot determine with full accuracy both velocity and position of an electron. Clearly if one could, the electron would be recognized as a particle and not as a wave. The Heisenberg principle states that no measurement can be performed with sufficient accuracy to decide between the wave or the particle nature of the electron. This principle expresses a negative statement that certain measurements are impossible. We must recognize, however, the highly important fact that this impossibility of certain measurements is more than a mere technical limitation that some day might be overcome by clever instrumentation. If it were possible to perform such measurements, the coexistence of wave and particle properties in a single object would collapse, since these measurements would prove one of the two alternatives to be wrong. We know from a great wealth of observations that our objects exhibit both wave and particle properties. Hence the Heisenberg restrictions must have a deeper root: they are a necessary corollary to the dual nature of atomic objects. If they were broken, our interpretation of the wide field of atomic phenomena would be nothing but a web of errors, and its amazing success would be based upon accidental coincidence.

Quantum mechanics has given us an unexpected but wonderful answer to a great dilemma. On the one hand, atoms are the smallest parts of matter; they are supposed to be indivisible and endowed with every detailed specific property of the substance. On the other hand, atoms are known to have an internal structure; they consist of electrons and nuclei, which necessarily must perform mechanical motions not unlike the planets around the Sun, and therefore cannot be imagined to exhibit the required properties.

The answer lies in the discovery of the quantum states which fulfill to some extent the first requirement. Their wavelike behavior endows them with the properties of identity, wholeness, and specificity, but the range of this behavior is limited. Only if they are exposed to perturbances smaller than a characteristic threshold will they retain their identity and their specific properties. If they are exposed to stronger perturbations, the atoms lose their typical quantum properties and exhibit the untypical behavior expected from the mechanical properties of their internal structure.

The quantum state cannot be described in terms of a mechanical model. It is a new state of matter, different from what we have experienced with large objects. It has a particular way of escaping ordinary observation because of the fact that such observation necessarily will obliterate the conditions of its existence. The great Danish physicist Niels Bohr, who has contributed most to the clarification of these ideas, uses a special term for this remarkable situation; he calls it complementarity. The two descriptions of the atom—the wavelike quantum state on the one hand, and the planetary model on the other—are complementary descriptions, each equally true but applicable in different situations.

The quantum properties can unfold only when the atom is left undisturbed, or when it is exposed to perturbations which are less energetic than the quantum threshold. Then we find the atom with its characteristic symmetries, and it behaves like an indivisible entity. This is the case when we are dealing with matter under normal conditions. But when we try to look into the details of the quantum state by some sharp instrument of observation, we necessarily pour much energy into the atoms. Under these conditions the atoms behave as they would at very high temperature, that is as a plasma. We then observe the electrons as ordinary particles moving under the attractive force of the nuclei, without any quantum phenomena, and exactly as one would expect if one had to deal with ordinary old-fashioned particles.

Atomic phenomena present us with a much richer reality than we are accustomed to meeting in classical macroscopic physics. The wavelike properties of quantum states, the indivisibility of these states, the fact that we cannot describe the atom completely in terms of familiar things such as particles or classical waves, are features that do not occur with objects in our macroscopic experience. Hence the description of the atom cannot be as "detached" from the observing process as classical descriptions were. We can describe atomic reality only by telling truthfully what happens when we observe a phenomenon in different ways, although it may seem incredible to the uninitiated that the same electron can behave so differently as we observe it in the two complementary situations. These features, however, do not make electrons less real than anything else we observe in nature. Indeed the quantum states of the electron are the very basis of what we call reality around us.

Substance or Form?

The Importance of Form *
by Erwin Schrödinger (1951)

The effect of a single fast particle can be observed as it impinges on a fluorescent screen and causes a faint flash of light, a scintillation. (If you have a watch with luminous figures, take it into a dark room and observe it with a moderately strong magnifying glass: you will then observe the scintillations caused by the impact of single helium ions, alpha particles, as they are called in this context.) In a Wilson cloud chamber you can observe the paths of single particles, alpha particles, electrons . . . their traces can be photographed and you can determine their curvature in a magnetic field; cosmic ray particles passing through a photographic emulsion produce nuclear disintegrations there, and both the primary and the secondary particles (if they are charged, as they usually are) trace their paths in the emulsion, so that the paths become visible when the plate is developed by the ordinary photographic procedure. I could give you more examples (but these will suffice) of the very direct way in which the old hypothesis of the particle structure of matter has been confirmed far beyond the keenest expectation of previous centuries.

Still less expected is the modification which our ideas about the nature of all these particles underwent during the same time—had to undergo willy-nilly—in consequence of other experiments and of theoretical considerations.

Democritus and all who followed on his path up to the end of the nineteenth century, though they had never traced the effect of an individual atom (and probably did not hope ever to be able to), were yet convinced that the atoms *are* individuals, identifiable, small bodies just like the coarse palpable objects in our environment. It seems almost ludicrous that precisely in the same years or decades which let us succeed in tracing single, individual atoms and particles, and that in various ways, we have yet been compelled to dismiss the idea that such a particle is an

---

individual entity which in principle retains its "sameness" forever. Quite
the contrary, we are now obliged to assert that the ultimate constituents
of matter have no "sameness" at all. . . . It is not a question of our being
able to ascertain the identity in some instances and not being able to do
so in others. It is beyond doubt that the question of "sameness," of identity, really and truly has no meaning.

FORM, NOT SUBSTANCE, THE FUNDAMENTAL CONCEPT

The situation is rather disconcerting. You will ask: What are these
particles then, if they are not individuals? . . .

It is useful to consider this question in some detail, for it will give us
the clue to what a particle or an atom really is—what there is permanent
in it in spite of its lack of individuality. On my writing-table at home I
have an iron letter-weight in the shape of a Great Dane, lying with his
paws crossed in front of him. I have known it for many years. I saw it on
my father's writing-desk when my nose would hardly reach up to it.
Many years later, when my father died, I took the Great Dane, because
I liked it, and I used it. It accompanied me to many places, until it stayed
behind in Graz in 1938, when I had to leave in something of a hurry. But
a friend of mine knew that I liked it so she took it and kept it for me.
And three years ago, when my wife visited Austria, she brought it to me,
and there it is again on my desk.

I am quite sure it is the same dog, the dog that I first saw more than
fifty years ago on my father's desk. But *why* am I sure of it? That is quite
obvious. It is clearly the peculiar *form* or *shape* (German: *Gestalt*) that
raises the identity beyond doubt, not the material content. Had the material been melted and cast into the shape of a man, the identity would be
much more difficult to establish. And what is more: even if the material
identity were established beyond doubt, it would be of very restricted
interest. I should probably not care very much about the identity or not
of that mass of iron, and should declare that my souvenir had been
destroyed.

I consider this a good analogy, and perhaps more than an analogy, for
pointing out what the particles or atoms really are. For we can see in this
example as in many others how in palpable bodies, composed of many
atoms, individuality arises out of the structure of their composition, out of
shape or form, or organization, as we might call it in other cases. The
identity of the *material,* if there is any, plays a subordinate role. You may
see this particularly well in cases when you speak of "sameness" though
the material has definitely changed. A man returns after twenty years of
absence to the cottage where he spent his childhood. He is profoundly

moved by finding the place unchanged. The *same* little stream flows through the *same* meadows, with the cornflowers and poppies and willow trees he knew so well, the white-and-brown cows and the ducks on the pond, as before, and the collie dog coming forth with a friendly bark and wagging his tail to him. And so on. The shape and the organization of the whole place have remained the same, in spite of the entire "change of material" in many of the items mentioned, including, by the way, our traveller's own bodily self! Indeed, the body he wore as a child has in the most literal sense "gone with the wind." Gone, and yet not gone. For, if I am allowed to continue my novelistic snapshot, our traveller will now settle down, marry, and have a small son, who is the very image of his father as old photographs show him at the same tender age.

Let us now return to our ultimate particles and to small organizations of particles as atoms or small molecules. The *old* idea about them was that *their* individuality was based on the identity of matter in them. This seems to be a gratuitous and almost mystical addition that is in sharp contrast to what we have just found to constitute the individuality of macroscopic bodies, which is quite independent of such a crude materialistic hypothesis and does not need its support. The *new* idea is that what is permanent in these ultimate particles or small aggregates is their shape and organization. The habit of everyday language deceives us and seems to require, whenever we hear the word "shape" or "form" pronounced, that it must be the shape or form of *something*, that a material substratum is required to take on a shape. Scientifically this habit goes back to Aristotle, his *causa materialis* and *causa formalis*. But when you come to the ultimate particles constituting matter, there seems to be no point in thinking of them again as consisting of some material. They are, as it were, *pure shape*, nothing but shape; what turns up again and again in successive observations is this shape, not an individual speck of material.

The Roots of Atomic Science *

by Werner Heisenberg (1958)

The concept of the atom goes back much further than the beginning of modern science in the seventeenth century, it has its origin in ancient Greek philosophy and was in that early period the central concept of materialism taught by Leucippus and Democritus. On the other hand, the modern interpretation of atomic events has very little resemblance to genuine materialistic philosophy; in fact, one may say that atomic physics has turned science away from the materialistic trend it had during the nineteenth century. It is therefore interesting to compare the development of Greek philosophy toward the concept of the atom with the present position of this concept in modern physics. . . .

In the philosophy of Democritus the atoms are eternal and indestructible units of matter, they can never be transformed into each other. With regard to this question modern physics takes a definite stand against the materialism of Democritus and for Plato and the Pythagoreans. The elementary particles are certainly not eternal and indestructible units of matter, they can actually be transformed into each other. As a matter of fact, if two such particles, moving through space with a very high kinetic energy, collide, then many new elementary particles may be created from the available energy and the old particles may have disappeared in the collision. Such events have been frequently observed and offer the best proof that all particles are made of the same substance: energy. But the resemblance of the modern views to those of Plato and the Pythagoreans can be carried somewhat further. The elementary particles in Plato's *Timaeus* are finally not substance but mathematical forms. "All things are numbers" is a sentence attributed to Pythagoras. The only mathematical forms available at that time were such geometric forms as the regular solids or the triangles which form their surface. [Figure 3–21.]

Figure 3–21. (*After Guy Murchie,* Music of the Spheres.)

In modern quantum theory there can be no doubt that the elementary particles will finally also be mathematical forms, but of a much more complicated nature. The Greek philosophers thought of static forms and found them in the regular solids. Modern science, however, has from its beginning in the sixteenth and seventeenth centuries started from the dynamic problem. The constant element in physics since Newton is not a configuration or a geometrical form, but a dynamic law. The equation of motion holds at all times, it is in this sense eternal, whereas the geometrical forms, like the orbits, are changing. Therefore, the mathematical forms that represent the elementary particles will be solutions of some eternal law of motion for matter. Actually this is a problem which has not yet been solved. The fundamental law of motion for matter is not yet known and therefore it is not yet possible to derive mathematically the properties of the elementary particles from such a law. But theoretical physics in its present state seems to be not very far from this goal . . .

If we follow the Pythagorean line of thought we may hope that the fundamental law of motion will turn out as a mathematically simple law, even if its evaluation . . . may be very complicated. It is difficult to give any good argument for this hope for simplicity—except the fact that it has hitherto always been possible to write the fundamental equations in physics in simple mathematical forms. This fact fits in with the Pythagorean religion, and many physicists share their belief in this respect, but no convincing argument has yet been given to show that it must be so. . . .

It may seem at first sight that the Greek philosophers have by some kind of ingenious intuition come to the same or very similar conclusions as we have in modern times only after several centuries of hard labor with experiments and mathematics. This interpretation of our comparison would, however, be a complete misunderstanding. There is an enormous difference between modern science and Greek philosophy, and that is just the empiristic attitude of modern science. Since the time of Galileo and Newton, modern science has been based upon a detailed study of nature and upon the postulate that only such statements should be made, as have been verified or at least can be verified by experiment. The idea that one could single out some events from nature by an experiment, in order to study the details and to find out what is the constant law in the continuous change, did not occur to the Greek philosophers. Therefore, modern science has from its beginning stood upon a much more modest, but at the same time much firmer, basis than ancient philosophy. Therefore, the statements of modern physics are in some way meant much more seriously than the statements of Greek philosophy. When Plato says, for instance, that the smallest particles of fire are tetrahedrons, it is not quite easy to see what he really means. Is the form of the tetrahedron only symbolically attached to the element fire, or do the smallest particles of fire mechanically act as rigid tetrahedrons or as elastic tetrahedrons, and by what force could they be separated into the equilateral triangles, etc.? Modern science would finally always ask: How can one decide experimentally that the atoms of fire are tetrahedrons and not perhaps cubes? Therefore, when modern science states that the proton is a certain solution of a fundamental equation of matter it means that we can from this solution deduce mathematically all possible properties of the proton and can check the correctness of the solution by experiments in every detail. This possibility of checking the correctness of a statement experimentally with very high precision and in any number of details gives an enormous weight to the statement that could not be attached to the statements of early Greek philosophy.

All the same, some statements of ancient philosophy are rather near to those of modern science. This simply shows how far one can get by combining the ordinary experience of nature that we have without doing experiments with the untiring effort to get some logical order into this experience to understand it from general principles.

Physics and Reality *

by Albert Einstein and Leopold Infeld (1938)

What are the general conclusions which can be drawn from the development of physics indicated here in a broad outline representing only the most fundamental ideas?

Science is not just a collection of laws, a catalogue of unrelated facts. It is a creation of the human mind, with its freely invented ideas and concepts. Physical theories try to form a picture of reality and to establish its connection with the wide world of sense impressions. Thus the only justification for our mental structures is whether and in what way our theories form such a link. . . .

Physics really began with the invention of mass, force, and an inertial system. These concepts are all free inventions. They led to the formulation of the mechanical point of view. For the physicist of the early nineteenth century, the reality of our outer world consisted of particles with simple forces acting between them and depending only on the distance. He tried to retain as long as possible his belief that he would succeed in explaining all events in nature by these fundamental concepts of reality. . . .

Later developments both destroyed old concepts and created new ones. . . .

The quantum theory again created new and essential features of our reality. Discontinuity replaced continuity. Instead of laws governing individuals, probability laws appeared.

The reality created by modern physics is, indeed, far removed from the reality of the early days. But the aim of every physical theory still remains the same.

With the help of physical theories we try to find our way through the maze of observed facts, to order and understand the world of our sense impressions. We want the observed facts to follow logically from our

* From Albert Einstein and Leopold Infeld, *The Evolution of Physics.*

concept of reality. Without the belief that it is possible to grasp the reality with our theoretical constructions, without the belief in the inner harmony of our world, there could be no science. This belief is and always will remain the fundamental motive for all scientific creation. Throughout all our efforts, in every dramatic struggle between old and new views, we recognize the eternal longing for understanding, the ever-firm belief in the harmony of our world, continually strengthened by the increasing obstacles to comprehension.

Some Problems of Philosophy *

by James Jeans (1942)

APPEARANCE AND REALITY

The doctrine of materialism asserted that this space, time and material world comprised the whole of reality; it regarded consciousness as only a minor incident in the history of the material world, a somewhat exceptional episode in the haphazard muddle resulting from the chaotic movements of photons, electrons and matter in general. It interpreted thought as a mechanical motion in the brain, and emotion as a mechanical motion in the body. It seemed at one time to receive substantial support from science. For consciousness was never experienced except in conjunction with matter; a man's mental state was obviously influenced by the food, drink and drugs given to his body; and many thought it possible that all mental activities might be interpreted in terms of various physico-mental processes occurring in the associated body. At the same time astronomy was finding that only an inconceivably minute fraction of space provided any possibility for the existence of the kind of life we know, and it seemed impossible that the rest of the universe should contain anything but inanimate matter. It was hard to imagine that consciousness should be of fundamental importance in such a world.

The new physics suggests that, besides the matter and radiation which can be represented in ordinary space and time, there must be other ingredients which cannot be so represented. These are just as real as the material ingredients, but do not happen to make any direct appeal to our senses. Thus the material world as defined above constitutes the whole world of appearance, but not the whole world of reality; we may think of it as forming only a cross-section of the world of reality.

We may picture the world of reality as a deep-flowing stream; the world of appearance is its surface, below which we cannot see. Events deep down in the stream throw up bubbles and eddies on to the surface of the stream. These are the transfers of energy and radiation of our common life, which affect our senses and so activate our minds; below these lie deep waters which we can only know by inference. These bubbles and eddies show atomicity, but we know of no corresponding atomicity in the currents below.

This dualism of appearance and reality pervades the history of philosophy, again dating back to Plato. In a famous parable, Plato depicts mankind as chained in a cave: . . .

". . . Imagine mankind as dwelling in an underground cave with a long entrance open to the light across the whole width of the cave; in this they have been from childhood, with necks and legs fettered, so they have to stay where they are. They cannot move their heads round because of the fetters, and they can only look forward, but light comes to them from fire burning behind them higher up at a distance. Between the fire and the prisoners is a road above their level, and along it imagine a low wall has been built, as puppet showmen have screens in front of their people over which they work their puppets."

"I see," he said.

"See, then, bearers carrying along this wall all sorts of articles which they hold projecting above the wall, statues of men and other living things, made of stone or wood and all kinds of stuff, some of the bearers speaking and some silent, as you might expect."

"What a remarkable image," he said, "and what remarkable prisoners!"

"Just like ourselves," I said. "For, first of all, tell me this: What do you think such people would have seen of themselves and each other except their shadows, which the fire cast on the opposite wall of the cave?"

"I don't see how they could see anything else," said he, "if they were compelled to keep their heads unmoving all their lives!"

"Very well, what of the things being carried along? Would not this be the same?"

"Of course it would."

"Suppose the prisoners were able to talk together, don't you think that when they named the shadows which they saw passing they would believe they were naming things?"

"Necessarily."

"Then if their prison had an echo from the opposite wall, whenever one of the passing bearers uttered a sound, would they not suppose that the passing shadow must be making the sound? Don't you think so?"

"Indeed I do," he said.

"If so," said I, "such persons would certainly believe that there were no realities except those shadows of handmade things." *

* From *The Great Dialogues of Plato,* translated by W. H. D. Rouse, The New American Library of World Literature, Inc. (Mentor Books), 1956. Reprinted by permission of J. C. G. Rouse, London, England.

Our phenomenal world consists of the activities of matter and photons; the theatre of this activity is space and time. Thus the walls of the cave in which we are imprisoned are space and time; the shadows of reality which we see projected on the walls by the sunshine outside are the material particles which we see moving against a background of space and time, while the reality outside the cave which produces these shadows is outside space and time.

Many philosophers have regarded the world of appearance as a kind of illusion, some sort of creation or selection of our minds which had in some way less existence in its own right than the underlying world of reality. Modern physics does not confirm this view; the phenomena are seen to be just as much a part of the real world as the causes which produce them, being simply those parts of the real world which affect our senses, while the space and time in which they occur have the same sort of reality as the substratum which orders their motions. The walls of the cave and the shadows are just as real as the objects outside in the sunshine.

As the new physics has shown, all earlier systems of physics, from the Newtonian mechanics down to the old quantum theory, fell into the error of identifying appearance with reality; they confined their attention to the walls of the cave, without even being conscious of a deeper reality beyond. The new quantum theory has shown that we must probe the deeper substratum of reality before we can understand the world of appearance, even to the extent of predicting the results of experiment.

Two Worlds Are One *

by Eugene Rabinowitch (1963)

There is another aspect of modern science which also should affect man's idea of the world he lives in. Since science first arose, man has lived in two separate worlds. One is the world of physical existence, populated by material objects—from stars to atoms—which follow certain discoverable causal or statistical laws. The other is the world of mind and emotion. The first is dominated by concepts such as heavy or light, fast or slow, positively or negatively charged; the second by concepts such as good or bad, beautiful or hideous, virtuous or evil. Our growing understanding of the physical world—in which observations are reproducible and future behavior can be predicted on the basis of past history—has gradually narrowed the field of human experience dominated by emotional and spiritual concepts. Arbitrary manipulation of material objects by gods, once thought to explain many events, is used in today's religious systems only to explain exceptional cases, "miracles" interrupting the natural course of events. This narrowing of the realm of the spiritual and broadening of the realm of the material, susceptible to scientific analysis, has led many to believe that ultimately everything in human experience will be interpreted in material terms, and that concepts taken from man's emotional and spiritual experience are merely temporary tools, useful to describe material phenomena of such complexity that their interpretation by means of the laws of the material world is as yet impossible.

However, as justifiable as is the reaction against the past belief in the constant, crude intervention of spiritual forces into material events, this belief should not be replaced by the opposite—the extension of laws derived from observation of the material world to the spiritual aspects of human existence. Spiritual experience is as much an incontestable part of human existence as the experience of material phenomena. Everybody knows the experience of free will, of capacity to choose, of distinguishing between ethical or esthetic values. Some men can be brought to deny this experience, to say that it is based on self-deception, and to find satisfaction in considering themselves only very complex machines acting on the basis of the causal or statistical laws of science.

But does scientific analysis of the material world really require such denial of personal spiritual experience? Certain developments in theoretical physics suggest that man does not need to do violence to himself by denying his spiritual existence. The relevant theoretical principle, which has emerged from the extension of experimental physics into the world of elementary particles, is Bohr's principle of complementarity. It asserts the legitimacy and the inevitability of the parallel existence of two apparently mutually exclusive pictures in the description of physical events in microphysics. It further asserts that these two descriptions cannot contradict each other, because, as shown by Heisenberg, every time man attempts by any conceivable experiment whatsoever to obtain an increasingly precise definition of magnitudes belonging to one picture, he makes, by this very act, the magnitudes belonging to the other picture more and more vague. Together, the two sets of concepts give a full description of all we know now about the material universe; separately, each can represent only one aspect of it. . . .

There are eminent scientists who are dissatisfied with this dual picture, which implies renunciation of strict causal interpretation of the behavior of elementary particles, replacing it by statistical laws of probability determined by the propagation of the correlated waves. But the majority believe that this duality is not a temporary weakness of theory, but represents the ultimate realization of the capacity to understand the material world possible for man as a sensing organism. They consider the dualistic picture created by Bohr's complementarity principle and Heisenberg's uncertainty relation as logically satisfactory. The apparent contradiction of the wave and the particle pictures is, in their eyes, only a weakness of traditional ways of thinking, based on observations of macroscopic objects.

I believe that acceptance of the legitimate existence of two physical pictures—incompatible on the surface but never contradictory in predicting future observations—implies a major revolution in man's concept of the world. It offers a glimpse of how the apparent contradiction between the material and the spiritual elements in human existence could be ultimately resolved.

There is obviously no simple analogy between the particle and the wave aspects of the material world and the spiritual and the material aspects of human existence; but it suggests that the modes of interaction between man and the world around him may, by their very nature, make it impossible to form a unified picture, and requires "coexistence" of two (or perhaps more) independent systems of concepts and relations. If the analogy holds, the two systems can become contradictory only if one of them is applied to the types of observations which rightfully belong to the other.

The spiritual aspect of the world is, then, not contradictory to and not separable from its material aspect; it is complementary to it. The existence of spiritual forces cannot reveal itself, as many believe, in occasional violations of the laws which govern the material world. Rather, the whole world confronted by man has its spiritual and its material aspects. The material aspects reveal themselves to man through his sense organs, refined by instruments. These organs or instruments could not reveal the existence and operation of the spiritual forces even if each event in the world has its physical as well as its spiritual aspects, because by the very process of observation of material parameters, the spiritual ones are made diffuse and escape observation.

The more we will learn about the physical aspects of the physiological processes which accompany man's thoughts and emotions, the vaguer will become their spiritual content. We may be able to induce emotions and visions by drugs; but this only illustrates the coupling of physicochemical and spiritual experience, and does not make the one "explain" the other.

4

What Is the Secret of Atomic Energy?

The exciting story of the development of the atomic
bomb shows how a new understanding of nature that
came out of pure theoretical research can be used in
ways that deeply affect the future of man. The fundamental secret was one of understanding; once that had
been achieved could any other secrets prevent the
exploitation of this knowledge for destructive ends?

What Is the Secret of Atomic Energy?

Introduction

BEFORE DAWN on July 16, 1945 the first atomic bomb exploded in a flash of searing brilliance over the desert of Alamogordo. A dense cloud surged and billowed upward accompanied by an awesome roar that "warned of doomsday." In that moment the world of human experience was changed irreversibly. Mankind was presented on the one hand with untold opportunities, and on the other hand with dangers which he must learn to control before they destroy him. The speed with which this adjustment must be made is unprecedented in history. Science has created an accelerating rate of change and there is some concern that this rate has outstripped man's ability to grow with it.

The first reaction of a frightened public has been to look for scapegoats. Scientists have been blamed for opening Pandora's Box and turning loose a swarm of evils into the world. Scientists, so this argument goes, should have foreseen the consequences of their theories and kept these destructive ideas from reaching the hands of irresponsible people. Failure to do so clearly demonstrates a lack of concern for the good of mankind. And yet the fact is that the equation which led to the release of atomic energy was written down forty years before Alamogordo in the course of a purely theoretical study of the nature of light and motion by a gentle man who all his life was a "confirmed pacifist."

If the world dilemma cannot be blamed entirely on the scientists, then surely it can be blamed on the spies who gave away the details of the construction of atomic bombs to other nations. The door of the room into which Pandora released the swarm of evils should have been slammed shut to prevent these evils from reaching the rest of the world. As an example of this type of thinking: one of the bills presented in Congress provided the death penalty for giving away *the secret* of the atomic bomb. But the essential principles of the release of atomic energy were known to the entire scientific world by 1939. These "secrets" were an integral part of the advancing front of scientific knowledge.

The best way to dispel misconceptions is to know the facts, and yet many people feel that the American public is not informed about the origin and nature of atomic energy. As Eugene Rabinowitch says: "In some experience with atomic energy legislation, I have talked with enough public men to know that almost none of them understands even the most elementary principles underlying the release of atomic energy. The same is true for most well-educated laymen. And yet all of us must make decisions

135

about this weapon which is potentially destructive beyond the wildest nightmare of the imagination! These decisions cannot be made in ignorance; the public must be informed." [1]

The story of the development of atomic energy is one of the most fascinating and instructive chapters in the history of science. It illustrates how scientists work together, building on each other's ideas. It shows in a very vivid way the relationship between the search for pure knowledge and technological applications. What conditions are necessary for scientific knowledge to be used for practical purposes? Two billion dollars paid for the research and development that produced the atomic bomb in 1944. Would another two billion dollars buy us a superbomb or a cure for cancer?

As the discovery of atomic energy has so dramatically shown us, knowledge is power and power can be used either for good or for evil. Under the pressure of wartime military need the energy of the atom was first used for destructive purposes, but in the years since then constructive uses have also been developed. Atomic energy is being used today to power submarines, to generate electricity, to produce radioactive elements for medical treatment and research. Many other possibilities are being explored such as blasting new harbors, canals, and reservoirs, converting salt water into fresh water to increase the amount of arable land. Many difficult technical problems still remain to be solved but there is no doubt that in the years to come atomic energy will become an important factor in the reshaping of our environment to fit our needs unless we use it first to destroy not only ourselves but our world along with us. Centuries before man conceived of atomic energy this idea was expressed in a Buddhist proverb: "To every man is given the key to the gates of heaven; the same key unlocks the gates of hell."

1. From Selig Hecht, *Explaining the Atom*, "Prologue" by Eugene Rabinowitch.

The Story of the Development of Atomic Energy

Development of Atomic Energy *
by Selig Hecht (1947)

ISOTOPES: ATOMS DIFFERENT INSIDE BUT IDENTICAL OUTSIDE

[Before 1932 scientists believed that] atoms are made of protons and electrons. A proton weighs 1 unit, and an electron $\frac{1}{1840}$ or 0.00054 unit. Since the electron weighs so trifling an amount, why then are the atomic weights of the elements not whole or very nearly whole numbers?

The problem is an old one. Early in the nineteenth century after Dalton had suggested the atomic theory, Prout had proposed that all atoms were made up of hydrogen. Prout's hypothesis had to be discarded because the atomic weights of the elements were not exact multiples of the weight of hydrogen. This is not a matter of just ordinary accuracy. By 1900, atomic weights had been measured with a precision greater than any other constant of chemistry and were known to the fourth and fifth decimal places. They certainly were not whole numbers, nor were they multiples of hydrogen. Prout's hypothesis had long been abandoned, and yet here we are adopting essentially the same idea, by assuming that all atoms are made up of protons and electrons. If our theory of atomic structure is correct, why indeed are atomic weights not whole numbers?

Fortunately, this question did not bother investigators for very long, because by the time Rutherford had established the nuclear structure of the atom, other phenomena had already suggested the answer. The reason that atomic weights are not whole numbers is that the elements as usually isolated and purified chemically are not single elements, but mixtures. This statement needs to be explained and justified.

Take the element ionium. In 1906 this was a new element, which had just been discovered by B. B. Boltwood at Yale. He had isolated it from pitchblende, the mineral that contains a lot of uranium, and from which the Curies several years before had extracted radium and startled the world. Further study showed that the chemical properties of ionium were very much like those of thorium. It had the same appearance, the same

* From Selig Hecht, *Explaining the Atom.*

137

solubilities, the same melting point, and even the same color characteristics as thorium. Yet the two differed in atomic weight. The atomic weight
of ionium is 231.5; that of thorium is 232.1.

Direct comparison of ionium and thorium made certain that chemically
the two were not merely similar; they were identical. If the two were
mixed it became impossible to separate them. Separation is largely a
chemical procedure depending on differences between substances in sol-
ubility, boiling point, or combining capacity. When two different substances are dissolved in one solution, the addition of another liquid may
well precipitate one substance while the other remains in solution. But
thorium and ionium have identical chemical properties and cannot be
separated. Yet they cannot be the same because their atomic weights are
different.

True, the difference in atomic weight is only 0.6, and seems small.
However, the very fact that atomic weights can be determined with great
precision to several decimal places makes a difference of 0.6 as certain
and real as anything can be. Here, therefore, are two substances with the
same chemical properties but different atomic weights.

This is indeed a riddle. But in this case the riddles came in pairs. It will
be recalled that radium spontaneously gives off alpha particles, electrons,
and gamma rays, and leaves radium emanation or radon. Radon is itself
radioactive, and in a little while breaks down to radium-A, which is also
radioactive and leaves radium-B, which breaks down to radium-C, and
so on through several transformations ending in a substance that is stable
and that looks like lead. It has not only the same appearance, but the
same chemical properties, the same color characteristics, and all the common attributes of lead. If it is mixed with ordinary lead, the two cannot
be separated from the mixture. Yet the two have different origins.

What adds to the puzzle is that there exists still another form of lead.
The element thorium, whose atomic number is 90, is spontaneously radioactive and forms a family of radioactive sequences much as radium does.
The end of this sequence is a stable substance that also looks and behaves
like ordinary lead.

It was Frederick Soddy who as early as 1910 saw the meaning of these
riddles of ionium-thorium and of the three different leads that are alike.
With fine courage he predicted that the three leads would have different
atomic weights, and that the one from thorium would be greater than
ordinary lead while the one from radium would be less than ordinary
lead. Independently Kasimir Fajans made a similar prediction. Both
turned out to be correct. The atomic weight of ordinary lead is 207.2.
The atomic weight of thorium lead is 207.9, while the atomic weight of
radium lead is 206.1. The one is 0.7 greater and the other 1.1 less than

ordinary lead. These values were secured by the great masters of atomic weight determinations, Theodore W. Richards in America, and O. Hönigschmid in Germany, and there was no wishing them away. Here are elements identical chemically but with different atomic weights. How can this be?

Soddy called such substances isotopes, and explained what they represent in terms of atomic structure. In Greek *iso* means alike or the same; and *topos* means spot or space. Isotopes are elements that occupy the same space in the Periodic Table. They have the same atomic number, and the same chemical properties, regardless of what their atomic weights may be.

We have learned that the chemical properties of an element are determined by the number of its electrons outside the nucleus, which of course equals the net number of positive charges on the nucleus. Therefore, if two elements are indistinguishable chemically, they must have the same number of positive charges on the nucleus, the same number of electrons outside the nucleus, and the same arrangement of those electrons in their shells.

However, we have also learned that the nucleus contains more than the protons necessary to give it its net charge. For instance, helium has 2 protons in the nucleus, which gives it its 2 positive charges; but because its atomic weight is 4, it has something else in the nucleus that supplies the extra mass of 2.

At this time it had been tentatively supposed that this extra nuclear mass of 2 is furnished by 2 additional protons, each of which is neutralized by 1 electron inside the nucleus. In the same way lithium, with its atomic weight of 7 and atomic number of 3, has 7 protons in the nucleus, of which 4 are neutralized by 4 electrons inside the nucleus, leaving a net nuclear charge of 3.

Now suppose that a lithium atom is composed somewhat differently, as shown in Figure 4–1. Suppose that it has only 6 protons in the nucleus, and that 3 of these are internally neutralized by 3 electrons. The nucleus still has 3 positive charges, and the atom has 3 outside electrons arranged in two shells as before. Since the chemical properties are determined by the electrons in their shells, this atom would be indistinguishable chemically from the regular lithium atom. It would have the same atomic number 3, and occupy the same spot in the Periodic Table. Its atomic weight, however, would be less by 1 unit than normal lithium; its atomic weight would be 6 instead of 7.

Or suppose that an atom has 8 protons in the nucleus, of which 5 are internally neutralized by 5 electrons. The net charge on the nucleus would again be 3, and the atom would again have 3 outside electrons arranged

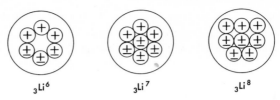

$_3\text{Li}^6$ $_3\text{Li}^7$ $_3\text{Li}^8$

Figure 4–1. Isotopes of lithium. All three isotopes have the same number of protons, and therefore the same net 3 positive charges of the nucleus. Three positive charges also mean 3 electrons. Hence the three isotopes are chemically alike. However, the extra mass of "neutralized protons" makes the difference between the masses of the isotopes, each being 1 unit heavier than its lighter neighbor.

in two shells. Such an atom would have all the chemical properties of lithium; its atomic number would be 3 and it would be in the same spot as lithium in the Periodic Table. But its atomic weight would be 8 instead of 7.

According to Soddy these three types of lithium would be isotopes: three chemically identical substances with different atomic weights. In this way Soddy explained ionium and thorium, and the three kinds of lead. Ionium and thorium are isotopes; they have the same atomic number (90), the same number of nuclear charges, the same number of electrons outside the nucleus arranged in the same shells. But they differ in the number of internally neutralized protons present in the nucleus to make up the different atomic weights. Similarly, lead, radium-lead, and thorium-lead are isotopes: they have the same atomic number (82), with the usual chemical consequences, but they differ in the number of internally neutralized protons in the nucleus that determine their atomic weights.

This idea of Soddy's explains why ionium and thorium, though identical chemically, differ in atomic weight. But how does it explain the fact that neither atomic weight is a whole number? Soddy knew the answer to this. Neither ionium nor thorium is a pure isotope; each is a mixture.

It is simpler to examine lithium. We saw a moment ago that it is conceivable to have three kinds of lithium, which are chemically indistinguishable isotopes: the normal one whose atomic weight is 7, a light one of atomic weight 6, and a heavy one of atomic weight 8. Suppose that ordinary lithium as found in nature is a mixture of two of these three isotopes, the normal one and the light one. If they were mixed in equal proportions the atomic weight of the mixture would be midway between 6 and 7 or 6.5. Actually the atomic weight of lithium is 6.94, which is so near 7 that the light isotope probably occurs about once in twenty atoms of the mixture.

Let us suppose that most elements as they are found in nature are mixtures of isotopes. It then follows that the deviations of atomic weights from whole numbers can serve as a clue to the relative amounts of the different isotopes in the elements as they occur naturally. This has turned out to be true. However, in 1910 it was guesswork, brilliant and sublime guesswork of the kind that gives one's heart a lift even in retrospect.

Before closing this section we may as well learn how to designate isotopes, because we need them later in the story. Again let us use lithium as an easy example. Lithium has an atomic number of 3. Its common isotope has an atomic weight of 7. This isotope is therefore written as $_3Li^7$; the subscript 3 indicates the atomic number, while the superscript 7 gives the atomic weight. Its less common isotope is $_3Li^6$. The theoretical isotope $_3Li^8$, which I described a while back, has never been found; it is inherently unstable. Frequently the isotopes are just referred to by their weights, and the atomic number is omitted because it is well known. Thus we speak of lithium-6 or lithium-7; and of the nonexistent isotope as lithium-8.

Now we can return to the story itself. Soon after this time many isotopes were discovered, but in a way quite different from what one would expect from the development that drove Soddy to invent them.

ISOTOPES IN BUNCHES

Let us [consider] Geissler tubes [1] and see what happened with them. A Geissler tube is a glass tube from which most of the air has been pumped out and through which an electric current passes between two metal electrodes. One of these plates is negative and from it a steady stream of electrons goes across the space to the other plate, which is positive. The negative plate is the cathode; the positive one is the anode.

As the current passes through the gas in the tube it tends to strip the negative electrons from the atoms of the gas and carry them along, from the cathode to the anode. What remains of the atoms are positively charged ions, which must be moving in the opposite direction, from the anode toward the negative cathode. These streams of positive ions were called positive rays when they were first discovered, and it was their study that developed our knowledge of isotopes.

In order to investigate these positive rays, J. J. Thomson designed a tube somewhat different from those previously used. If positive rays are coming from right to left, as they are shown in Figure 4-2, it would be a good idea to catch them and find out what they are. Therefore, Thomson used a thick cathode, and drilled a long hole in its center, in the hope that the positive rays on their way toward the cathode would go right through

1. Refer to page 52. Ed.

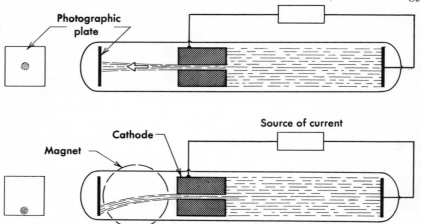

Figure 4–2. Demonstration of positive rays. The upper drawing shows the positive rays going through the hole in the cathode and falling on a photographic plate to make a round spot in the center. The lower drawing shows a magnet deflecting the beam so that it hits the photographic plate at a spot lower down on the photograph.

the hole and pass beyond it in a straight beam. For this reason he lengthened the tube to the left of the cathode and made arrangements to put a photographic plate at the extreme end. He argued that the beam of positive rays would impinge on the photographic plate and make a little black spot the diameter of the beam. And that is precisely what happened.

The next step was even more exciting than the mere demonstration of the existence of positive rays. If these rays are really the atoms of the gas stripped of some electrons, that is, if they are ions, then they should have essentially the mass of the atoms of the gas in the nearly evacuated tube. Thomson knew how to measure such masses, for it was he who had measured the mass of the electron several years before. He used the same principle here. A powerful magnet placed near the tube should divert the positively charged particles from their direct path. Instead of hitting the photographic plate dead center, the beam should hit below or above depending upon the orientation of the magnet. Moreover, the beam of charged particles should be deflected more or less, depending upon the mass of particles. Heavy particles should be deflected less than light particles, and if there are several kinds of ion in the beam of positive rays, there should be several spots on the photographic plate at distances from the center depending on the masses of the ions.

The first gas that Thomson used in this apparatus was neon. Nowadays the red color of neon under such conditions is familiar in the common neon signs. In 1910 it was relatively rare. The gas that J. J. Thomson used was highly purified neon, and when its positive rays were deflected by a magnet and photographed at the other end of the tube, it showed a dense dark spot at a distance from the center corresponding to a mass of 20. Neon has an atomic weight of just over 20 and this fits the requirements.

In addition to this dark spot corresponding to neon, there was a very much lighter spot farther from the center at a place corresponding to something with an atomic weight of 4. This lighter spot was clearly helium. We already know that helium and neon are both inert gases belonging in the same vertical column in the Periodic Table, and it is easy to understand why one could not remove all the slightest impurities of elements similar to neon. In fact, there was still another spot evident on the photographic plate; this one at a place corresponding to an atomic weight of 40. This also seemed sensible, because argon has an atomic weight of 39.9, and argon is another of the inert noble gases in the same column of the Periodic Table.

So far, so good. However, close examination of the photograph showed a very fine shadow of a spot at a place near neon but corresponding to an atomic weight of 22. J. J. Thomson purified his neon several times; but whenever any tube showed a spot for neon at 20, it always showed a faint shadow at 22. Could it be that there are two kinds of neon, which cannot be separated from each other by chemical purification, a neon of atomic weight 20, and a neon of atomic weight 22? If there were two kinds of neon, then the reason that even the most purified neon gas has an atomic weight of 20.18 is that it is a mixture of the two neon isotopes, with neon-22 present as a small fraction of the mixture.

These observations were made about 1913 in the Cavendish Laboratory, Cambridge University, where J. J. Thomson was the director. F. W. Aston, one of the younger men there, thought he saw a way of making certain that these ideas were correct. Aston argued that even if one cannot separate the two neons by chemical means, one should be able to separate them by physical means, using some property that depends on the mass of the nucleus, rather than on the number of electrons. For example, suppose we liquefy neon, and then let it evaporate slowly. The atoms of neon-22 are 10 per cent heavier than the atoms of neon-20. The atoms of the heavier isotopes should therefore find it a little more difficult to hurl themselves from liquid neon into the air and become gaseous neon. The lighter neon will thus evaporate faster than the heavier neon, and after most of the liquid neon has evaporated, the residue should contain a larger fraction of heavy neon than before.

Aston tried out his idea in this way, but failed to find any differences.

He therefore tested another method involving the same idea. He allowed neon to diffuse from one container into another through a barrier of baked clay like that used for clay pipes. This clay is a porous material full of microscopic holes, through which the neon atoms would have to travel. Aston argued that the heavy neon isotope should not be able to move so rapidly as the light neon, and therefore that the gas that had passed through the clay barrier would contain less of the heavier isotope, whereas the gas remaining in the original container would have more of the heavier isotope. Aston found a just measurable difference between the gases in the two containers, enough to show the probability of the idea, but not enough to settle the matter.

These two methods are mentioned here because they are typical of the kind that were later used successfully. Indeed, much later they were important in the manufacture of materials for the atomic bomb. Unfortunately their first trials by Aston resulted in little more than encouragement.

This was in 1914, just when the First World War began. Most of the young men in England became occupied with the war, and nothing much happened in the laboratories. Aston survived the war and in 1919, when he again began working in this field, he did not return to the separation experiments, but followed more directly in J. J. Thomson's footsteps.

Aston elaborated the negative end of the Geissler tube to an even greater extent than had J. J. Thomson. In addition to the one hole in the cathode through which positive ions passed, he placed another block of metal with another hole farther to the left, as in Figure 4–3. In this way the stream of positive ions that goes through the first hole, and that has become slightly divergent by the time it reaches the second hole, is sharpened because the second hole permits the passage of only those ions that have gone in a straight line between the first and second holes. By this means a very precise beam of ions is formed, which makes a small spot when it hits the photographic plate at the end of the tube. When a large magnet is put outside near this beam of ions, the beam curves away from its original direction in an arc whose curvature is determined by the mass of the ion. In this way one gets a series of spots on the photographic plate, and the spacing of the spots depends on the masses of the ions which make up the beam. Since the mass of an ion is essentially the mass of its nucleus, this procedure is a method of separating isotopes.

Before the First World War Thomson had found the secondary light spot of neon-22 associated with the darker spot of neon-20, and had recognized them as the two isotopes of neon. With his new and precise instrument Aston found that practically all elements, even when thoroughly

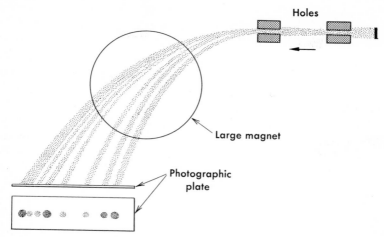

Holes

Large magnet

Photographic plate

Figure 4–3. Mass spectrometer for isotope separation. This is the left or cathode end of a Geissler tube, enlarged and modified. The large magnet curves the particles of different mass to different extents, the lighter being deflected more than the heavier.

purified, have these secondary spots associated with them. It was comparatively easy to determine the relative weights of the ions corresponding to the various spots, and in a short time Aston found the isotopes of many elements. Moreover, since the degree of blackening of a spot depends on the number of ions that hit it, Aston could also gauge the relative abundance of the isotopes of any element. The sketch at the bottom of Figure 4–3 shows how such a photographic plate looks.

Aston found that almost all the elements he studied have isotopes. His work was later taken up by K. T. Bainbridge in the United States, and between them they examined the whole series of elements. Every element has from one to eight isotopes; the first ninety-two elements together have about two hundred and fifty isotopes. A strange regularity has turned up here. Those elements whose atomic number is even usually have a greater number of isotopes than those elements whose atomic number is odd.

Our original question of why the atomic weights of the elements are not whole numbers can now be answered with confidence. Most elements are mixtures of isotopes. The fractions in their atomic weights depend on the relative proportions in which the isotopes exist in nature. If an element has an atomic weight that is very nearly an integer, it is overwhelmingly composed of just one isotope. This is true of fluorine, with its atomic weight of 19.00; of sodium, with its weight of 23.00; and of helium, with its weight of 4.00.

A SPECIAL ISOTOPE: HEAVY HYDROGEN

The existence of numerous isotopes presents us with a pretty problem. Very early the atomic weight of oxygen had been assigned the arbitrary value of 16.000. This was fine before anyone knew about isotopes and would still be fine if oxygen had no isotopes and were just $_8O^{16}$. But oxygen has two naturally occurring isotopes, O^{17} and O^{18}. For every five hundred atoms of O^{16} there is an atom either of O^{17} or of O^{18}. If we assign the value of 16.000 to the isotope O^{16}, then the atomic weight as determined with the naturally occurring mixture of oxygen isotopes will have to be higher by nearly 3 parts in 16,000, that is, it will be 16.003.

For most purposes this difference need not even be remembered, because it is so trifling. It does make a difference in the atomic weights of the other elements, which would all have to be raised by the same fraction. Therefore to avoid confusion, the old value of 16.000 for natural oxygen has been retained as the standard. But the difference, slight as it is, did set people thinking about hydrogen.

Without going into the details of the argument one can report that if the hydrogen atom is really just one proton and one electron, then the atomic weight of ordinary hydrogen is too high by the same amount, that is, by 3 parts in 16,000, or about 1 part in 5000. Please remember that even twenty years ago the atomic weight of hydrogen had been measured repeatedly with the greatest precision, and was known as precisely 1.00778. An error of 0.02 per cent was out of the question. Therefore this difference had to be accounted for.

It could be explained most easily if hydrogen had a heavy isotope. But unfortunately neither Aston nor Bainbridge had been able to find any trace of an isotope of hydrogen. Hydrogen purified and put through the glorified Geissler tube (now called a mass spectrometer) showed only one spot in the proper place, and no more.

There was always the bare possibility that a heavy isotope of hydrogen does exist, but is present in so small a concentration as not to affect the photographic plate of Aston's and Bainbridge's mass spectrometer. Computation had shown that if a heavy isotope of hydrogen exists, then its presence as only 1 part in 5000 parts of normal hydrogen would account for the discrepancy in atomic weight. But how can one demonstrate a suspected isotope in such great dilution that no trace of it can be found by the latest and most refined physical method of measurement?

The possibility, however, was fascinating, and for an excellent reason. The usual hydrogen atom has 1 proton, 1 electron, and an atomic weight of 1. The suspected isotope must have 2 protons in its nucleus, one of which is presumably neutralized internally by an electron. This leaves a net charge of 1 on the nucleus, as before, which is balanced by 1 electron outside the nucleus. The weight of this atom is 2, which is twice as much as that of the normal hydrogen atom. This is a real difference in weight.

The difference between neon-20 and neon-22 is only 10 per cent, and Aston's efforts to separate them by diffusion and by evaporation had been largely unsuccessful. Moreover, the efforts to separate chlorine isotopes had also succeeded only very slightly because of the small difference in weight between the two isotopes Cl^{35} and Cl^{37}. However, with hydrogen there was the possibility of an isotope with twice the weight of common hydrogen. If the ideas behind Aston's effort at separating the neon isotopes by diffusion or evaporation are sound, they should work with hydrogen, if they worked at all.

So Harold C. Urey thought, and as a consequence he decided to make the attempt. Urey argued that if liquid hydrogen were allowed to evaporate slowly, the normal light isotope should go off into the air more easily than the suspected isotope which is twice as heavy. Therefore, as the hydrogen evaporates, the liquid residue should become richer in the heavy isotope, until it becomes sufficiently concentrated to show up on the photographic plate of a mass spectrometer.

Urey interested F. G. Brickwedde at the Bureau of Standards, who proceeded to make a gallon of liquid hydrogen. Brickwedde then allowed the liquid to evaporate slowly until only a gram ($\frac{1}{28}$ of an ounce) of liquid hydrogen was left, which he shipped to Urey. At Columbia University, Urey and G. M. Murphy introduced a little of this presumably enriched hydrogen into a mass spectrometer, and photographed the positive rays produced, as worked out by Aston. They got the usual spot of hydrogen on the plate, but in addition they found another spot, never seen before, at the place corresponding to an atomic weight of 2. This spot could mean nothing else but the heavy isotope of hydrogen, $_1H^2$.

For this exciting discovery Urey was awarded a Nobel Prize in 1934. For some reason this heavy isotope of hydrogen, $_1H^2$, seemed such a unique particle at the time that it was given a special name, "deuterium," and a separate symbol, D. And just as the nucleus of ordinary hydrogen is called a "proton," the nucleus of deuterium was called a "deuteron."

Water is composed of two atoms of hydrogen and one of oxygen. Obviously deuterium can replace hydrogen in all chemical reactions because the two are isotopes. Therefore, it is to be expected that the compound D_2O exists, with two heavy hydrogens in place of ordinary hydrogen. Such a molecule of water is called "heavy water." A small fraction of normally occurring water must be heavy water. It now became a problem of separating these heavy-water molecules from ordinary water molecules, or at least of increasing their concentration. Such enriched water was prepared by evaporation of ordinary water according to the same principles that led to the discovery of deuterium in the first place.

The concentration of heavy water in the enriched mixture can be measured by weight. The ordinary water molecule weighs 18, its 1 oxygen atom contributing 16 and its 2 hydrogen atoms 1 each. The heavy-water molecule weighs 20 because the 2 deuterium atoms contribute 2 each. This is a difference of 2 parts in 20, or 1 in 10. In the laboratory one can easily weigh with a precision of 1 part in 10,000. Therefore one can detect by weight 1 part of heavy water in 1000 of ordinary water. . . .

Deuterium has served as a tool in the further exploration of atomic structure, and heavy water later played a role in the release of atomic energy. The discovery of deuterium and heavy water in itself helped to confirm the explanation of isotopes and to strengthen the meaning of atomic weights.

THE BASIS FOR ISOTOPES: NEUTRONS

The discovery of isotopes and the explanation of their structure brought into focus a problem that we have lightly passed over. It concerns the mass of the nucleus in excess of the protons furnishing its net positive charge.

It will be recalled, for example, that lithium with an atomic number of 3 and an atomic weight of 7 has 3 protons in the nucleus and 3 electrons outside. Four units of mass left in the nucleus must be accounted for. For a number of years, this extra mass was tentatively regarded as due to 4 protons whose charges have been neutralized by electrons inside the nucleus; and the diagrams in Figure 4-1 were drawn according to this idea.

All the elements above hydrogen have this extra mass in the nucleus; for the heavier atoms it is greater than the mass of the protons responsible for the atomic number and the net charge. Thus uranium has 92 protons with their positive charges, and 146 other units of mass, which were tentatively supposed to be protons whose charges have been neutralized by an electron each within the nucleus.

There were lively arguments as to how an electron can be inside the nucleus and why the positive and negative charges did not annihilate each other. The whole idea semed strange and no one was satisfied with it. However, the only way to deal with strange things is to ask questions, make experiments, and think about them. Many physicists therefore devoted their attention to the nucleus and tried to explore its structure further by bombarding it with alpha particles from radium, and with protons.

In 1930 W. Bothe and H. Becker sent streams of alpha particles at beryllium, the light metal that is number 4 in the series of elements. What came from the beryllium was a beam of rays with very high penetrating power. Bothe and Becker thought that these rays might be gamma rays like those given off by radium. In this they were later shown to be mistaken.

Frédéric Joliot and his wife Irène Curie, the daughter of Pierre and Marie Curie, made similar experiments in 1932 with beryllium and found that some of the radiation given off by beryllium was able to penetrate a lead shield that normally absorbs gamma rays. In addition, they observed that if a paraffin shield or any other hydrogen-containing compound were placed around the beryllium, the rays that entered the paraffin caused the ejection of protons of very high energy. This phenomenon was difficult to understand, and prompted others to investigate it.

Within the year, James Chadwick repeated these experiments with beryllium, and found, of course, the same powerful rays as had Bothe and Becker and the Joliot-Curies. He determined that the rays could not be deflected by a magnet—a finding that showed them to be neutral and in this respect like gamma rays or X rays. Chadwick, however, noticed that these rays traveled only at about one-tenth the velocity of light, a speed too slow for gamma rays. Gamma rays travel with the speed of light, since they are a form of light.

Furthermore, Chadwick found that these rays from beryllium, when directed against nitrogen, would give an occasional nitrogen atom a terrific wallop, something that gamma rays could not do, since they will bounce off even such tiny particles as electrons. This impact with the nitrogen atom indicated that the rays must be made of particles, and if they are particles, then they must be neutral particles, because they are not deflected by a magnet.

It was not long before Chadwick was able to show that this neutral particle has a mass of 1, the same as a proton. Very properly he called it a "neutron." For its discovery Chadwick was awarded a Nobel Prize in 1935.

The discovery of the neutron resulted in a huge surge of activity in nuclear physics, and is one of the definitive steps on the road to the atomic bomb. For our immediate purposes, however, its discovery resolved the problem of the extra mass in the nucleus. The extra mass is composed of neutrons. The particles inside the nucleus that give it the necessary weight in addition to its protons are the neutrons. The helium nucleus now contains 2 protons and 2 neutrons, and no hypothetical intranuclear electrons are needed. The lithium nucleus contains 3 protons and 4 neutrons, and so on for the other elements.

We may now rest easy. The charge on the nucleus is entirely due to the protons in it. Its mass, and therefore its atomic weight, is determined by the combined mass of its protons and its neutrons. And since the atomic weight of all elements except hydrogen is at least twice its atomic number, there are at least as many neutrons in a nucleus as there are protons.

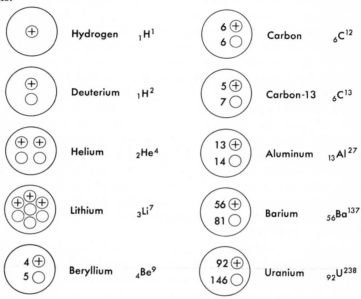

Figure 4–4. Nuclei of atoms. The number of protons and neutrons in the nuclei are shown for some interesting atoms. For convenience, all nuclei are drawn the same size; actually they differ in size depending on the number of particles in them.

The nuclei of some of the elements are shown in Figure 4–4. Notice particularly aluminum with its 13 protons and 14 neutrons; and barium with its 56 protons and 81 neutrons. And above all, look at uranium with its 92 protons and 146 neutrons. All these elements and their isotopes will interest us later.

From now on our task will be to show how the nucleus can be split to release the fabulous energy that radium and radioactivity have shown it to contain.

MATTER AND ENERGY

By 1935, three fundamental particles of which all matter seemed to be constructed were known: the electron, the proton, and the neutron. We also knew how these particles are distributed inside and outside the nucleus to form that significant sequence of elements represented by the Periodic Table. The picture appeared complete, and its pattern seemed logically sensible and esthetically satisfying.

True. But it left some old questions unanswered, and it raised some new ones. Take the matter of radium. Its atomic number is 88 and its atomic weight 226. We can therefore construct its atom by taking 88 protons and 138 neutrons in a tight bunch and surrounding them with 88 electrons arranged in their proper shells. This structure is designed to satisfy the requirements of the Periodic Table and of a host of chemical and physical properties. But why is this structure so unstable that a small grain of radium, all by itself, steadily pours out a powerful stream of alpha particles, beta particles, gamma rays, and heat? Where do the particles and rays come from? Where does the energy come from?

Take the even simpler problem of the neutron. The proton and the neutron both have a mass of 1. Are they related? Is it possible that the neutron is a proton that has captured an electron internally, and has become permanently neutralized? Or, consider the reverse. Perhaps the basic particle is really the neutron, and a proton is merely a neutron that has captured a unit of positive electricity.

This last question requires a moment of explanation, because it has introduced a new concept, a unit of positive electricity. Before 1932 the unit charge of positive electricity had always been associated with the particle of mass 1, the proton. However, there were some possibilities that a positive charge might exist separately from this large mass and that there is a unit of positive electricity with a mass of the same order as the electron but opposite in charge. In fact, P. A. M. Dirac predicted in 1931 that such a positive particle must exist, and in 1932 it was actually found by C. D. Anderson. It is called a "positron." It has a mass as small as the electron and is positively charged. It is not very common, and it lasts only a short time, because it is neutralized almost as soon as it is formed.

What about the positive charges within the nucleus? How do they manage to come so close to one another and remain stable? We know that like charges repel each other, whereas unlike charges attract each other. This principle can be demonstrated by such simple means as bits of paper similarly charged by contact with charged amber. The same is true of magnets: similar poles repel, whereas opposite poles attract each other. Yet in the helium nucleus, for example, there are 2 protons—2 positive charges—held close together as a unit. The same problem arises in the nucleus of all elements except hydrogen. There is carbon with 6 positive charges in the nucleus, aluminum with 13 positive charges, and uranium with 92 positive charges. How are these numerous similar charges held so closely together as they must be in the small space of the nucleus?

The neutrons may possibly have something to do with it. Notice that helium, the first nucleus that has more than one positive charge, also has 2 neutrons in it. One of the striking facts of nuclear structure, indeed, is that the number of neutrons in the nucleus is at least equal to and usually greater than the number of protons. Do the neutrons serve as the binding medium to keep the protons from flying apart? And if so, where do these binding energies come from? To answer some of these questions we have to examine what at first may appear to be a completely different problem.

Since nuclei are made only of protons and neutrons, it was to be expected that the atomic weight of each pure isotope would be a whole-number multiple the atomic weight of hydrogen. This is true of a few of the lighter elements such as helium, carbon, and nitrogen to the second decimal place. But as the masses of isotopes began to be determined more and more accurately, it was found not to be true for most of them, and not even for the lighter ones to the third and fourth decimal places. For example, the mass of helium $_2He^4$ turned out to be 4.0028, and carbon $_6C^{12}$, 12.0036.

Remember that this is all on the basis of oxygen as 16.0000. Therefore it might seem that if oxygen were given a slightly different value, everything would come out right. Unfortunately this cannot help, because some of the isotopes actually weigh less than they should, and no amount of arithmetical juggling can make them come out whole numbers. Close study of these circumstances brings out something of first-rate importance.

As usual, let us first work it out for a light element like helium. Many accurate measurements have established that, compared with oxygen as 16.00000, the mass of the proton is 1.00758, and the mass of the neutron is 1.00893. Helium is $_2He^4$ and has 2 protons and 2 neutrons.

$$
\begin{array}{rl}
2 \text{ protons} & = 2.01516 \\
2 \text{ neutrons} & = 2.01786 \\
\hline
\text{sum} & = 4.03302 \\
_2He^4 & = 4.00280 \\
\hline
\text{Difference} & = 0.03022
\end{array}
$$

As the table shows, the whole of helium $_2$He^4 is less than the sum of its parts. There is no wishing this difference away; it results from the most accurate measurements imaginable. In the formation of helium from its components 0.03022 unit of mass remains to be accounted for.

One cannot say that the mass is lost. Nothing can be lost. Every physical and chemical transaction balances both in mass and energy. What then has happened? The interesting thing is that Einstein had thought about this back in 1905 in connection with the special theory of relativity. At that time, he had suggested that energy and mass are different aspects of the same basic cosmic stuff, and that the two can be converted one into the other. He wrote a simple equation for the relation between the two, which says merely that energy E is equal to mass m.

Energy is measured in units such as ergs or calories or kilowatt-hours, whereas mass is measured in different units such as grams or pounds. To make mass and energy equal, the unit of mass must be translated into the unit of energy. The same holds even when one unit of mass is translated into another. To translate kilograms into pounds we multiply by a constant number 2.2. So 1 kilogram equals 2.2 pounds. To translate inches into centimeters we multiply by a constant whose value is 2.5. Thus 1 inch equals 2.5 centimeters. Einstein showed that the translating constant for converting mass measured in grams into energy measured in ergs is equal to the square of the velocity of light measured in centimeters per second. The velocity of light is usually designated by the letter c, and its value is 30,000,000,000 centimeters per second. (This is 186,000 miles per second.) The translation constant is c^2, and Einstein's equation becomes $E = mc^2$, probably the most important equation in history.

In 1905 Einstein wondered how to test this equation experimentally, and suggested that it might apply to the enormous energies released in radioactivity, which had only recently been discovered. Einstein's equation was actually tested with alpha particles from the disintegration of lithium-7 by protons by J. D. Cockcroft and E. T. S. Walton. But little did Einstein imagine then that his equation would be demonstrated forty years later on so large a scale as it was at Hiroshima, Nagasaki, and Bikini.

If you compute the energy that the transformation of 0.030 unit of mass yields in terms of the equation, the result is startling. The loss of 0.030 unit of mass in the formation of helium from 2 protons and 2 neutrons represents a disappearance of 3 parts of mass in 400 parts, or about ¾ of 1 per cent. In one gram (⅛₈ of an ounce) this is a loss of 0.0075 gram. Multiply this by c^2 and you get over 650 million billion ergs of energy. Translated into common units, this is about 200,000 kilowatt-hours, which is the current used to run 200,000 lamps of 100 watts each for a 10-hour day. And all this from the slight loss in mass that occurs when ½ gram each of protons and neutrons unite to form 1 gram of helium.

MASS IS CONVERTED TO ENERGY

What happens when ¾ of 1 per cent of matter is transformed into energy and is liberated in the formation of helium from protons and neutrons? The same thing that happens when a rock rolls down the mountainside and settles in the valley: the final situation is more stable than the initial one. The rock high on the mountain is in a relatively unstable position; if it is dislodged, it will roll downhill. When it comes tearing down the slope, it gives out the energy that it had by virtue of its high location. When the rock ends in the valley, it has less energy available than before, and is more stable; it can no longer roll down that hill.

Stated formally, this means that when a system emits energy during a change it is more stable after the emission than before. A ball, when it falls from the top of a house, gives off energy in its fall, and is in a much more stable position on the ground than on the roof. Water in the ocean has poured down from the hilltops and has given off energy that can be used to make electricity. The water in the ocean is certainly in a more stable condition than it would be on top of a hill.

What is true for these physical changes is also true for chemical changes. When a chemical reaction is accompanied by the emission of energy, the final compounds are more stable than the initial compounds. . . .

Precisely the same circumstances attend the emission of energy in the formation of a helium nucleus from protons and neutrons: the helium nucleus is more stable than the neutron or the proton. Neutrons quickly become attached to other elements, whereas helium nuclei, which are the same as alpha particles, stand a good deal of knocking around without becoming attached to anything or without being broken into their components.

One way to judge the relative stability of a system is to determine the energy necessary to change it into some other state. Our rock in the valley is more stable than on the mountaintop because a lot of energy is required to drag it up the mountainside to its original position. It takes a lot of energy to break up a helium nucleus into its protons and neutrons. And since it is difficult to concentrate such an amount of energy in order to supply it to the small nucleus, the result is that an alpha particle, or a helium atom, is a very stable particle indeed. However, it is by no means the most stable nucleus. In fact, it is one of the relatively less stable elements, as we shall see.

The loss of mass that occurs in the formation of a nucleus from protons and neutrons is spoken of as its "packing loss." The idea is that the protons and neutrons are packed more tightly in the nucleus than when they are free. The packing loss of an element per unit of atomic mass is secured by dividing its packing loss by the number of units in its nucleus; this we can call its "packing factor." Obviously, the greater the packing factor of an element, the greater is the energy emitted in its formation, and the greater is its stability. It is as if the protons and neutrons were bound more tightly together in the nucleus as a result of the loss in mass and the emission of energy. Because of this idea, the emitted energy is often spoken of as the "binding energy" of the protons and neutrons in the nucleus.

Aston measured the relative masses of the various isotopes in his mass spectrometer and found that the packing factor of all the elements is not the same. So many regularities have already been discovered in the properties of the elements that it is not surprising to learn that even in their packing factor the elements show a regular behavior. The new regularity that Aston found is simple enough, but it is pregnant with meaning for every inhabitant of the earth. It lies at the very foundation of the process for the release of atomic energy.

Look at the packing factors of the elements shown in Figure 4–5. Hydrogen has a packing factor of 0, because its nucleus is just a single proton. The value for any other element is secured by subtracting its actual atomic weight from the sum of the weights of the protons and neutrons in its nucleus. This gives the packing loss, which when divided by the number of protons and neutrons in the nucleus gives the packing factor. For example, krypton-78 has 36 protons and 42 neutrons in its nucleus.

$$36 \times 1.0076 = 36.2736$$
$$42 \times 1.0089 = 42.3738$$
$$\text{sum} = 78.6474$$
$$\text{atomic weight of Kr-78} = 77.9262$$
$$\text{packing loss} = 0.7212$$
$$\text{packing factor}$$
$$\text{referred to hydrogen} = 0.0091, \text{ or 91 parts per 10,000}$$

Clearly, krypton-78 has a loss of 91 parts per 10,000 for each of the 78 protons and neutrons that enter into the structure of its nucleus. It must be a stable nucleus indeed.

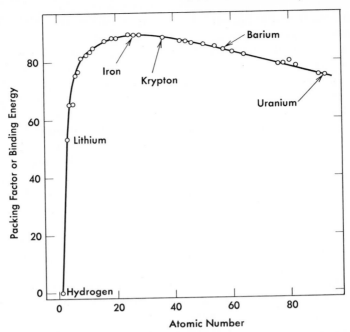

Figure 4–5. Packing factor. When protons and neutrons form atomic nuclei, they lose some of their mass as a result of the packing or binding of the particles in the nucleus. This loss per particle is the packing factor. It corresponds to the binding energy which is emitted, and its magnitude is shown for some interesting elements. The packing factor is given in hundredths of 1 per cent.

Figure 4–5 shows the packing factor of many of the elements. They lie on a curve that starts low at hydrogen, rises rapidly to reach a maximum at iron and nickel, and then decreases steadily to uranium. In other words, the light elements and the heavy elements of the Periodic Table have smaller packing factors than have the middle elements. Iron, which is at the top of the curve, has the largest packing factor. It is therefore the most stable element, whereas the lighter and the heavier elements are less stable than it is.

Look again at the sequence in Figure 4–5. Suppose it were possible to convert the elements into one another by rearranging their nuclear protons and neutrons. Then by starting at either end of the Periodic Table and constructing the elements in the middle, we could release energy, since we would be going from less stable to more stable elements. If we started with hydrogen we would combine smaller atoms to make larger ones. If we started with uranium, however, we would break large atoms into smaller ones. In both cases, the final mass would be less than the initial mass, and the difference would be given off as energy. Since we know that a trifling mass becomes tremendous energy, either process would yield vast amounts of energy.

Both procedures actually occur. The first type of process supplies the energy of the sun and the stars; [and is used] . . . in connection with the so-called hydrogen bomb.[2]

The second way of releasing energy in atomic transformations, from the heaviest elements, occurs on earth. For many years the only known course was through radioactivity. Remember that radium breaks up spontaneously to release helium and radon. The atomic weight of radium is 226, whereas the weights of helium and radon are 4 and 222, respectively. The large unstable nucleus of radium yields the smaller nuclei of helium and radon; mass is decreased because of the larger packing factors, and energy is therefore released. The energy is large, and we computed it earlier in our story.

Several other elements are naturally radioactive, but much less so than radium. The process, however, is the same. Smaller nuclei are formed, and energy is released, because of the packing-factor relations as shown in Figure 4–5.

Natural radioactivity is entirely spontaneous. The rate at which radium, uranium, thorium, and actinium normally break up to emit alpha particles, beta particles, and gamma rays is independent of man's activity and nothing we do has any influence on it. However, since 1939 we have learned another method of releasing energy by use of the change in packing factor from heavy-to-lighter elements. It consists in breaking the uranium nucleus up in such a way that the resulting nuclei are substantially lighter than the uranium nucleus and yield up vast amounts of energy. This is the method of the atomic bomb. It can be done at will and is entirely under the control of man.

ATOMS SPLIT AND RELEASE ENERGY: NUCLEAR FISSION

This is a good place to emphasize the fact that in all this work so far physicists were not concerned with the problem of releasing energy to produce atomic bombs. They were concerned with understanding the structure of matter. They wished to explore the nucleus, to determine why protons that are positively charged, and should repel each other, can be in intimate stable contact in so small a space as the nucleus. They wanted to know what a neutron is and how it functions inside the nucleus.

2. See also *Exploring the Universe*, pp. 315–17, and *fusion bomb* in Glossary. Ed.

Naturally they could not help speculating on occasions about the release of atomic energy. Some even wrote about the possibilities in the popular press; or at least they talked enough so that the news reporters wrote about the possibilities. However, the experiments that they performed were designed to answer the fundamental questions about matter and energy. The procedure was to bombard matter in bulk with alpha particles, with protons, with deuterons, and after 1932 with neutrons, and to see what happened.

In reviewing this work, one can see now that there were three kinds of result achieved. The first is quite simple and may be illustrated by the work of Cockcroft and Walton at the Cavendish Laboratory. They found that if a stream of protons at a relatively low velocity is directed against a film of the alkali metal lithium, there emerge alpha particles traveling at a very high velocity. It can be shown that for each proton that hits a lithium nucleus, two alpha particles appear.

The transformation is simple and straightforward. It is illustrated in Figure 4–6. A proton is a hydrogen nucleus $_1H^1$. Lithium is $_3Li^7$, its

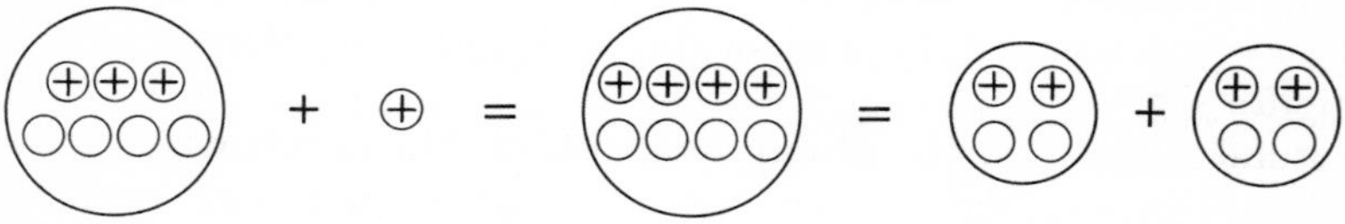

Figure 4–6. Lithium fission. A lithium nucleus after absorbing a proton splits into two helium nuclei with the release of energy.

nucleus containing 3 protons and 4 neutrons. An alpha particle is the helium nucleus $_2He^4$ containing 2 protons and 2 neutrons. The process of their interaction may be written as

$$_3Li^7 + _1H^1 = _2He^4 + _2He^4$$

In reading this equation, first add the subscripts: 3 protons + 1 proton = 4 protons. Then add the superscripts: a mass of 7 + a mass of 1 = a mass of 8. Probably what first happens is that the lithium nucleus takes up the proton and for an instant it contains these 4 protons and 4 neutrons, making a mass of 8 with a charge of 4. This nucleus is so unstable that it breaks in two, forming 2 helium nuclei, each of mass 4 and charge 2.

Actually the two helium nuclei fly apart with great speed as if considerable energy were released in the readjustment of the unstable nucleus. That considerable energy is released can be shown in two ways.

One is to determine the energy that the proton has before it hits the lithium atom, and the energy of the 2 alpha particles after they have been formed. This is done by measuring the speeds with which the particles travel and computing the energy by the usual equations of standard physics. The difference between the two velocities shows that considerable energy was released in the formation of the 2 alpha particles. After each collision the 2 alpha particles are released with a combined energy of 27.2 millionths of an erg for each atom of lithium.

The other way of showing the release of energy is to consider the loss of mass due to the changed packing factor. The lithium nucleus weighs 7.0165 and the proton weighs 1.0076; together they weigh 8.0241. An alpha particle weighs 4.0028, and two weigh 8.0056. Therefore the formation of 2 helium nuclei from lithium and hydrogen has resulted in the loss of 0.0185 unit of mass. This mass is responsible for the energy with which the 2 helium atoms are endowed, and by using Einstein's equation we can compute how much energy this is. The lost 0.0185 unit of mass actually weighs 3.07×10^{-26} gram, which when substituted in Einstein's equation equals 27.6-millionths of an erg per atom of lithium.

Notice how good an agreement the two methods give. In fact, for an experiment of this kind the agreement is almost perfect, and it demonstrates the complete equivalence of mass and energy. This, of course, is a proof of Einstein's equation.

One more thing needs to be pointed out about this lithium-proton reaction. It results in the breaking up of the lithium-proton mass into two equal fragments—2 helium nuclei. In biology when a cell divides to produce two equal daughter cells, the process is called "fission." By analogy the breaking of the nucleus into 2 equal helium nuclei may be called nuclear fission. Actually this term was not used till much later, when in 1939 the uranium nucleus was broken into two nearly equal fragments.

The interesting point at the moment is that when a proton and a lithium nucleus collide the result is 2 helium nuclei and considerable energy. Since the whole procedure is man-made, it might seem that this is a method for releasing atomic energy at will. And so it is; but not a very efficient method.

A little reflection shows why. Remember how small a nucleus is compared to the rest of the atom: the diameters are in the ratio of 1 to 10,000. Areas are proportional to the square of their diameters. The ratio of the diameters are as 1 is to 10,000. Therefore the cross-section areas are as 1 to 100,000,000—which means that in passing through a single lithium atom a proton has at best 1 chance in 100,000,000 of hitting the lithium nucleus. Actually, the chances are even fewer, because the proton and the lithium nucleus are both positively charged and repel each other. As the proton continues through the atoms, it hits electrons and becomes slowed down until it is finally stopped after having traversed about 100,000 atoms at best. Thus it has about 100,000 chances in 100,000,000 of hitting a lithium nucleus, or 1 chance in 1000. Even if the energy released is high, it hardly equals the energy required to get the protons moving, since at best only 1 in 1000 will hit a lithium nucleus. In short, this is a wasteful and inefficient method. The atomic energy is there, and it can be released, but only at the cost of a much greater expenditure of electrical energy.

RADIOACTIVE ATOMS ARE PRODUCED ARTIFICIALLY

In summarizing the action of atomic projectiles, I said that three kinds of result were achieved. The first is comparatively simple, like the fission of lithium just described. The second is somewhat more complex, and much more revolutionary.

Consider aluminum, the thirteenth element, with an atomic weight of 27. Its nucleus contains 13 protons and 14 neutrons, and it has no known isotope. When aluminum is hit with alpha particles, neutrons are emitted and a substance is formed whose nucleus has 15 positive charges and a mass of 30. This substance should be one whose nucleus contains 15 protons and 15 neutrons. The equation

$$_{13}Al^{27} + {}_2He^4 = {}_{15}P^{30} + {}_0n^1$$

bears this out; notice that the neutron is written as $_0n^1$ because it has a charge of 0 and a mass of 1.

Now a substance with 15 protons in its nucleus is the fifteenth element in the Periodic Table, and this corresponds to phosphorus. Note, however, that the atomic weight of this newly formed substance is 30, whereas the atomic weight of phosphorus is 31, and it has no known isotope. These experiments were made by Frédéric Joliot and his wife, Irène Curie. The Joliot-Curies made chemical tests of this newly formed substance and found it actually to be phosphorus. Here then was a phosphorus lighter than common phosphorus, which had never been found in nature. It looked as though a new artificial isotope had been produced.

This indeed was exciting; but what was more exciting was that even while the chemical measurements and tests were being made the material seemed to vanish. In a quarter of an hour no phosphorus was left. And most exciting of all, as it disappeared, it was radioactive. . . .

The significant aspect of this discovery is not that one element has been transformed into another, because such transmutations had become relatively common by 1933. The revolutionary discovery is that there has been produced artificially a radioactive element like radiophosphorus, which so far as we know does not exist in nature.

Within a year, most of the easily available elements were tested in this way and practically all of them yielded radioactive isotopes. A whole new group of isotopes was thus artificially produced—isotopes that are radioactive. It is a curious quirk of destiny that artificial radioactivity should have been discovered by the daughter of the Curies, who had discovered the most potent source of natural radioactivity. In 1935 a Nobel Prize was awarded to the Joliot-Curies for this work.

The discovery that most elements can be produced in the form of radioactive isotopes opened the most wonderful possibilities . . . in biological experimentation to chart the passage of an element through the body. . . .

In the first place, the radioactive isotope always shows its presence by its radioactivity. No matter where it is, it steadily gives off positrons and gamma rays, which can be detected by the delicate means developed by physicists for their own atomic work. This can be done without killing the animal or destroying its organs.

In the second place almost any element may be prepared as a radioactive isotope, and the preparation of one is about as easy as another. Moreover, the radioactive isotope need not be separated for purposes of concentration; it can be directly produced by irradiation with neutrons of elements or chemicals used in the preparation of feed, or of material to be injected into animals or plants.

There is one possibility for using radioactive isotopes which is particularly fascinating. Some organs of the body have a special affinity for one element. For example, the thyroid gland in the neck has a special affinity for iodine, and the bones have a special affinity for phosphorus. We take iodine ordinarily in food and drinking water, and a large part of it goes to the thyroid gland to be stored as part of the material that the thyroid gland secretes. If the iodine were radioactive, a good deal of radioactivity could thus be concentrated in the thyroid gland. All tissues are sensitive to radioactivity because its gamma rays are powerfully destructive to living cells. However, cancer cells are much more sensitive to gamma rays than are ordinary normal cells. Therefore if there were cancer cells in the thyroid, the radioactivity would kill them more easily than it would kill normal cells, and the concentration could be so regulated that the cancer cells would be destroyed locally without injuring the normal thyroid cells. In the same way radioactive phosphorus would settle in the bones so as to destroy a bone cancer.

Successful treatment of malignant growth and other diseases of the thyroid gland with radioactive iodine has in fact been proved to be possible. In certain other cases—such as leukemia, a cancerous disease of blood corpuscles—other radioactive elements have proved of considerable help. Concentration of radioactive phosphorus in tumor tissue has been found useful to establish exact location and extension of tumors in the brain for operative purposes.

Radioactive cobalt, an isotope that has radiations similar to those of radium, can be produced artificially at much lower prices—and in much larger quantities—than natural radium. The Canadians showed the way by producing the first cobalt "irradiation bomb" in their atomic-energy plant at Chalk River, Ontario; Oak Ridge has followed suit. Radium therapy, which is still the greatest weapon short of the knife that we have against cancer—is thus becoming more powerful and accessible. . . .

The American atomic-energy installation at Oak Ridge began to sell radioactive isotopes at cost to medical, scientific, and industrial users in July 1947. Its sales have rapidly snowballed since. It has been joined by Canadian, French, and British atomic-energy plants; Russian research reports indicate that radioactive isotopes are available there, too.

But it is time to return from this excursion into the present to our historical narrative.

THE NEUTRON BECOMES EFFECTIVE

For our story the most effective particle used in the exploration of the structure of the nucleus is the neutron. The protons, deuterons, and alpha particles, whose actions against various elements have been described, are all positively charged particles. The proton is the nucleus of ordinary hydrogen, the deuteron is the nucleus of heavy hydrogen, and the alpha particle is the nucleus of helium. Because of their positive charge these particles are repelled by the nuclei of the elements against which they are directed. In order for them to collide with another nucleus and to enter it, they have to travel at great speeds. For years the cry had been for more and more speed, and for more powerful devices to send these particles hurtling at speeds closer and closer to the velocity of light.

Neutrons have the same mass as protons, but have no charge. Therefore they are not repelled by the positive nuclei of atoms against which they are moving, and can more easily come into contact with them. Soon after neutrons had been discovered by Chadwick in 1932, Enrico Fermi in Rome began to use them as missiles to send into the interior of the nucleus. As his work and that of his associates developed in Rome, it was duplicated and amplified by George B. Pegram and John R. Dunning at Columbia University in New York.

The results achieved were not dissimilar from the two types already described. New atoms were formed from other atoms, and radioactive isotopes of various elements were produced. However, the most important result of the work concerned the speed of neutrons. Because the other particles were being used at high speeds, when neutrons were first used they were also jacked up to high speeds. But it soon became obvious that not only was this unnecessary, but even wrong. Slow neutrons were apparently much more effective than fast ones. In fact, neutrons that were so slow as to resemble in speed the ordinary random movements of atoms in a gas were found to be the most effective.[3]

Such slow neutrons easily penetrate the nucleus. Then, if the combination of nucleus plus neutron is stable, the neutron simply remains in the nucleus and a new isotope of the original element is formed. But if the arrangement of nucleus plus neutron is unstable, it breaks up to liberate positrons or electrons and gamma rays, and to form a stable isotope of a different element; or the product may be a radioactive element that in its turn liberates positrons or electrons and gamma rays.

The slower the neutrons, the better for these purposes. Neutrons can be slowed down by letting them pass through paraffin or similar substances containing hydrogen or carbon, substances called "moderators," which we meet again later. The neutrons are slowed down because they are constantly bouncing against the protons of the hydrogen atoms or against the light and stable nuclei of the other moderators, and the collisions gradually dissipate their energies.

Many things were done with these very slow neutrons. But the one that belongs in our stream of history deals with the relation between neutrons and the heavy elements. Uranium is the last and heaviest natural element in the Periodic Table. Can one artificially produce still heavier elements? Fermi argued that if uranium were surrounded by slowly moving neutrons, some neutrons might enter the uranium nucleus, and possibly stay there. After some slight rearrangement of charges, involving the emission of a positron or an electron or of some small fragment, the result might be a new element, heavier than uranium. These possible elements were referred to as the transuranic elements.

The experiments that Fermi made for this purpose were encouraging. Electrons were liberated from uranium, but the results as a whole were not clear. The experiments were duplicated by others, but the results still remained puzzling. In fact, it was five years before these experiments were understood.

Such a delay is not uncommon in the history of science. However, this was 1934 and the state of the world may have contributed to the delay.

3. These are also called "thermal neutrons." Ed.

First Germany, then Austria, and then Italy were being made uninhabitable for many scientists, who were forced to look for refuge in other countries. Forced migration is not conducive to creative thought—peace of mind is a prime requisite. By 1939, America, England, France, and Denmark had become the homes of an international galaxy of atomic physicists.

THE URANIUM ATOM SPLITS

Early in January 1939 the first clue was discovered that made the uranium-neutron experiments understandable. Otto Hahn and F. Strassmann, two chemists in Germany, had made chemical studies of the products of slow neutron action on uranium. Among the products they were astonished to find barium.

Remember that the uranium nucleus has 92 protons and 146 neutrons. Barium is $_{56}Ba^{138}$, and therefore has only 56 protons and 82 neutrons in its nucleus. Barium is so far from uranium in the Periodic Table that it does not seem sensible for it to appear as a product of neutron action on uranium. All previous experience leads one to expect the emission of a small fragment by uranium, perhaps an electron or a positron, and the appearance of some element immediately near the atomic weight of uranium. But what was barium doing here?

O. R. Frisch and Lise Meitner, in Copenhagen and Stockholm as refugees from Germany, had worked on uranium-neutron reactions; and as Lise Meitner meditated on this curious point, she had a revolutionary idea. Perhaps when uranium absorbs a neutron it splits into two roughly equal fragments. This would account for barium, which has about half the mass of uranium. She told this idea to her nephew and co-worker Frisch. They both discussed it with Niels Bohr, the director of the laboratory in Copenhagen and one of the great physicists, who was just about to leave for a stay at Princeton in order to discuss some theoretical problems with Einstein. Bohr arrived on January 16, 1939, and communicated Meitner's suggestion to his friends in Princeton and Columbia.

The effect of Bohr's news was immediate. As a biophysicist—one who applies physics to biology—working in my laboratory in the Physics Building at Columbia, I had some contact with the nuclear physicists who were working there at the time. It was fun to see the effect of Lise Meitner's suggestion. The weeks immediately following Bohr's arrival were filled with suppressed excitement, with lively speculation, and with critical experimentation. Everybody was working hard, thinking hard, and trying to appear nonchalant.

Meitner's suggestion was that when uranium absorbs a neutron it splits into two approximately equal fragments. Why all the excitement?

Uranium has 92 protons. When it splits, barium is formed. Barium has 56 protons, which leaves 36 protons for the other fragment. Look up number 36 in the Periodic Table; it is krypton. Now look up barium and krypton in the packing-factor diagram (Figure 4–5). They are among the elements with the highest packing factor. This means that when they are formed from uranium the final mass will be considerably less than the original mass, and a vast amount of energy will be liberated according to Einstein's equation for the conversion of mass into energy.

However, this was essentially no new story, and it should have been no cause for excitement. For instance, we learned that when lithium absorbs a proton it splits by perfect fission into two helium atoms and releases considerable energy as a result of the mass loss in terms of the packing factor. Moreover, we know that several such energy-releasing transformations have been investigated and that the whole situation is well understood. The energy release is certainly great, but as we have seen, it is useless for technical purposes. Much more energy is required to supply the protons or neutrons necessary to keep it going than can be got out of the reaction. The process stops the moment we stop supplying protons or neutrons.

Precisely here is where the excitement comes in. Look at Figure 4–7. Uranium-238 has 146 neutrons. Add to this number the one neutron that has caused fission. Barium-138 has 82 and krypton-83 47; together 129 neutrons. That leaves 18 neutrons to be accounted for. Even if some of these neutrons become converted to protons by the emission of beta rays, there is the possibility that several neutrons may remain free. It was the finding of these free neutrons that caused all the excitement.

When one neutron is absorbed by uranium, the latter breaks in two to give barium and krypton, with the release of lots of energy *and with the release of neutrons.* These released neutrons might then be absorbed by other uranium atoms, each of which would split into barium and krypton, and release energy and more neutrons. In this way one might get not only

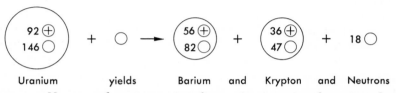

| Uranium | yields | Barium | and | Krypton | and | Neutrons |

Figure 4–7. Neutron release in uranium fission. A uranium nucleus after absorbing a neutron splits into two fragments and releases the extra neutrons. This is the basic fact that makes an atomic bomb possible.

a lot of energy as the result of fission, but one or several neutrons to keep the process going as a chain reaction until all the uranium was changed into barium and krypton. The result would be the emission of truly enormous amounts of energy at the expense of just one original neutron, which started the first uranium atom on its path of fission. For the first time the efficient release of atomic energy on a large scale seemed possible.

The first job, however, was to determine whether Meitner's suggestion was true. If the uranium atom that has absorbed a neutron really splits in two, the resulting large fragments will fly apart with great energy. These heavy pulses of energy can easily be detected. Frisch looked for them, and found them almost immediately. Within a few days of one another several groups of investigators here and abroad confirmed the results. Uranium fission was a reality.

The second job was to see whether neutrons are really emitted during fission. The idea that neutrons might be given off occurred independently to Joliot in Paris, to Fermi, and to Szilard, the last two both at Columbia University. With the help of colleagues they set about determining whether it is true. On March 8, 1939, H. von Halban, F. Joliot, and L. Kowarski sent their report for publication, and on March 16, 1939, H. L. Anderson, E. Fermi, and H. B. Hanstein, as well as L. Szilard and W. H. Zinn, sent their respective papers in for publication. All three groups of investigators by different methods found that neutrons are emitted during uranium fission. Atomic energy seemed around the corner.

WHICH URANIUM ISOTOPE FISSIONS?

The months following the demonstration of uranium fission with the emission of neutrons were full of such activity by many workers in different parts of the world that, in December 1939, when L. A. Turner summarized the year's work in the *Review of Modern Physics*, he covered about a hundred papers on fission. . . .

The most important thing about uranium fission that was discovered in 1939 concerns the uranium isotopes. Uranium has three naturally occurring isotopes. The main bulk of pure uranium—99.3 per cent of it— is $_{92}U^{238}$, which for short is written U-238. A small fraction, 0.7 per cent, is a lighter isotope, of atomic weight 235. It is $_{92}U^{235}$, and is written as U-235. Finally, there is a trace of a still lighter isotope, $_{92}U^{234}$, to the extent of 0.006 per cent. Do all three isotopes of uranium undergo fission?

To answer this question it was necessary to separate the three isotopes and to test them individually for fission. We already know that the separation of isotopes is not easy. Moreover, the differences among the masses of U-238, U-235, and U-234 are relatively trifling; at best about 1 per cent. However, not much material is necessary for these tests; so A. O. Nier was able to separate them by a modification of Thomson's and Aston's method, which had originally demonstrated the existence of isotopes.

In the mass spectrograph uranium is converted into a stream of positive ions as in the old Geissler tube. The stream is passed through holes in the cathode and curved into an arc by means of a magnetic field. The lighter isotope curves more than the heavy one, and the two hit the photographic plate at different spots, as shown in Figure 4–3. Instead of letting the beams fall on a photographic plate as Thomson and Aston had done, Nier permitted them to become deposited on a surface upon which they could accumulate. Then each spot of isotope was separately tested with neutrons and the results observed and measured. It was quickly apparent that only one of the isotopes, namely U-235, underwent fission. Uranium-238 merely captured a neutron but did not undergo fission. Uranium-234 hardly enters the picture because of its trifling concentration.

Further investigation showed that U-235 can capture slow neutrons ever so much more easily than it can fast neutrons. For purposes of fission, slow neutrons are therefore best. On the other hand, U-238 captures fast neutrons more easily and does not fission.

This information was not a good augury for the release of atomic energy. Uranium-235 needs slow neutrons in order to fission. When U-235 fissions it releases fast neutrons. Uranium-238, however, captures fast neutrons and does not fission. To maintain a chain reaction at least one of the neutrons released by U-235 must be captured by a nucleus of U-235. But the liberated fast neutrons are most easily captured by U-238, which does not fission. Moreover, in natural uranium there is 140 times as much U-238 as U-235. The fast neutrons released in the fission of U-235 will therefore be gobbled up by the U-238 nuclei before any of them can be absorbed by a U-235 nucleus to keep the chain reaction going.

There is an obvious way out of this fix: separate the isotopes so that you can have pure U-235 only. Then whatever neutrons are produced in its fission will have a good chance of being captured by U-235 nuclei without competition by U-238, and the chain reaction can have a good chance of going. Alas, this is an obvious way, but not an easy way. We have had experience with isotope separation before, from Aston's first attempts with neon-20 and neon-22 to Urey's successful hydrogen-deuterium separation, and the difficult oxygen-18 and oxygen-16 separation. The 1-per-cent difference in mass between U-235 and U-238 did not look propitious for easy isotope separation. Therefore, along this road, the release of atomic energy in terms of a chain reaction seemed possible but not likely.

NEWLY PRODUCED ATOMS THAT FISSION

The isotope U-238 absorbs fast neutrons but does not fission. What does it do? Nobody was entirely certain, but both evidence and theory seemed to indicate that the usual emission of small fragments might be occurring. Indeed in terms of some theoretical ideas that Bohr had formulated, one could guess what might be going on.

It is important to consider these guesses. Admittedly, the theory of nuclear structure at that time was poor and limited. Admittedly, prediction in terms of it was more of an art than a science. However, in this particular case, the theory predicted correctly.

What can happen when U-238 absorbs a neutron? If the nucleus absorbs the neutron and retains it, we should get a new isotope of uranium, U-239, because the neutron would merely add to the mass of the nucleus and hence to its atomic weight. Such a first step may be written as

$$_{92}U^{238} + _{0}n^{1} = _{92}U^{239}$$

Add the subscripts for the charges and the superscripts for the masses.

According to theory, this is an unstable system with too many neutrons. A rearrangement of charges and masses will therefore take place and the nucleus will emit an electron. If a negative charge leaves the nucleus, this can come about if a neutron has emitted an electron to become a positively charged proton. The result is a nucleus with one less neutron but with one more proton than U-238. Uranium has 92 protons; the new nucleus will have a total of 93 protons. An element with 93 protons is a completely different element from uranium, and will occupy the next place in the Periodic Table.

This new element would be called neptunium, with its symbol Np, after the planet Neptune which lies beyond the planet Uranus, after which uranium was named. It would thus be one of the transuranic elements which Fermi and the others had speculated about beginning in 1934.

The theory also predicted that when neptunium is formed, there would be emitted not only an electron (written as $_{-1}e^{0}$) but a fair amount of energy in the form of powerful X rays or gamma rays. The formation of neptunium Np from the transitory isotope U-239 can therefore be written as

$$_{92}U^{239} = _{93}Np^{239} + _{-1}e^{0} + \text{gamma rays.}$$

The process does not stop here. According to the theoretical ideas about nuclear structure, Np^{239} should be relatively unstable. In a short while it too will emit from its nucleus an electron and powerful X rays. The emission of an electron from the nucleus again means the transformation of a neutron into a proton by the removal of a negative charge. From neptunium, which has 93 protons, we thus derive a nucleus with 94 protons, which constitutes still another new element.

No significant mass has been lost by the successive emission of the 2 electrons. Therefore the atomic weight is still 239. But the new element will be number 94 in the Periodic Table. It was named plutonium, after Pluto, the planet farthest out in the solar system. The equation for its production from neptunium is

$$_{93}Np^{239} = {}_{94}Pu^{239} + {}_{-1}e^0 + \text{gamma rays.}$$

The final prediction from theory is perhaps the most significant. It says that the new element plutonium, Pu-239, is relatively stable and that it will absorb slow neutrons preferentially and undergo fission much as U-235 does.

If these theoretical predictions are true, then the absorption of a neutron by U-238 will yield the new element plutonium, Pu-239, which is just as fissionable as U-235 but which can be secured in much larger quantities because of the greater concentration of its parent, U-238, in natural uranium. Moreover, since plutonium is a chemically different element from uranium, there will be no difficulty in separating it from uranium after it is formed, and purifying it.

A mass of plutonium can then be prepared in which to start a chain reaction. A single neutron supplied from an outside source will be absorbed by a plutonium nucleus. It will fission into two flying fragments with the emission of heat, gamma rays, and several neutrons. These neutrons will be absorbed by plutonium nuclei, each of which will fission, emit energy and more neutrons, and this chain process will go on until all the mass of plutonium has been converted into fission fragments and enormous energy.

Thus theory at the end of 1939. And thus fact in 1945.

CAN ATOM SPLITTING BE KEPT UP?

All that I have written up to now, and much more, was common knowledge among those all over the world who were capable of understanding it. Much of it is to be found in elementary textbooks; all of it is available in advanced textbooks and in professional journals of physics. Far from being secretive, atomic physicists were a gregarious international group, and communicated information and ideas to one another by word of mouth, by mail, by telephone, and even by transatlantic cable. Everybody knew everybody else and everyone knew everything. Ideas were circulated freely, and were discussed critically. As a result enthusiasm ran high and science progressed rapidly.

The year 1939 saw the termination of this free exchange. In September the Germans invaded Poland, and Europe was at war. Many scientists reluctantly abandoned their regular work and turned to the problems of war. Some in the United States and in England began to think of the military possibilities of a uranium or plutonium chain reaction in the production of atomic energy.

The mere computations were terrifying. . . . If a chain reaction could become established and all the atoms in a pound of U-235 be fissioned, the energy produced would be over 400 billion billion ergs, or in common units, 12,000,000 kilowatt-hours.

If this energy were released slowly under control it would furnish the electric current that keeps 12 million 100-watt lamps going for a 10-hour day, or about enough to illuminate all the homes in New England for an evening.

If, however, it were released quickly, say in a fraction of a second, it would have the explosive force of about 10,000 tons of TNT. . . . Clearly a new order of explosive force was possible, and the sleep of those who made these calculations was not easy.

This is very nice on paper. But in reality no one had established such a chain reaction. No one had separated more than a hundred-millionth of a gram of U-235; this was a microscopic speck on a slide and was used to test which uranium isotope undergoes fission. A pound of U-235, indeed! One had better stay with ordinary uranium with its three isotopes and see what can be done about the possibilities of a chain reaction.

The basic fact is that an atom of U-235 when it absorbs a slow neutron undergoes fission and liberates fast neutrons. In ordinary uranium many things can then happen, and a chain reaction will result only if several factors are just right.

The first is fission capture. Uranium-235 will fission when it captures a slow neutron. Will U-235 fission if it captures a fast neutron? It is quite likely. But we cannot know, because in natural uranium there is 140 times as much U-238 as U-235 and it captures all the fast neutrons without undergoing fission.

Can one slow down the neutrons produced in the fission of U-235 so that they will be captured mainly by other atoms of U-235? One did not know, but there were ideas as to how it could be done. Light elements such as helium, carbon, beryllium, and heavy hydrogen do not absorb neutrons easily but bounce them back and therefore slow them down. These are the moderators that Fermi and Pegram and Dunning had been using all along to produce very slow neutrons. Could one of these moderators be mixed with uranium so as to slow down the fast neutrons emitted by fission and in this way supply the slow neutrons to be captured by U-235 for further fission?

The second factor concerns purity. Most substances capture neutrons and do not fission. Any impurities present in uranium would absorb the emitted neutrons and they would be wasted. Therefore the uranium has to be very pure. Also any moderators for slowing down the neutrons must be pure. The degree of purity is not trivial. Computations showed that impurities cannot be present as more than 1 part per million. Could one purify uranium or any of the moderators to this extent?

A third factor is the matter of neutron escape. Take a lump of uranium and send in a slow neutron. It hits a U-235 atom, which undergoes fission and releases some neutrons. If the lump is small, these neutrons have a good chance of getting out through the surface of the lump into the air before they are absorbed by some other U-235 atom. Once they get out they are lost, and if more get out than are captured, there will be no chain reaction.

THE CRITICAL SIZE OF AN ATOMIC BOMB

There is an amusing and vital point here. In a piece of uranium the loss of neutrons is through the surface, whereas the capture of neutrons is by the mass of the material.

Simple geometry tells us that the volume of a sphere varies as the cube of its radius, while the surface of a sphere varies as the square of the radius. Therefore as a lump of uranium increases in size, its surface does not increase as rapidly as its volume or mass. In other words, the larger the lump is, the less surface it offers per unit mass. Since the loss is through the surface, and capture is by the mass, the larger the lump the greater is the chance of the released neutrons staying inside the mass to be captured by U-235 for fission purposes.

The next question is how large a lump must be so that most of the neutrons get caught, and are not lost through the surface. The critical mass will be that chunk of uranium just large enough so that more neutrons will be retained than are lost. A piece of uranium smaller than this critical mass can never give a chain reaction. A piece larger than the critical mass will do so if all other factors are right.

What is the critical size? This depends on the range of the neutrons in uranium. How far can a neutron go before it is captured? This was known only very roughly, and therefore the critical mass was known only roughly. The available measurements indicated a value between 2 and 200 pounds of U-235 as the critical mass.

Most of the information on the fission of uranium had been secured from specks of the material less than a millionth of a gram in weight. (In case the reader has forgotten, 28 grams make 1 ounce.) A critical mass of U-235 weighing between 2 and 200 pounds was just fantastic. No one had ever seen more than a few grams of uranium as a metal all in one place. It was used in making ceramics and steel, but in the most trifling concentrations.

Uranium constitutes between 40 and 90 per cent of the mineral pitchblende, and pitchblende was known to be available in Czechoslovakia, Canada, and Belgian Congo. Other, less rich uranium minerals were known to occur in the Colorado plateau and in many other localities on the earth, including Asiatic Russia. To secure 200 pounds of U-235 would mean first processing tons of pitchblende to get the uranium metal pure, and then separating the isotope U-235 from the 140-times-more-prevalent U-238 in it. To work with the isotope mixture as it is plus a moderator to slow the neutrons would mean tons of the purified metal.

A similar situation existed with regard to the moderators for slowing the neutrons. Possible moderators were beryllium, heavy water, and carbon; and tons of these would be required just to try out a chain reaction.

Beryllium is a common element, and several hundred pounds of the metal were being produced yearly in the United States. It was not very pure, because there was no need for it.

Heavy water exists normally, as we learned earlier, about 1 part in 5000 parts of ordinary water. Heavy water can be concentrated by several means, and a large-scale factory for producing a few hundred quarts a year existed in Norway. In the United States a few quarts had been prepared, mostly for scientific purposes.

Carbon would be an excellent moderator. It was being produced in relatively large amounts—many hundreds of tons per year—as graphite for lubricating purposes. It was not purified to the necessary extent, but it was at least available and could probably be purified. Its use was suggested very early by Szilard and Fermi.

Suppose one could get enough pure uranium and enough pure moderator to exceed the critical mass and to establish a chain reaction. It might get out of hand. It might blow up. Even if it did not blow up, it might give off enough radioactivity and X rays to devastate a whole area and make it uninhabitable for months. Therefore one had to look for efficient neutron absorbers—substances that capture neutrons but do not themselves change very much. These could be inserted into the mass so as to control the reaction. A few such absorbing substances were known. One is cadmium, a metal belonging to the ancient triad of cadmium, zinc, and mercury. Others were suspected of being absorbers and would have to be tried out. There seemed to be plenty of work before a chain reaction could be attempted.

APPEAL FOR GOVERNMENT SUPPORT

In January 1939, Frisch and Meitner had suggested uranium fission. In a few weeks it had been tested and found true. In a few more weeks most of the computations and ideas just described had been gone through by several people, notably by Szilard and by Fermi at Columbia. The military possibilities had become clear, particularly to a small group of physicists centering around Szilard and including Eugene Wigner, Edward Teller, Victor F. Weisskopf, and Fermi. These were all European scientists who had found refuge in this country from Nazi and Fascist persecution, and they recognized the war clouds in Europe early. Most of our American-born scientists did not think in political and military terms quite so soon as the spring of 1939.

This small group, with the help of Bohr, immediately tried to organize a voluntary stop to the publication of critical data. American and British physicists entered the agreement, but Joliot refused, apparently because of a small paper that had been published before all American physicists had accepted voluntary censorship. Therefore the year 1939 saw the flood of papers on fission that has already been referred to. Actually, voluntary censorship did not begin until April 1940. This voluntary censorship was completely successful and went on for several years, long before any secrecy was established by the military.

It was obvious that to get on with the chain-reaction problem large amounts of materials would be required, more than any university laboratory can afford. Since the military implications were compelling it was logical to turn to the government for help.

In March 1939 Pegram arranged a conference between Fermi and representatives of the Navy Department. The Navy expressed interest and asked to be kept informed.

Goaded by the possibilities and by the delays, Szilard and Wigner conferred with Einstein in July and decided to appeal to President Roosevelt. This appeal was finally made in the fall by Alexander Sachs, who carried a letter from Einstein with a memorandum by Szilard, and who explained to the President the nature of the problem and the necessity for financial support of the work.

Letter to President Roosevelt *

by Albert Einstein

Albert Einstein
Old Grove Road
Nassau Point
Peconic, Long Island
August 2, 1939

F. D. Roosevelt
President of the United States
White House
Washington, D. C.

Sir:

Some recent work by E. Fermi and L. Szilard, which has been communicated to me in manuscript, leads me to expect that the element uranium may be turned into a new and important source of energy in the immediate future. Certain aspects of the situation seem to call for watchfulness and, if necessary, quick action on the part of the Administration. I believe, therefore, that it is my duty to bring to your attention the following facts and recommendations.

In the course of the last four months it has been made probable—through the work of Joliot in France as well as Fermi and Szilard in America—that it may become possible to set up nuclear chain reactions in a large mass of uranium, by which vast amounts of power and large quantities of new radium-like elements would be generated. Now it appears almost certain that this could be achieved in the immediate future.

This new phenomenon would also lead to the construction of bombs, and it is conceivable—though much less certain—that extremely powerful bombs of a new type may thus be constructed. A single bomb of this type, carried by boat or exploded in a port, might very well destroy the whole port together with some of the surrounding territory. However, such bombs might very well prove to be too heavy for transportation by air.

The United States has only very poor ores of uranium in moderate quantities. There is some good ore in Canada and the former Czecho-

* From *Einstein on Peace*, edited by Otto Nathan, and Heinz Norden, Simon and Schuster, New York, 1960. Reprinted by permission of the estate of Albert Einstein.

slovakia, while the most important source of uranium is the Belgian Congo.

In view of this situation you may think it desirable to have some permanent contact maintained between the Administration and the group of physicists working on chain reactions in America. One possible way of achieving this might be for you to entrust with this task a person who has your confidence and who could perhaps serve in an unofficial capacity. His task might comprise the following:

a) To approach Government Departments, keep them informed of the further developments, and put forward recommendations for Government action, giving particular attention to the problem of securing a supply of uranium ore for the United States.

b) To speed up the experimental work which is at present being carried on within the limits of the budgets of University laboratories, by providing funds, if such funds be required, through his contacts with private persons who are willing to make contributions for this cause, and perhaps also by obtaining the cooperation of industrial laboratories which have the necessary equipment.

I understand that Germany has actually stopped the sale of uranium from the Czechoslovakian mines which she has taken over. That she should have taken such early action might perhaps be understood on the ground that the son of the German Under-Secretary of State, von Weizsäcker, is attached to the Kaiser Wilhelm Institut in Berlin, where some of the American work on uranium is now being repeated.

Yours very truly,
A. Einstein

The First Self-Sustaining Chain Reaction *

by Selig Hecht (1947)

The President appointed a committee of three—one civilian, one Navy ordnance man, and one Army ordnance man—to look into the matter and to advise him.

This committee met several times and listened to evidence; and it made recommendations. Finally on February 20, 1940, the first funds from the Army and Navy were transferred to Columbia for the purchase of critically necessary materials. Total transferred—$6000.

---

* From Selig Hecht, *Explaining the Atom.*

The committee met again on April 28, 1940, and listened to reports of progress. By this time research had demonstrated that of the three uranium isotopes only U-235 would fission, and that slow neutrons are more effective than fast ones. Also the measurements on graphite at Columbia had shown that it would be a good moderator. Above all, news had reached various scientists that a large section of one of the Kaiser Wilhelm Institutes—the greatest research organization in Germany—had been set aside for work on uranium. A special advisory group that met in June 1940 reported to the committee that $100,000 worth of uranium and graphite was required to try out a chain reaction, and that $40,000 would be necessary to make the fundamental measurements. . . .

CAN URANIUM FISSION MAINTAIN ITSELF?

During 1940 and 1941 material was being purified and accumulated to test the possibilities of a chain reaction. This work was under the general leadership of Pegram at Columbia with Fermi and Szilard in actual charge. In the early months of 1941 a sufficient amount of extremely pure carbon in the form of graphite had been prepared to make a column 3 by 3 by 8 feet. By placing a neutron source at the bottom of this pile, and measuring instruments in various positions inside, one was able to study the properties of the neutrons as they traveled through carbon.

As a result a most important new idea was developed, which in practice came to be called a "lattice pile."

A lattice pile is essentially a pile of graphite bricks arranged with small spaces between them. At regular locations equally distributed throughout the pile are placed small pieces of ordinary uranium metal. This sharp separation of graphite as moderator from uranium as neutron producer has a special virtue. The fast neutrons emitted by the fission of U-235 leave the small uranium lumps easily, but before they reach the next lump of uranium in the pile, they must go through a given thickness of graphite carbon and therefore are slowed down so that they will be absorbed by the U-235 atoms and cause them to fission. Figure 4-8 illustrates the idea. . . .

While this was going on at Columbia other groups in other universities were investigating different possibilities. The most important of these was at the University of California under the general leadership of E. O. Lawrence and the immediate direction of E. Segré. This group concentrated on the problem of what happens to U-238 when it captures fast neutrons. We know what the theory is; but is it really true that after U-238 absorbs a neutron it gives off an electron and becomes $_{93}Np^{239}$, the new element neptunium? And does this new element give off still

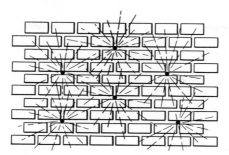

Figure 4–8. Lattice pile. Bricks of graphite separate small lumps of ordinary uranium. In this way fast neutrons released by U-235 in any one lump must pass through a lot of moderating graphite (carbon) before reaching another lump of uranium. This passage through the carbon slows down the neutrons, so that they may be captured by U-235 in another lump.

another electron from its nucleus to become $_{94}Pu^{239}$, the new element plutonium? And is plutonium just as fissionable as U-235?

The importance of the reactions is apparent when we recall two points. One is that U-238 constituted 99.3 per cent of ordinary purified uranium. If U-238 can be converted into fissionable material resembling U-235, then the mere fact that 140 times as much of it is available is a great asset. The other point is that plutonium is a different chemical species from uranium. After formation it can be separated from the unchanged uranium by relatively simple chemical procedures.

Before the end of the year 1941 the California group had established that U-238 by the capture of one neutron does go through neptunium to form plutonium, and that plutonium is actually fissionable with slow neutrons just like U-235. . . .

[In 1942 most of the Columbia group was moved to the University of Chicago under A. H. Compton.] By the fall enough materials were available to have another try at a lattice pile that would yield a self-sustaining chain reaction.

The pile was constructed under the squash courts in the stadium of the University of Chicago. As before, bricks of graphite were set up between which lumps of uranium were placed at regular distances. One precaution was taken. Removable rods of cadmium were inserted in various parts of the pile. Cadmium absorbs neutrons and is not changed by them. A rod or plate of cadmium serves as a shield to retard neutron transmission from point to point, and thus serves to control the speed of the reaction. And a good thing it was to have these retarding rods, because the pile worked better than its producers expected. By December 1, 1942, everything at the squash courts was ready to go.

Selections from an Eye-Witness Account of the First Atomic Pile °

An outsider looking into the squash court where Fermi was working would have been greeted by a strange sight. In the center of the 30 by 60-foot room, shrouded on all but one side by a gray balloon-cloth envelope, was a pile of black bricks and wooden timbers, square at the bottom and a flattened sphere on top. Up to half of its height, its sides were straight. The top half was domed, like a beehive. During the construction of this crude-appearing but complex pile (the name which has since been applied to all such devices) the standing joke among the scientists working on it was: "If people could see what we're doing with a million and a half of their dollars, they'd think we are crazy. If they knew why we were doing it, they'd be sure we are." . . . [Figure 4–9.]

At Chicago during the early afternoon of December 1, tests indicated that critical size was rapidly being approached. At 4 P.M. [Walter] Zinn's group was relieved by the men working under [Herbert L.] Anderson. Shortly afterward the last layer of graphite and uranium bricks was placed on the pile. Zinn, who remained, and Anderson made several measurements of the activity within the pile. They were certain that when the control rods were withdrawn, the pile would become self-sustaining. Both had agreed, however, that should measurements indicate the reaction would become self-sustaining when the rods were withdrawn, they would not start the pile operating until Fermi and the rest of the group could be present. Consequently, the control rods were locked and further work was postponed until the following day.

That night the word was passed to the men who had worked on the pile that the trial run was due the next morning.

About 8:30 on the morning of Wednesday, December 2, the group began to assemble in the squash court.

At the north end of the squash court was a balcony about ten feet above the floor of the court. Fermi, Zinn, Anderson, and [Arthur] Compton were grouped around instruments at the east end of the balcony. The remainder of the observers crowded the little balcony. R. G. Noble, one of the young scientists who worked on the pile, put it this way: "The control cabinet was surrounded by the 'big wheels'; the 'little wheels' had to stand back."

° From *The First Atomic Pile: An Eye-Witness Account Revealed by Some of the Participants and Narratively Recorded by Corbin Allardice and Edward R. Trapnell* (1946, published in 1949 by the United States Atomic Energy Commission).

Figure 4-9. Photograph of an original painting by Gary Sheahan which depicts the artist's version of the scene when scientists observed the world's first nuclear reactor (CP-1) as it became self-sustaining. (Reprinted courtesy of the Chicago Tribune.)

On the floor of the squash court, just beneath the balcony, stood George Weil, whose duty it was to handle the final control rod. In the pile were three sets of control rods. One set was automatic and could be controlled from the balcony. Another was an emergency safety rod. Attached to one end of this rod was a rope running through the pile and weighted heavily on the opposite end. The rod was withdrawn from the pile and tied by another rope to the balcony. Hilberry was ready to cut this rope with an ax should something unexpected happen, or in case the automatic safety rods failed. The third rod, operated by Weil, was the one which actually held the reaction in check until withdrawn the proper distance.

Since this demonstration was new and different from anything ever done before, complete reliance was not placed on mechanically operated control rods. Therefore a "liquid-control squad," composed of Harold Lichtenberger, W. Nyter, and A. C. Graves, stood on a platform above the pile. They were prepared to flood the pile with cadmium-salt solution in case of mechanical failure of the control rods.

Each group rehearsed its part of the experiment.

At 9:45 Fermi ordered the electrically operated control rods withdrawn. The man at the controls threw the switch to withdraw them. A small motor whined. All eyes watched the lights which indicated the rods' position.

But quickly the balcony group turned to watch the counters, whose clicking stepped up after the rods were out. The indicators of these counters resembled the face of a clock, with "hands" to indicate neutron count. Nearby was a recorder, whose quivering pen traced the neutron activity within the pile.

Shortly after ten o'clock, Fermi ordered the emergency rod, called "Zip," pulled out and tied.

"Zip out," said Fermi. Zinn withdrew "Zip" by hand and tied it to the balcony rail. Weil stood ready by the "vernier" control rod which was marked to show the number of feet and inches, which remained within the pile.

At 10:37 Fermi, without taking his eyes off the instruments, said quietly: "Pull it to 13 feet, George." The counters clicked faster. The graph pen moved up. All the instruments were studied, and computations were made.

"This is not it," said Fermi. "The trace will go to this point and level off." He indicated a spot on the graph. In a few minutes the pen came to the indicated point and did not go above that point. Seven minutes later Fermi ordered the rod out another foot.

Again the counters stepped up their clicking, the graph pen edged upwards. But the clicking was irregular. Soon it leveled off, as did the thin line of the pen. The pile was not self-sustaining—yet.

At 11 o'clock, the rod came out another six inches; the result was the same: an increase in rate, followed by the leveling off.

Fifteen minutes later, the rod was farther withdrawn and at 11:25 was moved again. Each time the counters speeded up, the pen climbed a few points. Fermi predicted correctly every movement of the indicators. He knew the time was near. He wanted to check everything again. The automatic control rod was reinserted without waiting for its automatic feature to operate. The graph line took a drop, the counters slowed abruptly.

At 11:35, the automatic safety rod was withdrawn and set. The control rod was adjusted and "Zip" was withdrawn. Up went the counters, clicking, clicking, faster and faster. It was the clickety-click of a fast train over the rails. The graph pen started to climb. Tensely, the little group watched and waited, entranced by the climbing needle.

Whrrrump! As if by a thunderclap, the spell was broken. Every man froze—then breathed a sigh of relief when he realized the automatic rod had slammed home. The safety point at which the rod operated automatically had been set too low.

"I'm hungry," said Fermi. "Let's go to lunch."

Perhaps, like a great coach, Fermi knew when his men needed a "break."

It was a strange "between halves" respite. They got no pep talk. They talked about everything else but the "game." The redoubtable Fermi, who never says much, had even less to say. But he appeared supremely confident. His "team" was back on the squash court at 2:00 P.M. Twenty minutes later, the automatic rod was reset and Weil stood ready at the control rod.

"All right, George," called Fermi, and Weil moved the rod to a predetermined point. The spectators resumed their watching and waiting, watching the counters spin, watching the graph, waiting for the settling down, and computing the rate of rise of reaction from the indicators.

At 2:50 the control rod came out another foot. The counters nearly jammed, the pen headed off the graph paper. But this was not it. Counting ratios and the graph scale had to be changed.

"Move it six inches," said Fermi at 3:20. Again the change—but again the leveling off. Five minutes later, Fermi called: "Pull it out another foot."

Weil withdrew the rod.

"This is going to do it," Fermi said to Compton, standing at his side. "Now it will become self-sustaining. The trace will climb and continue to climb. It will not level off."

Fermi computed the rate of rise of the neutron counts over a minute period. He silently, grim-faced, ran through some calculations on his slide rule.

In about a minute he again computed the rate of rise. If the rate was constant and remained so, he would know the reaction was self-sustaining. His fingers operated the slide rule with lightning speed. Characteristically, he turned the rule over and jotted down some figures on its ivory back.

Three minutes later he again computed the rate of rise in neutron count. The group on the balcony had by now crowded in to get an eye on the instruments, those behind craning their necks to be sure they would know the very instant history was made. In the background could be heard William Overbeck calling out the neutron count over an annunciator system. Leona Marshall (the only girl present), Anderson, and William Sturm were recording the readings from the instruments. By this time the click of the counters was too fast for the human ear. The clickety-click was now a steady brrrrr. Fermi, unmoved, unruffled, continued his computations.

"I couldn't see the instruments," said Weil. "I had to watch Fermi every second, waiting for orders. His face was motionless. His eyes darted from one dial to another. His expression was so calm it was hard. But suddenly, his whole face broke into a broad smile."

Fermi closed his slide rule—

"The reaction is self-sustaining," he announced quietly, happily. "The curve is exponential."

The group tensely watched for twenty-eight minutes while the world's first nuclear chain reactor operated.

The upward movement of the pen was leaving a straight line. There was no change to indicate a leveling off. This was it.

"O.K., 'Zip' in," called Fermi to Zinn, who controlled that rod. The time was 3:53 P.M. Abruptly, the counters slowed down, the pen slid down across the paper. It was all over.

Man had initiated a self-sustaining nuclear reaction—and then stopped it. He had released the energy of the atom's nucleus and controlled that energy.

Right after Fermi ordered the reaction stopped, the Hungarian-born theoretical physicist Eugene Wigner presented him with a bottle of Chianti wine. All through the experiment Wigner had kept this wine hidden behind his back.

Fermi uncorked the wine bottle and sent out for paper cups so all could drink. He poured a little wine in all the cups, and silently, solemnly, without toasts, the scientists raised the cups to their lips—the Canadian Zinn, the Hungarians Szilard and Wigner, the Italian Fermi, the Americans Compton, Anderson, Hilberry, and a score of others. They drank to success—and to the hope they were the first to succeed.

A small crew was left to straighten up, lock controls, and check all apparatus. As the group filed from the West Stands, one of the guards asked Zinn:

"What's going on, Doctor, something happen in there?"

The guard did not hear the message which Arthur Compton was giving James B. Conant at Harvard, by long distance telephone. Their code was not prearranged.

Figure 4–10. Plaque commemorating the first self-sustained nuclear chain reaction at Chicago. (Reprinted courtesy of the Argonne National Laboratory.)

"The Italian navigator has landed in the New World," said Compton.
"How were the natives?" asked Conant.
"Very friendly."

The Atom Bomb *

by George Gamow (1946)

When it was shown beyond any doubt that plutonium can be produced and separated from uranium by the method of a graphite pile,
construction on a larger scale was started at the United States Government project at Clinton, Tennessee, where several isotopes-separation
plants were already in operation. . . . By March 1944, the pile delivered
several grams of pure plutonium, and the production was going on at
full speed.

Although making several grams of an element which does not exist
anywhere in the Universe can be considered as quite an achievement on
the part of practical alchemy, the rate of production of a single Clinton-
pile was far from enough to produce in a comparatively short time the
kilograms of plutonium which were needed for the construction of
atomic bombs. Thus under the pressure of war, a new and much larger
plutonium production plant was built by the United States Government
in the State of Washington on the shores of the Columbia River, the cold
waters of which were very useful for cooling the giant graphite piles in
which the plutonium was cooked. It may be remarked here that the
cooling problem is very important when plutonium is being produced on
a large scale. For example, a plant producing one kilogram of plutonium
per day must operate at a power of one million kilowatts, liberating
enough heat to bring to boiling point 150 tons of ice-cold water every
minute. This giant enterprise, known as *Hanford Plant*, started in June
1943, and was in full operation by the summer of 1945. It covers an area
of nearly one thousand square miles, in which are located numerous
laboratories, work-shops, and chemical separation plants, all subordinated
to the three giant piles cooking plutonium day and night and heating the
Columbia River by the streams of hot water coming out of their cooling
systems.

The materials produced in this giant alchemical plant, as well as those
coming from Clinton, are being carefully stored in neutron-tight con-

* From George Gamow, *Atomic Energy in Cosmic and Human Life*, Cambridge
University Press; The Macmillan Company, New York, 1947. © 1946 The Macmillan
Company. Reprinted by permission.

tainers, and are undoubtedly destined to play much more important roles in the future economic and political position of this country than all the gold resting in the underground vaults of Fort Knox!

ATOMIC EXPLOSIONS

Now that we know how to produce in sufficient quantities such fissionable elements as U-235 or plutonium, the next question is how this highly concentrated energy can be used. There are, of course, two different ways to utilize the atomic energy which the progress of science has put into our hands. We can either release it instantaneously in the form of a violent explosion, destroying everything for miles around, or we can let it flow out in a steady stream to supply power to various kinds of machinery. Since the discovery of uranium-fission coincided with the beginning of the greatest war in the entire history of the human race, it was only natural that the main interest of the people working on that problem was directed towards the first objective: the atomic bomb. Provided we have a sufficient amount of U-235, plutonium, or some other fissionable transuranium element, how can we make it explode? Well, it does not seem to be so difficult, and probably a more reasonable form of the question would be: how can we keep these materials from exploding?

We have seen that neutron-chain-reaction in fissionable materials is in principle a self-accelerating, or explosive, reaction, being much more similar to the chemical reactions in nitroglycerine or TNT than to those taking place in the burning of coal or oil. We have seen that in order to prevent these chain-reactions from developing into an explosion, one has to use such small samples of fissionable materials that most of the neutrons formed in their interiors escape through the surface, thus coming out of play. It follows that *all we have to do in order to produce an atomic explosion is to take several pieces of fissionable material, each one smaller than critical size, and bring them rapidly together, thus forming one large lump.*

The construction of an atomic bomb, according to the above described simple principle, is however not at all an easy task. The main point is that due to the scarcity of fissionable material and to the comparatively large amounts of these materials needed for each single explosion, one could not proceed in the way of ordinary military practice in which dozens of bombs of new construction are dropped just to see how their fuses are functioning. Thus, one had to work precisely, which meant calculating in advance every single detail of the nuclear chain-reaction involved, the sizes and the shapes of separate pieces used, and all the phenomena expected to take place in the process of the "assembly" which had to lead to the explosion. This giant task was undertaken under the general leadership of J. R. Oppenheimer, theoretical physicist from the University of California, in the third secret atomic bomb site at Los Alamos near Santa Fe, New Mexico. The work carried out here included both detailed experimental study of various processes participating in neutron-chain reactions, as well as the advance-calculations of the functioning of the bomb. As everybody knows, this work resulted in the first, experimental atomic bomb which was exploded in the New Mexican desert on the morning of July 16th, 1945, and verified in all details the expectations of its constructors.

The Secret Is Out *
by Selig Hecht (1960)

No theory is acceptable until it has been put to the test of experiment. The theory that underlies the atomic bomb is an elaborate structure that has grown from simple beginnings. We started with salt dissolving in water, which yielded the concept of atoms. Since then we have enlarged and complicated this basic atom until its architecture is a mass of whirling electrons in shell after shell around a nucleus that has its own inner complexities of neutrons, protons, and charges tied in knots by binding energies.

Sometime in the course of the story the reader has probably said to himself that this theoretical piling of Pelion on Olympus and of Ossa on Pelion is too much. First we measure the combining ratios of substances. They turn out to be almost whole numbers, and we have an explanation. Then because they are not really whole numbers we devise a theory to explain the differences: we invent isotopes. But even in terms of the new theory there still are differences from whole numbers, so we invent packing factors. Then we invent fast neutrons and slow neutrons and nuclear fission. Finally we predict a theoretical atomic bomb, which cannot be demonstrated on a small scale. And we expect the world to supply hundreds of millions of dollars to build factories employing thousands of people to produce a few pounds of something that we insist must be kept in small packages.

It seems fantastic. It *is* fantastic. To the scientist who works daily in the laboratory in terms of a theory, it becomes a familiar reality. He watches it grow. He predicts a piece here or there, and either he or a

* From Selig Hecht, *Explaining the Atom*.

colleague elsewhere tests it and finds it true or false. The whole structure gradually assumes a kind of certainty that to the outsider who has not followed its development, seems wholly visionary and a little mad.

The atomic bomb project was infinitely more complex than the usual scientific experiment. Ordinarily, the step from prediction to practice is not large or long delayed, and in the course of the development, progress can be established by small-scale experiments. With the atomic bomb the realization of theoretical prediction involved thousands of people, vast amounts of money, factories, towns, secrets, the Army, the Navy, and the highest echelons of government and science. And nothing to show for it until the final single all-or-nothing test.

Alamogordo: Selections from an Interview with Brigadier General Thomas F. Farrell *

The scene inside the shelter was dramatic beyond words. In and around the shelter were some twenty-odd people concerned with last-minute arrangements. Included were Dr. Oppenheimer, the director who had borne the great scientific burden of developing the weapon from the raw materials made in Tennessee and Washington, and a dozen of his key assistants, Dr. Kistiakowsky, Dr. Bainbridge, who supervised all the detailed arrangements for the test; the weather expert, and several others. Besides those, there were a handful of soldiers, two or three army officers and one naval officer. The shelter was filled with a great variety of instruments and radios.

For some hectic two hours preceding the blast, General Groves stayed with the director. Twenty minutes before the zero hour, General Groves left for his station at the base camp, first because it provided a better observation point and second, because of our rule that he and I must not be together in situations where there is an element of danger which existed at both points.

Just after General Groves left, announcements began to be broadcast of the interval remaining before the blast to the other groups participating in and observing the test. As the time interval grew smaller and changed from minutes to seconds, the tension increased by leaps and bounds. Everyone in that room knew the awful potentialities of the thing that they thought was about to happen. The scientists felt that their

* From "The War Department Release on the New Mexico Test," July 16, 1945.

figuring must be right and that the bomb had to go off but there was in everyone's mind a strong measure of doubt.

We were reaching into the unknown and we did not know what might come of it. It can safely be said that most of those present were praying —and praying harder than they had ever prayed before. If the shot were successful, it was a justification of the several years of intensive effort of tens of thousands of people—statesmen, scientists, engineers, manufacturers, soldiers, and many others in every walk of life.

In that brief instant in the remote New Mexico desert, the tremendous effort of the brains and brawn of all these people came suddenly and startlingly to the fullest fruition. Dr. Oppenheimer, on whom had rested a very heavy burden, grew tenser as the last seconds ticked off. He scarcely breathed. He held on to a post to steady himself. For the last few seconds, he stared directly ahead and then when the announcer shouted "Now!" and there came this tremendous burst of light followed shortly thereafter by the deep growling roar of the explosion, his face relaxed into an expression of tremendous relief. Several of the observers standing back of the shelter to watch the lighting effects were knocked flat by the blast.

The tension in the room let up and all started congratulating each other. Everyone sensed "This is it!" No matter what might happen now all knew that the impossible scientific job had been done. Atomic fission would no longer be hidden in the cloisters of the theoretical physicists' dreams. It was almost full grown at birth. It was a great new force to be used for good or for evil. There was a feeling in that shelter that those concerned with its nativity should dedicate their lives to the mission that it would always be used for good and never for evil.

Dr. Kistiakowsky threw his arms around Dr. Oppenheimer and embraced him with shouts of glee. Others were equally enthusiastic. All the pent-up emotions were released in those few minutes and all seemed to sense immediately that the explosion had far exceeded the most optimistic expectations and wildest hopes of the scientists. All seemed to feel that they had been present at the birth of a new age—The Age of Atomic Energy—and felt their profound responsibility to help in guiding into right channels the tremendous forces which had been unlocked for the first time in history.

As to the present war, there was a feeling that no matter what else might happen, we now had the means to insure its speedy conclusion and save thousands of American lives. As to the future, there had been brought into being something big and something new that would prove to be immeasurably more important than the discovery of electricity or any of the other great discoveries which have so affected our existence.

The effects could well be called unprecedented, magnificent, beautiful,

Figure 4–11. Los Alamos, New Mexico . . . The Trinity fireball, 15 seconds after detonation of the first atomic bomb on July 16, 1945, rises into the air above the desert near the town of San Antonio, New Mexico. This first bomb was developed and built by the University of California's Los Alamos Scientific Laboratory in New Mexico. The Trinity explosion had an approximate yield of 20 kilotons (20,000 tons) of TNT. (Photograph courtesy of Los Alamos Scientific Laboratory.)

stupendous and terrifying. No man-made phenomenon of such tremendous power had ever occurred before. The lighting effects beggared description. The whole country was lighted by a searing light with the intensity many times that of the midday sun. It was golden, purple, violet, gray and blue. It lighted every peak, crevasse and ridge of the nearby mountain range with a clarity and beauty that cannot be described but must be seen to be imagined. It was that beauty the great poets dream about but describe most poorly and inadequately. Thirty seconds after, the explosion came first, the air blast pressing hard against the people and things, to be followed almost immediately by the strong, sustained, awesome roar which warned of doomsday and made us feel that we puny things were blasphemous to dare tamper with the forces heretofore reserved to the Almighty. Words are inadequate tools for the job of acquainting those not present with the physical, mental and psychological effects. It had to be witnessed to be realized.

Implications, Social and Political

Editor's Note. As the time for the first atom bomb test approached an Interim Committee was appointed by the Secretary of War to recommend war and post-war policy on the use of atomic energy. One of the major decisions to be made by this Committee was whether to use the atomic bomb against Japanese cities if the test was successful. The Committee requested the scientists working on the Manhattan Project at the University of Chicago to comment on the best ways of continuing their work after the war. The Franck Report from which the following selections have been taken was prepared by a group of scientists at the "Metallurgical Laboratory": James Franck, chairman, D. Hughes, L. Szilard, T. Hogness, G. Seaborg, E. Rabinowitch, and J. J. Nickson. It was transmitted to the Secretary of War on June 11, 1945.

Selections from the Franck Report (June 11, 1945)

In making suggestions for the postwar organization of nucleonics, a discussion of political problems cannot be avoided. The scientists on this project do not presume to speak authoritatively on problems of national and international policy. However, we found ourselves, by the force of events, during the last five years, in the position of a small group of citizens cognizant of a grave danger for the safety of this country as well as for the future of all the other nations, of which the rest of mankind is unaware. We therefore feel it our duty to urge that the political problems, arising from the mastering of nuclear power, be recognized in all their gravity, and that appropriate steps be taken for their study and the preparation of necessary decisions. We hope that the creation by the Secretary of War of the Committee to deal with all aspects of nucleonics indicates that these implications have been recognized by the Government. We believe that our acquaintance with the scientific elements of the situation and prolonged preoccupation with its world-wide political implications, imposes on us the obligation to offer to the Committee some suggestions as to the possible solution of these grave problems.

All of us, familiar with the present state of nucleonics, live with the vision before our eyes of sudden destruction visited on our own country, of a Pearl Harbor disaster magnified a thousand-fold and repeated in every one of our major cities.

Among all the arguments calling for an efficient international organization for peace, the existence of nuclear weapons is the most compelling one. In the absence of an international authority which would make all resort to force in international conflicts impossible, nations could still be diverted from a path which must lead to total mutual destruction, by a specific international agreement barring a nuclear armaments race. . . .

[The question of using the atomic bomb against Japan should be weighed very carefully, not only by military authorities, but by the highest political leadership of this country.] It may be very difficult to persuade the world that a nation which was capable of . . . suddenly releasing a new weapon as indiscriminate as the rocket bomb and a thousand times more destructive, is to be trusted in its proclaimed desire to see such weapons abolished by international agreement.

Thus, the military advantages and the saving of American lives achieved by the sudden use of atomic bombs against Japan may be outweighed by the ensuing loss of confidence and by a wave of horror and repulsion sweeping over the rest of the world and perhaps even dividing public opinion at home.

From this point of view, a demonstration of the new weapon might best be made, before the eyes of representatives of all the United Nations, on the desert or a barren island. The best possible atmosphere for the achievement of an international agreement could be achieved if America could say to the world: "You see what sort of a weapon we had but did not use. We are ready to renounce its use in the future if other nations join us in this renunciation and agree to the establishment of an efficient international control." . . .

One thing is clear: any international agreement on prevention of nuclear armaments must be backed by actual and efficient controls. No paper agreement can be sufficient, since neither this nor any other nation can stake its whole existence on trust in other nations' signatures. Every attempt to impede the international control agencies would have to be considered equivalent to denunciation of the agreement.

We believe that these considerations make the use of nuclear bombs for an early unannounced attack against Japan inadvisable. If the United States were to be the first to release this new means of indiscriminate destruction on mankind, she would sacrifice public support throughout the world, precipitate the race for armaments, and prejudice the possibility of reaching an international agreement on the future control of such weapons.

Much more favorable conditions for the eventual achievement of such an agreement could be created if nuclear bombs were first revealed to the world by a demonstration in an appropriately selected uninhabited area.

A Poll of Scientists at Chicago, July, 1945 *

by Arthur H. Compton and Farrington Daniels (1948)

Four days before the first experimental test in New Mexico, A. H. Compton asked Farrington Daniels, as Director of the Metallurgical Laboratory, to take an opinion poll regarding the use of the bomb. The scientists working in their laboratories at Chicago on July 12, 1945 were asked, one at a time, to vote in this poll by secret ballot without previous discussion. The poll was entirely voluntary and informal. It read as follows:

Which of the following five procedures comes closest to your choice as to the way in which any new weapons that we may develop should be used in the Japanese war:
    1. Use them in the manner that is from the military point of view most effective in bringing about prompt Japanese surrender at minimum human cost to our armed forces.
    2. Give a military demonstration in Japan to be followed by a renewed opportunity for surrender before full use of the weapon is employed.
    3. Give an experimental demonstration in this country, with representatives of Japan present; followed by a new opportunity for surrender before full use of the weapon is employed.
    4. Withhold military use of the weapons, but make public experimental demonstration of their effectiveness.
    5. Maintain as secret as possible all developments of our new weapons and refrain from using them in this war.

After reading the questions, each of the scientists placed a number in an envelope expressing his opinion. The poll did not reach everyone, but all those who were approached voted and the number comprised more than half of the scientists.

The scientists were physicists, chemists, biologists, and metallurgists who had received an academic degree. The results were as follows:

Procedure indicated above	1	2	3	4	5
Number voting	23	69	39	16	3
Per cent of votes	15	46	26	11	2

* From Arthur H. Compton and Farrington Daniels, "A Poll of Scientists at Chicago, July, 1945," *Bulletin of the Atomic Scientists*, February, 1948. © by *Bulletin of the Atomic Scientists*. Reprinted by permission.

These five procedures were undoubtedly interpreted differently by different scientists, as they undoubtedly will be by present readers, but no definition or amplification of these procedures was made at the time of the poll. The results of this poll together with several petitions and letters were transmitted to the White House. A reply from Washington was immediately received, showing that the opinions expressed were being considered.

A Difficult Question *

by Arthur H. Compton (1956)

The meeting at which Truman told Stalin of our intention to use the new bomb was on 24 July. It was the previous day that Colonel Nichols came to me at Oak Ridge with the word, "Washington wants at once the results of the opinion polls on the use of the bomb." I knew of the conference at Potsdam, but of course knew nothing of the state of its discussions. The votes and petitions were by now in my hands. I accordingly wrote out a message summarizing the results as objectively as I could and handed it to the Colonel. An hour later he came to me again. "Washington wants to know what you think."

What a question to answer! Having been in the very midst of these discussions, it seemed to me that a firm negative stand on my part might still prevent an atomic attack on Japan. Thoughts of my pacifist Mennonite ancestors flashed through my mind. I knew all too well the destruction and human agony the bombs would cause. I knew the danger they held in the hands of some future tyrant. These facts I had been living with for four years. But I wanted the war to end. I wanted life to become normal again. I saw a chance for an enduring peace that would be demanded by the very destructiveness of these weapons. I hoped that by use of the bombs many fine young men I knew might be released at once from the demands of war and thus be given a chance to live and not to die.

"My vote is with the majority. It seems to me that as the war stands the bomb should be used, but no more drastically than needed to bring surrender."

Colonel Nichols took my message and sent it at once to Washington. Two weeks later the first bomb fell on Hiroshima.

* From Arthur H. Compton, *Atomic Quest*, Oxford University Press, Inc. © 1956 by Oxford University Press. Reprinted by permission.

Pictures taken by Japanese photographers in the first hours after the atom bombs dropped on Hiroshima and Nagasaki. These photographs were suppressed by U.S. Military censors throughout the seven years of occupation. In August, 1952, when U.S. censorship was abolished, these and other similar pictures were published in Japan. (Life magazine, September 29, 1952.)

Figure 4–12. Last drink—and her first since the bomb fell—is sucked hungrily by girl the morning after. Shortly she and other victims sprawled here awaiting aid died. (Yosuke Yamahata from "Atom Bombed Nagasaki," Daüchi Shuppan-Sha, Tokyo, Japan.)

Figure 4–13. Hurt and homeless, child, masked in dressings, and dazed girl are carted to suburbs by home guards man. (Photograph by Masatoshi Yama-mura from "Atom Bomb No. 1," Asahi Shuppan-Sha, Tokyo, Japan.)

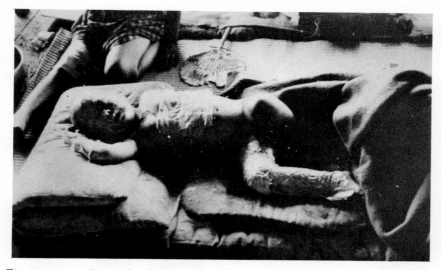

Figure 4-14. Doomed child, sprawled grotesquely in a makeshift first-aid station, lies dying of severe burns and can never again be cooled by fan on mat beside him. (Hajime Muyatake for Asahi Graph, *Tokyo, Japan.)*

Correspondence Between the Japanese Publication *Kaizo* and Albert Einstein * (1952–53)

[Letter to Einstein from editor of *Kaizo*, September 15, 1952]

. . . Recently—that is to say, seven years after the war—the ban on publication of pictures of the destruction wrought by the atomic bomb was lifted; for the first time the Japanese people have come face to face with actual scenes of the catastrophe, vividly showing the most destructive, not to say annihilating, effects of an atomic bomb. Once more the whole Japanese nation has been forcibly reminded of the fruit of its own guilt. . . . Yet we are left with a bewildered feeling as to why science, whose primary aim is to serve the welfare and happiness of mankind, should have been instrumental in producing such horrible results. As a great scientist who played an important role in producing the atomic bomb, you are eminently qualified to relieve the mental anguish of the Japanese people. I therefore venture to ask you the following questions:

    1. What is your reaction to photographs showing the destructive effect of atomic bombs?

    2. What do you think of the atomic bomb as an instrument of human destruction?

    3. The next world war, it is commonly predicted, will be an atomic war. Does this not mean the destruction of mankind?

* From *Einstein on Peace.*

Figure 4–15. *Single picture tells full story of an incident—twisted tracks, the blast-crushed trolley, riders hurled into the ditch, their shirts blown from their backs.* (*Yosuke Yamahata from* "*Atom Bombed Nagasaki,*" Daüchi Shuppan-Sha, *Tokyo, Japan.*)

Figure 4–16. *Ten minutes after the blast Yoshito Matsushige snapped Hiroshima's "Walking Dead," later washed this developed film in creek near city. (From "Atom Bomb No. 1," Asahi Shuppan-Sha, Tokyo, Japan.)*

4. Why did you co-operate in the production of the atomic bomb although you were well aware of its tremendous destructive power?

I know how busy you are with your own research, but I would be most grateful if you were able to reply within the month in order to mitigate the agony of that nation which alone has been exposed to the deadly rays of the atomic bomb.

In case no reply is received from you, I assume you will have no objection to having that fact duly recorded in our magazine.

Einstein replied immediately, on September 20, 1952, specifying that he would assume responsibility only for his German text and not for any Japanese translation which *Kaizo* might prepare:

My participation in the production of the atomic bomb consisted of one single act: I signed a letter to President Roosevelt, in which I emphasized the necessity of conducting large-scale experimentation with regard to the feasibility of producing an atom bomb.

I was well aware of the dreadful danger which would threaten mankind were the experiments to prove successful. Yet I felt impelled to take the step because it seemed probable that the Germans might be working on the same problem with every prospect of success. I saw no alternative but to act as I did, *although I have always been a convinced pacifist.*

I believe that the killing of human beings in a war is no better than common murder; but so long as nations lack the determination to abolish war through common action and find means of solving their disputes and safeguarding their interests by peaceful arrangements according to existing laws, they will continue to consider it necessary to prepare for war. They will feel compelled to engage in the manufacture of even the most detestable weapons in their fear that they may lag behind in the general arms race. Such an approach can only lead to war, and warfare today would mean universal annihilation of human beings.

There is little point, therefore, in opposing the manufacture of *specific* weapons; the only solution is to abolish both war and the threat of war. That is the goal toward which we should strive. We must be determined to reject all activities which in any way contradict this goal. This is a harsh demand for any individual who is conscious of his dependence upon society; but it is not an impossible demand.

Gandhi, the greatest political genius of our time, indicated the path to be taken. He gave proof of what sacrifice man is capable once he has discovered the right path. His work in behalf of India's liberation is living testimony to the fact that man's will, sustained by an indomitable conviction, is more powerful than material forces that seem insurmountable.

Einstein's statement to *Kaizo* apparently did not find a sympathetic reception in some Japanese quarters. Seiei Shinohara, a Japanese pacifist, who had translated Einstein's statement for *Kaizo,* made himself the spokesman of those in Japan who felt dissatisfied with the statement. In a letter of January 5, 1953, written in almost flawless German, Shinohara asked Einstein how he, who considered himself an "absolute" pacifist, had found it possible to write that letter to President Roosevelt in 1939.

[On June 23, 1953, Einstein wrote]

. . . I am a *dedicated* [*entschiedener*] but not an *absolute* pacifist; this means that I am opposed to the use of force under any circumstances, except when confronted by an enemy who pursues the destruction of life as an *end in itself.* I have always condemned the use of the atomic bomb against Japan. However, I was completely powerless to prevent the fateful decision for which I am as little responsible as you are for the deeds of the Japanese in Korea and China.

I have never said I would have approved the use of the atomic bomb against the Germans. I did believe that we had to avoid the contingency of Germany under Hitler being in *sole* possession of this weapon. This was the real danger at the time.

I am not only opposed to war against Russia but to all war—with the above reservation.

P.S. You should endeavor to form an opinion of others and of their actions only on the basis of sufficient information.

Correspondence Between Jules Isaac and Albert Einstein * (1955)

Einstein's emphatic statements to a Japanese publication and to friends in Japan concerning the role which he had played in initiating research on atomic explosives in 1939 had not become widely known. Inquiries on the subject were frequent.

. . . Professor Jules Isaac, a French historian of advanced years, sent Einstein a recently published article, "Atomic War or Coexistence," and asked whether Einstein should not have had the foresight to predict the possible dangerous technological "consequences of his equations" when he first published the Relativity Theory in 1905. Professor Isaac further posed the question as to whether scientists, as a group, should not, long ago, have sought ways of averting the catastrophic developments which would result from their discoveries. Einstein replied on February 28, 1955:

I have read your illuminating pamphlet with great interest, as well as the straightforward letter which you attached to the essay on the history of our people.

One cannot avoid the feeling that one ought to do something to avert the threatening doom. Such action may possibly appear more promising to you than it does to me; for I live in one of the two prime centers of political fever. Things have reached a point where only a handful of people are left with whom one can enjoy a quiet talk. Fear, hatred, and petty personal concerns dominate the actions of everyone, driving nations and men, including scientists, toward the final catastrophe. One can no longer ascertain who does the driving and who is driven. Virtually everyone is aware that the alternative is either a secure peace on a supranational basis or universal doom. But when men are given even the slightest chance of acting in accordance with this knowledge, they fail to do anything; they are victims of the very social pressure to which they themselves have contributed. I suppose this has always been the case, but never before have the consequences been of such global scope.

Now you seem to believe that I, poor fellow that I am, by discovering and publishing the relationship between mass and energy, made an important contribution to the lamentable situation in which we find ourselves today. You suggest that I should then, in 1905, have foreseen the possible development of atomic bombs. But this was quite impossible since the accomplishment of a "chain reaction" was dependent on the existence of empirical data that could hardly have been anticipated in 1905. But even if such knowledge had been available, it would have been ridiculous to attempt to conceal the particular conclusion resulting from the Special Theory of Relativity. Once the theory

---

* From *Einstein on Peace.*

existed, the conclusion also existed and could not have remained concealed for any length of time. As for the theory itself, it owes its existence to the efforts to discover the properties of the "luminiferous ether"! There was never even the slightest indication of any potential technological application.

Secrecy and Scientific Progress *
by Eugene Rabinowitch (1964)

For several years after 1945, the "secret of the atomic bomb" had been agitating the public mind in America, particularly after it became known that Soviet spies with the help of a Canadian physicist, Alan Nunn May, and of a German-born British physicist, Claus Fuchs, had transmitted to Soviet Russia valuable information about the Manhattan Project, including a description of the mechanism of the bomb itself. At first, widely erroneous ideas about the meaning and worth of the "secret of the atomic bomb" gained wide circulation. The atom bomb appeared to many as something that could be kept an American monopoly for a long time, if not indefinitely, simply by guarding better a few pieces of paper, on which its "secret" (perhaps a single magic formula) was written down. As time went on, more realistic attitudes prevailed. The development of thermonuclear weapons in the Soviet Union in 1952–53 almost simultaneously with, and obviously independently from, the U.S., clearly demonstrated what American scientists have been saying from the beginning—that basic scientific knowledge is a common property of scientists all over the world; and that technological developments, based on this common basic knowledge, are within the capability of any nation possessing sufficiently numerous, qualified, and well-supported teams of researchers and engineers.

In 1945, American scientists, in disagreement with official views, predicted that it would take the Soviet scientists about five years to produce their own bombs. It did take one year less, and that may have been the measure of acceleration made possible by the "atomic spies." This acceleration was brought about mainly through an earlier start of Soviet atomic weapons research. It probably began in 1943, in the midst of the Soviet-German war, rather than in 1945, after Hiroshima.

The possibility of making an even more powerful type of bomb was known and discussed by American scientists immediately after the war. The theoretical background of this thermonuclear type of explosion had been published in 1946 in a book by the Viennese physicist Hans Thirring.

* Written especially for *The Mystery of Matter*.

However, many American scientists believed that this bomb would cause too much wide-spread destruction to be effective against isolated military targets and would only serve to increase the horror of atomic warfare. Therefore, a conspiracy of silence surrounded the thermonuclear bomb for the years between 1945 and 1950. Then, when Russia exploded her first atomic bomb, the argument that America must maintain her lead in the atomic weapons race won the day.

In 1952, the thermonuclear bomb (fusion bomb, or "hydrogen bomb") made its entrance, almost simultaneously in the U.S. and in the U.S.S.R. It is a device in which the explosion of a fission bomb is used as a detonator to cause explosive fusion of a mass of heavy hydrogen (deuterium and tritium) to helium. The explosive power is thus magnified by another factor of a hundred or more—to an equivalent of between 10 and 100 millions of tons (megatons) of TNT. By surrounding the fusionable material with a shell of so-called "stable" uranium, U-238, the latter can be brought to fission, too, thus further increasing not only the explosive power of the bomb, but also the "fallout" of radioactive fission products.

The thermonuclear bomb has no theoretical upper limit, similar to that imposed on fission bombs by the critical size. It is limited only by the weight which can be delivered. However, bombs with a megaton yield can be made light enough to be carried by intercontinental missiles halfway around the globe. It is truly destruction unlimited.[1]

In view of the history of the development of atomic weapons the question can be raised: is it possible (and advisable) to keep certain discoveries of science secret, making them available only to a nation's own engineers? As far as basic science is concerned, the answer to this question is negative because openness is in the very nature of science; its violation may slow down a nation's own progress as well as that of its competitors. The root of steady progress of science since the beginning of modern science has been this openness—the ready submission of every theoretical or experimental result by publication, to scrutiny and verification. After initial hesitation immediately after the end of the Second World War, this principle was again recognized by all major nations, the U.S.S.R. as well as the U.S.; and free publication of research results in pure science has again become as it had been before—a general rule throughout the world. This does not mean that all technological data also have to be, or are, freely published; in this case, a careful weighing of the advantages and disadvantages of secrecy is needed; with clear recognition that such secrecy can be only temporarily effective, and that it may impress handicaps on your own progress.

1. See *fusion, nuclear,* and *fusion bomb* in Glossary for a more detailed description of the reactions which cause the release of energy in this type of bomb. Ed.

In the long run we cannot stop the progress of science—and we would not want to even if we could! Stopping science would mean not only stopping economic progress, but making return to a life of squalor, hunger, and disease inevitable. If we had prevented the discovery of nuclear energy, mankind would now be facing the certainty of impending exhaustion of fossil fuels, and thus the end of industrial civilization, which alone offers a chance to support the present (and growing) population of several billion humans on earth.

The great challenge now facing mankind, that of preventing the misuse of science for evil and destruction, cannot be solved by stopping science, or keeping parts of it under wrap. It can be solved only by educating mankind to make it fit for life in the scientific age.

Scientists have an important role to play in this re-education. Being better aware than anybody else of the immensity of forces which have become available to man with the release of nuclear energy, they must do all in their power to spread this knowledge, and to make mankind conscious of the immense possibilities opened by constructive utilization of science, including atomic science, for the common benefit. As Selig Hecht wrote in 1946, "Man really has his fate in his hands. If he can put into the practice of world relations the same honesty, the same courage, the same intellect, and the same drive that have gone into science and the accumulation of knowledge, then the future will indeed be a happy one. If he cannot, then anyone can envision the hell that may be on earth."

Questions To Consider

If the war had occurred three years earlier, could the atom bomb have been developed?

Should all scientific knowledge be made fully available to the whole world?

If you had been in Einstein's position in 1939, would you have written to President Roosevelt? If you had been in Roosevelt's position, what would you have done about it?

Do you agree with Professor Jules Isaac that Einstein should have had the foresight to predict the possible dangerous technological consequences of his equations when he published the Relativity Theory?

Is it true that science's primary aim is to serve the welfare and happiness of mankind, as stated by the editor of *Kaizo?*

Suggestions for Further Reading

Bishop, Amasa S.: *Project Sherwood: The U.S. Program in Controlled Fusion,* Anchor Books, Doubleday & Co., Inc., 1960. An account of the development of the United States program in controlled thermonuclear reactions. The presentation is intended for the non-specialist who is interested in knowing more about the peacetime uses of atomic energy.

Compton, Arthur H.: *Atomic Quest,* Oxford University Press, Inc., 1956. A first-hand account of the development of atomic energy with special emphasis on the attitudes and motivations of the men who were engaged in this research.

° Fermi, Laura: *Atoms in the Family: My Life with Enrico Fermi,* Phoenix Books, University of Chicago Press, Inc., 1961. Mrs. Fermi's delightful biography of her famous husband who directed the first self-sustaining chain reaction.

Hecht, Selig: *Explaining the Atom,* with revisions and additional material by Eugene Rabinowitch, the Viking Press, 1964. Chapters 7, 8, and 9 give more detailed information about the technology of atomic bomb construction than the excerpts which have been included in these readings. Chapters 11 and 12 deal with attempts to outlaw the atom bomb and the development of atomic energy.

° *Scientific American,* Editors of: *Atomic Power,* Simon and Schuster, 1956. A collection of articles dealing with power reactors, uranium resources, fuel and fission products, the economics and politics of atomic power, radio biology, and thermonuclear reactions.

(See also *Suggestions for Further Reading,* Part 2.)

° Paperback edition

5

Is the Universe Asymmetric?

Science has made the simplifying assumption that the universe is symmetric and that physical laws must therefore be independent of direction in space. Many aspects of nature such as crystal structure and the newly discovered particles of anti-matter seem to confirm this assumption. But a few experimental results from such widely divergent fields as biology and nuclear physics point to an intrinsic distinction between right- and left-handedness. Could it be that the universe is really asymmetric? And what is the origin of our deep emotional attachment to the concept of symmetry?

Is the Universe Asymmetric?

Introduction

THE IDEA of symmetry was important to mankind long before the dawn of science. It was implicit in all artistic work. The beauty of a building, a painting, a piece of music depends upon the balance and harmony of its composition, and yet complete symmetry is dull. A sphere is less beautiful than a snowflake because some degree of asymmetry, some differentiation adds interest and movement within the framework of a symmetrical composition.

What is symmetry and why is it so pleasing to us? Philosophers and poets as well as mathematicians and scientists have considered this question. In both the physical and biological sciences, a study of the symmetry of natural processes has led to a new understanding of the world.

The traditional separation of the different fields of science has sometimes obscured the extent of cross-fertilization between them. The readings in this part illustrate the way in which concepts from one area of thought are taken over and tested in other areas. By bringing together selections from such widely divergent fields as the origin of life and the conservation of parity, the discussion of symmetry connects the very early biological experiments of Pasteur with some of the latest and most sophisticated experiments in nuclear physics, thus building a bridge between the two sciences.

Physics took over the concept of symmetry from philosophy. Leibniz's statement that "two states indiscernible from each other are the same state," served as the foundation of one of the pillars of physical science. Since no absolute direction had been found in space (north and south, right and left, up and down were all relative terms) the assumption was made that space was symmetrical in all directions.

It is important to recognize that this was an assumption. Like all scientific assumptions it was the simplest one to make under the circumstances. Science always tries the simplest solution first and only goes to solutions of greater complexity when they are demanded by overwhelming evidence. This general principle, known as Ockham's Razor, was first stated by William of Ockham about 1320: "It is unsound to set up many hypotheses when one will suffice." [1]

The first indication that the assumption of symmetry in the physical world may not be universally valid, came from Pasteur's experiments on

1. "Entia non sunt multiplicanda praeter necessitatem." *Commentarium in Libros IV, Sententiarum Petri Lombardi* (1318–23).

crystals when biology was still in its infancy. Starting with an examination of the asymmetry of certain crystalline structures, Pasteur discovered that living organisms differentiate between right-handed and left-handed molecules.

Was the principle of symmetry immediately changed to accommodate this new experimental fact? Not at all. Contrary to popular conception, science does not usually change its basic framework of thought in response to each new piece of contradictory evidence. The case is treated as an exception, an unexplained phenomenon, and only when a considerable body of contradictory evidence has accumulated is any revolutionary change made in the basic framework of thought.

Just recently physics has come upon an exception in its own field. In the experiment which marked the overthrow of parity, physicists found that atoms undergoing certain types of radioactive disintegration did show an intrinsic difference between right and left. Further research growing out of this discovery may result in a modification of one of the great fundamental principles of science. As Philip Morrison says, "We have entered an exhilarating time." The overthrow of a basic assumption often marks an important turning point in the history of science.

Because the concepts described in these selections involve a three-dimensional perception, they are difficult to illustrate on paper or to describe in words. The reader will find these ideas much easier to grasp if he takes the time to perform the few simple demonstrations which are suggested. The readings have been kept as short as possible in order to allow time for the actual physical examination of these examples of three-dimensional form. In Part 3 we learned that matter may be thought of as pure form; so it is not surprising that the degree of symmetry of the form in space may prove to be a new key to the understanding of matter.

The Concept of Symmetry

Symmetry *
by Hermann Weyl (1952)

BILATERAL SYMMETRY

If I am not mistaken the word *symmetry* is used in our everyday language in two meanings. In the one sense symmetric means something like well-proportioned, well-balanced, and symmetry denotes that sort of concordance of several parts by which they integrate into a whole. *Beauty* is bound up with symmetry. Thus Polykleitos, who wrote a book on proportion and whom the ancients praised for the harmonious perfection of his sculptures, uses the word, and Dürer follows him in setting down a canon of proportions for the human figure. In this sense the idea is by no means restricted to spatial objects; the synonym "harmony" points more toward its acoustical and musical than its geometric applications. *Ebenmass* is a good German equivalent for the Greek symmetry; for like this it carries also the connotation of "middle measure," the mean toward which the virtuous should strive in their actions according to Aristotle's Nicomachean Ethics, and which Galen in *De temperamentis* describes as that state of mind which is equally removed from both extremes. . . .

The image of the balance provides a natural link to the second sense in which the word symmetry is used in modern times: *bilateral symmetry*, the symmetry of left and right, which is so conspicuous in the structure of the higher animals, especially the human body. Now this bilateral symmetry is a strictly geometric and, in contrast to the vague notion of symmetry discussed before, an absolutely precise concept. . . . Because of their complete rotational symmetry, the circle in the plane, the sphere in space were considered by the Pythagoreans the most perfect geometric figures, and Aristotle ascribed spherical shape to the celestial bodies because any other would detract from their heavenly perfection. It is in this tradition that a modern poet addresses the Divine Being as "Thou great symmetry":

* From Hermann Weyl, *Symmetry*, Princeton University Press, Princeton, 1952. Copyright 1952 by Princeton University Press. Reprinted by permission.

> *God, Thou great symmetry,*
> *Who put a biting lust in me*
> *From whence my sorrows spring,*
> *For all the frittered days*
> *That I have spent in shapeless ways*
> *Give me one perfect thing.*[1]

Symmetry, as wide or as narrow as you may define its meaning, is one idea by which man through the ages has tried to comprehend and create order, beauty, and perfection. . . .

I open the discussion on bilateral symmetry by using this noble Greek sculpture from the fourth century B.C., the statue of a praying boy (Figure 5–1) to let you feel as in a symbol the great significance of this type of symmetry both for life and art. One may ask whether the aesthetic value of symmetry depends on its vital value: Did the artist discover the symmetry with which nature according to some inherent law has endowed its creatures, and then copied and perfected what nature presented but in imperfect realizations; or has the aesthetic value of symmetry an independent source? I am inclined to think with Plato that the mathematical idea is the common origin of both: the mathematical laws governing nature are the origin of symmetry in nature, the intuitive realization of the idea in the creative artist's mind its origin in art; although I am ready to admit that in the arts the fact of the bilateral symmetry of the human body in its outward appearance has acted as an additional stimulus.

Of all ancient peoples the Sumerians seem to have been particularly fond of strict bilateral or heraldic symmetry. A typical design on the famous silver vase of King Entemena, who ruled in the city of Lagash around 2700 B.C., shows a lion-headed eagle with spread wings *en face*, each of whose claws grips a stag in side view, which in its turn is frontally attacked by a lion (the stags in the upper design are replaced by goats in the lower) (Figure 5–2). Extension of the exact symmetry of the eagle to the other beasts obviously enforces their duplication. Not much later the eagle is given two heads facing in either direction, the formal principle of symmetry thus completely overwhelming the imitative principle of truth to nature. This heraldic design can then be followed to Persia, Syria, later to Byzantium, and anyone who lived before the First World War will remember the double-headed eagle in the coats-of-arms of Czarist Russia and the Austro-Hungarian monarchy. . . .

In contrast to the orient, occidental art, like life itself, is inclined to mitigate, to loosen, to modify, even to break strict symmetry. But seldom is asymmetry merely the absence of symmetry. Even in asymmetric

1. Anna Wickham, "Envoi," from *The contemplative quarry*, Harcourt, Brace and Co., 1921.

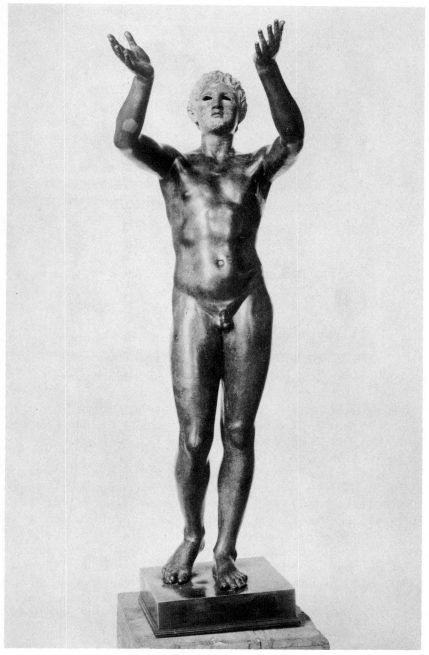

Figure 5–1. Greek statue of a praying boy, 4th century B.C. (Reprinted through the courtesy of Staatliche Museen Zu Berlin, Berlin, Germany.)

Figure 5–2. Design from silver vase of King Entemena, Louvre Museum.

designs one feels symmetry as the norm from which one deviates under the influence of forces of non-formal character. I think the riders from the famous Etruscan Tomb of the Triclinium at Corneto (Figure 5–3) provide a good example. . . .

Clearly we touch ground here where the precise geometric notion of bilateral symmetry begins to dissolve into the vague notion of *Ausgewogenheit*, balanced design with which we started. "Symmetry," says Dagobert Frey in an article *On the Problem of Symmetry in Art*, "signifies rest and binding, asymmetry motion and loosening, the one order and law, the other arbitrariness and accident, the one formal rigidity and constraint, the other life, play and freedom." Wherever God or Christ are represented as symbols for everlasting truth or justice they are given in the symmetric frontal view, not in profile. Probably for similar reasons public buildings and houses of worship, whether they are Greek temples or Christian basilicas and cathedrals, are bilaterally symmetric. . . .

While we are about to turn from art to nature, let us tarry a few minutes and first consider what one may call the *mathematical philosophy of left and right*. To the scientific mind there is no inner difference, no polarity

Figure 5–3. Riders from Etruscan Tomb of the Triclinium at Corneto. (Photograph courtesy of The American Academy in Rome.)

between left and right, as there is for instance in the contrast of male and female, or of the anterior and posterior ends of an animal. It requires an arbitrary act of choice to determine what is left and what is right. But after it is made for one body it is determined for every body. . . .

Position, direction, left and right are *relative* concepts. In language tinged with theology this issue of relativity was discussed at great length in a famous controversy between Leibniz and Clarke, the latter a clergy-

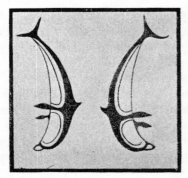

Figure 5–4. Floor patterns at the Megaron in Tiryns, circa 1200 B.C.

man acting as the spokesman for Newton.[2] Newton with his belief in absolute space and time considers motion a proof of the creation of the world out of God's arbitrary will, for otherwise it would be inexplicable why matter moves in this rather than in any other direction. Leibniz is loath to burden God with such decisions as lack "sufficient reason." Says he, "Under the assumption that space be something in itself it is impossible to give a reason why God should have put the bodies (without tampering with their mutual distances and relative positions) just at this particular place and not somewhere else; for instance, why He should not have arranged everything in the opposite order by turning East and West about. If, on the other hand, space is nothing more than the spatial order and relation of things then the two states supposed above, the actual one and its transposition, are in no way different from each other . . . and therefore it is a quite inadmissible question to ask why one state was preferred to the other." By pondering the problem of left and right Kant was first led to his conception of space and time as forms of intuition. Kant's opinion seems to have been this: If the first creative act of God had been the forming of a left hand then this hand, even at the time when it could be compared to nothing else, had the distinctive character of left, which can only intuitively but never conceptually be apprehended. Leibniz contradicts: According to him it would have made no difference if God had created a "right" hand first rather than a "left" one. One must follow the world's creation a step further before a difference can appear. Had God, rather than making first a left and then a right hand, started with a right hand and then formed another right hand, He would have changed the plan of the universe not in the first but in the second act, by bringing forth a hand which was equally rather than oppositely oriented to the first-created specimen.

Scientific thinking sides with Leibniz. Mythical thinking has always taken the contrary view as is evinced by its usage of right and left as symbols for such polar opposites as good and evil. You need only think of the double meaning of the word *right* itself. In this detail from Michelangelo's famous *Creation of Adam* from the Sistine Ceiling (Figure 5-5). God's right hand, on the right, touches life into Adam's left.

People shake right hands. *Sinister* is the Latin word for left, and heraldry still speaks of the left side of the shield as its sinister side. But *sinistrum* is at the same time that which is evil, and in common English only this figurative meaning of the Latin word survives. Of the two malefactors who were crucified with Christ, the one who goes with Him to paradise is on His right. St. Matthew, Chapter 25, describes the last judg-

2. See G. W. Leibniz, *Philosophische Schriften*, ed. Gerhardt (Berlin 1875 seq.), VII, pp. 352–440, in particular Leibniz' third letter, section 5.

Figure 5–5. "God Creates Man" by Michelangelo. Detail of God's finger touching that of Adam. Sistine Chapel. (Photograph courtesy of the Bettmann Archive.)

ment as follows: "And he shall set the sheep on his right hand but the goats on the left. Then shall the King say unto them on his right hand, Come ye, blessed of my Father, inherit the Kingdom prepared for you from the foundation of the world. . . . Then he shall say also unto them on the left hand, Depart from me, ye cursed, into everlasting fire, prepared for the devil and his angels." . . .

This half-philosophical excursion was needed as a background for the discussion of the left-right symmetry in nature; we had to understand that the general organization of nature possesses that symmetry. But one will not expect that any special object of nature shows it to perfection. Even so, it is surprising to what extent it prevails. There must be a reason for this, and it is not far to seek: a state of equilibrium is likely to be symmetric. More precisely, under conditions which determine a unique state of equilibrium the symmetry of the conditions must carry over to the state of equilibrium. Therefore tennis balls and stars are spheres; the earth would be a sphere too if it did not rotate around an axis. The rotation flattens it at the poles but the rotational or cylindrical symmetry around its axis is preserved. . . .

The most striking examples of symmetry in the inorganic world are the crystals. The gaseous and the crystalline are two clear-cut states of matter which physics finds relatively easy to explain; the states in between these two extremes, like the fluid and the plastic states, are somewhat less amenable to theory. In the gaseous state molecules move freely around in space with mutually independent random positions and velocities. In the crystalline state atoms oscillate about positions of equilibrium as if they were tied to them by elastic strings. These positions of equilibrium form a fixed regular configuration in space.

Symmetry in Nature

Crystals, Examples of Symmetry in Nature *
by Alan Holden and Phylis Singer (1960)

THE THREE STATES OF MATTER

Since the physicist says, "Crystals are solid," look first at the familiar word "solid." One physicist has written that solids are those parts of the material world which support when sat on, which hurt when kicked, which kill when shot. Roughly, but graphically, he has distinguished solids from fluids. Fluids include both liquids and gases, and indeed another physicist has said, "We distinguish three *states of matter:* solid, liquid, and gas." Following this clue, think critically for a moment about those three familiar states.

Some materials can take any of the three forms, with no change in their chemical composition. Steam, water, and ice are common names for the three forms taken by a single material. Another familiar liquid, one of the most convenient to use in making thermometers, is the metal mercury. It is a "liquid metal." But it will freeze to a solid metal at a low enough temperature and then, as long as you keep it cold enough, it will behave much like the more familiar solid metals. At a high enough temperature, mercury will vaporize to a gaseous metal; it forms the gas in mercury-vapor lamps, for example.

Bubbles of carbon dioxide fizz out of beer and soft drinks, showing that carbon dioxide is a gas under ordinary conditions. At a low enough temperature the same material forms the solid called "dry ice." Unlike ordinary ice, that "ice" is "dry" because the liquid form of carbon dioxide never appears at ordinary pressure. The material disappears into thin air when you put it in a warm place because it turns directly from a solid into a gas. But you can make liquid carbon dioxide if you seal the stuff up and put it under a higher pressure.

Even common salt or a quartz rock will melt into a liquid if you get it

* From Alan Holden and Phylis Singer, *Crystals and Crystal Growing* (Anchor Books), Doubleday & Company, Inc., Garden City, New York. Reprinted by permission of Educational Services, Inc.

217

Figure 5–6. Snow Crystals. (Courtesy of the United States Department of Commerce, Weather Bureau.)

hot enough. In fact, if you get these things even hotter than that, you can make gases out of them.

But you cannot make liquids and gases of all solids—not even out of most of them. If you heat gunpowder, it goes off with a bang, and you might say you have turned it into gas. But the change of solid gunpowder into "gunpowder gas" is not the same kind of change as that of ice into steam: you cannot get the gunpowder back by cooling the gas, as you can get ice by cooling steam. The change in gunpowder is . . . called a "chemical" change, and the change in ice a "physical" change.

If you heat sugar very carefully, it melts into a clear liquid. But if you heat it too much, it turns brown, and you do not get all the sugar back when you cool it. The sugar decomposes chemically into new materials, which are sometimes collectively called "caramel." If you try to boil the sugar to form a gas, it will decompose completely, giving off steam and leaving a crust of charcoal.

In their ability to stand heat, most solids are more nearly like sugar than salt: they decompose chemically at temperatures below their melting points. This is the reason why vastly more materials are known in the form of solids than in the form of liquids or gases.

The best way to picture the difference in the three states of matter is to think about a material that can appear in any one of them—mercury, for example. Picture what happens when you cool it from the form of a gas, first, into a liquid and, finally, into a solid.

In the gas the mercury atoms seem to be taking up quite a lot of space. An amount of mercury gas of the same volume as a drop of mercury, does not weigh nearly as much as the drop because there is very much less matter in it. Another way of looking at the difference is to notice that if you turned a drop of liquid mercury into mercury gas at the same pressure and temperature, the gas would occupy about a thousand times as much space as the drop did. Figure 5–7 contrasts the volumes of liquid and gas.

You might think that each atom of the mercury in the gas had swelled up like a balloon and was a thousand times bigger in the gas than it was in the liquid. But that is not so; the atoms stay nearly the same size. They use up more room by dashing about. As they travel, they bounce off each other and off the walls of their container. Each bounce off the wall gives the wall a little kick, and the combination of all these little kicks is the pressure of the gas on the wall.

But the important thing to notice is that the gas is a completely disorderly collection of mercury atoms. Indeed, it is disorderly in two distinguishable ways. Except during a collision, no atom pays any attention to what the speed and direction of any other atom may happen to be. The

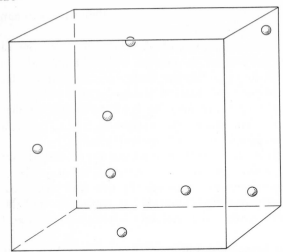

Figure 5–7. A comparison of volumes shows that the atoms in a gas are far from one another and hence can move independently; the atoms in a liquid or a solid are closely packed and restrict one another's motions. At the normal temperature and pressure of the atmosphere a given number of atoms in a gas occupies about a thousand times the volume—ten times the linear dimension— of the same number of atoms in liquid or solid form.

atoms are moving about quite independently, except during the instants when two collide, and thus their *motions* are entirely disorderly. And if you could take a quick picture of the collection at any instant, you would see no pattern in the picture: in other words, the *positions* of the atoms are entirely disorderly too.

To keep the gas together in one place, you must confine it, so that the atoms do not speed off into space in all directions. If you cool the confined gas, the atoms move less rapidly. And finally, at some lower temperature, the activity of the atoms slacks off enough to give the *attractions* of the atoms for one another a chance to have a big effect. Then the attractions bring most of the atoms together into a liquid, and drops of mercury form in the container.

Not all the mercury gas collapses in this way; there is still a gas of mercury atoms in the container. If you remove the confining walls, that gas will escape, and mercury atoms will leave the surfaces of the drops in an effort to regenerate the lost gas. In other words, the mercury will slowly evaporate.

The evaporation shows that the mercury atoms are still moving about in the liquid. Even when the confining walls are there, mercury atoms are leaving the liquid to join the gas, but just as many atoms are leaving the gas to join the liquid. Such a balance of escape and capture is often called "dynamical equilibrium." In short, both the mercury gas and the mercury drop, apparently stationary and unchanging after equilibrium has been established in the container, are really the seats of a great deal of activity.

Look for a moment at the pool of liquid mercury which forms as the drops gather together. Since the liquid flows freely, the atoms must be able to move past one another quite easily. But it holds together in drops if you spill it, showing that there are attractive forces between the atoms —the same forces which brought them together to form the liquid from the gas, and which now keep them associated in densely packed liquid communities.

You can get a good idea of how close this association must be if you contrast the effects of pressure on the gas and on the liquid. If you apply pressure to the gas, you can easily squeeze it into a smaller volume. But even quite a high pressure does not reduce the volume of the liquid much. From this you can guess that the atoms in the liquid are packed together almost as tightly as they can be.

Of course, there is still a little free space in the liquid—space enough for the atoms to move about irregularly. And there is a constant competition between the attractive forces which hold the atoms together and the irregular motions which tend to knock them apart. The atoms evaporating from the surface, for example, are those which get a powerful enough kick, from the atoms beneath the surface, to knock them out of the liquid despite the attractive forces tending to keep them there. When you cool the liquid, the motions are less vigorous, the evaporation is less rapid, and the attractive forces can pull the atoms even closer together so that the liquid contracts slightly.

As you continue to cool the mercury, it finally reaches a temperature at which it solidifies. When that happens, there is usually very little change of volume, because the atoms are already packed together so closely in the liquid that solidification cannot bring them much closer. But the solid does not flow freely, as the liquid did, and you can guess that the atoms can no longer move past one another easily. In other words, liquid and gas are alike in their ability to flow but unlike in the volumes they occupy, while liquid and solid are alike in the volumes they occupy but unlike in their ability to flow. Figure 5–8 may help you to picture the differences in the structures of gas, liquid, and solid.

From the rigidity of solids, which suggests that the atoms cannot move past one another, you might jump to the conclusion that the atoms have stopped moving altogether. But that would be going too far. Remember that dry ice evaporates: the molecules of carbon dioxide escape from the solid to form carbon dioxide gas. Hung wet on the clothesline in winter,

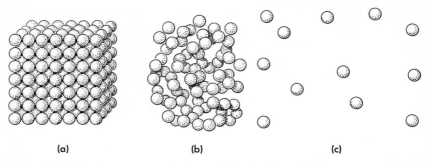

Figure 5–8. *The three states of matter.* (a)—*In the solid, atoms are close to-gether. They vibrate but cannot move past one another.* (b)—*In the liquid the atoms are almost as closely packed as in the solid, but they can move past one another.* (c)—*In the gas the atoms are widely separated, and can move almost independently.*

the week's wash may freeze stiff, yet it will dry out. Just as the mercury atoms leave a drop of liquid mercury when it evaporates, the molecules escape from ice because they are moving all the time, and occasionally one is kicked by its neighbors hard enough to go flying off. But the departure of molecules from most solids at ordinary temperature is so infrequent that the evaporation is imperceptible.

Since the atoms in a solid are moving but cannot pass one another, each atom stays in one place *on the average,* and its motion is a vibration about that place. It has a fixed average position from which it keeps making little excursions. The atoms box one another in, so to speak, and the average position of each atom is in the middle of its own private box.

ORDER AND DISORDER

The atoms in a solid exhibit another feature, a most important one. The fixed average positions, about which the atoms vibrate, are arranged in an orderly way. And the orderliness is of a particular sort: the solid consists of a pattern of atoms repeated again and again. In two dimensions you can liken the result to the repeated design of wallpaper. In three dimensions it is like a large hotel with floor upon floor of identical rooms, identically furnished. Usually any one material has only one preferred orderly arrangement, and usually different materials have different orderly arrangements.

The orderliness of solids is a rather astonishing fact of nature. Physicists have become used to the fact, and they often forget that they do not really know why atoms adopt orderly arrangements. Nevertheless, more than any other property, this orderliness distinguishes solids from liquids:

the atoms are packed closely together in both, but they have a constantly shifting, disorderly arrangement in a liquid and an orderly arrangement about which they vibrate in a solid. Orderliness of this regularly repeated sort is called "crystallinity"; anything having crystallinity is a "crystal" or a collection of crystals. That includes almost all solids and it includes very little else.

You may ask, "How far must order extend to make a material solid?" Of course, an atomic hotel can be pretty large from an atom's point of view, and at the same time pretty small from a human point of view. An atom is only about one hundred millionth of an inch in diameter. If an atom were as large as a golf ball, the atoms in an inch would stretch from New York to San Francisco. There are a hundred million times a hundred million times a hundred million atoms in a cubic inch of crystal.

A millionth of an inch is a fairly long distance from an atom's viewpoint—a hundred times its own size. Certainly you can say a substance is crystalline if it has regular arrays of atoms extending over a millionth of an inch. If the component crystals in a piece of matter are that large, each crystal contains a million atoms in orderly array, but you still cannot see it through a microscope.

Thus a crystal is not necessarily a single beautiful solid with plane faces bounding it. If you break a piece from the solid, the fragment is

Figure 5–9. A cast slab of zinc, when broken apart, will often show the outlines of component crystals, because it has broken along boundaries between crystals.

still a crystal, because the orderly arrangement of atoms extends a "long" distance. If you pound the fragment to dust, you have many crystals, for each of the dust particles is much larger than a millionth of an inch.

All pieces of metal are crystalline as Figure 5–9 suggests: they are like the crystalline dust, but perfectly dense, with no space between the individual crystals. The crystals are jumbled together every which way, but within each of them the arrangement of atoms is orderly. . . .

If you melt the dust or the metal, however, you destroy most of the orderly arrangement. There is some fluctuating, local, temporary order in the liquid—groups of a hundred atoms become ordered for a short time perhaps—but order is to be found only here at one instant, there at the next. And when you vaporize the liquid, even those relics of orderliness disappear.

How do we know that solids are orderly? Today we have powerful methods for confirming the idea. But long before those methods were available, the idea first arose in the minds of people who looked thoughtfully at the evidence gathered by their unaided eyes. The same evidence is accessible to you.

Consider mica. Glittering flakes of it are in the rocks all about you. The flakes easily come apart into thin sheets, and the only limit to their

Figure 5–10. Cleaving mica is easy. Push the point of a pin into the edge of a mica crystal; then work the pin back and forth along the edge, slowly pushing it at the same time.

thinness is your skill in picking at them by techniques such as that shown in Figure 5–10. It is hard to avoid the conclusion that the atoms in the mica are arranged in great sheets. Then if the attractive forces between atoms in each sheet are strong, and the forces between atoms in adjacent sheets are weak, you would expect what you actually observe.

Consider salt. If you dissolve it in water and then let the water slowly evaporate, you will get back the salt in little cubes, with flat faces. You can dry one of the little cubes on a paper handkerchief and cleave it with a razor blade along planes parallel to the cube faces, making more little cubes with flat faces out of the original. It is hard to avoid the conclusion that the atoms are all arranged in some orderly way which predisposes salt to form cubes. Salt in the salt shaker, even though it has been knocked about, usually consists of little cubes, as you could see with a low-power magnifying glass. (Figure 5–11.)

If you make a crystal of alum,[1] you will get a solid that looks like the crystal pictured in Figure 5–12. During its growth it retains its shape, just getting bigger. Why does it grow into that shape, all by itself, when you impose no shape on it? It is hard to avoid the conclusion that the whole crystal is made of regularly arranged little cubic units—atomic building blocks—stacked together in the way the picture shows. . . .

1. See *crystal* in Glossary for description of method for making an alum crystal. Ed.

Figure 5–11. *Table salt often has natural faces showing on individual grains. Under a magnifying glass the grains appear as cubes.*

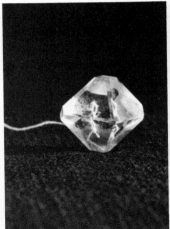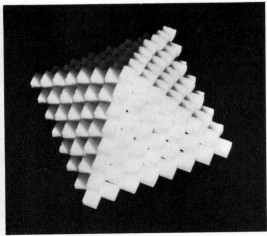

Figure 5–12. An alum crystal retains its characteristic symmetrical shape, no matter how large it grows. Because you can build this shape by piling up little cubes, you can think of an alum crystal as made of regularly arranged cubical blocks comparable to a molecule in size.

Experiments show, among other things, that many properties of crystals are somewhat like the cleavage of mica and salt: they depend on direction, and not on the point from which you start. It is difficult to see how a property of a material can depend on direction unless the material has some underlying orderliness.

Notice also that this evidence all suggests a particular sort of orderliness: the *repetitive* sort. The sheets of mica are all alike, whatever part of the crystal you take them from. And the fact that properties we discuss . . . later . . . depend on direction, but not on the starting point in the crystal, shows that the orderly arrangement must be repeating itself within very short distances—distances comparable to the size of an atom.

Of course, many other sorts of orderliness can be imagined, but they are not repetitive and therefore not the sorts the atoms in a crystal take up. To most people "orderliness" means anything done according to a clearly established rule. But there are many kinds of rule that do not lead to a repetition of any pattern, and hence are not possible kinds of order for the atoms in a solid.

In Figure 5–13A you see an orderliness that is *not* the kind that atoms adopt in a crystal. The atomic positions proposed there do follow a rule, and the continued application of the rule would continue to produce an orderly arrangement of a sort for the atoms. The arrangement would even give the whole piece of matter the same density in all its parts. But the

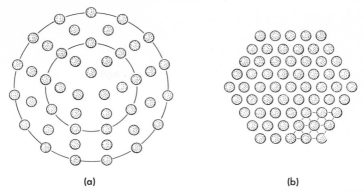

Figure 5–13. Contrasting kinds of order. (a)—*At left, proposed sites for atoms are located by a rule. Successively more atoms are placed on successively larger circles. The result is an orderly placement of sites without a repeated pattern and hence not "crystalline."* (b)—*At right, the sites are placed on the intersections of a regular triangular net of lines. They form a repeated pattern; their repetitive order is "crystalline."*

rule is not one that repeats the same pattern from place to place. On the other hand, Figure 5–13B proposes a kind of order that repeats itself again and again as you extend it. . . .

There are all kinds of solids—hard and soft, clear and colored, high melting and low melting—many more kinds than there are kinds of gases. The only way in which gases differ is in the kinds of molecules they are made of. In other ways all gases seem to be much alike; any gas will mix completely with any other gas, for example. Liquids show more differences, to be sure; oil floats on water without dissolving in it. But solids have endless variety.

One reason for the variety of solids is the fact that more substances are chemically stable in solid form, . . . But another reason is that solids are orderly. Solids differ not only in the kind of molecules they are made of, as gases do, but also in the kind of orderliness those molecules adopt in the solid. At first you might think that there were more kinds of disorder than kinds of order, but a second look will convince you that there is really only *one* kind of disorder for things as small and numerous as atoms.

The patterns in Figure 5–14 will help you to take that second look. They are made of two motifs, strewn in disorder at A and arranged in three different orderly patterns at B, C, and D. You may say, "The diagram at A is just as orderly as the rest; it is only more complicated." But you must contemplate the problem of continuing it in a disorderly way.

If you continue it by repeating it, you construct a form of orderliness:

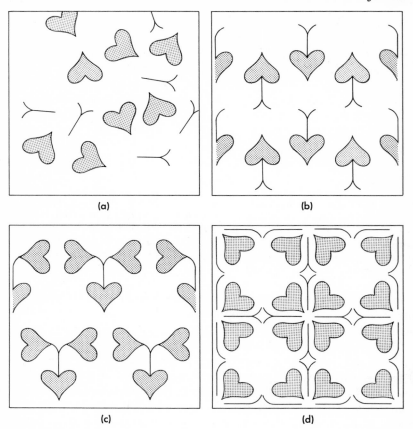

Figure 5–14. *Four different arrangements of the same motifs. There is only one kind of disorder* (a), *because random repetitions of the motifs cannot be told apart. On the other hand, there are many distinguishable ways of putting the motifs in repetitive order, such as are shown at* b, c, *and* d.

the orderly repetition of that pattern. You can continue it in a disorderly way only by making each added pattern different from every other. As you do this, you use up more and more of the possible ways of strewing the motifs in disorder within each pattern. In the resulting construction all the patterns would be different and placed next to one another at random.

Hence, any such effort will look like any other such effort. You cannot distinguish two different disorderly constructions in any other way than by specifying exactly where each item is located in each construction. When the items are as small and as numerous as the atoms in a solid, you have no way to see the exact specifications of a construction, and consequently all the constructions look alike.

A crowd of people at a college football game will often remind you that disorder is a single thing, whereas order is many things. Before the game begins, the members of the crowd will be arranged in a disorderly way. Looking down from the top of the stadium, you cannot distinguish the different arrangements from one minute to the next. But later the members of the college bands will leave the crowd, and you will see them march in many distinguishable sorts of orderliness.

Orderliness comprises so many different possibilities that almost every substance has a kind of orderliness of its own. Only when two substances are very much alike will they have the same kind of orderliness. For this reason, when several substances are all dissolved in a single solution, they will usually crystallize out separately. Crystals of a substance will usually contain very little, if any, of the other substances present when the crystals formed. If you add sugar to the salt solution which you evaporate to get salt cubes, the salt cubes will contain almost no sugar. . . .

CRYSTAL GROWTH

The orderliness of the atomic arrangement in a crystal is certainly its most important feature. But another feature, almost as important, is the fact that a crystal does not suddenly spring into being; it *grows* into being. If a solid is made of crystals—and the physicist says that most solids are made so—then you can understand solids only by understanding this aspect of crystals too. The fact that a crystal must grow may seem obvious, but once you get that fact out in the open and look at its consequences, you will quickly see that it explains many conspicuous properties of solids.

In the first place, a growing crystal clearly does not draw its nourishment from within. It has to grow from outside—from the stuff presented to its surface. The stuff must be the right stuff, able to accommodate itself to the particular kind of orderliness possessed by the growing crystal. And the stuff must be free to reach the crystal's surface.

In the growing of a crystal of alum in solution, aluminum sulfate and potassium sulfate diffuse through the water; and when they reach the surface of the crystal, they join with each other and with some of the water. They adopt positions on the surface that are forced on them by the kind of orderliness confronting them. Settling into those positions, they extend the orderliness outward, and thus the crystal grows.

Of course, nourishment cannot reach the parts of the surface resting on the bottom of the container, or butted against the sides, or in contact with the surfaces of other crystals growing in the same solution. This is why it is rare to see large single crystals, and especially rare to find them with many natural faces exposed and well developed.

Usually, both in nature and in man's manufacturing processes, a great many crystals of the same material start growing at about the same time in many different places. They grow until something gets in their way, or until they get in one another's way, and then they stop. Since they start with no knowledge of one another, they all have different orientations, and when they meet they cannot join to form a single big crystal. The result is a *polycrystalline mass*. Its component crystals all have the same kind of orderliness, but they all have different directions of that orderliness, as Figure 5–15 shows.

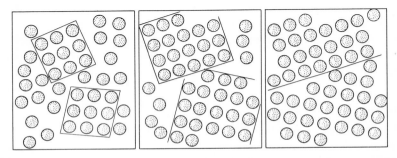

Figure 5–15. Two crystals growing independently from a molten material do not join to form a single crystal. They will have the same pattern of orderliness, but one ordered group of atoms will be turned in a different direction from the other.

It is especially easy to see why metals, in the forms in which we use them, are nearly all polycrystalline masses. Almost always they are solidified by fairly fast cooling of the molten metal. When the molten metal cools to its melting point, which is the same temperature as its solidification point, innumerable little crystals suddenly form, and grow quite rapidly until they touch one another in all directions and no metal is left molten. . . .

It is interesting to make an estimate of how rapidly molecules must get themselves ordered at the surface of a growing crystal. You find that, even when the growth rate of material on a face is no faster than one or two millimeters per day, about a hundred layers of molecules must be laid down per second on the surface. And if the crystal is to be truly perfect, all these molecules must be laid down in the right sort of orderliness.

Imagining the atomic hustle and bustle this implies, you will not be surprised that crystals are seldom perfect. Even crystals that seem perfect to the eye and under the microscope usually have imperfections on an atomic scale. The defects to which crystals are subject are of many kinds, some crude, some subtle. They manifest their presence in various ways, most of them too complicated to discuss here. . . .

SOLIDS THAT ARE NOT CRYSTALS

There is a kind of "solid" that is not crystalline—*glass.*

Perhaps "glasses" would be a better word than "glass," for there are more kinds of glass than most persons think. To see how they come about, visualize what happens as you cool a molten material made of atoms which are tightly connected together in groups to form molecules. The molecules are less agitated as the temperature goes down, and finally try to settle into orderly positions. But if the molecules are large and have an irregular shape, they may have difficulty getting into those positions. Each molecule may have to turn around, in order to jockey itself into the right place, and in this effort it may get so entangled with other molecules that it never succeeds.

Even in liquids you can see the effects of these difficulties. As you cool almost any liquid, it becomes more "viscous": it pours more slowly, and solid bodies do not fall through it as rapidly. Maple syrup fresh from the refrigerator pours very slowly indeed, and in winter you change to a "lighter" lubricating oil in your automobile because the summer oil would flow too sluggishly at the lower temperature. The increasing viscosity of liquids as their temperature goes down is a measure of the increasing difficulty with which the molecules move past one another.

In short, two factors control how well a molecule can accomplish its desires. It needs freedom and time—freedom to move, and time in which to move. The bigger the molecule and the more irregular its shape, the more of *both* freedom and time it needs. Ordinary glass is a material needing more freedom and time than anybody usually gives it. It will sit at ordinary temperatures for a lifetime, a mass of disordered, tangled molecules, quivering and unable to move enough to crystallize. . . . (Figure 5–16.)

The cut-glass punch bowl, which is "crystal" to the shopkeeper, is not crystal to the physicist. "Crystal gazers," who used to look into the future through spheres polished out of large single crystals of quartz, often look today through spheres of glass, because they are cheaper. It would be interesting to know whether the future seems as clear through a disorderly material as through an orderly one.

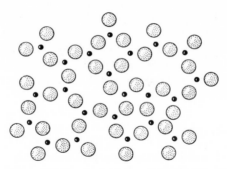

Figure 5–16. The atomic arrangement in a glass has no order extending a long distance, but there is usually some short-range orderliness. In this example each black atom has three white atoms around it, at a fixed distance and at the corners of an equilateral triangle.

THE SYMMETRY OF CRYSTALS

. . . The study of the symmetries of crystals, combined with the study of how they can be constructed from building blocks, led crystallographers to a systematic scheme for classifying crystals into "crystal systems." A knowledge of the kind of symmetry possessed by a particular crystal turns out to be important also in studying the physical behavior of that crystal, . . . And when you have learned how to look for symmetry, and how to describe the symmetry which you find, you will constantly be discovering it in the most unexpected places, and observing more and more the role it plays throughout nature and art.

THE IDEA OF SYMMETRY

Certainly the most familiar example of a kind of symmetry is the symmetry of a human being. Viewed from outside, his left half is "like" his right half. Inside, of course, his organs lack that symmetry; he has a heart on the left side and none on the right side, for instance. Even outside, he may show slight differences between left and right—more muscular bulge on his right arm, or a parting in his hair on the left side of his head. But you have little trouble visualizing a symmetrical "ideal man," just as you can visualize an ideal crystal.

The letters of the alphabet will give you more illustrations of the presence or absence of symmetry. The letter A has the symmetry of the ideal man, but the letter F has none. The letters B, C, and D have a different symmetry: the top half of each is like its bottom half. And the letters H and I have both of these symmetries: their tops are like their bottoms, and their left sides are like their right sides.

Now look at the symmetries of some *words*. The word MOM has all the symmetry of the latter A. The word POP has not as much symmetry as MOM, but it still has a kind of symmetry: it is *spelled* symmetrically. In other words, if you ignore the unsymmetrical shape of the letter P, and pay attention only to what letter it is, you would say that POP is spelled symmetrically and MOP is not.

This kind of thinking about the symmetry of words illustrates a general problem in the idea of symmetry. When somebody says something is symmetrical, you have a right to ask him just what he means by "symmetrical." Consider, for example, how a logician may use the word, and how a mathematician may use it.

The statement, "John is a neighbor of Paul," might interest a logician in different ways. He might want to know whether the statement was true or false. But in either case the statement has one property which the logician immediately recognizes: it is "symmetrical." It is symmetrical in the sense that when you turn it around, to say, "Paul is a neighbor of John," you are saying the same thing that you said in the first place. On the other hand, "John is a son of Paul" is unsymmetrical. In the logician's uses, the word symmetrical has moved from the realm of physical things into the realm of thoughts.

The familiar process of adding two numbers together furnishes a simple example of symmetry in mathematics. "Two plus three" is mathematically symmetrical, because "three plus two" gives the same answer. On the other hand, "three minus two" is unsymmetrical.

Notice that the mathematician's use of symmetrical is really very similar to the logician's use. The logician says, "It makes no difference if I interchange John and Paul in the statement that John is a neighbor of Paul." The mathematician says, "It makes no difference if I interchange two and three in the expression 'two plus three.'" In fact, going back to words, letters, and the shape of a man, you see that you can give symmetry a similar description there also. You can say, "It makes no difference if I interchange the beginning and ending of the word MOM, or the left and right sides of a man."

This is a clue to the ways of studying symmetry in almost all the places where the idea is used, including crystallography. You ask, "Is there a way by which I can interchange parts of the ideal crystal and produce a result which looks just like the original crystal?" There may be no way, and the crystal then "lacks symmetry" or "is asymmetric." There may be several ways, and you can then describe the symmetry of the crystal by specifying what those ways are. All those several ways bundled together define the "symmetry class" to which the crystal belongs.

It turns out that there are just thirty-two possible classes of symmetry to which a crystal can belong, including the class of crystals having no symmetry at all. Each of these classes represents a bundle of "symmetry operations," which we define as a collection of things you can do, or things you can imagine doing, to an ideal crystal and leave it looking the same as it did before you performed the operation. Turning a crystal end for end is an example.

SYMMETRY OPERATIONS

In studying symmetry operations, it is best to begin with two-dimensional figures because they are simpler and easier to picture than three-dimensional figures. The letters of the alphabet again make a good starting place. Look first at the letter S.

If you turn an S around its center in the way shown in Figure 5–17 until its top has replaced its bottom, you reproduce exactly its original appearance in exactly its original place. Here then is a symmetry operation for that letter. Figure 5–18 shows that you could think of this

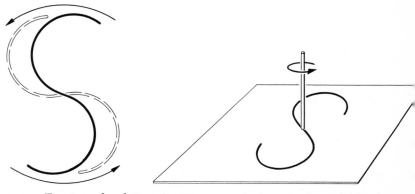

Figure 5–17. *Turning the letter S about its center by one-half of a full revolution leaves it looking as before.* Figure 5–18. *An axis of two-fold symmetry lies along the center line of the axle used to turn the S.*

operation as one in which you attach the center of the S to an axle perpendicular to the paper, and then turn the axle through one half of a full turn.

The center line of such an axle—the line about which the axle turns—is called the "axis of symmetry." For S it is called an axis of "two-fold" symmetry, because as you turn the axle through one full turn, you reproduce the appearance of the letter twice, once at a half turn and again at the full turn. Clearly an equilateral triangle has an axis of threefold symmetry, and a square has an axis of four-fold symmetry. The snowflakes pictured in Figure 5–6 have an axis of six-fold symmetry perpendicular to them.

In short, the idea of an axis of two-fold symmetry provides a precise way of saying that the top and bottom of the letter S look alike. Now examine the letter K, whose top and bottom also look alike, but they look alike in a rather different way. Turning the K as you turned the S does not reproduce its appearance. But you can describe the symmetry of the letter K by another sort of operation, often called "reflection in a plane of symmetry." These two kinds of symmetry elements—axes of symmetry and planes of symmetry—describe the two fundamental kinds of symmetry operations in three dimensions also.

Before examining the definition of the second operation, notice a helpful way of picturing it in your mind. This way of looking at the operation makes clear why it is called "reflection in a plane of symmetry." If you draw the K on a piece of paper, and hold a mirror against the paper so that one edge lies along the horizontal center line of the K as in Figure 5–19, you will see an entire K, of which one half comes from the K on the paper and the other half from its reflection in the mirror.

There is a very deep-seated distinction between axes of symmetry and planes of symmetry. Axes describe operations which you can actually perform physically. If your S is cut out of a piece of paper, you can stick a pin through its center and rotate it about the pin. Reflection in a plane

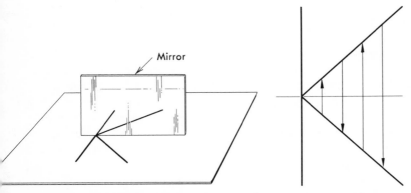

Figure 5–19. Reflecting the letter K in a mirror perpendicular to the paper and across the center of K makes K look the same as it looked before.

Figure 5–20. A plane of reflection symmetry intersects the paper through the middle of K. Moving every point of the letter perpendicularly to the plane and through it to an equal distance on the other side reproduces the letter.

of symmetry is an operation which you can perform only in imagination, or by an optical trick such as the use of a mirror. Figure 5–20 shows what the operation is. You draw a horizontal line through the center of the K, and you imagine moving every point of the K perpendicularly across the line, stopping when the distance of the point from the line is the same as its original distance on the opposite side.

This is the kind of symmetry possessed by the outside of an "ideal man": a single plane of symmetry dividing him vertically in half. For example, when you reflect him in that plane, you transform his right foot into his left foot, and you transform his left foot into his right foot. In the unlikely event you ever found yourself in the ridiculous plight of having two left shoes, you would quickly learn that there is no way of rotating one of them into a right-foot shoe. You would have to perform the imaginary operation of *reflecting* one of them into a right-foot shoe.

The fact that rotation is a "performable operation," whereas reflection is a "nonperformable operation," has another familiar consequence. Usually a person sees his own face only after it has been reflected by mirrors or shop windows. When he sees a photograph of himself, he may disagree with friends who say, "That looks just like you." For nobody has an "ideal face": there are subtle differences between anybody's left side and his right side. His friends are used to seeing those differences in their right places, while he is used to seeing those differences on the wrong sides, and no amount of twisting and turning will ever make his friends' image of him coincide with his image of himself.

This experience suggests that you look a little more generally at these operations, which are capable of being symmetry operations if they are performed in the right ways on the right objects, and notice what they do to an object when they are *not* symmetry operations for the object. Take a human hand, which has no symmetry, as an object to operate on; notice in Figure 5–21A what happens when you reflect it in any plane. You transform it from a right hand into a left hand. Now reflect that left hand in a second plane, at right angles to the first, as shown in Figure 5–21B. The operation transforms it back into a right hand, but upside down. You could have produced that last hand from the first hand by a single operation: rotating the first hand one-half turn about an axis lying along the intersection of the two planes, as shown in Figure 5–21C.

This is an example of a rule applying to all these operations. A succession of two nonperformable operations is equivalent to a single performable operation. If a person wants to see himself as others see him, he need not pay a photographer to take a picture of him. He can look at himself in two mirrors. The first turns him the wrong way round, and the second turns him back again. . . .

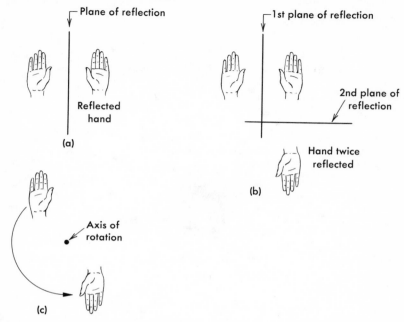

Figure 5–21. *Reflecting an object twice is equivalent to turning it. A reflection (a) is called a "nonperformable operation," because it accomplishes the impossible feat of turning a right hand into a left hand, for example. But a second reflection (b) turns the left hand back into a right hand. This succession of two "nonperformable" operations is equivalent (c) to the single performable operation of rotation about the line of intersection of the two planes.*

THE STRUCTURES OF REAL CRYSTALS

Until about fifty years ago there was no experimental way to find the atomic arrangement in a crystal—the way in which the building block is furnished. It was only possible to get two kinds of information about the arrangement. The shape of the building block could be determined by making the measurements of interfacial angles, and the symmetry of the atomic arrangement could often be learned from the habit of the crystal and other properties.

In 1912 three German physicists, Max von Laue, W. Friedrich, and P. Knipping, performed a very important experiment. They showed that a crystal will scatter a beam of X rays into a large number of separate beams, which come out of the crystal in definite directions. . . . The spots you see in Figure 5–22 were made by the beams of X rays scattered onto a photographic plate by a crystal of quartz.

Since that time the work of many investigators has perfected methods

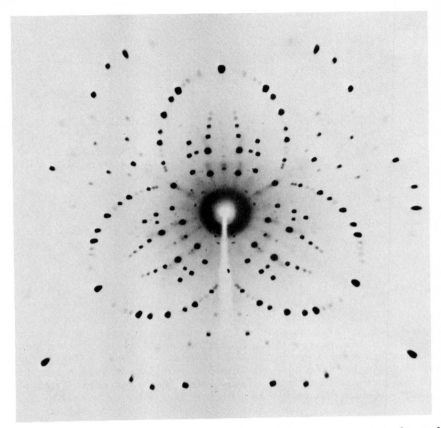

Figure 5–22. Laue photograph of quartz, Si O₂. The X-ray beam was directed along the c axis of the crystal. (Photograph by B. J. Wuensch and D. R. Peacor, Massachusetts Institute of Technology. Reprinted by permission.)

of scattering X-ray beams from crystals and interpreting the angles at which the scattered beams emerge. The investigations yield information on how the atoms are arranged and even how far apart the atoms are. Today the "crystal structures" of many materials have been worked out.

But there are still limitations to the information X rays can yield. Except in rare cases, X rays can only propose a few alternative structures and cannot assert which of those few is the most probable. In order to narrow the final choice down to a single structure, it is necessary to use other information. The habit of the crystal, its optical properties, . . . these properties may be useful.

For complicated crystals the final choice must depend on an "educated guess," based on a knowledge of how atoms combine into molecules in chemical compounds. In fact, the relationship of crystallography and chemistry has a long history and continues to work both ways. X-ray determinations of crystal structure often help the chemist to discover the manner in which the atoms are interconnected in complicated organic molecules—for example, in the molecule of penicillin.

After the structure of a crystal has been determined, one of the best ways to make a picture of it is to show how the atoms are arranged in just one of its building blocks. After all, no more is necessary, for the whole crystal is built up by simply repeating the block. Today the building block furnished with its atoms is usually called a "unit cell."

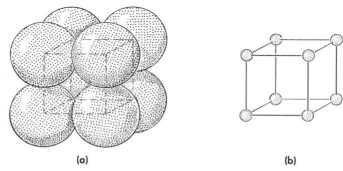

(a)   (b)

Figure 5–23. Indicating positions of atoms by small spheres gives a clearer picture (b) of the array than a diagram (a) in which the "atoms" are shown in their proper relative size.

It is a little more difficult to make a realistic picture of an arrangement of atoms in three dimensions than in two dimensions. If you make pictures in which the atoms have their proper sizes for the scale of the picture, the atoms hide one another, as you see in Figure 5–23A. For this reason drawings or models of the arrangement of atoms in a crystal usually have little spheres located where the centers of the atoms would be. The spheres are connected by enough lines, as in Figure 5–23B, to guide your eyes so that you can see the arrangement clearly.

Looking at diagrams and models such as these, you must be careful to avoid two tempting misconceptions. Because the spheres are widely separated, you may forget that the atoms themselves are really in contact with their neighbors. You may also feel that the lines in the drawings, and the sticks in the models, represent bonds between the atoms, but they are only visual aids in the drawings, and mechanical members necessary to the construction of the models.

Asymmetry in Nature

Pasteur's Experiments with Organic Crystals *

by René Dubos (1960)

In 1847 Pasteur buckled down to research work for his doctor's degree at the Ecole Normale Supérieure. He was then twenty-four and letters of the time to his boyhood friend Chappuis leave no doubt that, even so early in his career, there was deep in his heart the secret desire to accomplish some great feat. The problem that was then in his mind, as we shall see later, was the very origin of life on earth. In point of fact, however, the selection of his research project was not determined by some genial inspiration, or even by a philosophical preoccupation with some deep problem. As in the case with most graduate students, his project certainly arose from discussions that went on at the Ecole Normale among his schoolmates under the influence of teachers whom they respected. Problems of crystallography were then scientifically fashionable, and Pasteur showed no originality in electing to work on them for his doctor's thesis. But his originality began to become manifest as he went deeper into this field. His career illustrates well that what an individual achieves in life depends less upon the circumstances in which he has to function than upon what he brings to bear upon them. Napoleon meant something of this sort when he wrote in his diary, "No situation is good or bad in itself, everything depends upon what one makes out of it."

A CRYSTALLOGRAPHIC PROBLEM

In the science department at the Ecole Normale, there was much interest in the problems of crystallography, and Delafosse, one of the most respected teachers, had made significant observations revealing the existence in quartz crystals of right- and left-handed facets. [Figure 5–24.] It was also known at the time that quartz in the crystalline state can rotate the plane of polarized light. [Figure 5–25.] Jean Baptiste Biot, a

* From René Dubos, *Pasteur and Modern Science*, Doubleday & Co., Inc., Garden City, New York, 1960. Reprinted by permission of Educational Services, Inc.

Figure 5–24. A crystal showing little facets.

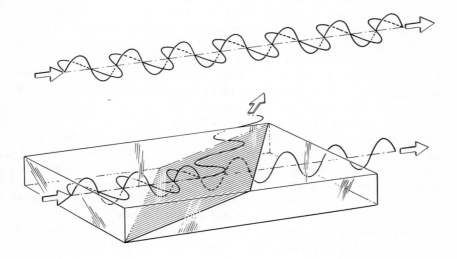

Figure 5–25. The polarization of light. The waves of light normally oscillate in all planes (top). The Nicol prism (bottom) lets through the oscillations in only one plane, reflecting away the others. The transmitted light is plane-polarized. A cross-section of a ray of ordinary light would show that the waves of which it consists undulate in all planes—up and down, from side to side, and obliquely. Such light is called "unpolarized." But when light passes through a crystal of the transparent substance called Iceland spar, for instance, it is refracted in such a way that the light emerges "polarized." It is as if the array of atoms in the crystal allows only certain planes of undulation to pass through (just as the palings of a fence might allow a person moving sideways to squeeze through but not one coming up to them broadside on). There are devices, such as the "Nicol prism" and the more modern "Polaroid" lenses, that let light through in only one plane. (Reflected light often is partly plane-polarized; this is true of moonlight, for instance. Polaroid sunglasses screen out much of the troublesome reflections of sunlight, because the reflected light is partly polarized). (Figure after Isaac Asimov, text from The Intelligent Man's Guide to Science. Copyright 1960 by Basic Books, Inc. Reprinted by permission.

celebrated French chemist who was to become one of Pasteur's scientific protectors, had shown furthermore that certain organic substances like sugar or tartaric acid can also rotate the plane of light but, in contrast to quartz, exhibit optical activity [1] even in solution. All these facts were much discussed at the Ecole Normale and it was under this influence that Pasteur began to work on the optical activity of crystals. He selected tartaric acid and tartrates as the object of his studies because a great deal was known about these substances, and also because they readily gave beautiful crystalline forms.

At precisely that time Jean Baptiste Biot presented before the Academy of Sciences in Paris a note in which the German chemist Mitscherlich described a very odd fact concerning the optical activity of tartrates. Mitscherlich pointed out that among the usual large crystals of tartaric acid always present in the "tartar" formed during the fermentation of wine, there were found occasionally smaller crystals, needlelike tufts, which proved to be another form of tartaric acid. The latter form was called "paratartaric acid" or also "racemic" acid to recall its origin from the grape (*racemus*). According to Mitscherlich, these two forms of tartaric acids and their respective salts, the tartrates and paratartrates, had "the same chemical composition, the same crystal shape with the same angles, the same specific gravity, the same double refraction, and therefore the same angles between their optical axes. Their aqueous solutions have the same refraction. But the solution of the tartrate rotates the plane of polarization, while the paratartrate is inactive."

Pasteur immediately saw an incompatibility here. Could the two forms of tartaric acid behave differently toward polarized light and still, according to Mitscherlich's claim, be identical in every other particular? He was convinced that there *had* to be some chemical difference between the two substances, and he hoped that this difference would express itself in the shape of the crystals. It was the recognition of this incompatibility that provided him with the first well-defined problem on which to test his skill as an experimenter. By seizing on the occasion, he demonstrated one of the most fundamental characteristics of the gifted experimenter: the ability to recognize an important problem, and to formulate it in terms amenable to experimentation.

A GREAT DISCOVERY

Immediately and without help, Pasteur prepared and crystallized nineteen different salts of tartrates and paratartrates, and examined the

---

1. Optical activity is the ability of a substance to rotate the plane of polarization of light. Ed.

crystals with great care under the microscope. With much satisfaction he found that they all exhibited small facets similar to those seen in quartz crystals [Figure 5–24]—a fact which had escaped the attention of other observers. Then he detected that these facets did not all have the same orientation in the different crystals. More precisely, the facets in each of the tartrate salts exhibited the same orientation, whereas in each of the paratartrates, some were oriented in one direction, and some in the opposite direction. But at this point it seems best to let Pasteur describe in his own words how he made the discovery that launched him on a scientific career.

The fortunate idea came to me to orient my crystals with reference to a plane perpendicular to the observer, and then I noticed that the confused mass of crystals of paratartrate could be divided into two groups according to the orientation of their facets of asymmetry. In one group, the facet of asymmetry nearer my body was inclined to my right with reference to the plane of orientation which I just mentioned, whereas the facet of asymmetry was inclined to my left in the other. The paratartrate appeared as a mixture of two kinds of crystals, some asymmetric to the right, some asymmetric to the left.

A new and obvious idea soon occurred to me. These crystals asymmetric to the right, which I could separate manually from the others, exhibited an absolute identity of shape with those of the classical right tartrate. Pursuing my preconceived idea, in the logic of its deductions, I separated these right crystals from the crystallized paratartrate; I made the lead salt and isolated the acid; this acid appeared absolutely identical with the tartaric acid of grape, identical also in its action on polarized light. My happiness was even greater the day when, separating now from the paratartrate the crystals with asymmetry at their left, and making their acid, I obtained a tartaric absolutely similar to the tartaric acid of grape, but with an opposite asymmetry, and also with an opposite action on light. Its shape was identical to that of the mirror image of the right tartaric acid and, other things being equal, it rotated light to the left as much in absolute amount as the other acid did it to the right.

Finally, when I mixed solutions containing equal weights of these two acids, the mixture gave rise to a crystalline mass of paratartaric acid identical with the known paratartaric acid.

It is easy to recapture the dramatic quality of the situation and the intense excitement it must have caused in the young investigator. Pasteur was so overcome with emotion that he rushed from the laboratory, and, meeting one of the chemistry assistants in the hall, embraced him, exclaiming, "I have just made a great discovery. . . . I am so happy that I am shaking all over and am unable to set my eyes again to the polarimeter!" To appreciate the magnitude of the achievement, it must be remembered that Pasteur was then barely twenty-five years old and had been working in a laboratory for only two years. Let us keep in mind also that this laboratory was very small and very primitive according to modern standards. Not only did Pasteur have to prepare all the chemicals that he used, he even had to build with his own hands the polarimeter and the goniometer [2] with which he made his measurements. He had no assistance, only the encouragement of his teachers and school friends, and faith in his destiny.

THE CONFIRMATION: A NEW FIELD OF SCIENCE

The news of Pasteur's discovery soon spread through the Paris scientific circles and eventually reached Jean Baptiste Biot—the very man who three years before had presented to the Academy of Sciences the Mitscherlich paper which had perplexed Pasteur and had served him as a springboard for his studies. Biot was so much interested in the new discovery that he was willing to present it to the scientific public, but before he did, he wanted to subject the findings to a stringent verification. Here again, let us read Pasteur's own account of his dealings with Biot.

He [M. Biot] sent for me to repeat before his eyes the several experiments and gave me a sample of racemic acid which he had himself previously examined and found to be quite inactive toward polarized light. I prepared from it, in his presence, the sodium ammonium double salt, for which he also desired himself to provide the soda and ammonia. The solution was set aside for slow evaporation in one of the rooms of his own laboratory, and when thirty to forty grams of crystals had separated, he again summoned me to the College de France [where Biot had his office] so that I might collect the dextro and levorotatory crystals [i.e., the crystals deviating the plane of polarized light to the right or to the left] before his eyes, and separate them according to their crystallographic character—asking me to repeat the statement that the crystals which I should place on his right hand would cause deviation to the right, and the others to the left. This done, he said that he himself would do the rest. He prepared the carefully weighed solutions, and at the moment when he was about to examine them in the polarimeter, he again called me into his laboratory. He first put into the apparatus the more interesting solution, the one which was to cause rotation to the left. At the first sight of the color tints presented by the two halves of the field in the "Soleil" polarimeter, and without having to make a reading, Biot recognized that there was a strong levorotation. Then the illustrious old man, who was visibly moved, seized me by the hand, and said, "My dear son, I have loved science so deeply that this stirs my heart."

Thus, at one stroke Pasteur had established himself as a masterful experimenter and created a new field of science—namely the relation of optical activity to molecular and crystalline structure. For three years he continued in this field and made concrete and lasting contributions to the chemical aspects of crystallography. . . .

2. A goniometer is an instrument for measuring the angles between crystal faces. Ed.

SEPARATING CRYSTALS WITH MOLDS

[His deep interest in this subject] reveals the complexity of his scientific personality—the constant interplay in his mind between rigorous, logical thinking and highly imaginative dreams about the mysteries of life. Throughout his scientific career, he engaged in thoughts of cosmic grandeur that went far beyond practical realities. But these romantic imaginings were always derived from factual observations, and often they led him to entirely new lines of investigation. It is to this aspect of his genius that we shall now turn.

As will be recalled, Pasteur's first fractionation of racemic acid into its two isomeric components was the painstaking process of separating the crystals under the microscope according to the orientation of their facets. In subsequent years much less laborious methods of separation were worked out in his laboratory, but only one will be mentioned here, a very original method of chemical fractionation based on a biological phenomenon. This method was discovered in 1857, the result of one of those accidents or "chance" occurrences that are meaningless to ordinary persons and are seized upon only by trained observers whose minds are receptive to the clues offered by nature. "In experimental science," Pasteur was wont to say, "chance favors only the prepared mind."

The fact that certain molds grow readily in solutions of calcium paratartrate during warm weather had been frequently observed, and it occurred in Pasteur's laboratory as it did in other places. The common reaction was, of course, to throw the solution down the sink because it was moldy. In contrast, Pasteur asked himself whether the two isomeric components of the solution, the half which rotated light to the left and the half which rotated it to the right, would be differently affected by the mold. To answer this question, he investigated the optical activity of a solution of paratartrate infected with a mold, and found, to his great excitement, that the solution became more active optically with time. He proved that only one of the components (the right rotating) was destroyed, whereas the other component was spared. As a result, the latter component persisted alone in the solution and thus caused it to become optically active. This observation led to an entirely novel and convenient method for the separation of the two isomeric forms by means of the mold, but more importantly it led Pasteur's mind into new channels that were to take him, and science, into completely uncharted territory.

THE ASYMMETRY OF THE UNIVERSE

It was already known that many organic substances, that is, substances produced by living things, have the ability to rotate the plane of polarized light in one direction or the other. In contrast, Pasteur was aware of the fact that if the same substances were synthesized in the laboratory, they were optically inactive. Now it appeared from the experience with paratartaric acid that at least one living thing, a mold, exhibited a striking selectivity with regard to its action on one of the two isomeric components. Putting all these facts together and extrapolating from them, Pasteur soon formed the view that only living agents could produce optically active asymmetric compounds and that an intensive study of molecular asymmetry would eventually throw light on the genesis of life. In his words, "This important criterion [molecular asymmetry of organic compounds] constitutes perhaps the only sharply defined difference which can be drawn at the present time between the chemistry of dead and of living matter." And to his friend Chappuis he confided in 1851, "I am on the verge of mysteries, and the veil which covers them is getting thinner and thinner. The night seems to me too long." These "mysteries" had to do with nothing less than the creation of life! He postulated that the peculiar selectivity of living processes for one or the other of isomeric forms of the same molecule might be the manifestation of asymmetric forces of the environment acting upon the living organism during the synthesis of protoplasmic constituents.

In his words,

Life, as manifested to us, is a function of the asymmetry of the universe and of the consequences of this fact. The universe is asymmetrical; for, if the whole of the bodies which compose the solar system moving with their individual movements were placed before a glass, the image in the glass could not be superposed upon the reality. Even the movement of solar light is asymmetrical. . . . Terrestrial magnetism, the opposition which exists between the north and south poles in a magnet and between positive and negative electricity, are but resultants of asymmetrical actions and movements. . . .

Life is dominated by asymmetrical actions. I can even imagine that all living species are primordially, in their structure, in their external forms, functions of cosmic asymmetry.

Pasteur was bold enough to attempt some experimentation in this highly speculative domain, hoping to duplicate in the laboratory the asymmetrical effects which he assumed to preside over the synthesis of organic materials in nature. He used powerful magnets in order to introduce asymmetrical influences during the formation of crystals. He also devised a clockwork arrangement with which he intended to reverse the natural movement of the solar rays striking a plant, from its birth to its death. He was thus trying to find out whether in such an artificial world—where the sun rose, so to speak, in the west and set in the east— the optically active substances would not appear in forms opposite to those occurring in the normal order of nature! He eventually abandoned these fantastic experiments without having obtained any results, but never gave up completely his alchemist's dream of unraveling the chemical riddle of life.

ASYMMETRY AND THE DEVELOPMENT OF BIOCHEMISTRY

I shall not deal further with these experiments, but I cannot refrain from mentioning that even today the fact that asymmetric molecules are always the products of living processes remains as much of a mystery as ever. Ever since Pasteur, it has been universally accepted that molecules with a certain degree of complexity exist in two forms, the structure of one being related to that of the other as the right hand is related to the left so that each is identical with the mirror image of the other. Both forms may occur in living organisms, but as a rule each species uses or synthesizes only one. Such asymmetric syntheses are hard to manage in the laboratory.[3] Pasteur's romantic preoccupation with this problem might acquire some new significance in the near future, since the chemical reactions involved in the origin of life are once more coming to the forefront of scientific preoccupation. One of the contributors to a recent symposium on this subject opened his paper on "The Origin of Optical Activity" with the remark that "no other chemical characteristic is as distinctive of living organisms as is optical activity." It might be mentioned also that the recent discovery of the non-conservation of parity in certain interactions of "fundamental particles" has led to a general acceptance of the notion that the structure of the universe is asymmetrical. This is what Pasteur had prophesied in 1874 before the French Academy of Sciences: "L'univers est un ensemble dissymétrique et je suis persuadé que la vie, telle qu'elle se manifeste à nous, est fonction de la dissymétrie de l'univers ou des consequences qu'elle entraine. *L'univers est dissymétrique.*"

While Pasteur's studies on the biological significance of stereo-isomerism (from the Greek: *stereos,* solid; *isos,* equal; and *meros,* part)

3. Even today the synthesis from symmetric materials of asymmetric molecules, without at the same time building up an equal number of asymmetric molecules of opposite configuration, can be accomplished only by introducing an asymmetric element into the reaction. Ed.

did not explain the genesis of life, they have yielded a number of facts which have had far-reaching influence on the development of bio-chemistry. Pasteur himself recognized that the differences in structural configuration between the isomeric forms of tartaric acids, as well as of other organic compounds, are reflected in the differential behavior of these isomeric substances toward living agents, for example, in their effect on taste buds and in their susceptibility to attack by micro-organisms. These observations have served as a springboard for a whole range of investigations on the chemical basis of biological speci-ficity, a problem which is such a characteristic feature of modern bio-chemistry. . . .

It was from his conviction that *asymmetric* molecules are always the product of life that he was led to the study of fermentation, to the recog-nition that microorganisms play an essential role in the economy of nature, and eventually to his epoch-making discoveries in the field of infectious diseases.

Explanation of Optically Active Isomers *

by Isaac Asimov (1960)

What was there about the two molecules that made them mirror images of each other? Pasteur could not say. And although Biot, who had sug-gested the existence of molecular asymmetry, lived to be 88, he did not live long enough to see his intuition vindicated.

It was in 1874, twelve years after Biot's death, that the answer was finally presented. Two young chemists, a twenty-two-year-old Dutchman named Jacobus Hendricus Van't Hoff and a twenty-seven-year-old Frenchman named Joseph Achille Le Bel, independently advanced a new theory of the carbon valence bonds which explained how mirror-image molecules could be constructed.

Chemists had drawn the four bonds of the carbon atom all in the same plane, not necessarily because this was the way they were actually arranged but because it was the convenient way of drawing them on a flat piece of paper. Van't Hoff and Le Bel now suggested a three-dimen-sional model in which the bonds were directed in two mutually per-pendicular planes, two in one plane and two in the other. A good way to picture this is to imagine the carbon atom as standing on any three

* From Isaac Asimov, *The Intelligent Man's Guide to Science.*

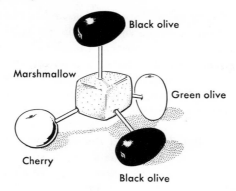

Black olive

Marshmallow

Green olive

Cherry

Black olive

Figure 5–26.

of its bonds as legs, in which case the fourth bond points vertically upward [Figure 5–26]. If you suppose the carbon atom to be at the center of a tetrahedron (a four-sided geometrical figure with triangular sides), then the four bonds point to the four vertices of the figure. The model is therefore called the "tetrahedral carbon atom."

Now let us attach to these four bonds two hydrogen atoms, a chlorine atom, and a bromine atom. Regardless of which atom we attach to which bond, we will always come out with the same arrangement. Try it and see. With four toothpicks stuck into a marshmallow (the carbon atom) at the proper angles, you could represent the four bonds. Now suppose you stick two black olives (the hydrogen atoms), a green olive (chlorine), and a cherry (bromine) on the ends of the toothpicks in any order. Let us say that when you stand this on three legs with a black olive on the fourth pointing upward, the order on the three standing legs in the clockwise direction is black olive, green olive, cherry. You might now switch the green olive and cherry so that the order runs black olive, cherry, green olive. But all you need to do to see the same order as before is to turn the structure over so that the black olive serving as one of the supporting legs sticks up in the air and the one that was in the air rests on the table. Now the order of the standing legs again is black olive, green olive, cherry.

In other words, when at least two of the four atoms (or groups of atoms) attached to carbon's four bonds are identical, only one structural arrangement is possible. (Obviously this is true when three or all four of the attachments are identical.)

But when all four of the attached atoms (or groups of atoms) are different, the situation changes. Now two different structural arrangements are possible—one the mirror image of the other. For instance, suppose you stick a cherry on the upward leg and a black olive, a green olive, and a cocktail onion on the three standing legs. If you then switch the black olive and green olive so that the clockwise order runs green olive, black olive, onion, there is no way you can turn the structure to make the order come out black olive, green olive, onion, as it was before you made the switch. Thus with four different attachments you can always form two different structures, mirror images of each other. Try it and see.

Van't Hoff and Le Bel thus solved the mystery of the asymmetry of optically active substances. The mirror-image substances that rotated light in opposite directions were substances containing carbon atoms with four different atoms or groups of atoms attached to the bonds. One of the two possible arrangements of these four attachments rotated polarized light to the right; the other rotated it to the left.

Figure 5–27. Mirror image structural formulas of a simple organic compound (glyceraldehyde, a relative of the sugars).

More and more evidence beautifully supported Van't Hoff's and Le Bel's tetrahedral model of the carbon atom, and by 1885 their theory was universally accepted. . . .

This preoccupation with the minutiae of optical activity has turned out to be more than a matter of idle curiosity. As it happens, almost all the compounds occurring in living organisms contain asymmetric carbon atoms. And in every such case the organism makes use of only one of the two mirror-image forms of the compound. Furthermore, similar compounds generally fall in the same series. For instance, virtually all the simple sugars found in living tissue belong to the *D*-series, while virtually all the amino acids (the building blocks of proteins) belong to the *L*-series.

Symmetry and Asymmetry in Modern Physics

Editor's Note. Ever since the positive electron, the positron, was discovered physicists have speculated about the possible existence of anti-matter. If an anti-electron could exist, why not an anti-proton? In 1956 the Bevatron,[1] the great new accelerator at the University of California, produced anti-protons. Man's intuitive expectation of symmetry in the Universe seemed to be confirmed.

Anti-Matter and Strange Particles *
by Isaac Asimov (1960)

With the Bevatron, man at last came within reach of creating the anti-proton. The California physicists set out deliberately to produce and detect it. In 1955 Owen Chamberlain and Emilio G. Segrè, after bombarding copper with protons of 6.2 billion electron volts hour after hour, definitely caught the anti-proton—in fact, 60 of them. It was far from easy to identify them. For every anti-proton produced, 40,000 particles of other types came into existence. But by an elaborate system of detectors, so designed and arranged that only an anti-proton could touch all the bases, they recognized the particle beyond question. For their achievement, Chamberlain and Segrè received the Nobel Prize in physics in 1959.

The anti-proton is as evanescent as the positron—at least in our universe. Within a tiny fraction of a second after it is created, the particle is snatched up by some normal, positively charged nucleus. There the anti-proton and one of the protons of the nucleus annihilate each other, turning into energy and minor particles. (Figure 5–28.)

Once in a while a proton and an anti-proton have only a near-collision

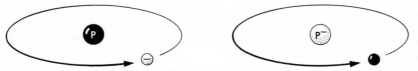

Figure 5–28. An atom of hydrogen and an atom of its anti-matter counterpart, consisting of an anti-proton and a positron.

1. See *Bevatron* in Glossary for description of this accelerator. Ed.
* From Isaac Asimov, *The Intelligent Man's Guide to Science.*

instead of a direct one. When that happens, they mutually neutralize their respective charges. The proton is converted to a neutron, which is fair enough. But the anti-proton becomes an "anti-neutron"! What can an "anti-neutron" be? The positron is the opposite of the electron by virtue of its opposite charge, and the anti-proton likewise, but what is the uncharged anti-neutron the opposite of?

Here we have to digress a little into the subject of the spin of particles. Every known type of particle spins on its axis, like a top or the earth or the sun or our Galaxy or, for all we know, the Universe itself. In spinning, the particle generates a tiny magnetic field; such fields have been measured and thoroughly explored, notably by the American physicist Isidor Isaac Rabi, who received the Nobel Prize in physics in 1944 for his work on this phenomenon.

Now it is easy to understand how a charged particle sets up a magnetic field, but not so easy to see why the uncharged neutron should. Yet it unquestionably does. The most direct evidence of this is that when a neutron beam strikes magnetized iron, it behaves differently from the way it does when the iron is not magnetized. The neutron's magnetism remains a mystery; physicists can do no better than to guess that the neutron may contain positive and negative charges which add up to zero but which somehow manage to set up a magnetic field when the particle spins.

In any case, the spin of the neutron gives us the answer to the question as to what the anti-neutron is. It is simply a neutron with its spin-direction reversed; its south magnetic pole, say, is up instead of down. Actually the proton and anti-proton and the electron and positron show exactly the same pole-reversed phenomenon.

Naturally some intriguing thoughts arise from the discovery that the three chief particles making up matter—the proton, the neutron and the electron—all have anti-particles. Were particles and anti-particles created in equal numbers at the beginning of the Universe? If so, does the Universe contain worlds, remote from ours, which are made up of anti-particles? Such a world would be like ours and follow exactly the same laws with only one trifling difference: the plus and minus signs would be reversed. It would be a mirror-image of our world. Of course, if the two worlds ever came together—matter encountering anti-matter—they would instantly destroy each other.

Astronomers have lately taken to looking speculatively at distant galaxies to see if they can find anything odd about them. An individual galaxy composed of anti-matter would not betray itself in any way we can recognize. But two colliding galaxies might. Fred Hoyle believes that the tremendous output of radio energy from the two colliding galaxies in Cygnus [Figure 5–29] may just possibly signify a meeting of matter and anti-matter. He also points out that Messier 87, a galaxy which has a bright jet of luminosity sticking out of its globular main body, may represent a collision of matter with a small cloud of anti-matter, or vice versa. [Figure 5–30.]

Maurice Goldhaber of Brookhaven suggests that the original cosmic egg from which the universe was born may have been formed of equal parts of matter and anti-matter which promptly split into two universes —a "cosmon" made of normal matter and an "anti-cosmon" made of anti-matter. They may have been pushed apart by some kind of repulsion between them. (If anti-matter, why not anti-gravity?) So somewhere, entirely beyond our reach or observation, there may be an anti-universe made up almost entirely of anti-matter.

Figure 5–29. Cygnus "A," a strong emitter of radio waves, may be a pair of colliding galaxies which appear as the blob in the center of this 200-inch telescope photograph. Its observed radio energy can be calculated if the galaxies are assumed to contain some anti-matter. (Photograph from the Mount Wilson and Palomar Observatories.)

Figure 5–30. Messier 87 is apparently a single galaxy, but the radiation of light and radio waves by the bright jet at right is unusually strong. This radiation may be caused by the annihilation of anti-matter in the jet. The photograph was made with the 200-inch telescope. (Photograph from the Mount Wilson and Palomar Observatories.)

STRANGE PARTICLES

The discovery of the anti-particles did not disturb physicists; on the contrary, it was a pleasing confirmation of the symmetry of the universe. What did disturb them was a quick succession of discoveries showing that the proton, the electron, and the neutron were not the only "elementary particles" they had to worry about.

The first of these complications had arisen even before the neutron was discovered. It had to do with the emission of beta particles by radioactive nuclei.[2] The particle emitted by a radioactive nucleus generally carries a considerable amount of energy. Where does the energy come from? It is created by conversion of a little of the nucleus's mass into energy; in other words, the nucleus always loses a little mass in the act of expelling the particle. Now physicists have long been troubled by the fact that often the beta particle emitted in a nucleus's decay did not carry enough energy to account for the amount of mass lost by the nucleus. What was the reason for this deficiency, or, to put it another way, what happened to the missing energy?

In 1931 the Austrian physicist Wolfgang Pauli (who was to receive the Nobel Prize in physics in 1945 for his "exclusion principle," having to

2. Refer back to p. 84. Ed.

do with the distribution of electrons in the atom) suggested a solution for the riddle of the missing energy. His solution was very simple: another particle carrying the missing energy came out of the nucleus along with the beta particle. This mysterious second particle had rather strange properties. It had no charge and practically no mass; all it had was a certain amount of energy. It looked, in fact, like a fictional item created just to balance the energy books.

And yet, no sooner had it been proposed than physicists were sure that the particle existed. When the neutron was discovered and found to break down into a proton, releasing an electron which, as in beta decay, also carried a deficiency of energy, they were still surer. Enrico Fermi in Italy gave the putative particle a name—*"neutrino,"* Italian for "little neutral one."

In neutron decay a single particle (the neutron) has formed two particles (the proton and the electron), and if we include the neutrino, actually three particles. It seems more reasonable to suppose that the neutron is converted into two particles and an anti-particle, or a net of one particle. In other words, what we really need to balance the books is not a neutrino but an *anti-neutrino*.

The neutrino itself would arise from the conversion of a proton into a neutron. There the products would be a neutron (particle), a positron (anti-particle), and a neutrino (particle). This, too, balances the books.

To summarize, then, neutrinos are produced in any process involving the conversion of protons to neutrons. The most important of these are the nuclear reactions that go on in the sun and other stars. Stars therefore emit vast floods of neutrinos, and it is estimated that perhaps 6 to 8 per cent of their energy is carried off in this way. Anti-neutrinos are produced in any process involving the conversion of neutrons to protons. The most important of these are natural radioactivity and uranium fission.

Our list of "elementary" particles has grown, then, to eight: proton, neutron, electron, neutrino, and their respective anti-particles. Be patient: we have only begun to count. A fantastic new crop of particles materialized before physicists had had time to digest the ones they had.

The new particles came from the simple question: what holds the nucleus together? How do all those protons—up to 92 of them in the natural elements—stick together in the nucleus despite the fact that ordinarily protons repel one another so strongly?

The search for the nuclear "cement" has engrossed physicists, and still engrosses them, perhaps more than any other single problem in modern physics. The first fruitful lead came in 1932 when Werner Heisenberg suggested that the protons were held together by "exchange forces." He pictured the protons and neutrons in the nucleus as continually interchanging identity, so that any given particle was first a proton, then a neutron, then a proton, and so on. This might keep the nucleus stable in the same way that you might be able to hold a hot potato by tossing it quickly from hand to hand. Before a proton could "realize" (so to speak) that it was a proton and try to flee its neighbor protons, it had become a neutron and could stay where it was. Naturally it could get away with this only if the changes took place exceedingly quickly, say within a trillionth of a trillionth of a second.

In 1935 the Japanese physicist Hideki Yukawa tried to work out this notion mathematically. His reasoning led to the conclusion that the transfer of charge back and forth between the proton and neutron had to be conveyed by a particle with a certain mass. It turned out that the mass of the appropriate particle lay somewhere between that of the proton and the electron; Yukawa estimated it to be between 200 and 300 times the mass of an electron.

Barely a year later this very kind of particle was discovered. At the California Institute of Technology Carl Anderson (the discoverer of the positron), investigating the tracks left by secondary cosmic rays in a cloud chamber,[3] came across a short track which was more curved by a magnetic field than a proton's and less curved than an electron's. In other words, the particle had an intermediate mass. Soon more such tracks were detected, and the particles were named "mesotrons," or "mesons" for short.

The meson proved to have a mass about 200 times that of the electron and to be extremely unstable, as Yukawa had predicted. But in other respects it failed to fill the specifications of a cementing particle. For one thing, it showed no strong tendency to be absorbed by atomic nuclei. How could mesons be the cement that held nuclei together if they avoided nuclei?

Then in 1947 the British physicist C. F. Powell discovered another type of meson in cosmic-ray photographs. It was a little more massive— about 270 times the mass of an electron. Powell named this one the "pi-meson" and the earlier one the "mu-meson" (they are now usually called "pion" and "muon," respectively). The pi-meson was found to react strongly with nuclei and to be just the particle predicted by Yukawa. So it now appears that even protons and neutrons are not the simple particles they were thought to be but may have nuclei of some sort surrounded by clouds of mesons, just as atoms have nuclear cores surrounded by clouds of electrons.

The pi-mesons and mu-mesons themselves break down into electrons

---

3. See Glossary for description of the *cloud chamber*. Ed.

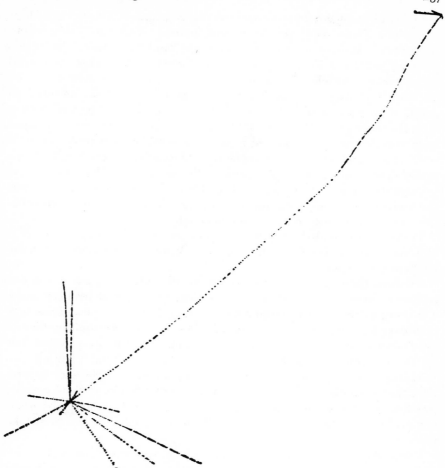

Figure 5–31. Meson collision with a nucleus. A high-energy meson struck a nucleus and produced a star made up of mesons and alpha particles (lower left), the energetic meson then traveled along the wavering path to the upper right, where it was finally stopped by collision with another nucleus.

(or positrons) and neutrinos. All the mesons have short lives, breaking down in a millionth of a second or even less. Both pions and muons come in positively charged and negatively charged forms, and the pion also has a neutral variety.

The pions and muons, it developed, were only forerunners—the advance scouts of an army, so to speak. Now came a parade of new particles, discovered by the increasingly sophisticated eyes of the physicists in the products of giant accelerators such as the Brookhaven Cosmotron. [Figure 5–32.] There were heavier mesons named "K-mesons"; there were "hyperons," subdivided into types called the "lambda particle," the "sigma particle," and the "xi particle." These could exist in charged or uncharged forms and as particles or anti-particles. Thus, in 1959, the "xi-zero," an uncharged xi particle, was detected, as well as the "anti-lambda." In addition, in 1962, it was discovered that muons were associated with a second variety of neutrino and anti-neutrino, different in some mysterious fashion from the ones produced along with electrons and positrons.

All in all, nuclear physics is currently a wonderland—or a jungle, if you prefer—awaiting further exploration. At the latest count there were some 32 particles, detected or predicted, and no one could say that this was the end. In fact, *very* short-lived "resonance particles" such as the rho-meson and omega-meson have been detected.

The K-mesons and the hyperons introduced physicists to a fourth field of force different from the three already known: gravitational, electro-magnetic, and nuclear.

Of these three, gravitational force is by all odds the weakest, electro-magnetic force comes next, and the nuclear force is still stronger—some 130 times as strong as electromagnetic forces. But the nuclear force acts only over an extremely short distance. Whereas the electromagnetic and gravitational forces decrease only as the square of the distance, nuclear forces drop off so rapidly with distance that the force between two nucleons falls almost to zero if they are separated by a distance greater than their own diameter. (This is as if the earth's gravity were to become practically zero 4,000 miles above the surface.) Consequently inter-actions between particles under the influence of nuclear forces must take place very quickly.

For instance, imagine a pi-meson and a proton approaching each other. If the nuclear force is to cause them to interact, it must do so while they are within a proton's width of each other. A proton's width is about 0.000000000001 centimeter. Flying mesons are traveling at almost the speed of light, which is 30 billion centimeters a second. Thus the pi-meson will be within the influence of the nuclear force for only about 0.0000000000000000000001 second (a hundred billionth of a trillionth of a second). And yet, even in this short time, the nuclear force brings about an interaction. The pi-meson and the proton can react to produce a lambda-hyperon and a K-meson.

This is an example of what physicists call a "strong interaction." A "weak interaction" is one that requires a considerably longer time. An example of such an interaction is the breakdown of a K-meson or a hyperon. This takes one ten-billionth of a second or so. That may seem

	PARTICLE	SYMBOL	MASS	LIFETIME IN SECONDS
LEPTONS	PHOTON	γ	0	Stable
	NEUTRINO	ν	0	Stable
	ANTI-NEUTRINO	$\bar{\nu}$	0	Stable
	ELECTRON	e^-	1	Stable
	POSITRON	e^+	1	Stable
MESONS	MU MESONS	$\mu^-\ \mu^+$	206	2.22×10^{-6}
	PI MESONS	$\pi^-\ \pi^+$	273	2.56×10^{-8}
	NEUTRAL PI MESON	π°	264	$<10^{-15}$
	K MESONS	$K^-\ K^+$	967	1.2×10^{-8}
	NEUTRAL K MESON$_1$	K_1°	~ 973	10^{-10}
	NEUTRAL K MESON$_2$	K_2°	~ 973	$\sim 8 \times 10^{-8}$
NUCLEONS	PROTON	p	1836	Stable
	ANTI-PROTON	$\bar{p}$	1836	Stable
	NEUTRON	n	1839	1010
	ANTI-NEUTRON	$\bar{n}$	1839	1010
HYPERONS	LAMBDA	Λ°	2182	2.6×10^{-10}
	ANTI-LAMBDA	$\bar{\Lambda}^\circ$	2182	2.6×10^{-10}
	SIGMA POSITIVE	Σ^+	2328	$\sim 8 \times 10^{-11}$
	ANTI-SIGMA POSITIVE	$\bar{\Sigma}^+$	2328	$\sim 8 \times 10^{-11}$
	SIGMA NEGATIVE	Σ^-	2342	1.7×10^{-10}
	ANTI-SIGMA NEGATIVE	$\bar{\Sigma}^-$	2342	1.7×10^{-10}
	NEUTRAL SIGMA	Σ°	2326	$<10^{-11}$
	NEUTRAL ANTI-SIGMA	$\bar{\Sigma}^\circ$	2326	$<10^{-11}$
	XI NEGATIVE	Ξ^-	2585	$\sim 10^{-10}$
	ANTI-XI NEGATIVE	$\bar{\Xi}^-$	2585	$\sim 10^{-10}$
	XI NEUTRAL	Ξ°	....	....
	ANTI-XI NEUTRAL	$\bar{\Xi}^\circ$	....	....

Figure 5–32. A list of identified subatomic particles. (From Isaac Asimov, The Intelligent Man's Guide to Science.)

a breathlessly short time, but compared to the time it takes for a pi-meson and proton to interact, it is very long. It is, in fact, about a trillion times as long as the physicists had expected, considering the speed of most nuclear interactions.

They concluded that the "weak interactions" were governed by forces much weaker than the nuclear forces, and they took to calling the particles that broke down as a result of weak interactions "strange particles." This name applied not only to K-mesons and hyperons but also to the light mesons and to neutrinos, which likewise were involved in weak interactions.

Physicists began to study weak interactions with increasing fascination. And in time they came to a discovery which rocked physics to its foundations.

The Overthrow of Parity *

by Philip Morrison (1957)

In the days when philosophers, acute in observation but as yet unaided by the tools of modern science, were primary founts of insight into the nature of the physical world, the philosopher Gottfried Wilhelm von Leibniz formulated a "great principle" which was to bear greater fruits than he knew. It was a proposition which at first thought seems absurdly simple and self-evident: namely, that "two states indiscernible from each other are the same state." Leibniz argued it on grounds which today we would find theological rather than scientific. Yet it has become one of the firmest pillars of modern physics. It underlies the theory of relativity and those laws of conservation—of energy, momentum and so on—upon which our understanding of nature is built. And it is now given deeper and sharper meaning than ever by the amazing event in physics which is the topic of this article—the overthrow of the "parity principle" and the unraveling of the nature of left and right.

The important word in Leibniz's axiom is "indiscernible." Modern physics has been profoundly concerned with what is discernible and what is not. One of its strongest and most fruitful assumptions has been that among the indiscernibles are absolute space, time and direction. It is not hard to present examples. Think of the conventional world map.

To each place are assigned a latitude and a longitude—a pair of numbers. The numbers are of great utility and convenience, but they are in no sense real attributes of the places; they have no physical significance. If the starting point for counting were to be shifted from Greenwich to Timbuktu, the numbers would change but no mountains would be moved. The numbers are merely arbitrary labels. And this is the manner in which space in general is treated in physics. The coordinates specifying positions in space describe only relative positions. We try to formulate our physical laws by the use of mathematical schemes in which absolute positions in space never enter. Whatever our frame of reference, we say, space remains invariant.

Let us take a more dramatic and comprehensive example. Suppose that a skilled director is going to produce on a stage before you some physical event or phenomenon—any whatever—without offering you clues to the date of the event, the directional orientation of the stage or the location of the theater. Could you determine any of these by any certain evidence? Indeed not. You may, of course, date the performance as lying within your lifetime, but this is clearly a subjective (i.e., relative) time. (Indeed, Rip van Winkle could not succeed even in that.) You can judge which direction within the theater is up and which down, but "up" and "down" are merely relative to the earth; consider that you are in a theater in Australia and you will begin to realize the problem of attempting to determine the absolute orientation. A sharper test would be to use a compass to find "north," but this fails too, for the director can falsify the magnetic field, and in any case locating "north" on the earth tells you nothing about your absolute orientation in space. Nor can you locate the theater, even if you can look out a window and see a familiar landmark or a familiar star. The earth itself moves, and so do all the external reference points. No, in principle and in practice absolute location in time or space and absolute direction are all indiscernibles.

These facts are of basic importance in physics. The indiscernibility of absolute coordinates lies at the basis of Albert Einstein's construction of the special theory of relativity, as is emphasized by the very name of his theory. And the fact that physical equations cannot refer to absolute time, space or orientation leads logically, by mathematical reasoning which we need not review here, to the classical laws of the conservation of energy and momentum.

The conservation "law" that concerns us now is the conservation of "parity," which rests upon the assumed indiscernibility of right from left. The indiscernibility principle can be put this way: there is no absolute distinction between a real object (or event) and its mirror image. A right-hand glove, and a left-hand glove are surely different, but if accurately made they are precise counterparts; looking at a right-hand glove in a mirror, you cannot tell from its properties that you are not looking at a left-hand glove. The looking-glass world of people is admittedly unusual. Your mirror image is badly brought up: it offers to greet you with its left hand instead of its right, and it writes oddly. But the curiousness of the mirror world is largely conventional. There is no reason to doubt that such a world could exist. Indeed, any good director could set and coach a performance so that you could not distinguish it from the mirror image of a conventional performance.

The physical principle of the indistinguishability of right and left implies that for every scene, every experiment, an exact mirror counterpart is possible. It is true that nature seems to favor a specific orientation (right-handed or left-handed) for the spiraling shells of snails [Figure 5–33] and other animals, and for molecules of living matter. But this provides no conclusive evidence for the physicist: he sees that the molecule would function exactly the same way were it mirrored, and he can envision a world of living beings just like our own in which the "handedness" was simply reversed. The looking-glass world of life could function exactly like the actual world.

Until the startling events of the past few months, it seemed that the invariance of left and right was as unassailable as the invariance of time or space. All experience had buttressed the idea that no intrinsic difference could be found to distinguish physical phenomena in a looking-glass world from the real world. All the seeming guides for distinguishing left from right failed on analysis to do any such thing. A student of electricity might cite the famous right-hand rule for telling the direction of an electromagnetic field: if you grasp a wire with your right hand so that the thumb points in the direction of the current's flow, your finger tips point in the direction in which a north pole moves in the magnetic field around the wire. But not so fast. What distinguishes a north pole from a south pole? True, you may refer me to a compass needle. The "north"-seeking end of the needle is colored blue and stamped with a big N. But this convention could be reversed without the least difficulty. If we switched the label N to the other end of the needle, the experiment would work with the left hand. So only convention distinguishes our experiment from its mirror counterpart. No intrinsic physical distinction, either in the macroscopic or the microscopic world, exists between a north magnetic pole and a south. All our right-hand rules are pure convention: there is nothing in the laws of electromagnetic fields that permits an absolute distinction between right and left.

The power of this idea of spatial symmetry ought now to be clear. If we begin by postulating mirror invariance, we can infer the indistinguish-

Figure 5–33. Chambered shell of nautilus forms a logarithmic spiral in this X-ray photograph. The animal makes a partition after each period of growth. It occupies an outer chamber which has volume equal to all other chambers. Gas in shell helps animal float. (Photograph reprinted courtesy of the Eastman Kodak Company, Rochester, New York.)

ability of magnetic north and south poles. The latter in turn is an important principle in the microworld of particles, permitting us to give an orderly account of certain phenomena in that world. It implies the principle of the conservation of "parity," just as the invariance of space and time implies the conservation of energy.

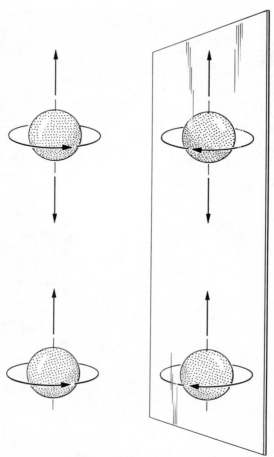

Figure 5–34. *Mirror reflection of a spinning ball could not be detected if the ball ejected particles equally in both directions along its axis. Image at top right looks just like the real ball turned upside down. Reflection can be detected if there is a preferred direction for the ejection of particles. Thus the image at bottom cannot be mistaken for the real thing.*

"Parity" is a mathematical concept, impossible to define in physical terms. It is a property of the so-called wave function by which quantum mechanics describes the wave characteristics of a particle and represents its position in space. The variables of a wave function are just those coordinates that we use to locate spatial positions. Now it is not hard to see that if we change the sign of one coordinate (i.e., from plus to minus), this is equivalent to reflecting the system in a mirror. Parity is the term that describes the effect of such a reversal upon the wave function. If

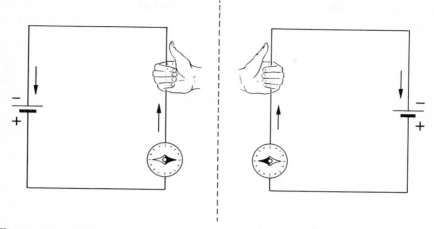

Figure 5–35. Right-hand rule relating the directions of an electric current and its resulting magnetic field (thumb points with current, fingers point with the north-seeking pole of a test compass needle) becomes a left-hand rule when the experiment is reflected in a mirror. In this drawing, the "real" experiment is seen at the left and its mirror image at the right.

the wave function remains unchanged when the sign of one of its three spatial variables is reversed, we say that the function has "even" parity. If reversal of the sign of the variable reverses the sign of the wave function, we call its parity "odd." In short, parity has one of two values— even or odd. And all our experience, as well as theory, has indicated that in an isolated system parity never changes its value—i.e., parity is always conserved.

Or rather, almost all. We are now confronted with a flat failure of parity conservation. The story goes back to about a year ago, when two extremely imaginative and ingenious investigators of the newly discovered "strange" particles of the atomic world made a really novel suggestion.

The two—Tsung Dao Lee of Columbia University and Chen Ning Yang of the Institute for Advanced Study—were absorbed in what was perhaps the most baffling paradox in this new realm of strangeness: the so-called "tau-theta puzzle." There were two mesons, called tau and theta. Tau, in the course of time, disintegrated into three pi mesons; theta, into two pi mesons. What was baffling was that in every property except the mode of decay, tau and theta were identical twins. Could they be one and the same particle? Decay of a particle by two different modes was certainly permitted by theory and precedent, but in this case the principle of conservation of parity stood in the way. Tau decayed to a set of pions of odd parity, theta to even-parity pions. The law of unchanging parity said that tau and theta must have different parity and therefore be different particles.

Yet the undownable question remained: Why were tau and theta exactly alike in every respect except this one? Lee and Yang boldly faced up to an embarrassing but insistent possibility: perhaps the parity-conservation law simply broke down in the realm of particle decays like tau's and theta's!

Their boldness was not rash. They could take the stand that while mirror invariance, from which the parity-conservation idea was derived, might hold in all other realms, it need not necessarily apply in the world of tau and theta. For the decay of tau and theta belongs to a very special class of reaction known as "weak interactions." The forces involved in them are very weak indeed—much weaker even than the forces which bind electrons in atoms. The forces are measured by the time it takes, with a given amount of available energy, for a particle emission to occur. By this measure the force entailed in a weak interaction such as the decay of tau or theta is smaller by a factor of 100 billion than the binding force on an atomic electron. Yang and Lee felt that the previous tests of mirror invariance in other fields of phenomena might have no validity in this untested realm of weak and subtle interactions.

They proposed an experiment to test whether right and left could or could not be distinguished in this realm. Tau and theta particles themselves were poor candidates as subjects for such a test, for their lifetime is short—only about a billionth of a second. But the beta-decay (emission of beta particles) of radioactive atomic nuclei also belongs to the family of weak interactions, and these decays, taking place at much lower levels of available energy, have conveniently long lifetimes—measured in seconds or even years (e.g., the beta-decay half life of cobalt 60 is 5.3 years). In essence Yang and Lee's proposal for the test experiment was simply to line up the spins of beta-emitting nuclei along the same axis, and then see whether the beta particles were emitted preferentially in one direction or the other along the axis. Neither direction would have any significance, conventional or otherwise: there is no arrowhead on the axis. But the preferred direction of beta-emission by the spinning nuclei would in fact define an arrowhead—the direction of advance of a right-hand or left-hand screw—and its mirror image would be discernibly reversed from the real thing. The experiment should leave no doubt about a distinction between left and right in beta-decay.

A powerful team of laboratory experimenters took up the challenge. Chien Shiung Wu of Columbia contributed her art in designing experiments and her experience in beta-decay work. A team at the National

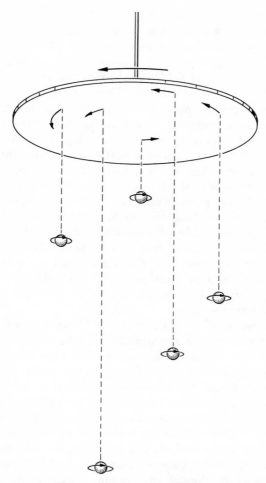

Figure 5–36. Screw direction could theoretically be specified by an aluminum disk, mounted to rotate around vertical axis, and coated on underside with cobalt 60. Electrons ejected downward have predominantly one spin, and impart opposite spin to disk. Upward electrons are absorbed by aluminum. Thus the disk always spins in direction shown. The device was suggested by J. R. Zacharias of the Massachusetts Institute of Technology.

Bureau of Standards under Ernest Ambler undertook the task of lining up the nuclei. Ambler's job was to provide the straight line; Wu's, to look for the tip of the arrow (i.e., the preferred direction of beta-emission).

Nuclear alignment is a new art, no more than three or four years old. The sole handle by which the nuclei of atoms can be manipulated is their magnetic moment. No laboratory generator can produce magnetic fields strong enough to align these tiny moments; only within atoms themselves do sufficiently strong fields exist. So special atoms are lined up to produce a field, and their field in turn lines up the magnetic nuclei. But to make orderly alignment possible at all, thermal agitation of the atoms must be reduced to a minimum, which means cooling the system to very low temperature—considerably less than one degree above absolute zero. Shielded by the best sort of vacuum bottle, cooled by streams of liquid helium, the cobalt 60 atoms which served as the beta-emitters were kept aligned for 15 minutes or so at a time.

Six months to design, prepare and carry out the 15-minute experiments —these times proved just long enough to settle the issue beyond doubt. The beta particles emitted by the lined-up cobalt nuclei went predominantly in the direction against the magnetic field. This meant that, from the standpoint of beta-emission, the nuclei had an intrinsically left-handed spin. Left could be distinguished from right. Mirror invariance was dead. However valid it was elsewhere, in the realm of weak interactions it unambiguously failed.

Within a few weeks after that first test in December, 1956, the conclusion was again unequivocally confirmed by another experiment. This time the weak interaction tested was the decay of the mu meson. The experiment rested on a hypothesis which seeks to explain the failure of mirror invariance in beta-decay. The theory assumes that in the decay of a mu meson both a neutrino and an anti-neutrino are emitted, along with the beta particle, and that the neutrino always has a right-handed spin while the anti-neutrino's is left-handed. It was reasoned that when a pi meson decays into a mu meson and an anti-neutrino, the mu meson must be emitted with a left-handed spin to balance that of the anti-neutrino. As a consequence, when aligned mu mesons, under suitable conditions, decay with emission of electrons, the electrons should come out in a preferential direction. The theory was tested, first by a group at Columbia and later in other laboratories, and the preference for the specified screw direction was verified. The Columbia group have used the effect very ingeniously to measure the magnetic moment of the mu meson, and thus already have made a useful application of the failure of mirror invariance.

Theoretical physicists have only begun to speculate about the more general implications of this profound overthrow of a basic principle in the world of weak interactions. But there is an over-all lesson which can be put simply: The great invariance principles of nature may be relied upon within the domains of their application, but they are not *a priori* self-evident or necessarily of universal application. It is worth while to test to higher and higher precision the great foundation principles, including the conservation of energy. So far as we have gone, even in weak particle interactions, energy conservation appears to hold, but does it still hold for the weakest interactions of all, those involving the weak force of gravity? Here one thinks of the hypothesis that matter may arise spontaneously from a space containing no energy, and the possibilities are exciting. It may also be that there is some connection between the two major asymmetries we now see in the physical world—the right-left asymmetry of weak particle reactions and the fact that our world is overwhelmingly made up of one kind of matter, to the near-exclusion of anti-matter. Perhaps this lead could forge a bridge between the microphysics of the fundamental particles and the physics of the great distances —that is, cosmology. It is fair to say that the discovery of the limitations of the mirror invariance principle is not a setback but an opportunity. We have entered an exhilarating time.

"It seems very pretty," Alice said when she had finished it, "but it's *rather* hard to understand!" (You see she didn't like to confess, even to herself, that she couldn't make it out at all.) "Somehow it seems to fill my head with ideas— only I don't exactly know what they are! . . ."

          ✿   ✿   ✿

"She's coming," cried the Larkspur. "I hear her footsteps, thump, thump, along the gravel-walk!"

Alice looked around eagerly and found that it was the Red Queen. . . .

"I think I'll go meet her," said Alice, . . .

"You can't possibly do that," said the Rose: "*I* should advise you to walk the other way."

This sounded nonsense to Alice, so she said nothing, but set off at once towards the Red Queen. To her surprise she lost sight of her in a moment, and found herself walking in at the front-door again.

Lewis Carroll
Through the Looking Glass

Questions To Consider

Why does symmetry seem beautiful to us?

What is the relationship between symmetry and simplicity?

Why does asymmetry suggest movement? Is it necessary to have some degree of asymmetry in living things?

Is the scientific assumption that the universe is symmetrical an example of man imposing an order on nature?

If science establishes a fundamental asymmetry in nature will the universe seem less orderly and beautiful?

Suggestions for Further Reading

Blin-Stoyle, R. J., *et al.: Turning Points in Physics*, Torchbooks, Harper & Brothers, 1961. Chapter VI deals with the new concepts in elementary particles.
° Holden, Alan, and Phylis Singer: *Crystals and Crystal Growing*, Anchor Books, Doubleday & Co., Inc., 1960. For the reader interested in exploring further the beautiful world of crystals we strongly recommend reading the rest of this book from which the selection beginning on p. 217 was taken.
° Weisskopf, Victor F.: *Knowledge and Wonder*, Anchor Books, Doubleday & Co., Inc., 1963. One of the best recent books for the non-scientist. It synthesizes the basic ideas of physics, chemistry, astronomy, biology, and evolution. Chapter 7 describes some of the most recent work in elementary particle physics. The selection beginning on p. 95 in Part 3 was taken from this Science Study Series book. The chapters on life and evolution will be useful for Parts 6 and 9.
Whyte, Lancelot Lon: *Accent on Form*, Harper & Row, 1954. An original and provocative essay on the growing importance of the concept of form in scientific thought.
° Wilson, Robert R., and Raphael Littamer: *Accelerators: Machines of Nuclear Physics*, Anchor Books, Doubleday & Co., Inc., 1960. A Science Study Series book that traces the development of particle accelerators. It describes the design and construction of the latest accelerators and the purposes they serve in studying the nature of matter.

° Paperback edition

6

What Is the Origin of Living Matter?

Can life arise spontaneously from non-living matter or does it require the presence of a vital force? The development of early scientific theories of the origin of life from Greek times up to the twentieth century highlights the conflict between these two views. Are they mutually exclusive or do they, in some sense, encompass one another?

What Is the Origin of Living Matter?

Introduction

THE QUESTION of the origin of life has occupied mankind since the beginning of conscious thought. The first answers were found in religion and philosophy. Now, in recent times, science has undertaken to discover its own answer.

The earliest theories about life fell into two schools of thought. One believed that life arose by natural processes from non-living matter, while the other believed that a special "vital force" was present in all living things. It is an interesting fact that adherents of both schools of thought believed that simple forms of life could arise "spontaneously." Anyone could see the swarms of maggots and flies which seemed to appear from nowhere on the surface of decaying meat or rotting fruit. These common-sense observations were further confirmed with the invention of the microscope, which revealed a world teeming with microscopic forms of life. They were found in sour milk, in the sediment in old gutter pipes, and in puddles of rain water. Any organic matter left in a warm place soon became infested with tiny forms of life. Since organic matter was believed at that time to be formed only by living things, it was reasonable to suppose that organic matter contained the special vital force which was capable of creating more life from the same raw materials.

However Francisco Redi's experiments in 1668 and Pasteur's two hundred years later demonstrated that organic matter does not in itself have the power of creating life. If all microorganisms are removed and excluded from an organic substance, no microorganisms appear.

In 1827, the synthesis of an organic substance from inorganic compounds bridged the gap which the vitalists had believed to be unbridgeable. As a result of this experiment, organic materials could no longer be believed to contain a special vital principle.

During the next century, evidence accumulated to support the position of the so-called mechanists that there is no element or principle in living matter which is different from non-living matter. Yet, on the other hand, life seems to spring only from pre-existing life. In spite of all attempts, no living organism has been created in the laboratory from non-living matter.

If it is true that under certain conditions life could result from the chance shuffling of random combinations of molecules, then the conditions on earth today do not appear to be favorable for this event. Perhaps at some other place or time in the universe conditions were favorable and then life began. It might, for example, have occurred on some other celestial body and the spores might have been carried here in meteoric dust, under the action of light and gravity. This theory (or variations of it) had many adherents during the nineteenth century, but fell into disrepute later when it was discovered that the spores would be subjected to intense electromagnetic radiation during the long journey through space. However, in the last few years, evidence has been found in meteorites of complex organic molecules and organized elements which may have been formed outside of the earth's atmosphere. The evidence is still controversial but it does reestablish the possibility that an elementary form of life arrived on earth from another place in the universe. As George Wald says: "No great idea is ever lost. . . . It is dismissed only to return, yet never quite the same. Its rejection is only a step in its further development." [1] In the next few years, the exploration of space may throw more light on this idea.

The theory most generally held by the scientific world today is that the conditions suitable for the beginning of life occurred at some earlier period in the earth's history and, once formed, life evolved to the state of complexity which we witness today. The details of this modern theory of evolution will be examined later. For the moment, it should be accepted that scientists believe this could have happened. The question in these readings is the origin of the first living thing. If scientists succeed in recreating in the laboratory conditions approximating the primeval conditions on earth and synthesize some simple living organism, will it prove that this is the way life appeared on earth? Will it disprove once and for all that there is anything special about living matter? Will it disprove a divine creation?

The significance of scientific experiments are sometimes exaggerated by the people who live at the time those experiments are made. Pasteur's contemporaries thought he had proved that life could never arise spontaneously from non-living matter. Now we are trying to accomplish this in the laboratory. "If the day comes," Loren Eiseley warns us, "when the slime of the laboratory for the first time crawls under man's direction, we shall have great need of humbleness. . . . there will be few to consider—so deep is the mind-set of an age—whether the desire to link life to matter may not have blinded us to the more remarkable characteristics of both." [2]

1. See p. 326.
2. See p. 334.

Theories of the Origin of Life

Genesis *

And God said, Let the earth bring forth grass, the herb yielding seed, and the fruit tree yielding fruit after his kind, whose seed is in itself, upon the earth: and it was so.

And the earth brought forth grass, and herb yielding seed after his kind, and the tree yielding fruit, whose seed was in itself, after his kind: and God saw that it was good.

And the evening and the morning were the third day.

And God said, Let there be lights in the firmament of the heaven to divide the day from the night; and let them be for signs, and for seasons, and for days, and years:

And let them be for lights in the firmament of the heaven to give light upon the earth: and it was so.

And God made two great lights; the greater light to rule the day, and the lesser light to rule the night: he made the stars also.

And God set them in the firmament of the heaven to give light upon the earth,

And to rule over the day and over the night, and to divide the light from the darkness: and God saw that it was good.

And the evening and the morning were the fourth day.

And God said, Let the waters bring forth abundantly the moving creature that hath life, and fowl that may fly above the earth in the open firmament of heaven.

And God created great whales, and every living creature that moveth which the waters brought forth abundantly, after their kind, and every winged fowl after his kind: and God saw that it was good.

And God blessed them, saying, Be fruitful, and multiply, and fill the waters in the seas, and let fowl multiply in the earth.

And the evening and the morning were the fifth day.

And God said, Let the earth bring forth the living creature after his kind, cattle, and creeping thing, and beast of the earth after his kind: and it was so.

* From Genesis, 1.11–31, Authorized King James Version.

And God made the beast of the earth after his kind, and cattle after their kind, and every thing that creepeth upon the earth after his kind: and God saw that it was good.

And God said, Let us make man in our image, after our likeness: and let them have dominion over the fish of the sea, and over the fowl of the air, and over the cattle, and over all the earth, and over every creeping thing that creepeth upon the earth.

So God created man in his own image, in the image of God created he him; male and female created he them.

And God blessed them, and God said unto them, Be fruitful, and multiply, and replenish the earth, and subdue it: and have dominion over the fish of the sea, and over the fowl of the air, and over every living thing that moveth upon the earth.

And God said, Behold, I have given you every herb bearing seed, which is upon the face of all the earth, and every tree, in the which is the fruit of a tree yielding seed; to you it shall be for meat.

And to every beast of the earth, and to every fowl of the air, and to every thing that creepeth upon the earth, wherein there is life, I have given every green herb for meat: and it was so.

And God saw every thing that he had made, and, behold, it was very good. And the evening and the morning were the sixth day.

Theories of Spontaneous Generation of Life *

by A. I. Oparin (1938)

The question of the origin of life, of its first appearance on Earth, still occupies the human mind, as it has done since the most remote antiquity. It may be safely said that it is one of the most important problems of natural history. No religious or philosophical system, no outstanding thinker ever failed to give this question serious consideration. During different epochs and at different stages of civilization the question was answered differently, but this question was always the focal point of a sharp philosophical struggle which reflected the underlying struggle of social classes. For a very long time the question of the origin of life was treated not as a subject of scientific research but entirely from the point of view of religio-scholastic concepts. The ancient religious teachings of

China, Egypt, Babylon traced the origin of life to various traditions and legends, and invariably attributed the appearance of life to some creative act of God. But we will not concern ourselves with these theories and shall consider only . . . those philosophical systems which, though no longer of any significance so far as our modern approach to this problem is concerned, have a purely historical interest. E. Lippmann [1] in a recent book . . . draws the interesting parallel between the ancient conceptions of the architecture of the World and the conceptions of the origin of life. "Everyday experience gave irrefutable evidence in the course of thousands of years of the movement of the Sun around the Earth with such probability that there could be no doubt on this score. Similarly evident was the 'fact' that very frequently, under favorable conditions, living things originate from lifeless matter. This 'fact' seemed so obvious that there was no necessity for a more detailed study of this phenomenon. Therefore, since the most remote times, we find among the various peoples all over the world the solid conviction, based frequently on observation, that the simplest animals, both of the lowest and highest order, can originate spontaneously." And this author notes further that these everyday, superficial observations so powerfully affect human concepts, that the belief in the possibility of spontaneous generation of various living things from all sorts of rotting material has been sustained for thousands of years and persists even to the present day. Even in our own time of crowning achievement in the exact natural sciences the layman of civilized European countries not infrequently believes that worms are generated in manure, that the enemies abounding in garden or field, the various parasites operative in our daily existence arise spontaneously from refuse and every sort of filth.

It is easy to understand the tremendous significance of such daily experience in the formulation of conceptions among the ancient peoples, who lacked the methods for an exact study of natural phenomena. Such "irrefutable evidence" formed the basis of theories of many philosophers of the Ionian school (600 B.C.) according to which living organisms originated in sea slime by the action of heat, sun and air. Thus, for instance, the oldest philosopher of this Greek school, Thales, taught that living things developed from the amorphous slime under the influence of heat. Anaximander (611–547 B.C.) claimed that everything living arises in sea ooze and goes through a succession of stages in its development. Xenophane (560–480 B.C.) taught that all organisms originate from earth and water.

It is necessary to point out, however, that the conception of spontaneous generation of living things, entertained by Greek philosophers on

1. E. Lippmann, *Urzengung und Lebenskraft,* Berlin, 1933.

the basis of everyday observation, was intimately interwoven with their teaching of the perpetuity of life. Although they considered the origin of life from lifeless inorganic matter, this strictly speaking did not imply a primary phenomenon, since in the view of these philosophers the entire universe was conceived to be living. Thus, according to Anaxagorus (510–428 B.C.), neither creation nor destruction of life was possible and, although in his opinion plants, animals and man all came from the earth's slime, nevertheless it was essential that this should be fructified by unchanging and infinitely small seeds (spermata), the ethereal embryos, which were carried into the earth from the air with rain water.

Democritus, like Anaximander, thought that the organic world took its origin in water and that animals passed through a long developmental process before they became such as we find them today. But this philosopher already advanced the theory of the mechanical self-creation of life resulting from an inherent movement of the atoms: the atoms of lifeless, moist earth meet accidentally and unite with atoms of the live and energizing fire. . . .

The views developed by Aristotle (384–322 B.C.) have an entirely different and particular significance for the future history of the study of the origin of life. . . . According to this theory animals not only originate from other similar animals but living things do arise and always have arisen from lifeless matter. Aristotle teaches that living things, as well as other concrete things, are produced by the union of some passive principle "matter" (by which Aristotle apparently refers to what we now designate as substance) with an active principle "form," this form being the "entelechy" or soul of living things. It imparts organization and movement to the body. Thus, matter by itself is devoid of life but is vivified, purposefully molded and organized by the aid of the energy of the soul, whose inner essence (entelechy) endows matter with life and keeps it alive. But the soul is already present in the primary elements of which living things are made; to a lesser degree it is a property of the earth, but to a greater degree of water, air and fire. Therefore, what form the soul will endow depends first of all on the predominance of one or the other element. Thus, the earth produces principally plants; water produces aquatic animals; air, terrestrial organisms; while fire gives rise to the supposed denizens of celestial bodies, such as the Moon. The form of living things originating from their like depends upon the "animal heat," but of those generated spontaneously from inorganic matter upon the "sun's heat." Slime, manure, and similar decaying matter do not of themselves produce living organisms but only under the fructifying influence of rain saturated with air and of the Sun's heat.

Aristotle suggested the possibility of spontaneous generation of a great variety of living organisms. He maintained that not only plants but also a number of animals could be observed to originate from the earth. According to Aristotle ordinary worms, larvae of the bee or wasp, ticks, fireflies and many other insects develop from the morning dew, or from decaying slime and manure, from dry wood, hair, sweat and meat, while tapeworms are born in the rotting portions of the body and excreta. Mosquitoes, flies, moths, manure beetles, cantharides, also fleas, bed bugs and lice (either full grown or as larvae) are generated in the slime of wells, rivers or sea, in the humus of the fields, in manure, in decaying trees or fruits, in animal excreta and filth of every sort, in vinegar dregs as well as in old wool.

However, not only insects and worms but even more highly organized living creatures may originate spontaneously according to Aristotle. Crabs and various molluscs were thought to come from the moist soil and decaying slime, eels and many kinds of fish to come from the wet ooze, sand, slime and rotting seaweeds; even frogs and under certain conditions salamanders may come from slime. Mice are generated in moist soil. Some higher animals and even man may have a similar origin, though in the case of the latter his first appearance is in the form of a worm.

We have dwelt to such length on the views of Aristotle because the entire history of the problem of the origin of living things has been dominated by the teachings of this philosopher. By his overwhelming authority Aristotle gave credence to data derived from naive direct observation and thus predetermined for many centuries in advance the future fate of the theory of spontaneous generation. An important part in this matter was played by the acceptance of Aristotle's teachings by the Roman and more particularly by the neoplatonic (Plotinus) philosophers and through them by the fathers of the Christian Church, in particular by Basilius (315–379) and Saint Augustine (354–430).

Basilius taught that just as the Earth once upon a time produced various grasses, trees and animals by the command of God so to this day this ability has been retained in full force and living creatures such as grasshoppers, mice, etc., may be produced from the earth. Saint Augustine accepted the spontaneous generation of living creatures as an irrefutable truth and in his teachings was concerned only to reconcile this phenomenon of nature with the viewpoint of the Christian Church. He argued that just as God usually makes wine from water and earth by way of the grape and grape juice but on occasion, as in Canaan of Galilee, can dispense with the grape and make wine directly from water, so also in the case of living creatures He can cause them to be born either from the seed or from inorganic matter containing invisible seeds (occulta semina). Saint Augustine thus beheld in the phenomenon of spontaneous generation of living things the will of God, which interferes with the usual orderly sequence of events, and established the theory of spontaneous generation as a dogma sustained by all the force of authority of the Christian Church.

It is, therefore, clear why further development of the problem of the origin of life remained for a long time within the framework of the teaching of spontaneous generation. The medieval scholars in their works merely corroborated the "facts" described by Aristotle of the origin of living creatures from decaying matter, or even supplemented these with still more phantastic observations and experiments of their own. As a fitting comment upon the typical methods of studying nature in the Middle Ages mention may be made of the widely accepted tales of the goose tree, of the vegetable lamb . . .

On the authority of very prominent scholars and numerous travellers of that period geese and ducks came from sea shells, which themselves had come from the fruit of trees. Birds could also be born directly from these fruits. This legend of the goose tree was already expounded by Cardinal Pietro Damiani at the beginning of the eleventh century. The English encyclopedist Alexander Neckam (1157–1217) evolved the theory of the origin of birds from fir trees which came in contact with the salt of sea water. Subsequently this theory of the vegetable source of geese and ducks was so generally accepted that the use of their meat became common on fast days, a practice which was later prohibited by a special edict of Pope Innocent III.

It is interesting that this theory of the goose tree survived until the end of the seventeenth and even the beginning of the eighteenth century. A number of authors gave their own observations and produced more or less phantastic drawings which portrayed the gradual development of birds from the fruit of trees. Evidently this legend originated from a naive interpretation of superficial observations of a peculiar species of barnacle, the so called sea ducks (Lepas anatifera). The full-grown specimens of these sea animals attach themselves to rocks, stones, bottoms of boats and occasionally to a tree which has fallen into the water, and they form a calcareous membrane resembling a shell. On the shores of northern Scotland, Ireland and of the neighboring islands this occurs at the same time of year when the young polar geese arrive from the North. These two events were somehow associated with each other and phantasy filled in the rest of the imaginary picture of the relation of these birds, which came no one knew whence, with the little "sea ducks" attached to the trunks of trees.

Possibly analogous superficial observations were the basis of another legend, the vegetable lamb, which many travellers to the Orient have reported (Odorico da Pordenone, 1331; Maundeville, 1300–1372; and others). According to their reports these travellers had heard tales of or had even seen plants and whole trees whose melon-like fruit contained full formed lambs which the local population used for meat. . . .

Although in the last half of the sixteenth and especially in the seventeenth century observation of natural phenomena becomes more exact and experimentation is already achieving a place for itself, the idea of a primary spontaneous generation of living things still dominates completely the minds of the investigators and scholars. The famous Brussels physician Van Helmont (1577–1644), who had so mastered the technique of exact, critical experimentation that he could tackle the complex problem of the nutrition of plants, still considered the possibility of spontaneous generation of living creatures as beyond the peradventure of doubt. Furthermore, he actually supported this theory with many observations and experiments. It is to Van Helmont that we owe the well known recipe for obtaining mice from wheat kernels. Since he believed that human sweat can furnish the generating principle, it was enough to place a dirty shirt into a vessel containing wheat germ and after 21 days, when fermentation would cease, the vapors from the shirt together with the vapors of the seeds would generate live mice. Van Helmont was particularly surprised to find that these artificially produced mice were the exact replicas of natural mice originating from the semen of their parents.

Harvey (1578–1657), the discoverer of the circulation of the blood, did not reject spontaneous generation although he coined the famous phrase "Omne vivum ex ovo" (all living from the egg). But he interpreted the word "egg" very broadly and considered entirely possible the "generatio aequivoca" (spontaneous generation) of worms, insects, etc., through the action of special forces liberated in decay and analogous processes.

Thus the dogma enunciated by Saint Augustine of God's will, which arbitrarily interrupts the usual inherent order of things, continued to dominate over the minds of leading men even as late as the first half of the seventeenth century, when in all other branches of knowledge the exact and inflexible laws of nature had already been established. Even such luminaries of the human intellect as Descartes (1596–1650) and Newton (1643–1727) accepted unqualifiedly the theory of spontaneous generation of living organisms from lifeless matter. It is true that Descartes considered spontaneous generation as a natural process, occurring under still imperfectly understood circumstances, particularly when moist earth is exposed to sunlight or when there is decay. He believed that various plants and animals such as worms, flies and other insects can originate in this manner. Newton gave little attention to biological problems but he was firmly convinced in the possibility of spontaneous generation and even pointed out that plants were produced from the attenuated emanation from the tail of comets.

The experiments of the Tuscan physician Francesco Redi (1626–97), who had the honor of being the first to demolish by experimental proofs the faith in spontaneous generation which held uninterrupted sway for many centuries, constitute justly the turning point in the history of the spontaneous generation theory. . . .

At about the same time when Redi performed his famous experiments, the Dutch investigator Leeuwenhoek (1632–1723) discovered, with the aid of a microscope which he constructed, a new world of living things unperceived by the unaided eye. In his letters to the London Royal Society, Leeuwenhoek described, in great detail, these tiny "live beasts" (viva animalcula) which he found in rain water exposed for a long time to the air, in various infusions, excreta, etc. With his primitive microscope Leeuwenhoek examined representatives of practically every class of microorganism known at the present time, and furnished pictures and remarkably exact descriptions of infusoria, yeast, bacteria, etc.

The curious discoveries of this Dutch investigator attracted wide attention and inspired numerous followers. Wherever decay or fermentation of organic substance took place, observers found microorganisms present. They were found in all sorts of vegetable infusions and decoctions, in rotting meat, in spoiled bouillon, in sour milk, in fermenting wort, etc. It was only necessary to put easily decomposing substances for a short time into a warm place when almost immediately live microscopic creatures developed where they were absent before. With the belief in spontaneous generation still widely held, the idea that the origin of living microorganisms from lifeless matter was actually taking place before one's eyes in these infusions and decoctions, easily gained ground.

Selections from Letters
by Antony Van Leeuwenhoek

ON CERTAIN ANIMALCULES FOUND IN THE SEDIMENT IN GUTTERS ON THE ROOFS OF HOUSES.* (1675)

On the 25th of August, I saw in a leaden gutter at the fore part of my house, for the length of about five feet, and the breadth of seven inches, a settlement of rain water, which appeared of a red colour; and, upon considering that perhaps this colour might proceed from some red Animalcules, similar to those which I had seen in muddy ditches, I took a drop of this water, which I placed before the microscope, and in it I discovered a great number of Animalcules, some of them red, and others of them green. The largest of these, viewed through the microscope, did not appear bigger than a large grain of sand to the naked eye; the size of the others was gradually less and less: they were, for the most part, of a round shape; and in the green ones, the middle part of their bodies was of a yellowish colour. Their bodies seemed composed of particles of an oval shape; they were also provided with certain short and slender organs or limbs, which were protruded a little way out of their bodies, by means of which they caused a kind of circular motion and current in the water: when they were at rest and fixed themselves to the glass they had the shape of a pear with a short stalk. Upon more carefully examining this stalk, or rather this tail, I found that the extremity of it was divided into two parts, and by the help of these tails the Animalcules fixed themselves to the glass; the lesser of these appeared to me to be the offspring of the larger ones.

ON HUMAN TEETH †

It is my custom, every morning, to rub my teeth with salt, and afterwards to wash my mouth, and after eating I always clean my large teeth with a tooth-pick, and sometimes rub them very hard with a cloth. By these means, my teeth are so clean and white, that few persons of my age [over fifty] can shew so good a set, nor do my gums ever bleed, although I rub them hard with salt; and yet I cannot keep my teeth so clean, but that upon examining them with a magnifying glass, I have

* From the *Proceedings of The Royal Society of London,* 1675.
† From *The Select Works of Antony Van Leeuwenhoek,* translated by Samuel Hoole, 1800.

observed a sort of white substance collected between them, in consistence like a mixture of flour and water. In reflecting on this substance, I thought it probable, (though I could not observe any motion in it,) that it might contain some living creatures. Having therefore mixed it with rain water, which I knew was perfectly pure, I found, to my great surprise, that it contained many very small animalcules, the motions of which were very pleasing to behold. The largest sort of them . . . had the greatest, and the quickest motion, leaping about in the fluid, like the fish called a Jack; the number of these was very small. The second sort . . . often had a kind of whirling motion . . . these were more in number. Of the third sort, I could not well ascertain the figure, for sometimes they seemed roundish but oblong, and sometimes perfectly round. . . . The motion of these little creatures, one among another, may be imagined like that of a great number of gnats, or flies sporting in the air. From the appearance of these, to me, I judged that I saw some thousands of them in a portion of liquid, no larger than a grain of sand, and this liquid consisted of eight parts water, and one part only of the before-mentioned substance taken from the teeth. [Figure 6–1.]

With the point of a needle, I took some of the same kind of substance from the teeth of two ladies, who I knew were very punctual in cleaning them every day, and therein I observed as many of these animalcules as I have just mentioned. I also saw the same in the white substance taken from the teeth of a boy about eight years old; and upon examining in like manner, the same substance taken from the teeth of an old gentle-

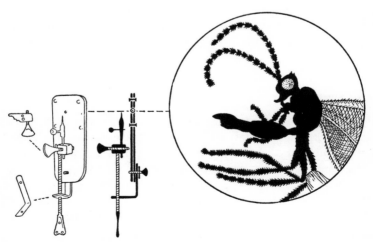

Figure 6–1. Leeuwenhoek's microscope and one of the "little animals" he saw on its pinpoint. (From Ruth Moore, The Coil of Life.*)*

man, who was very careless about keeping them clean, I found an incredible number of living animalcules, swimming about more rapidly than any I had before seen, and in such numbers, that the water which contained them, (though but a small portion of the matter taken from the teeth was mixed in it) seemed to be alive.

Francisco Redi's Experiments *

by James Conant (1951)

The relations between observation and experiment are very simply illustrated by Francisco Redi's study of the alleged spontaneous generation of worms in putrefying flesh. . . . this early investigator combined the habits of the naturalist and physician with the experimental methods of the Accademia del Cimento. In 1668 Redi published the results of his studies of the formation of worms in meat. He demonstrated quite convincingly that contrary to opinions previously held the worms which appeared in meat after several days were *not* formed spontaneously. On the contrary they originated from eggs deposited by flies. In his account Redi starts with a description of the careful observations of a natural phenomenon under usual conditions. He clearly indicates how he proceeded from observation to experiment.

Redi first recounts what he observed on the surface of the meat kept in an open box for many days in Florence in mid-July. Not only worms but also small objects he calls eggs (actually they were pupae) appeared on the surface of the meat. He also noted the hatching of many flies. Of these Redi said: "There were to be seen many broods of small black flies . . . and almost always I saw that the decaying flesh . . . was covered not alone with worms but with the eggs from which, as I have said, the worms were hatched. *These eggs made me think of those deposits dropped by flies on meats, that eventually became worms,* a fact noted by the compilers of the dictionary of our Academy, and also well known to hunters and to butchers who protect their meats in summer from the filth by covering them with white cloths."

Here is the record of the naturalist, the fieldworker, the careful observer of biological processes as they naturally occur. These observations as emphasized by the words I have italicized in the quotation seem to have led to the hypothesis that all the worms originated in the deposits of flies. For Redi in the next paragraph notes, "Having considered these

* From James B. Conant, *Science and Common Sense.*

things, I began to believe that all worms found in meat were derived from the droppings of flies and not from the putrefaction of the meat." Here is an example of the grand working hypothesis in a biological field. From it consequences follow which can be tested by specific experiment, that is, by observation of some artificial situation. Redi was clearly following the pattern of the members of the Accademia del Cimento who were at this time studying pneumatics and hydrostatics. The experiments which he performed were quite simple but he felt them to be essential, for he writes, "Belief would be in vain without the confirmation of experiment."

So Redi, to test his hypothesis that flies are essential for the production of worms in putrefying flesh, proceeds to eliminate the flies. To this end he seals up the meat in glass flasks and notes with satisfaction that even "though many days had passed" no worm was seen. But in the same paragraph he tells of another highly significant observation, namely that samples of the same meat placed in similar *open* flasks at the same time soon "became wormy and flies were seen." Here is a good example of a recurring phenomenon in experimental biology, the *control experiment*. I shall have more to say about it after we complete the summary of Redi's work.

In keeping out the flies Redi likewise had prevented the air from circulating. One might say it was this rather than the absence of the flies that was responsible for the absence of worms. To test this point Redi used a simple procedure; he closed the flasks with a "fine Naples veil that allowed the air to enter." Again he observed no worms. With this evidence before him he considered the problem solved, and as far as I am aware, this particular case of alleged spontaneous generation was never reopened. Yet it is worth taking a moment to see just how far a skeptic might push his doubts as to what conclusions can be drawn. In so doing some similarities and some differences between biological and physical experimentation may be brought to light.

THE CONTROL EXPERIMENT

The important principle [of] the *control of* variables appears in these experiments . . . One may analyze Redi's procedures and say that he in effect recognized three variables: (1) the flies, (2) the circulating air, (3) a sum total of effects such as time, place, warmth, kind of meat. The methods of testing the effect of the first two variables are as clear a case of common-sense experimentation as could possibly be found . . . The third variable is the peculiar one. Redi makes no specific mention of it but it is clearly implied by the circumstance of his "control experiment." By placing side by side open and closed flasks containing samples of the *same* meat, Redi in effect answered any critic who might say, "but perhaps the meat wouldn't have produced worms on that particular day even if it had not been sealed up."

The essence of the control experiment . . . is an attempt to insure that only the variable being tested is affecting the results. The method is not confined to the biological sciences. Perier was using a control experiment when he had an observer watch a second barometer at the foot of the Puy-de-Dôme.[1] But the method has special importance in biological experimentation because so often a host of variables of unknown nature may be involved. One endeavors to eliminate them by running in parallel two or more experiments identical in every respect except one, so that whatever differences are observed will be due only to the single, known variable.

There are other differences between the techniques of the biological and the physical sciences which are revealed by an examination of Redi's experiments and his conclusions. It is often hard to decide how wide a generalization may be made on the basis of the experimental facts. Indeed, what were the "facts" in the restricted sense in which we are using the word in Redi's case? The reproducible experimental situation would seem to be: "If flies have no access to the meat, there are no worms." But this has only been shown to be true in Florence in mid-July. Will it be true in all parts of the world and for all kinds of meat? What do you mean by the words "meat" and "flies"? Something no vaguer in 1668, to be sure, than what was implied by the words "fire," "oil," and "sulfur" as then used, but far vaguer than the words "red oxide of mercury" as used by Lavoisier and Priestley. In short, to assure reproducible material, to define conditions accurately, is a matter of great difficulty in the field of experimental biology. Although the same problem arises throughout all the sciences, the degree of difficulty is certainly greater here than in physics or chemistry. How Pasteur handled this problem and how even he stumbled we shall soon see.

It would clearly be unsafe to conclude that spontaneous generation never occurs, even if experiments with all kinds of meats in all manner of climates showed there were worms only when flies had access. Indeed, Redi himself believed that worms spontaneously appeared in plant galls.

Jumping to the mid-twentieth century, it seems quite clear that there is no way of testing and therefore no way of disproving some such state-

1. In 1648 Blaise Pascal asked his brother-in-law, Monsieur Perier, to perform an experiment which would test Pascal's theory concerning the change of atmospheric pressure with altitude. Perier made readings of atmospheric pressure at different altitudes on the mountain Puy-de-Dôme, leaving an observer at the foot of the mountain to watch a second barometer. For further information on this experiment see *Exploring the Universe*, Part 2, pp. 34–8. Ed.

ment as "Somewhere on the earth's surface living organisms are today being formed from nonliving matter" (though I doubt if anyone at all versed in biology believes such a statement). On the other hand, if someone were to come forward as people have from Redi's time almost to the present day and declare, "Under such-and-such conditions spontaneous generation occurs," then this becomes a testable proposition, although it is by no means a simple matter on which to obtain conclusive evidence, as the controversies of the later nineteenth century prove.

Organic and Inorganic Substances *

by Isaac Asimov (1960)

Toward the end of the 1700's, chemists were beginning to recognize two broad classes of substances. One class consisted of those minerals that were found in the soil and ocean, together with the simple gases of the atmosphere. These substances could withstand rough treatment, such as strong heat, without change in their essential nature. Moreover, the existence of these substances seemed to be independent of the existence of living organisms.

On the other hand, there was another class consisting of substances found only in living things or in the dead remains of once-living things. This second class consisted of relatively delicate substances. Under the influence of heat, these chemicals would smoke, char, burn, even explode.

Examples of the first class are salt, water, iron, air, rock; of the second, sugar, alcohol, gasoline, olive oil, rubber, hair.

In 1807, a Swedish chemist, Jöns Jakob Berzelius, suggested that the two classes be named *inorganic* and *organic,* the inorganic being those substances that occurred in nature independently of life, and the organic being those substances produced only by living things.

Berzelius then lent the great weight of his authority (for he was the most renowned chemist of his day) to the belief that the gulf between these two classes was deep and, in part, unbridgeable.

Chemists had learned how to convert one inorganic substance into another in many ways. For instance, they knew how to dissolve zinc in acid to form hydrogen gas. They had also learned to convert one organic substance into another as when sugar was so treated as to ferment and become alcohol. They could even convert an organic substance into an inorganic one, as when alcohol (organic) was burnt to carbon dioxide and water (both considered inorganic).

However, and this was the crucial point, no chemist had yet succeeded in crossing the gulf between the classes in the opposite direction. No one had, by purely chemical means and without the intervention of a living organism, converted an inorganic substance into an organic one. In the opinion of Berzelius, that had not been done because it could not be done.

To produce an organic substance from an inorganic one was, he thought, entirely the province of living organisms; it required the presence of a mysterious "vital force," which the chemist would forever be incapable of duplicating in his test tubes.

For a couple of decades, the theory of the "vital force" held sway. Berzelius' "vitalism" was destroyed by one of the chemist's own pupils and by accident.

That pupil was the German chemist Friedrich Wöhler. In 1827, while gently heating a compound called *ammonium cyanate*, which was considered an inorganic chemical, he found that it was converted into another chemical which Wöhler recognized as urea.

This dumfounded Wöhler, for urea was definitely an organic substance. It had been discovered a hundred years before in urine and, in fact, it was the chief solid substance left behind when urine was evaporated to dryness. It was a waste product formed by living organisms and, according to Berzelius' theory, could never be formed from inorganic substances by the ordinary methods of the chemical laboratory.

Yet Wöhler had done just that, and very simply and easily, too. He repeated the experiment a number of times, making certain nothing had gone wrong, that it was indeed ammonium cyanate he began with and urea he ended with. Finally, in 1828, he published his results and there was a sensation. As so often happens in science, it needed only one break in the dike to start a flood. At once, other chemists began to synthesize other organic substances out of inorganic ones.

Berzelius himself was forced to change his mind, and soon chemists were quite satisfied that organic chemicals, although more complex, on the whole, than inorganic chemicals and far more difficult to handle and understand, nevertheless followed the same rules as inorganic chemicals. No one has doubted it since.

The death of "vitalism" implied that the chemistry of organic compounds and, eventually, of living tissue itself was found to follow the fundamental laws that governed "ordinary" chemicals.

To be sure, we still divide chemistry into inorganic and organic, but as a matter of convenience only. Organic chemistry is now defined as the chemistry of those compounds containing carbon atoms in their molecules, whether those molecules had ever been formed by any living thing or not.

The narrower concept of organic chemistry—the study of those substances found primarily in living tissue, together with the changes they undergo there—is what is now known as *biochemistry*, the prefix "bio-" coming from the Greek word for "life."

The Controversy Concerning Spontaneous Generation *

by James Conant (1951)

To return to the discussion of the doctrine of spontaneous generation we may note that as a consequence of Redi's experiments and similar observations, the idea of the spontaneous generation of common plants and animals seems to have been given up. But the discovery of the world of microscopic organisms by the microscopists of the late seventeenth century opened up a new area in which the controversy could flourish. The origin of the mass of minute organisms revealed by the microscope in all manner of animal and plant extracts and scrapings was a subject of debate among the biologists of the eighteenth century. One highly placed French naturalist, the Comte de Buffon, became a powerful protagonist of the doctrine of heterogenesis, as the notion of spontaneous generation was later designated. Buffon considered all living matter to consist of organized particles essentially indestructible but capable of entering into different combinations. These "organic molecules" constituted the essence of life. These ideas were put forward, it must be noted, before the chemical revolution and a half-century before Dalton's atomic theory. Buffon strongly opposed those who maintained that microscopic organisms, like larger plants and animals, had specific living precursors. Microscopic germs—the equivalent of eggs or seeds—he thought to be nonexistent.

An English amateur biologist, John T. Needham, collaborated with Buffon in some of the latter's writings and supplied what he regarded as convincing experimental evidence as to the ability of dead material to *regenerate* living matter. He seems to have been the first to use elevated temperatures in an effort to kill or destroy all living organisms in a liquid or solid material. Thus he corked up "mutton gravy" in a glass phial and heated the phial in hot ashes. This procedure he claimed would kill all pre-existing germs. Yet in a few days the phial after cooling off swarmed with microscopic organisms. We would say today Needham's experimen-

* From James B. Conant, *Science and Common Sense.*

tal ideas were good but his interpretation of the results was erroneous. Indeed, this was the opinion of a contemporary, the Italian naturalist Spallanzani. Like Needham he used elevated temperatures to destroy any "germs" present in the various mixtures of plant and animal tissues whose putrefaction and decay he wished to study. Infusions made by soaking a variety of seeds in warm water were his favorite objects of investigation. He concluded from his experiments that if one took adequate precautions and heated the infusions *long enough,* no living organisms would subsequently appear.

Some who have studied Spallanzani's papers feel that his experiments should have settled the matter. That he was ahead of his time is clear; for the upshot of the Needham-Spallanzani controversy was that both remained unconvinced and the scientific world continued to be divided. Pasteur, reviewing the work of these two opponents from the vantage point of nearly a hundred years later, points out clearly why the issue was not settled by Spallanzani's work. The point is of more than passing interest for it is another illustration of the difficulty of defining biological concepts in experimental terms. Needham's defense against Spallanzani boiled down to this: in order to prevent the subsequent growth of microorganisms in infusions of plant and animal material the Italian had subjected the materials to the temperature of boiling water for periods of time far longer than Needham believed were necessary in order to destroy living organisms; Spallanzani had "weakened or perhaps totally destroyed the vegetative force of the infusions"; he had tortured the material, the Englishman maintained. Needham and Buffon, we must remember, postulated the presence in dead animal and plant material of a "vital force" which was different from specific living "germs." The germs should be killed by short exposure to boiling water, for this exposure would cook an egg and "kill" small plants and animals, but the vital force could stand only short periods of "cooking"; it was far too sensitive to stand such prolonged boiling as Spallanzani used. Such was Needham's position.

If you define a vital force or even "organized molecules" in terms of resistance to elevated temperatures you end with a doctrine of heterogenesis that Spallanzani's experiments do not invalidate. While we may feel that the notion of a vital force represents prescientific thinking, the idea of sensitive organized molecules which are altered by exposure to boiling water is by no means foreign to the twentieth-century chemistry of proteins.

Not only was the controversy between Needham and Spallanzani a draw as far as scientific opinion was concerned, but a remarkable experimental discovery in the early nineteenth century still further complicated the issue. Shortly after 1800 an enterprising French confectioner by the name of Appert had applied the methods of Needham and Spallanzani to the preservation of food. He was the inventor of the process we now call "canning," for he showed that if you fill a bottle practically full of food material, heat it in boiling water for some time, and stopper it well while still hot, the material will keep for long periods of time. Here, by the way, is another example of the success of a highly empirical procedure, for when this scientific discovery was taken over by the practical arts it was still an open question what were in fact the variables which were altered by the process we call "sterilization by heat."

Not only was what occurred in this sterilization by heat an open question, but the rapidly developing new science of chemistry yielded a false clue. A distinguished French chemist soon submitted Appert's procedure to chemical test and found that the air which remained above the "canned" foodstuff *contained no oxygen.* He therefore concluded that the significant variable in the preservation or putrefaction of animal or plant material was the presence of oxygen. Oxygen, in other words, might be the vital principle which Needham complained Spallanzani had destroyed.

One more bit of history before we come to the detailed examination of Pasteur's classic work on spontaneous generation. In 1837 a German investigator introduced a new experimental technique which was to play an important role in later work on heterogenesis. He showed that air which had been *heated* could be introduced into a flask containing meat juice without causing the latter to putrefy. These findings showed that the presence or absence of oxygen was not the significant variable. They indicated that it was the dust in the air which mattered, dust presumably carrying germs. This was rendered still more probable by the work of two other Germans twenty years later in which air filtered through cotton proved to be in general the equivalent of heated air in experiments with material capable of putrefaction. In retrospect the evidence seems convincing, for we have become accustomed to the view that "germs" must be present as a necessary condition for the appearance of microorganisms in foodstuffs or other plant and animal mixtures. . . .

Pasteur's interest in spontaneous generation was a natural outcome of his study on fermentation. Indeed, in his first important paper on spontaneous generation he also discusses his views on fermentation. But as his biographers have made clear, Pasteur felt impelled to study the question because of a paper by Pouchet. This naturalist, the director of the Museum of Natural History in Rouen, had become convinced of the possibility of spontaneous generation. Pouchet's experiments in support of his views were published in 1858 and an elaborate reply by Pasteur in

1862. The controversy continued vigorously for the next few years, and then, Pasteur appearing to have won a complete victory, interest subsided. But in the seventies an English doctor, Henry C. Bastian, took up the cudgels for the doctrine of spontaneous generation and the subject was reopened with highly beneficial results for the progress of science. By the end of the eighties, however, the evidence against heterogenesis seemed overwhelming, and though Bastian gave his views in a book published as late as 1910, few proponents of heterogenesis survived into the twentieth century.

Pasteur's paper of 1862 on "The Organized Corpuscles Which Exist in the Atmosphere" is one of the great documents of experimental science. In the historical introduction the author, after reviewing the work of Redi, Needham, Spallanzani, and the more recent experiments in Germany, writes as follows (the remarks in brackets are mine):

When after the researches of which I have just spoken, a skillful naturalist of Rouen, Pouchet (corresponding member of the Academy of Sciences) announced to the academy the results on which he thought he could base in a definitive manner the principles of heterogeneity [spontaneous generation] no one could point out the true cause of error in his experiments. Soon the French academy, realizing how much remained to be done, offered a prize for a dissertation on the following subject: Attempts by well-conceived experiments to throw new light on the question of spontaneous generations.

The problem then appeared so obscure that Biot [a distinguished French physicist], whose kindness with regard to my work has always been unfailing, expressed his regret at seeing me engaged on these researches. He exacted a promise from me to abandon the subject after a limited time if I had not overcome the difficulties which were then perplexing me. Dumas [the dean of French chemists], who has often joined with Biot in showing kindness to me, said about the same time, "I should not advise anyone to spend too long on this subject."

What need had I to concern myself with it? Chemists ran into a collection of extraordinary phenomena twenty years before which are designated by the generic name *fermentations*. All require the concurrence of two substances: one known as *fermentable* material, such as sugar; the other nitrogenous material, always in the form of an albumin-like substance. The theory which was universally then accepted was as follows: the albuminous substances undergo a change on exposure to air (a special oxidation of unknown nature); this gives them the character of a *ferment*, that is to say, the property of subsequently acting, through contact, on fermentable substances.

Pasteur then discusses his work on the lactic acid fermentation . . . and contrasts his conclusion with Liebig's ideas. He then continues:

One knew that ferments originated from the contact of albuminous substances with oxygen gas. One of two things must be true, I said to myself: either ferments are organized entities and they are produced by oxygen alone, considered merely as oxygen, in contact with albuminous materials, in which case they are spontaneously generated; or if they are not of spontaneous origin, it is not oxygen alone as such that intervenes in their production, but the gas acts as a stimulant to a germ carried with it or existing in the nitrogenous or fermentable materials. At this point, to which my study of fermentation had brought me, I had to form an opinion on the question of spontaneous generation. I might perhaps find here a powerful weapon to support my ideas on those fermentations which are properly called fermentations.

The researches which I am about to describe were consequently only a digression I was forced to make from my work on fermentations. It was thus that I was led to occupy myself with a subject which up till then had taxed only the skill and wisdom of naturalists.

. . . Pasteur clearly states the problem of the relation between putrefaction and fermentation and the question of spontaneous generation. He had to determine for himself whether procedures like Appert's worked because the oxygen was used up or because the germs were destroyed by the boiling process. He proceeds to amass an amount of experimental evidence which, as compared to the work of his predecessors, was overwhelming.

I shall make no attempt to summarize even this one paper by Pasteur. However, I shall discuss the type of experiment he used and some of the difficulties of interpretation. We are here dealing with *converging evidence,* it will be noted, for no single set of experiments by themselves would appear sufficient to answer the objection of his opponents, the believers in spontaneous generation. Pasteur repeated and confirmed the work of his immediate predecessors in this field. He showed that air which had been passed through a red-hot tube (calcined air) could be introduced into a vessel (suitably sterilized by boiling) containing fermentable material without starting fermentation. On the other hand, when ordinary air was passed into a similar vessel containing the same material, fermentation soon started (note the control experiment). The vessels were placed in a warm closet in every case to hasten the fermentation. The fermentable material Pasteur employed was what he called "sugared yeast water." It was an extract of yeast, to which sugar was added; it contained no living yeast, but in addition to the added sugar, nitrogenous substances and mineral salts from the yeast were present. In other words, by purely empirical procedures Pasteur had prepared a good "nutrient" medium from yeast. This choice of one particular experimental material had important consequences, as will be noted shortly. Pure empiricism is an important part of almost every experimental procedure.

Pasteur convinced himself that he could repeatedly prepare "sugared yeast water" under conditions which would prevent its subsequent fermentation in a warm closet. He then proceeded to use this knowledge as a basis for experiment. He collected the dust from ordinary air on a bit of cotton wool by sucking a considerable amount of air through a cotton wool filter. He then ingeniously contrived to introduce this bit of cotton into a sterile flask containing the sugared yeast water, under conditions where only *heated* air was likewise introduced (the experimental technique is illustrated by the simplified diagram shown in Figures 6–2 and 6–3). In due course the flasks which contained the cotton showed signs of vigorous fermentation, while others into which cotton was not introduced did not.

The use of the "control experiment" is evident in this example of Pasteur's work. No one maintaining the negative position in this debate on spontaneous generation could do otherwise than declare that the failure of precautions to destroy germs or keep them out would result in fermentation. Therefore, it was essential to show that if everything else was the same *except* for the cotton, there would be no fermentation. Pasteur went further and performed a special experiment which was in the nature of a "control" on the others. He substituted asbestos for the cotton; the results were the same. Therefore, since two quite different filters behaved in the same manner, he argued that it could not be the introduction of the filter which started the fermentation. With the

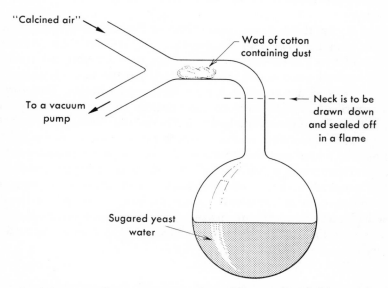

Figure 6–2. Diagram illustrating Pasteur's technique. The sugared yeast water is boiled and the wad of cotton introduced into the tube. By repeated evacuation and filling with "calcined air," the ordinary air is replaced by calcined air. The flask is then tilted so that the cotton falls into the liquid and the flask is sealed off (Figure 6–3).

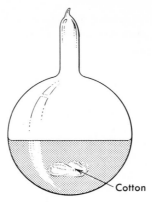

Figure 6–3. The flask of Figure 6–2 after being sealed off.

asbestos, however, he performed what seems to me his most striking experiment. He showed that an asbestos filter, filled with dust in the usual manner *but then heated,* when introduced into the flasks produced no fermentation; the same filter filled with dust but not heated caused fermentation to start when the experiment was performed in the usual manner.

Let us review these classic experiments of Pasteur for a moment in the light of what he wished to demonstrate. He believed that very small particles of living matter (germs) must be present before the fermentation of sugared yeast water could begin. These particles were too few and too small to detect *as such* even with a microscope. Therefore his demonstration had to be indirect. Nevertheless, he was able to show that a "something" in ordinary air had to be introduced into the flasks before fermentation commenced. Furthermore, this something could be collected with dust on a filter and was destroyed (or its effectiveness destroyed) by heating. What could a "something" thus defined in experimental terms be but a precursor of the microorganisms which grow in sugared yeast water under ordinary conditions? So far Pasteur was on safe ground; he never had cause to retreat an inch from the position taken as the result of these experiments. But his attempt to marshal still more evidence led him onto treacherous ground.

PASTEUR'S CONTROVERSY WITH POUCHET

To follow this part of the story, one must remember the view that had prevailed a few years earlier, namely that oxygen was the essential variable in putrefaction or fermentation. This was Pouchet's contention.

Many experiments in which putrefaction or fermentation could be induced by the introduction of a small quantity of air could be accounted for on *either* the germ theory or the oxygen theory. The "calcined air" experiments of Pasteur were convincing, but he devised some additional and very simple experiments. He placed his sugared yeast water in a flask, boiled the solution, and then sealed off the neck of the flask in a flame. After cooling, the tip of the neck could be broken and a small amount of air then rushed in, as a partial vacuum had been formed in the flask when it was sealed at a higher temperature. Pasteur then sealed the tip again and placed the flask in a warm room. Now, he argued, if oxygen is the significant factor, *all* the flasks thus treated should behave in the same way, for they all had received a small inrush of oxygen when opened and sealed again. But many experiments showed that whether the material in the flasks fermented or not depended on *where* they had been opened and closed. Only rarely did *all* the flasks in a dozen or so treated in the same way show the growth of microorganisms. Indeed, when opened in the country, only 8 out of 73 flasks showed signs of fermentation in experiments performed as just described. And in a spectacular demonstration Pasteur showed that of 20 flasks opened and closed on a glacier, the Mer de Glace, only one subsequently showed the presence of microorganisms; while 10 out of 13 opened in a room in the inn at Chamonix showed signs of growth.

Dust was certainly less widely distributed in the air on a mountain than in a village inn; therefore it was reasonable to conclude that the striking difference reflected a difference in the distribution of the germs in the air. But the vital point was that air could enter many, many flasks and *not* cause fermentation. The analysis of the air in Appert's preserves had yielded a false scent. There is no oxygen in the air above canned foods. This is due to a slow secondary effect—the absorption of the oxygen by some material in the food. Such was Pasteur's explanation and it is the one we accept today. Pasteur summarizes his findings in his paper of 1862 by the statement: "It is not true that the smallest quantity of ordinary air is sufficient to produce in an infusion the organized life characteristic of that infusion."

Pouchet and his supporters were by no means convinced by Pasteur's paper. They proceeded to experiment on mountain tops themselves and obtained results in complete contradiction to those Pasteur reported. Bottles containing fermentable material were opened and closed on the summits of Mont Blanc and Monte Rosa and on a glacier in the Pyrenees. All Pasteur's precautions were taken, it was said, yet *in every case* growths appeared when the vessels were kept in a warm place. Pasteur naturally attributed these results to poor experimentation, for it must be emphasized again that every experimental error would seem to favor the heterogenists; every failure to destroy or exclude germs would, on Pasteur's hypothesis, yield results that *appeared* to indicate spontaneous generation.

A committee of the French academy was formed to settle the controversy between Pasteur and Pouchet. Pasteur produced his flasks which showed no signs of fermentation although they had been opened and closed. His evidence was most convincing. For reasons that are not clear Pouchet and his collaborators raised trivial objections about the conditions set down by the committee for the test, refused to carry out their experiments, and finally withdrew. The committee decided in favor of Pasteur. The victory seemed complete in 1865. But ten years later it became apparent even to Pasteur that Pouchet had withdrawn from the field of battle far too soon.

Not that any evidence for heterogenesis was found that could stand the test of rigorous experimentation. But what was discovered indicated that Pouchet's experimental results were by no means the consequences of faulty manipulation. The trouble lay elsewhere. Pouchet had used infusions of hay, Pasteur sugared yeast water. Both investigators and the scientific onlookers had *assumed* that the nature of the fermentable material was of no consequence. Actually, it was a variable of the first order of importance. Why? Because the microorganisms naturally present in hay form spores, a sort of resting stage in the life history of these bacteria. These spores are highly resistant to heat but do not give rise to a vigorous growth of microorganisms *except in the presence of oxygen*. Therefore, the boiling sufficient to sterilize sugared yeast water is quite inadequate for hay infusions. The introduction of oxygen does start up growth *in every case* in hay infusions which have been inadequately sterilized (as were Pouchet's). In short, with Pouchet's flasks, the presence or absence of oxygen was the important thing, not the presence or absence of germs in the air.

All these difficulties with sterilizing certain types of infusions came to light in the 1870's as a consequence of still further controversy. The protagonist for heterogenesis was the English physician Bastian, already mentioned. On the other side Pasteur had a firm and expert ally in the physicist John Tyndall. To go into the details would require another chapter, but, in a word, Bastian forced Pasteur and Tyndall to revise their ideas on what procedures were required to destroy all precursors of living organisms. Temperatures above the boiling point of water were sometimes necessary; from this time on, Papin's digestor, now called an autoclave, became a feature of biological laboratories and, soon after, of hospitals as well.

One can almost hear the ghost of Needham raising an objection to the techniques of the bacteriologists as they were finally developed in the 1880's. If there were a sensitive vital principle in vegetable or animal matter, it was indeed tortured by heating to temperatures well above the boiling point of water and in some instances for long periods of time. But the day of such vague ideas as that of a vital principle was rapidly passing. Biochemistry and bacteriology were narrowing the definitions of their concepts. By the end of the nineteenth century the experiments of Pasteur and Tyndall had only historic interest insofar as the controversy about spontaneous generation was concerned. But their importance was recognized for other reasons; their significance lay in the fact that these experiments were the firm foundation for the techniques of the bacteriologist and microbiologist. Following the lead given by Pasteur in his first paper on lactic acid fermentation, scientists had learned how to isolate and grow pure strains of microorganisms. Therefore, instead of a miscellaneous collection of microorganisms forming when dust was introduced into a nutrient material such as sugared yeast water, one could at will grow one organism or another by suitable inoculation. One could come very close to realizing the condition of seeing (with a microscope) the single germs which when introduced into a sterile medium were the starting point of the subsequent growth. In other words, the advancing techniques and concepts of bacteriology placed any proponent of spontaneous generation in the position of having to specify what organism he claimed could spontaneously arise. And it would be difficult for even Needham's ghost to claim that a sensitive vital principle could yield one kind of organism when sugared yeast water was inoculated with a drop of one fluid and another when the same medium was inoculated with a different fluid. The nitrogenous materials from the yeast, the meat, the hay, whatever is fermenting or putrefying can hardly be imagined to be other than "the food of ferments" and not the "ferment," to use Pasteur's own words.

The outcome of the work we have just reviewed seems so obvious that we accept the results today as part of common sense. By so doing we fail to realize the difficulties of relating concepts to experiment in experimental biology, and the significance of the story is thus often lost. It is well worth restudying the whole history of spontaneous generation in order to appreciate that . . . one is here viewing the transformation of vague common-sense notions into scientific concepts. And how tortuous may be the process of transformation! How difficult it is to reformulate common-sense notions carrying with them so much of a nonlogical background into ideas and terms related to experiment. The common-sense ideas we express by such words as "living organisms," "living precursors of microorganisms," or as "germs" have a psychological and sociological basis. They became concepts of science only slowly and as the result of a vast amount of work. . . .

We . . . see some of these same troubles plaguing (but not blocking) the worker in pure and applied biology today. Is a "virus" alive or not? Is a disease agent not only a necessary but a sufficient "cause" of a disease? If not sufficient, what are the other variables? How do you define a disease? How specify a species of microorganism? How define a particular virus? To follow these and countless other questions would take us into the modern laboratories of departments of biology, agricultural stations, medical schools, hospitals, and special institutions. There we should see in progress investigations of problems Pasteur never even dreamed of, but we should certainly find methods and modes of thought essentially the same as those he employed. And if we were lucky enough to meet with a pioneer, a driving genius, we would probably find him as bold with his hypotheses on a grand scale and as certain of his preconceived ideas (one may even say his scientific prejudices) as was Pasteur himself.

But how about the origin of living organisms, some reader may inquire? If they don't originate spontaneously, how did all the vast number of plants and animals large and small ever get started? . . . while no one can categorically deny that spontaneous generation is occurring on the earth today, one can say that no phenomena have been studied which cannot be accommodated far better by the concept that for every living organism there is a living precursor.

And, therefore, gentlemen, I could point to that liquid and say to you, I have taken my drop of water from the immensity of creation, and I have taken it full of the elements appropriated to the development of microscopic organisms. And I wait, I watch, I question it!—begging it to recommence for me the beautiful spectacle of the first creation. But it is dumb, dumb since these experiments were begun several years ago; it is dumb because I have kept it from the only thing man does not know how to produce: from the germs which float in the air, from Life, for Life is a germ and a germ is Life. Never will the doctrine of spontaneous generation recover from the mortal blow of this simple experiment.

Louis Pasteur
Lecture at the Sorbonne, 1864.

The Origin of Life [*]
by A. I. Oparin (1938)

THEORIES OF THE CONTINUITY OF LIFE

By his experiments Pasteur demonstrated beyond peradventure of doubt the impossibility of autogeneration of life in the sense as it was imagined by his predecessors. He showed that living organisms cannot be formed suddenly before our eyes from formless solutions and infusions. A careful survey of the experimental evidence reveals, however, that it tells nothing about the impossibility of generation of life at some other epoch or under some other conditions. Incidentally, Pasteur himself, with his usual reserve, placed such an interpretation on his own experiments. His contemporaries, however, put a broader interpretation on his data, considering them as absolute proof of the impossibility of a transition from dead matter to living organisms. For instance, the famous English physicist Lord Kelvin (1871) expressed himself very clearly that, on the basis of Pasteur's experiments, the impossibility of autogeneration of life at any time or anywhere must be regarded established as firmly as the law of universal gravitation. The same viewpoint has been shared by a number of investigators, for whom life is radically different from the rest of inanimate nature. Therefore, in their opinion, it is wrong even to pose the question of the origin of life, since life is as much an eternal category as matter itself. Life is eternal, it only changes its form but is never created from dead substance.

At first sight the impression is gained that Pasteur's experiments caused a complete reversal in the conceptions of naturalists with regard to the origin of life. Previously it was believed that living organisms were easily generated from dead matter, before our very eyes, so to speak; then the attitude was taken that life can never originate but must exist eternally. This contradiction in viewpoints is only apparent and a careful examination of the question shows that both the theory of spontaneous generation and the theory of the continuity of life are based on the same dualistic outlook on nature. Both theories start essentially with the same assumption that life is endowed with absolute autonomy determined by special principles and forces, applicable only to organisms, the nature of which is radically different from the principles and forces operative in the inanimate kingdom.

[*] From A. I. Oparin, *The Origin of Life*.

But from the opposite point of view, from the point of view of the unity of forces operative in living and non-living nature, the spontaneous generation of organisms . . . is altogether impossible and unthinkable. . . . even the simplest of living organisms possesses a very complex structure or organization. We are not familiar with physical or chemical forces which could cause under the described experimental conditions the appearance of organisms from structureless solutions of organic substances. Therefore, the sudden generation of organisms can be explained either with St. Augustine as an act of divine will (miracle) or as the result of some special vital force. Actually, throughout the history of this problem, the conception of a spontaneous generation is intimately associated with the idea of a "vital force." It is the Aristotelian "entelechy" embracing all matter and forming it purposefully into living organisms. It is the spirit of life, "spiritus vitae" of Paracelsus, the "archai" of Van Helmont which, according to his views, reside in seeds and direct the processes of creation and of autogeneration. Finally, it is Leibniz' "monads" which represent the immutable centers of force of a spiritual character. Similarly, the later adherents of the spontaneous generation of life, Buffon, Needham, Pouchet, are all among the most convinced vitalists who believe that a vital force, capable of vivifying the organic substance of solutions and infusions, is dormant in every microscopic particle of organic matter. The action of this force is not bound by any general physical laws, it is entirely "sui generis" and, therefore, can transform non-living into living matter in the wink of an eye.

It is hardly necessary to prove that the same vitalistic conception, the same dualism is at the bottom of the theory of the continuity or eternity of life. No matter what form the theories of continuity of life may assume, they always leave an unbridgeable gap between the kingdom of organisms and of inorganic nature. But to say that life never had an origin and existed eternally, is to imply that there is an absolute autonomy of living organisms.

F. Engels in his "Dialectics of Nature" subjected both the theory of spontaneous generation and the theory of eternity of life to a withering criticism. . . . with regard to experiments attempting to prove the primary generation, he remarks ironically: "It would be foolish to try and force nature to accomplish in twenty four hours, with the aid of a bit of stinky water, that which it took her many thousands of years to do."

But Engels likewise rejects the conception of the eternity of life. He quotes a very characteristic statement by Liebig: "It is sufficient to admit that life is as old and as eternal as matter itself, and the entire argument about the origin of life loses apparently all sense by this simple admission. And, really, why can we not imagine that organic life is just as much without beginning as is carbon and its combinations, or as is all uncreated and indestructible matter and the forces which are eternally bound up with the movement of matter in universal space." Engels shows that such a view can only be based upon the recognition of some special life force as the form-giving principle, which is entirely incompatible with the materialistic world conception. Engels notes further that Liebig's assertion about carbon compounds being as eternal as carbon itself, is inexact if not actually erroneous. Engels points out that carbon compounds are eternal in the sense that under constant conditions of mixing, temperature, pressure, electrical potential, etc., they repeat themselves always. But to this day no one has ever asserted that, for instance, even such simple carbon compounds as CO_2 or CH_4 are eternal in the sense of having existed at all times, instead of being constantly formed from certain elements and decomposed again into the same elements. If living protein is eternal in the same sense as other carbon compounds, it must not only break up constantly into its elements, as actually happens, but it must also be constantly formed anew from these elements without the cooperation of preexisting protein. This is diametrically opposed to Liebig's results.

The same holds true, even in a larger measure, with regard to living organisms. The idea that living things always arise under definite conditions has nothing to do with the conception of the eternity of life. On the contrary, it emphasizes the necessity of generation of organisms from non-living matter. But the adherents of the theory of the eternity of life assume that at all times some principle existed eternally, which passed on from organism to organism, and without which the origin of living things would be impossible. Following this path of reasoning we invariably fall into the pit of vitalistic conceptions.

Engels shows that a consistent materialistic philosophy can follow only a single path in the attempt to solve the problem of the origin of life. Life has neither arisen spontaneously nor has it existed eternally. It must have, therefore, resulted from a long evolution of matter, its origin being merely one step in the course of its historical development. . . .

The *cosmozoa* theory attempted to reconcile the principle of eternity of life with the conception of the origin of our planet. All adherents of this theory assumed that life existed eternally, that it was never created, never separated from dead material. But how then did life originate on the Earth? The Earth itself is not eternal, since it must have had a beginning sometime, having separated from the Sun, and certainly during the early period of its existence could not have been populated with organisms, simply because of unfavorable temperature conditions. To overcome this difficulty, the idea was promoted that germs of life dropped to the

Earth from the interstellar and interplanetary spaces just as they get into Pasteur's flasks from the outside air. This conception was first elaborated in 1865 by Richter, who proceeded from the assumption that, owing to the very fast movement of cosmic bodies, small fragments or hard particles could have become detached, and that viable spores of microorganisms could also have been carried away from the cosmic bodies together with these detached particles. The particles, floating in the interstellar space, could be carried accidentally to other cosmic bodies and, landing on a planet where conditions for life were already favorable (moderate humidity and temperature), commence to develop and later become the ancestors of the entire organic kingdom of that planetary body. Richter assumed that somewhere in the universe there were always cosmic bodies present on which life exists in cellular form. Later this idea was also developed by Liebig who believed that "the atmosphere of celestial bodies as well as of whirling cosmic nebulae can be regarded as the timeless sanctuary of animate forms, the eternal plantations of organic germs." Therefore, the existence of living organisms in the universe is eternal, organic life is never really created but only transmitted from one planet to the next. The problem, according to Richter, is not how life originates but how the germs of life can be carried from one celestial body to the other.

Richter paid special attention to the possibility of transfer of viable germs through the universal spaces separating celestial bodies. He pointed out that organic germs in a dormant state can exist a long time without water or nourishment but become revivified as soon as the conditions favor this, and therefore germs can endure very long journeys. The only danger to the existence of these germs comes from the rise in temperature resulting from the tremendous friction as the body falls through the Earth's atmosphere. However, some meteorites contain traces of carbon and other easily inflammable substances. If those substances could reach the Earth without burning up, it is quite possible for germs also to traverse the atmosphere without losing their viability.

H. von Helmholtz developed a similar idea a number of years after Richter. This well known German physiologist . . . thought that live germs were brought to the Earth by meteorites. He based this possibility upon the fact that meteorites, on passing through the Earth's atmosphere, are heated only on the surface while the interior remains cool. He comments as follows: "Who would deny that such bodies floating everywhere in the universal space do not leave behind them the germs of life, wherever the planetary conditions are already suitable to promote organic creation!"

However, in his introduction to Thomson's "Treatise on Theoretical

Physics" Helmholtz had this to say about the theory of cosmozoa: "If anyone is inclined to regard this hypothesis as not very probable or indeed highly questionable, I have nothing to say against this. But it seems to me that if every attempt to create organisms from inanimate matter has failed us, it is entirely within the domain of scientific discussion to inquire whether life had ever been created, whether it is not just as old as matter itself and, finally, whether germs are not carried from one celestial body to another, taking root and developing wherever they find favorable soil."

Thus, even Helmholtz did not feel entirely convinced in the correctness of his reasoning. The theory itself, too, soon disappeared from the scientific horizon, since the most painstaking search of meteorites failed to reveal in them not only organisms or their remnants, but even traces of sedimentary or biochemical formations. Only in the very last few years Ch. Lipman attempted once more to resuscitate these ideas. He examined a number of rocky meteorites for possible traces of living organisms. Using a very intricate technique to preclude the possibility of contaminating the meteorites with earth bacteria, he came to the conclusion that live bacteria and their spores are found in the interior of the meteorites. The organisms which he succeeded in isolating were identical with the bacterial forms existing on the Earth. This makes it very probable that, in spite of all his precautions, Lipman did not succeed in preventing earth bacteria from contaminating the meteorites while they were ground to a powder. Even in different regions of our planet there are different forms of microorganisms, and it would be extremely strange if exactly the same bacterial forms found on the Earth were present also on some remote planets.[1]

At the beginning of the twentieth century the idea of the transfer of germs from one celestial body to another was again revived in the form of the so-called theory of panspermia, originated by the great Swedish physical chemist S. Arrhenius. Being a strong adherent of the conception that life is scattered throughout universal space, he showed very convincingly, by means of direct calculations, the possibility of transfer of particles from one celestial body to another. The principal activating force is the pressure exerted by light rays, discovered by Clerk Maxwell and brilliantly verified experimentally by P. Lebedev.

Arrhenius draws the following picture of the transfer of small particles, including microorganismal spores, through the interstellar and interplanetary space. The upward air currents, which are especially powerful during large volcanic eruptions, may carry the tiniest particles of matter to a tremendous height of sixty miles or more above the Earth's surface. In the upper layers of the atmosphere, due to a number of causes, there are

1. See page 320 for more recent evidence on this subject. Ed.

always electrical discharges which are strong enough to shoot these material particles from the Earth's atmosphere into the interplanetary space, where they are driven farther and farther by the one-sided pressure of the Sun's light rays. Under certain conditions, this results in the formation by our planet of something like a comet's tail but, of course, of incomparably smaller dimensions. This tail is formed by the finest particles of matter always leaving the Earth and repelled by the action of the Sun's rays. According to Arrhenius, similar phenomena occur on the other planets also.

In this way tiny particles of substance must be cast off all the time from the Earth's surface as well as from the surface of other celestial bodies. If a planet is inhabited by live organisms, particularly microorganisms, their spores would be thus carried off into the interstellar space. Arrhenius calculated that bacterial spores with a diameter of 0.0002–0.00015 mm. move with very great speed in the empty space under the influence of pressure of the Sun's rays. Separated from the Earth, such spores will pass beyond the limits of our planetary system in 14 months, and in 9000 years will reach the nearest star, a-Centauri.

The movement of spores of microorganisms may be not only away from but also back towards the Sun. Living germs carried off into the interstellar space may meet with particles of cosmic dust of relatively large size. If a spore attaches itself to a particle with a diameter of over 0.0015 mm. its movement is reversed and it then moves towards the Sun, because the light pressure will no longer be able to overcome the gravitation of the heavy particles to the Sun. Arrhenius thinks that in this way the Earth could be covered with microorganismal spores arriving into our solar system from other stellar worlds. Of course, this could only happen if the spores were still in a viable condition after completing this very long journey through space.

This aspect of the problem naturally received special attention from Arrhenius and other adherents of this theory. Arrhenius discusses in detail all the dangers to living germs lurking along their path from planet to planet. According to Arrhenius the absence of moisture or oxygen and the extreme cold of the interplanetary space present no terrors for the microorganismal spores, nor does the heating of the particles, as they fall rapidly through the Earth's atmosphere, endanger their existence. From his calculations Arrhenius concludes that the heat does not exceed 100° and lasts only a short time. Since bacterial spores are known to remain viable after such treatment, he thinks it is reasonable to regard the transport of viable germs from one planetary system to another as the cause of the origin of life on Earth. This theory has many supporters, being especially energetically upheld by Kostychev.

However, . . . [recent discoveries and] new facts . . . make it seem less and less probable that such a transfer of viable germs from one celestial body to another really occurs. . . .

Life germs wayfaring in the interstellar space unprotected against cosmic radiation would not only be absolutely doomed to perish, but even their inner chemical structure would in a comparatively brief time suffer radical changes under the influence of radiant energy. We must, therefore, once and for all give up the idea that life germs floated towards our Earth from the outside cosmic spaces. We must, instead, search for the sources of life within the boundaries of our own planet.

THEORIES OF THE ORIGIN OF LIFE AT SOME DISTANT PERIOD OF THE EARTH'S EXISTENCE

From the preceding [remarks] we learned that neither the theory of the spontaneous generation nor the theory of the continuity of life solves rationally the problem of the origin of life on Earth. These theories invariably come in conflict with the objectively established facts derived from a careful and detailed study of the world around us. This is not hard to understand since these theories are based on the tacit assumption of an absolutely impassable hiatus between animate and inanimate nature.

Already in the second half of the last century attempts were made to solve the problem of the origin of life on the basis of materialistic conceptions and we find such tendencies in the work of Bastian. . . . Bastian considered it entirely possible that living things originated from inorganic substances without the intervention of any specific vital force. . . .

A. Weisman somewhat later developed the same idea. Rejecting decisively any vitalistic tendencies, he believed that life must have arisen sometime or other from inanimate matter. He thought that, at the very beginning and under conditions unknown to us now, the simplest, tiniest organismal forms, the "biophores" were created. The more highly organized beings developed from these at a later period.

Haeckel's theory . . . is based on similar ideas. . . . He could see no difference between the formation of a crystal and of a living cell. The simplest living thing, the "non-nucleated monera," crystallized out mechanically from inanimate substance. But herein lies Haeckel's fundamental error, because it implies that simplest organisms can actually arise all at once from inorganic matter, the whole thing depending merely on the presence of some peculiarly favorable external physical forces which determine the transformation of inanimate substance into an animate being. Furthermore, according to his theory, such forces existed only during the dim past of the Earth's history and have been so completely lost, that spontaneous generation is no longer possible at the present time. . . .

But just how these conditions and forces have formed such extremely complex systems as are represented even by the simplest living organisms remained a dark mystery as much for Haeckel as for all subsequent biologists.

The numerous objections which the adherents of the theory of the continuity of life raised against theories which assumed that living organisms have been generated at some remote period in the existence of our planet, become thus quite understandable, and can all be reduced to two points. The first was expressed by Preyer who referred with biting sarcasm to those mysterious conditions which were necessary for the appearance of life in geological epochs of long ago and pointed out that no one seems to understand what those conditions really were. If the conditions were the same as prevail now, the origin of life would be plainly impossible because, as Pasteur's investigations have shown, this does not occur at the present time. On the other hand, if those conditions were different, the generated organisms must have perished at once, because the viability is confined to a very narrow range of variation in external conditions.

The other objection has been formulated by S. Kostychev in his popular book: "The Appearance of Life on Earth" (Russian, 1921). He argues that even the most simply organized living things possess a very complex, delicate and perfect protoplasmic structure. The various vital processes are made possible by this protoplasmic structure and perfect functional differentiation. The metabolism of matter and energy characteristic for living things would be entirely impossible without a specially adapted apparatus, and it is highly improbable that such a complex apparatus could have arisen fortuitously. If the reader were asked to consider the probability that in the midst of inorganic matter a large factory with smoke stacks, pipes, boilers, machines, ventilators, etc., suddenly sprang into existence by some natural process, let us say a volcanic eruption, this would be taken at best for a silly joke. Yet, even the simplest microorganism has a more complex structure than any factory, and therefore its fortuitous creation is very much less probable.

These arguments are of substantial significance only if we accept Haeckel's standpoint and assume that at some definite period in the Earth's existence, under the influence of some physical forces and of some unknown conditions, the living organism has originated all at once from non-living matter, just as a crystal is formed in the mother liquor. Even if this organism is the simplest monera, nevertheless it must have been endowed with every attribute of living matter, i.e., its inner structure must have been adapted to carry on definite vital functions. But it is in the highest degree improbable that this adaptation, this purposefulness of inner structure could result from the action of some blind external physical force.

All these difficulties, however, disappear if we discard once and for all the above mechanistic conception and take the standpoint that the simplest living organisms originated gradually by a long evolutionary process of organic substance and that they represent merely definite mileposts along the general historic road of evolution of matter. Then the arguments of both Preyer and Kostychev lose their force. . . . Unquestionably, a factory could never originate through some natural phenomenon and independently of man, simply because every factory is constructed in accordance with some set, previously worked out plan. Everything in the factory, beginning with the erection of the building and machinery down to the arrangement of different sections, has been calculated by the engineer with a view to fulfill definite and foreseen aims. The natural elements could not accomplish such human objectives or fulfill a previously laid-down plan.

It is inconceivable that such a preconceived plan of protoplasmic structure could exist unless one assumes a creative divine will and a plan of creation. But a definite protoplasmic organization and fitness of its inner structure to carry out definite functions could easily be formed in the course of evolution of organic matter just as highly organized animals and plants have come from the simplest living things by a process of evolution. Later we shall attempt to trace this evolution and to picture the gradual formation of living things from non-living matter. . . .

The generation of living things must have been inevitably preceded by a primary development on the Earth's surface of those organic substances of which the organisms are constructed. Now, under natural conditions, we do not observe the formation of those substances which are formed only secondarily by organisms as a result of their vital activity. . . .

Organic substance is the building material out of which the complex structure of living organisms could be formed. . . .

At the present time . . . if organic substance originated anywhere on the Earth's surface, it would be extremely rapidly devoured and destroyed by the countless microorganisms inhabiting the soil, air and water. But before life had yet appeared, the Earth, of course, was entirely sterile and the organic substances which were formed could evolve in many different directions for a very long period of time. However strange this may seem at first sight, a sterile, life-less period in the existence of our planet was a necessary condition for the primary origin of life. This condition prevailed only in the remote past but does not exist now, since the surface of the

Earth is already thickly populated by innumerable highly organized living things.

To establish the possibility for generation of life in the dim past of the Earth's history, it is necessary first of all to prove the possibility of a primary formation of organic substance on our planet.

The Chemistry of Life *

by Isaac Asimov (1960)

Biochemistry as an empirical study antedated its existence as a science by thousands of years, of course. Even in prehistoric times, people were interested in the properties of food, since it was important to learn how to store it without spoilage, how best to prepare it for eating and so on. And it was impossible to deal with food without becoming acquainted with the different broad classes of substances that comprised it.

For instance, in making bread one dealt with *starch,* a dry, white tasteless substance insoluble in water. Fruit juice and honey are sweet to the taste and contain *sugar* which, when isolated, is also white but is soluble in water.

About 1812, the French chemist Joseph Louis Gay-Lussac analyzed such substances as sugar and starch to determine the proportions of their elementary content. He found that both sugar and starch contained exactly three elements: carbon, hydrogen and oxygen. In both, the proportions were about the same: roughly 45 per cent carbon, 6 per cent hydrogen and 49 per cent oxygen, by weight.

The relative percentages, by weight, of hydrogen and oxygen in these substances was just about one to eight, which is the same as the relative percentage of those two elements in water. It seemed, therefore, that an organic compound like sugar or starch might be composed of carbon and water, and the name *carbohydrate* ("watered carbon" in Greek) arose. The name is inaccurate, since the structure of the compounds is not as simple as "watered carbon," but it has stuck, anyway.

Gay-Lussac found wood to have an elementary composition similar to that of both starch and sugar and so it, too, is largely carbohydrate in nature. The chief substance in wood is now called *cellulose,* because fibers of it are found mainly in between plant cells, forming stiff and rigid "cell walls."

* From Isaac Asimov, *The Wellsprings of Life.*

But carbohydrates are not the only class of substances to be found in food. Another group of substances, perhaps even better known, are the fats and oils. These have a greasy feel, leave translucent marks on paper, are liquid or semisolid, are usually yellowish in color, burn more easily than starches or sugars, and are insoluble in water.

Chemical analysis in the early nineteenth century showed that, like carbohydrates, they were composed of three elements: carbon, hydrogen and oxygen. However, the proportions were different. In fats and oils, the proportions were roughly: 77 per cent carbon, 12 per cent hydrogen and 11 per cent oxygen by weight. Fats and oils are much richer in carbon and much poorer in oxygen than carbohydrates are and no further reason is needed (though many others do exist) for considering two separate classes of compounds to exist here. (In modern times, fats and oils, plus certain related substances, are called *lipids,* from a Greek word for "fat.")

But not all substances in food contain simply carbon, hydrogen and oxygen. An example is a solid substance that can be obtained from egg white. This substance is soluble, but not sweet, and even gentle heating causes it to become insoluble and seems to change its properties radically.

The Latin word for "egg white" was "albumen" (from another Latin word meaning simply "white"), so any substance that behaved like egg white was said to be *albuminous.* Material derived from milk, from blood, and from meat generally was found to be albuminous.

In 1811, the French chemist Claude Louis Berthollet was able to break down albuminous substance in such a way as to liberate a gas which he recognized as ammonia. Ammonia is known to contain the element nitrogen. Albuminous substances, therefore, differ from carbohydrates and lipids in possessing a fourth element, nitrogen, in addition to the usual three.

In 1838, a Dutch chemist, Gerard Johann Mulder, went further and analyzed various albuminous substances carefully. He found, in addition to carbon, hydrogen, oxygen and nitrogen, still a fifth element, sulfur. Since the albuminous substances were clearly more complicated than the other types of substances in food, Mulder believed the albuminous class to be more important, as well, and probably the basis of living tissue and of life. He named the class of substances *proteins* from the Greek word for "first" and, all in all, it has turned out to be a pretty good name—at least until very recently.

Pasteur's experiments disproving spontaneous generation seemed to separate living matter from non-living matter by an eternal wall. And, indeed, living matter shared a common chemical structure that was alien to non-living matter. Chemically all life was a unit.

By the time of Pasteur it was quite plain that the organic matter in protoplasm fell for the most part, into one of the three classes: carbohydrates, lipids and proteins. It did not matter whether the protoplasm were that of an oak tree, a bacterium, an oyster, a snake or a man. Carbohydrate, lipid and protein; that, for the most part, was it.

To be sure, that fact and nothing more might seem to be insufficient grounds for making life a unit or for saying that all *protoplasm* of all species is essentially alike. Suppose, for instance, we consider the carbohydrates. The starch obtained from potatoes is not precisely like the starch obtained from rice, nor is either identical with the starch from wheat or from bananas. All these kinds of starch are different from the several distinct varieties of sugar, while cellulose is completely different from either starch or sugar. Further, the plant kingdom is rich in cellulose and in a certain sugar called sucrose. The animal kingdom contains neither. On the other hand, another sugar, called lactose, is found only in mammalian milk. It occurs nowhere else in the animal kingdom and certainly nowhere in the plant kingdom.

Is it fair, then, to make much of the fact that all protoplasm contains something so heterogeneous in nature and occurrence as what we choose to call "carbohydrate"?

Actually there is more to "carbohydrate" than just the presence of carbon, hydrogen and oxygen in certain proportions. For instance, in 1812, a German chemist named Gottlieb Sigismund Kirchhoff found that if he heated starch with weak acid, it dissolved. From the solution, he could separate a solid that was no longer starch, but something he recognized as identical to the sugar that was found in grape juice. As it turned out, it didn't matter which variety of the common starches one started with. They all broke down to grape sugar under the action of the acid. (The modern name for grape sugar is *glucose,* from the Greek word for "sweet.")

Then, in 1819, a French chemist H. Braconnot found that treating cellulose with acid broke it down to a sugar also—and the same sugar, glucose!

In fact, glucose occurs as such not only in fruit juices such as that of the grape, but (as was first discovered in 1844) also in human blood; and, as we now know, in blood of any variety. It is consequently called "blood sugar" as well as "grape sugar."

In short, the carbohydrates that seem so different are not so different after all. Most of the carbohydrate in the world is built up of a single building block, glucose.

There are some carbohydrates that involve sugars other than glucose. For instance, cane sugar or *sucrose* (which was mentioned before as a purely plant product) has molecules that are made up of one glucose unit combined with a unit of another sugar called *fructose*. In *lactose* (the sugar mentioned as occurring in milk) a glucose unit is combined with a unit of another sugar called *galactose*.

Fructose and galactose, however (together with other simple sugars that occur here and there in living tissues), are very similar in properties to glucose. All these sugars are white, crystalline solids, soluble in water and more or less sweet to the taste. All behave similarly in the presence of certain chemicals; all form yellow insoluble compounds with one chemical, or red soluble compounds with another, and so on.

In other words, the widely dissimilar carbohydrates are made up of a very few, very similar building blocks (of which one predominates), and this is true for all species without known exception.

As for lipids, the case is much the same. In 1811, the French chemist Michel Eugène Chevreul found that lipids broke down in the presence of an acid, forming new, somewhat simpler compounds which had the chemical properties of weak acids. These new compounds he therefore called *fatty acids*.

All fats and oils, from all species, break down to liberate, for the most part, the same few fatty acids. And in all cases, without exception, these fatty acids are held together by being joined with a substance called *glycerol*.

It seemed fair enough to assume, by mid-nineteenth century, that not only was all protoplasm built up out of the same three classes of substances, but that these classes were in turn built up out of a relatively few building blocks that all species held in common. The completed organisms might be as infinitely various as the completed musical compositions that have been and can be written, but, like the latter, the infinite variety is built upon the arrangement and rearrangement of a relatively small number of notes.

This point of view explained how it was that one form of life could live on another. Potato starch, olive oil, and beef protein are eaten by man and out of them are produced human glycogen, human fat, human protein. What is the mysterious alchemy that brings about the conversion? Nothing more than this: the process of digestion breaks down the foreign food substances to the building blocks that man holds in common with all creatures. It is the building blocks that are absorbed, the simple sugars, the fatty acids and so on; and it is the building blocks that are then put back together again in a fashion that suits our own requirements.

Chemically, all life is one.

Actually, though, I have not mentioned the building blocks of proteins and, at mid-century, information about them was not yet really satisfactory.

Proteins were more complicated than either carbohydrates or lipids in structure and behavior and were more important to the life processes. As long ago as 1816, it had been shown by the French physiologist François Magendie that dogs could not survive on diets of carbohydrates and lipids alone, but that proteins had to be added. (On the other hand, as was later discovered, animals could live on diets that were almost entirely protein.) It might, therefore, be maintained that carbohydrates and lipids are part of the dead, raw material used by the body, just as water and salt are; and that it was protein that was actually the "life-stuff." If carbohydrates and lipids were built up out of the same simple building blocks in all species, that was of no more importance than that all life depended on water. The question was: how alike were the proteins of the various species?

The first successful attempt to find a building block in proteins was by Braconnot (who had broken down cellulose to glucose in 1819). The next year, 1820, he tried to repeat his success on gelatin, a protein that was obtained by boiling animal gristle. He heated the gelatin with dilute acid, as he had done in the case of cellulose. Eventually, he obtained out of the mixture some white, sweet-tasting crystals, which he naturally took to be sugar, but which was definitely not glucose. He called it "sugar of gelatin." Later that year, he isolated another type of white crystal, which was tasteless and this he called *leucine* (from a Greek word for "white"). Leucine, he found, had nitrogen as part of its structure, which at once made it altogether different from sugars and fatty acids. It was a new kind of building block.

In 1838 it was discovered that Braconnot's "sugar of gelatin" also contained nitrogen and was therefore not a sugar for all its sweetness. It was renamed *glycine* (from the Greek word for "sweet").

In 1846, the German chemist Justus von Liebig heated a milk-curd cheese with an alkaline reagent (one opposite in properties to acids) and out of the resultant material obtained white crystals that were neither glycine nor leucine. He called the substance *tyrosine* (from the Greek word for "cheese").

By mid-century then, there were three entries among the candidates for building blocks of proteins. All contained nitrogen and had certain properties in common but it had to be admitted they did not form the neat, tight group formed by the simple sugars and by the fatty acids. Glycine was sweet, but leucine and tyrosine were not; glycine was quite soluble in water, leucine only slightly soluble, tyrosine practically insoluble. Still, proteins were beginning to yield.

Other crystalline substances were obtained from proteins as the years went by. By the end of the nineteenth century well over a dozen had been isolated. In some ways they were still a heterogeneous group, but the key point was this: every protein, no matter what its source and no matter what its properties, broke up to give these same building blocks. Glycine, leucine, tyrosine, and all the rest, could be obtained out of human protein, whale protein, bat protein, trout protein, snail protein, dandelion protein, bacterial protein. The tyrosine from one was identical with the tyrosine of all the rest, and so on for the remaining building blocks, too.

Formulas, which simply list the number of atoms of each element present in a compound, are quite adequate for the simple compounds that are generally met with in inorganic chemistry. The molecules of organic chemicals are much more complicated, and here unlooked for trouble arose. For instance, the formula of glucose, the chief building block of the carbohydrates, is made up of six carbon atoms, twelve hydrogen atoms and six oxygen atoms. It can be written $C_6H_{12}O_6$. So far, so good.

Yet fructose and galactose, two other sugars which serve as building blocks, have precisely the same number of the same kind of atoms in their molecules. They, too, have formulas which can be written $C_6H_{12}O_6$. And yet glucose, fructose and galactose are three different substances with different properties.

This situation, involving identical formulas and differing properties, bothered the early organic chemists, for the situation did not, to their knowledge, arise in inorganic chemistry. Such compounds were called *isomers* (from Greek words meaning "equal parts"), since each isomer contained equal parts of the various elements composing it. This name was first suggested by Berzelius.

The solution of the isomer problem came when chemists realized that it was not merely the number and kinds of atoms in a molecule that counted, but also their arrangement. (The simplest analogy is that of our numbering system, wherein 951 is quite different from 519 or 159, though all are composed of the same three digits.) In the simple inorganic molecules, there was generally only one arrangement possible, so a formula expressing mere numbers and kinds of atoms was enough to distinguish one substance from another. Not so in the more complex organics.

The first who realized this clearly was the German chemist Friedrich August Kekule. In 1858, he began to draw lines between atoms (represented by their symbols) to show their relationship within the molecule. Chemical knowledge already gained showed that the carbon atom has four valence bonds, nitrogen has three, oxygen two, and hydrogen one. In this way a *structural formula* could be prepared.

Kekule's system did not mean that structural formulas could at once be prepared for all known organic substances. It took long experimentation and clever deductive work to decide just which structural formulas to use for which isomers; to decide, in other words, on the exact shape of molecules that were far too small to be seen by any known instrument.

It was not until 1891, for instance, that the German chemist Emil Fischer, as a result of detailed and brilliant research (for which he received the Nobel prize in chemistry in 1902), worked out the structural formulas of glucose, fructose and galactose. They look like the diagram in Figure 6–4.

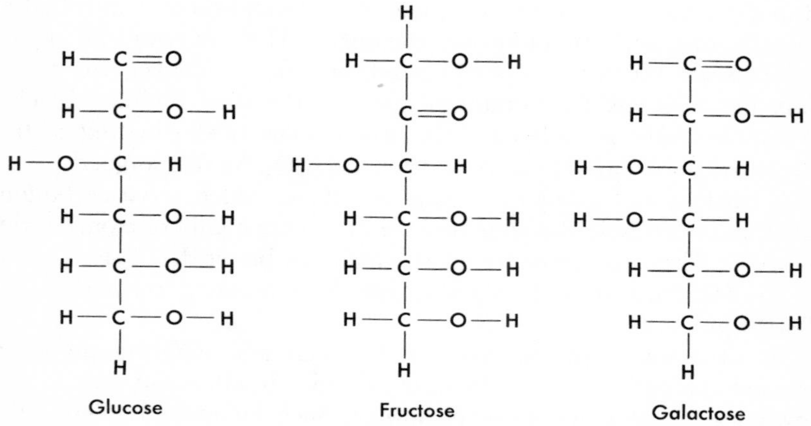

Glucose   Fructose   Galactose

Figure 6–4.

Notice that each formula has six carbon atoms, twelve hydrogen atoms and six oxygen atoms. Notice, too, that the differences in arrangement are minor. Still, out of such minor differences, large variations in properties can result, and upon that, the structure of life can be built.

The structural formula for glycine (which proved to be the simplest of all the building blocks of proteins) is shown in Figure 6–5. The group of three atoms on the left, a nitrogen and two hydrogens, is called an *amine group*, because the structure is similar to that of the molecule of the gas ammonia. The group of four atoms on the right, a carbon, two oxygens and a hydrogen, usually lends acid properties to any compound

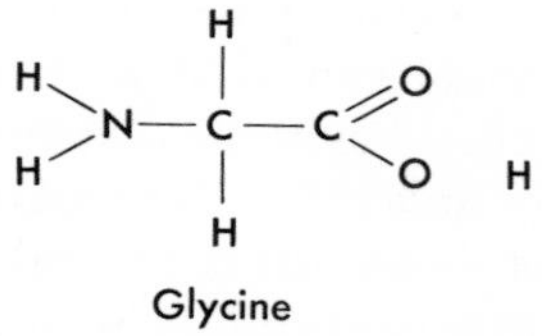

Glycine

Figure 6–5.

in which it occurs. A compound which possesses both these groups in the molecule is called an *amino acid*.

As it turned out, all the various building blocks of the proteins, so heterogeneous in some of their properties, turned out to be similar in chemical structure to this extent: they were all amino acids.

The structural formulas of leucine and tyrosine, for instance, are shown in Figure 6–6.

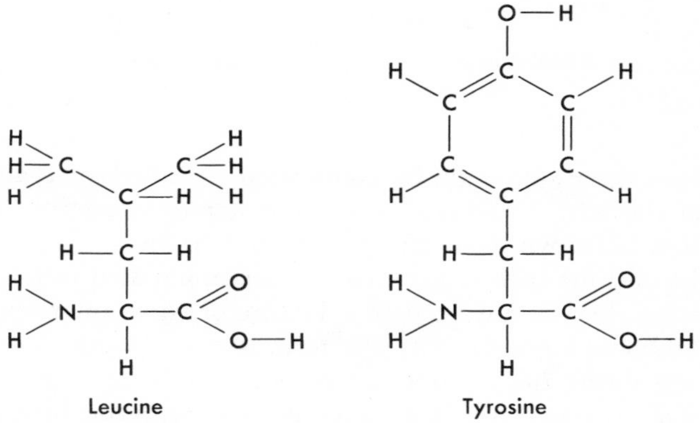

Leucine

Tyrosine

Figure 6–6.

The difference between these and between either and glycine is that different groups of atoms are, in each case, attached to the carbon atom between the amine group and the acid group. These differing atom combinations are termed *side-chains,* and the different amino acids that make up proteins differ only in the nature of their side-chains.

Emil Fischer (the chemist who had worked out the structure of the simple sugars) also tackled the amino acids. By 1918, he had definitely shown how the amino acids were combined to form protein molecules. The acid group of one combined with the amine group of its neighbor; the acid group of that neighbor combined with the amine group of a third; the acid group of that third combined with the amine group of a fourth, and so on indefinitely. This method of combination held universally among the proteins of all species.

There is a subtlety about some organic compounds that has already been mentioned.[1] It is possible to arrange the atoms of amino acids (with the exception in the case of glycine, the simplest) in two different, but equivalent, ways that are mirror images of each other. This can be shown clearly if the arrangement is made three-dimensionally, using small balls

1. See p. 250. Ed.

as atomic models. Restricting ourselves to the two-dimensionality of paper, the two ways are conventionally written as shown in Figure 6–7 (with the letter "R" representing the side-chain).

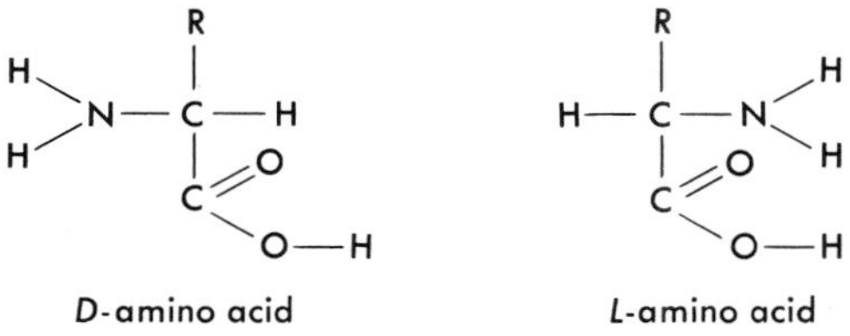

D-amino acid   L-amino acid

Figure 6–7.

The one on the right, again by convention, is called an L-amino acid, the one on the left, a D-amino acid (the letters stand for "levo" and "dextro" from Latin words meaning "left" and "right").

When the chemist tries to manufacture an amino acid in the test tube (which he can do), he always gets a mixture of equal quantities of each form. In the body, however, only one form is synthesized.

But which form? Both forms are equally stable and have an equal probability of existence. Are there some proteins with one form and some with another? Or do some species use one form while others use another?

No, there is uniformity. The human body contains proteins built up out of L-amino acids only. This is true of all other forms of life, vertebrate and invertebrate, animal and plant, multicellular and unicellular. So uniform is the chemistry of life, that the D-amino acids are often spoken of as "unnatural amino acids," even though they do exist in nature, in small quantities, in a few rare proteins, mostly of bacterial and fungal origin.

There is no known reason why all proteins might not have been built up out of D-amino acids. It is almost as though life began once (let us say as a single cell) and happened to settle on the L-amino acid as a building block, and all life thereafter has been stuck with the choice through descent from that original cell.

Now that we have looked into the chemical basis of living matter, are we sure that Pasteur's experimental disproof of spontaneous generation can stand? Or could a living cell have been formed from non-living matter over very long intervals of time under conditions markedly different from those prevailing today?

From all that has been said, it is obvious that the molecules which compose even the simplest living cell are themselves extremely complex and yet chemists have been able to take them apart step by step into simpler building blocks. In order to prove the possibility of the formation of a living cell from non-living matter it is necessary to show that these basic organic building blocks could have been synthesized from inorganic matter under conditions that prevailed at some early period in the earth's history.

From a consideration of the chemical make-up of the universe as a whole, and of the solar system in particular, it would seem that the earth's original atmosphere could not have been at all like the atmosphere it now has. The original atmosphere must probably have been composed of compounds rich in hydrogen, since it is estimated that the universe is about 90 per cent hydrogen and the sun is 85 per cent hydrogen.

As an example of a hydrogen-rich atmosphere, consider that of the planet Jupiter, which is mostly hydrogen and helium (in the proportion of three to one) with minor quantities of hydrogen-containing gases such as ammonia (NH_3) and methane (CH_4). The atmospheres of the other giant planets beyond Jupiter are similar.

The earth is much smaller than Jupiter, however, and the earth's gravitational field is not strong enough to hold on to the very light molecules of hydrogen and the almost-as-light atoms of helium. However, the field could hold on to methane and ammonia and the earth's original atmosphere may well have contained these, plus sizable quantities of carbon dioxide. There would be no free oxygen in this atmosphere.

Since carbon dioxide and ammonia are both quite soluble in water, the earth's original ocean must have been loaded with those two compounds. Furthermore, both air and water would have been exposed to a much harsher sunlight than we are exposed to today.

The sun emits a rich variety of ultraviolet rays, but these react with the oxygen in the upper reaches of our present atmosphere, forming a particularly energetic variety of oxygen, which is called *ozone*. Almost all the ultraviolet radiation of the sun is absorbed in the process, and goes into the maintenance of the ozone layer (or *ozonosphere*) fifteen miles above the surface of the earth. Very little of the ultraviolet radiation actually penetrates down to the surface, which is a good thing, for the sun's full supply would kill us. (Even the feeble quantity of the less energetic variety that does reach us can result in painful burns to the fair-skinned and unwary.)

In the earth's primordial atmosphere, however, where no free oxygen would have existed, there would have been no ozone formation. All the ultraviolet rays of the sun would reach the surface, or almost all. The energetic ultraviolet light, bombarding the ocean and dense surface atmosphere, would have supplied the energy necessary to convert the simple molecules of water, carbon dioxide, methane and ammonia into more complicated molecules, and still more complicated ones. (Earth, in primordial days, possessed more radioactivity than it does now, and radio-active radiations may have helped, too.)

In 1952, an American chemist, S. L. Miller, circulated a mixture of water, ammonia, methane, and hydrogen past an electric discharge for a week, trying to duplicate primordial conditions (with the electric discharge representing the energy supply of ultraviolet light). At the end of the week, he found organic compounds in his solution that had not been there to begin with. Even some of the simpler amino acids were present —and he had been working only a week. [Figure 6–8.] Such experiments

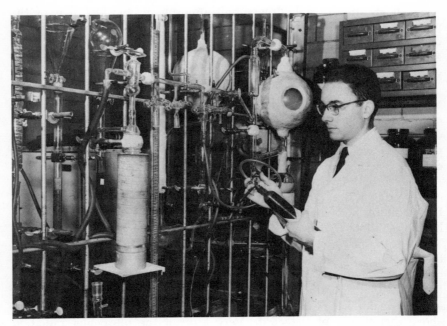

Figure 6–8. Stanley Miller's historic experiment creating amino acids in the laboratory. (United Press International Photo, May 16, 1953.)

have been repeated often since and in 1963, a molecule called *adenosine triphosphate,* a key compound in the utilization of energy by living tissue, was so synthesized.

Without being able to be certain, of course (and perhaps we never will be), we can speculate as to the possible course of events in the primordial ocean.

Under the drive of energy, ultraviolet or radioactive, the primordial ocean would have slowly filled with more and more complex compounds:

amino acids, sugars, etc. These would be built up further so that amino acids might combine into proteins.

This could continue at random for perhaps a billion years or more, until a time came when a molecule was put together which was complex enough to have the capacity of consummating replication. To have this happen on the basis of random chance seems to be asking a lot, but then a billion years is a long time.

And if this indeed happened (and surely something like it must have), then at least once in the history of our planet, there did, after all, take place a case of spontaneous generation. It was a stupendous event, too, the most stupendous in the history of our planet, for by it all of life may have been formed in one split-second of random synthesis.

To start really at the beginning, at the true wellsprings of life, we must answer the question "How did life begin?" something like this:

"Once upon a time, very long ago, perhaps two and a half billions years ago, under a deadly sun, in an ammoniated ocean topped by a poisonous atmosphere, in the midst of a soup of organic molecules, a nucleic acid molecule came accidentally into being that could somehow bring about the existence of another like itself—"

And from that all else would follow!

Organic Matter from Space *

by Brian Mason (1963)

In 1834 the great Swedish chemist Jöns Jakob Berzelius analyzed a peculiar meteorite that had fallen near Alais in southern France. He found that it contained carbonaceous material and he wondered: Does it contain humus or traces of other organic compounds? Does it possibly indicate the presence of organisms on extraterrestrial bodies? Berzelius thought not.

The exciting question asked and answered by Berzelius has recently been reopened to investigation, speculation and controversy. In 1961 a group of investigators discovered a variety of complex hydrocarbons in a meteorite of the same type as the one that fell at Alais. (Figure 6–9.) They found sufficient resemblance between these compounds and those formed on earth by living things to propose the possibility that the mete-

Figure 6–9. Meteorites in which organic compounds and "organized elements" have been discovered include the Orgueil carbonaceous chondrite. This sample, weighing 40 grams, is in the collection of the American Museum of Natural History. Carbonaceous chondrites are earthy, crumbly, hard to identify as meteorites, and quickly destroyed by weathering. (Photograph courtesy of the American Museum of Natural History.)

orite had arrived bearing products of extraterrestrial life. . . . The quantities of the hydrocarbons in the meteorite indicate that there can be no reasonable doubt that they were present when it entered the earth's atmosphere and are not the result of terrestrial contamination. They are truly extraterrestrial in origin. It was not the findings of [Bartholomew S.] Nagy and his co-workers but their interpretation of these findings that stirred debate: How close is the resemblance between the mass spectra of the Orgueil hydrocarbons and those of known biogenic hydrocarbons, and does this resemblance justify the conclusion that they had similar origins? (Figure 6–10.) . . .

The work on the organic compounds has been rather overshadowed by another kind of evidence. In November, 1961, George Claus of the New York University Medical Center and Nagy announced that they had discovered "microscopic-sized particles, resembling fossil algae, in relatively large quantities within the Orgueil and Ivuna carbonaceous meteorites." This finding, if confirmed—that is, if the particles are in fact the remains of organisms and are clearly not terrestrial contaminants—would certainly be evidence of life in the parent bodies of these meteorites. The announcement by Claus and Nagy aroused a hot controversy that is still far from resolved. In New York in spring 1962, interested workers representing several disciplines convened to discuss the identification and interpretation of these "organized elements." They agreed generally that at high magnifications certain regular and in many cases remarkably complex

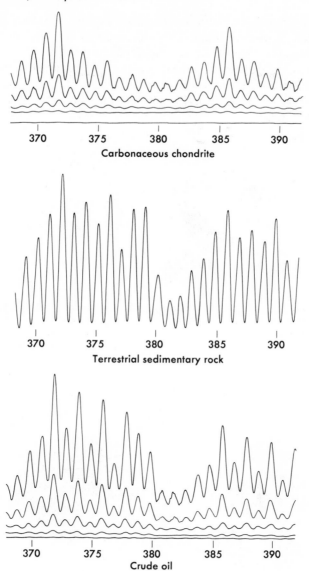

Figure 6–10. Material extracted from carbonaceous chondrite, a chunk of terrestrial sedimentary rock, and a blob of crude oil are fractionated in a silicagel chromatographic column. Then the fractions are analyzed on a mass spectrometer, which determines the amount of material present at various molecular weights. The results of the spectrometric analysis, which come in the form of the curves shown on the right, indicate similarities between the meteoritic and terrestrial hydrocarbons.

forms can be recognized in the meteoritic material and that these can be concentrated by chemical and physical methods such as acid extraction and centrifugation. But what are they? (Figure 6–11.)

The answers fall into three categories: The organized elements are indeed life forms, the vestiges of extraterrestrial organisms; they are merely crystals of organic or inorganic compounds; they are terrestrial contaminants. . . .

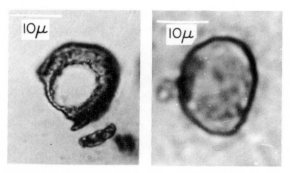

Figure 6–11A. Photomicrographs of "organized elements" found by Nagy et al. in the Orgueil meteorite. Electron probe X-ray microanalysis has shown that these particles are mineralized with inorganic compounds. Hydrochloric acid leaching removes the mineral matter, leaving behind acid-insoluble, organic residues.

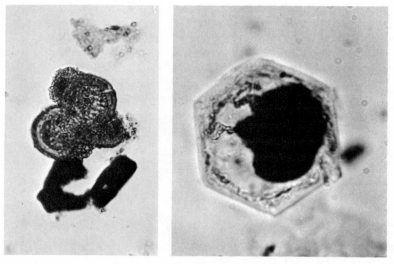

Figure 6–11B. Microfossils were identified in an Orgueil sample by Frank L. Staplin of Imperial Oil, Ltd., in Canada. (Photographs courtesy of Dr. Frank L. Staplin.)

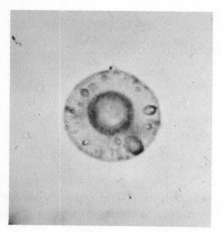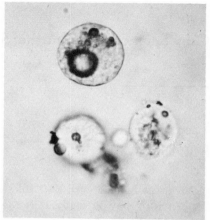

Figure 6–11C. *Complex structure of some of the meteoritic elements was paralleled, according to Edward Anders and Frank W. Fitch of the University of Chicago, in some terrestrial contaminants. They compared one of Claus and Nagy's particles (left) with furnace ash (right).*

While the reality of extraterrestrial life or the remains thereof in the carbonaceous meteorites is still in doubt, this should not obscure the great significance of the organic compounds they contain. The fact remains that under certain conditions and in certain regions of outer space rather complex hydrocarbons and other organic substances were produced in considerable amounts and survived for long periods of time. . . . Proof that the organic compounds and organized elements are the residues of living organisms indigenous to the meteorites would be, as Harold C. Urey of the University of California at La Jolla has said, "the most interesting and indeed astounding fact of all scientific study in recent years."

Can Science Fathom the Secret of Life?

The Creation of Life *
by George Wald (1958)

No great idea is ever lost. Like Antaeus, it is overthrown only to rise again with renewed vigor. It is dismissed only to return, yet never quite the same. Its rejection is only a step in its further development.

One could say better that all great ideas come in pairs, the one the negation of the other, and both containing elements of truth. Each generation has the satisfaction of overthrowing the idea in one of its forms, each succeeding generation the triumph of rediscovering it. The onlooker, watching this vacillation, has the illusion that no progress is made. Yet this is the very mechanism of progress. It is the progress of a screw, which advances as it rotates. Science turns the idea about and about, now accepting it, now rejecting it, giving it always fuller, more detailed and exact meaning.

The great idea emerges originally in the consciousness of the race as a vague intuition; and this is the form it keeps, rude and imposing, in myth, tradition and poetry. This is its core, its enduring aspect. In this form science finds it, clothes it with fact, analyzes its content, develops its detail, rejects it, and finds it ever again. In achieving the scientific view, we do not ever wholly lose the intuitive, the mythological. Both have meaning for us, and neither is complete without the other. The Book of Genesis contains still our poem of the Creation; and when God questions Job out of the whirlwind, He questions us.

Let me cite an example. Throughout our history we have entertained two kinds of views of the origin of life: one that life was created supernaturally, the other that it arose "spontaneously" from nonliving material. In the seventeenth to nineteenth centuries these opinions provided the ground of a great and bitter controversy. There came a curious point, toward the end of the eighteenth century, when each side of this controversy was represented by a Roman Catholic priest. The principal opponent of the theory of spontaneous generation was then the Abbé Lazzaro Spallanzani, an Italian priest; and its principal champion was John Turberville Needham, an English Jesuit.

Since the only alternative to some form of spontaneous generation is a belief in supernatural creation, and since the latter view seems firmly implanted in the Judaeo-Christian theology, I wondered for a time how a priest could support the theory of spontaneous generation. Needham tells one plainly. The opening paragraphs of the Book of Genesis can in fact be reconciled with either view. In its first account of the Creation, it says not quite that God made living things, but that He commanded the earth and waters to produce them. The language used is: "Let the waters

Figure 6–12. The creation is depicted in this woodcut from the Lübeck Bible, published in 1494. In the center God creates Eve out of Adam's rib. In the circle around this scene are the waters; in the next circle, the heavens. In the outermost circle are the angels. (Reprinted courtesy of the New York Public Library.)

bring forth abundantly the moving creature that hath life. . . . Let the earth bring forth the living creature after his kind." In the second version of the Creation, the language is different and suggests a direct creative act: "And out of the ground the Lord God formed every beast of the field, and every fowl of the air. . . ." In both accounts man himself—and woman —are made by God's direct intervention. The myth itself therefore offers justification for either view. Needham took the position that the earth and waters, having once been ordered to bring forth life, remained ever after free to do so; and this is what we mean by spontaneous generation.

This great controversy ended in the mid-nineteenth century with the experiments of Louis Pasteur, which seemed to dispose finally of the possibility of spontaneous generation. For almost a century afterward biologists proudly taught their students this history and the firm conclusion that spontaneous generation had been scientifically refuted and could not possibly occur. Does this mean that they accepted the alternative view, a supernatural creation of life? Not at all. They had no theory of the origin of life, and if pressed were likely to explain that questions involving such unique events as origins and endings have no place in science.

A few years ago, however, this question re-emerged in a new form. Conceding that spontaneous generation does not occur on the earth under present circumstances, it asks how, under circumstances that prevailed earlier upon this planet, spontaneous generation did occur and was the source of the earliest living organisms. Within the past ten years this has gone from a remote and patchwork argument spun by a few venturesome persons—A. I. Oparin in Russia, J. B. S. Haldane in England—to a favored position, proclaimed with enthusiasm by many biologists.

Have I cited here a good instance of my thesis? I had said that in these great questions one finds two opposed views, each of which is periodically espoused by science. In my example I seem to have presented a supernatural and a naturalistic view, which were indeed opposed to each other, but only one of which was ever defended scientifically. In this case it would seem that science has vacillated, not between two theories, but between one theory and no theory.

That, however, is not the end of the matter. Our present concept of the origin of life leads to the position that, in a universe composed as ours is, life inevitably arises wherever conditions permit. We look upon life as part of the order of nature. It does not emerge immediately with the establishment of that order; long ages must pass before it appears. Yet given enough time, it is an inevitable consequence of that order.

When speaking for myself, I do not tend to make sentences containing the word God; but what do those persons mean who make such sentences? They mean a great many different things; indeed I would be happy to know what they mean much better than I have yet been able to discover. I have asked as opportunity offered, and intend to go on asking. What I have learned is that many educated persons now tend to equate their concept of God with their concept of the order of nature. This is not a new idea; I think it is firmly grounded in the philosophy of Spinoza. When we as scientists say then that life originated inevitably as part of the order of our universe, we are using different words but do not necessarily mean a different thing from what some others mean who say that God created life. It is not only in science that great ideas come to encompass their own negation.

The cell consists of matter called protoplasm, composed chiefly of carbon, with an admixture of hydrogen, nitrogen and sulphur. These component parts, properly united, produce the soul and body of the animated world, and suitably nursed become man. With this single argument the mystery of the universe is explained, the Deity annulled and a new era of infinite knowledge ushered in.

Ernst Haeckel, 1877 *

The Secret of Life †
by Loren Eiseley (1946)

The notion that mice can be generated spontaneously from bundles of old clothes is so delightfully whimsical that it is easy to see why men were loath to abandon it. One could accept such accidents in a topsy-turvy universe without trying to decide what transformation of buckles into bones and shoe buttons into eyes had taken place. One could take life as a kind of fantastic magic and not blink too obviously when it appeared, beady-eyed and bustling, under the laundry in the back room.

It was only with the rise of modern biology and the discovery that the trail of life led backward toward infinitesimal beginnings in primordial sloughs, that men began the serious dissection and analysis of the cell. Darwin, in one of his less guarded moments, had spoken hopefully of the possibility that life had emerged from inorganic matter in some "warm little pond." From that day to this biologists have poured, analyzed,

* Cited by W. S. Lilley in the *Fortnightly Review,* 1886, Vol. 39, p. 35.
† From Loren Eiseley, *The Immense Journey,* Random House, New York. Copyright 1946 by Loren Eiseley. Reprinted by permission.

minced, and shredded recalcitrant protoplasm in a fruitless attempt to create life from nonliving matter. It seemed inevitable, if we could trace life down through simpler stages, that we must finally arrive at the point where, under the proper chemical conditions, the mysterious borderline that bounds the inanimate must be crossed. It seemed clear that life was a material manifestation. Somewhere, somehow, sometime, in the mysterious chemistry of carbon, the long march toward the talking animal had begun.

A hundred years ago men spoke optimistically about solving the secret, or at the very least they thought the next generation would be in a position to do so. Periodically there were claims that the emergence of life from matter had been observed, but in every case the observer proved to be self-deluded. It became obvious that the secret of life was not to be had by a little casual experimentation, and that life in today's terms appeared to arise only through the medium of preëxisting life. Yet, if science was not to be embarrassed by some kind of mind-matter dualism and a complete and irrational break between life and the world of inorganic matter, the emergence of life had, in some way, to be accounted for. Nevertheless, as the years passed, the secret remained locked in its living jelly, in spite of larger microscopes and more formidable means of dissection. As a matter of fact the mystery was heightened because all this intensified effort revealed that even the supposedly simple amoeba was a complex, self-operating chemical factory. The notion that he was a simple blob, the discovery of whose chemical composition would enable us instantly to set the life process in operation, turned out to be, at best, a monstrous caricature of the truth.

With the failure of these many efforts science was left in the somewhat embarrassing position of having to postulate theories of living origins which it could not demonstrate. After having chided the theologian for his reliance on myth and miracle, science found itself in the unenviable position of having to create a mythology of its own: namely, the assumption that what, after long effort, could not be proved to take place today had, in truth, taken place in the primeval past.

My use of the term *mythology* is perhaps a little harsh. One does occasionally observe, however, a tendency for the beginning zoological textbook to take the unwary reader by a hop, skip, and jump from the little steaming pond or the beneficent chemical crucible of the sea, into the lower world of life with such sureness and rapidity that it is easy to assume that there is no mystery about this matter at all, or, if there is, that it is a very little one.

This attitude has indeed been sharply criticized by the distinguished British biologist Woodger, who remarked some years ago: "Unstable organic compounds and chlorophyll corpuscles do not persist or come into existence in nature on their own account at the present day, and consequently it is necessary to postulate that conditions were once such that this did happen although and in spite of the fact that our knowledge of nature does not give us any warrant for making such a supposition . . . It is simple dogmatism—asserting that what you want to believe did in fact happen."

Yet, unless we are to turn to supernatural explanations or reinvoke a dualism which is scientifically dubious, we are forced inevitably toward only two possible explanations of life upon earth. One of these, although not entirely disproved, is most certainly out of fashion and surrounded with greater obstacles to its acceptance than at the time it was formulated. I refer, of course, to the suggestion of Lord Kelvin and Svante Arrhenius that life did not arise on this planet, but was wafted here through the depths of space. . . .

This theory had a certain attraction as a way out of an embarrassing dilemma, but it suffers from the defect of explaining nothing, even if it should prove true. It does not elucidate the nature of life. It simply removes the inconvenient problem of origins to far-off spaces or worlds into which we will never penetrate. Since life makes use of the chemical compounds of this earth, it would seem better to proceed, until incontrovertible evidence to the contrary is obtained, on the assumption that life has actually arisen upon this planet. The now widely accepted view that the entire universe in its present state is limited in time, and the apparently lethal nature of unscreened solar radiation are both obstacles which greatly lessen the likelihood that life has come to us across the infinite wastes of space. Once more, therefore, we are forced to examine our remaining notion that life is not coterminous with matter, but has arisen from it.

If the single-celled protozoans that riot in roadside pools are not the simplest forms of life, if, as we know today, these creatures are already highly adapted and really complex, though minute beings, then where are we to turn in the search for something simple enough to suggest the greatest missing link of all—the link between living and dead matter? It is this problem that keeps me wandering fruitlessly in pastures and weed thickets even though I know this is an old-fashioned naturalist's approach, and that busy men in laboratories have little patience with my scufflings of autumn leaves, or attempts to question beetles in decaying bark. Besides, many of these men are now fascinated by the crystalline viruses and have turned that remarkable instrument, the electron microscope, upon strange molecular "beings" never previously seen by man. Some are satisfied with this glimpse below the cell and find the virus a halfway station on the road to life. Perhaps it is, but as I wander about in the thin mist that is beginning to filter among these decaying stems and ruined spider webs, a kind of disconsolate uncertainty has taken hold of me.

I have come to suspect that this long descent down the ladder of life, beautiful and instructive though it may be, will not lead us to the final secret. In fact I have ceased to believe in the final brew or the ultimate chemical. There is, I know, a kind of heresy, a shocking negation of our confidence in blue-steel microtomes and men in white in making such a statement. I would not be understood to speak ill of scientific effort, for in simple truth I would not be alive today except for the microscopes and the blue steel. It is only that somewhere among these seeds and beetle shells and abandoned grasshopper legs I find something that is not accounted for very clearly in the dissections to the ultimate virus or crystal or protein particle. Even if the secret is contained in these things, in other words, I do not think it will yield to the kind of analysis our science is capable of making.

Imagine, for a moment, that you have drunk from a magician's goblet. Reverse the irreversible stream of time. Go down the dark stairwell out of which the race has ascended. Find yourself at last on the bottommost steps of time, slipping, sliding, and wallowing by scale and fin down into the muck and ooze out of which you arose. Pass by grunts and voiceless hissings below the last tree ferns. Eyeless and earless, float in the primal waters, sense sunlight you cannot see and stretch absorbing tentacles toward vague tastes that float in water. Still, in your formless shiftings, the *you* remains: the sliding particles, the juices, the transformations are working in an exquisitely patterned rhythm which has no other purpose than your preservation—you, the entity, the ameboid being whose substance contains the unfathomable future. Even so does every man come upward from the waters of his birth.

Yet if at any moment the magician bending over you should cry, "Speak! Tell us of that road!" you could not respond. The sensations are yours but not—and this is one of the great mysteries—the power over the body. You cannot describe how the body you inhabit functions, or picture or control the flights and spinnings, the dance of the molecules that compose it, or why they chose to dance into that particular pattern which is you, or, again, why up the long stairway of the eons they dance from one shape to another. It is for this reason that I am no longer interested in final particles. Follow them as you will, pursue them until they become nameless protein crystals replicating on the verge of life. Use all the great powers of the mind and pass backward until you hang with the dire faces of the conquerors in the hydrogen cloud from which the sun was born.

You will then have performed the ultimate dissection that our analytic age demands, but the cloud will still veil the secret and, if not the cloud, then the nothingness into which, it now appears, the cloud, in its turn, may be dissolved. The secret, if one may paraphrase a savage vocabulary, lies in the egg of night. . . .

Every so often one encounters articles in leading magazines with titles such as "The Spark of Life," "The Secret of Life," "New Hormone Key to Life," or other similar optimistic proclamations. Only yesterday, for example, I discovered in the *New York Times* a headline announcing: "Scientist Predicts Creation of Life in Laboratory." The Moscow-date-lined dispatch announced that Academician Olga Lepeshinskaya had predicted that "in the not too distant future, Soviet scientists would create life." "The time is not far off," warns the formidable Madame Olga, "when we shall be able to obtain the vital substance artificially." She said it with such vigor that I had about the same reaction as I do to announcements about atomic bombs. In fact I half started up to latch the door before an invading tide of Russian protoplasm flowed in upon me.

What finally enabled me to regain my shaken confidence was the recollection that these pronouncements have been going on for well over a century. Just now the Russian scientists show a particular tendency to issue such blasts—committed politically, as they are, to an uncompromising materialism and the boastfulness of very young science. Furthermore, Madame Lepeshinskaya's remarks as reported in the press had a curiously old-fashioned flavor about them. The protoplasm she referred to sounded amazingly like the outmoded *Urschleim* or *Autoplasson* of Haeckel—simplified mucoid slimes no longer taken very seriously. American versions —and one must remember they are often journalistic interpretations of scientists' studies rather than direct quotations from the scientists themselves—are more apt to fall into another pattern. Someone has found a new chemical, vitamin, or similar necessary ingredient without which life will not flourish. By the time this reaches the more sensational press, it may have become the "secret of life." The only thing the inexperienced reader may not comprehend is the fact that no one of these items, even the most recently discovered, is *the* secret. Instead, the substance is probably a part, a very small part, of a larger enigma which is well-nigh as inscrutable as it ever was. If anything, the growing list of catalysts, hormones, plasma genes, and other hobgoblins involved in the work of life only serves to underline the enormous complexity of the secret. "To grasp in detail," says the German biologist Von Bertalanffy, "the physico-chemical organization of the simplest cell is far beyond our capacity."

It is not, you understand, disrespect for the laudable and persistent patience of these dedicated scientists happily lost in their maze of pipettes, smells, and gas flames, that has led me into this runaway excursion to the wood. It is rather the loneliness of a man who knows he will not live to see the mystery solved, and who, furthermore, has come to believe that it will not be solved when the first humanly synthesized particle begins—if it ever does—to multiply itself in some unknown solution.

It is really a matter, I suppose, of the kind of questions one asks oneself. Some day we may be able to say with assurance, "We came from such and such a protein particle, possessing the powers of organizing in a manner leading under certain circumstances to that complex entity known as the cell, and from the cell by various steps onward, to multiple cell formation." I mean we may be able to say all this with great surety and elaboration of detail, but it is not the answer to the grasshopper's leg, brown and black and saw-toothed here in my hand, nor the answer to the seeds still clinging tenaciously to my coat, nor to this field, nor to the subtle essences of memory, delight, and wistfulness moving among the thin wires of my brain.

I suppose that in the forty-five years of my existence every atom, every molecule that composes me has changed its position or danced away and beyond to become part of other things. New molecules have come from the grass and the bodies of animals to be part of me a little while, yet in this spinning, light and airy as a midge swarm in a shaft of sunlight, my memories hold, and a loved face of twenty years ago is before me still. Nor is that face, nor all my years, caught cellularly as in some cold precise photographic pattern, some gross, mechanical reproduction of the past. My memory holds the past and yet paradoxically knows, at the same time, that the past is gone and will never come again. It cherishes dead faces and silenced voices, yes, and lost evenings of childhood. In some odd nonspatial way it contains houses and rooms that have been torn timber from timber and brick from brick. These have a greater permanence in that midge dance which contains them than ever they had in the world of reality. It is for this reason that Academician Olga Lepeshinskaya has not answered the kind of questions one may ask in an open field.

If the day comes when the slime of the laboratory for the first time crawls under man's direction, we shall have great need of humbleness. It will be difficult for us to believe, in our pride of achievement, that the secret of life has slipped through our fingers and eludes us still. We will list all the chemicals and the reactions. The men who have become gods will pose austerely before the popping flashbulbs of news photographers, and there will be few to consider—so deep is the mind-set of an age— whether the desire to link life to matter may not have blinded us to the more remarkable characteristics of both.

As for me, if I am still around on that day, I intend to put on my old hat and climb over the wall as usual. I shall see strange mechanisms lying as they lie here now, in the autumn rain, strange pipes that transported the substance of life, the intricate seedcase out of which the life has flown. I shall observe no thing green, no delicate transpirations of leaves, nor subtle comings and goings of vapor. The little sunlit factories of the chloroplasts will have dissolved away into common earth.

Beautiful, angular, and bare the machinery of life will lie exposed, as it now is, to my view. There will be the thin, blue skeleton of a hare tumbled in a little heap, and crouching over it I will marvel, as I marvel now, at the wonderful correlation of parts, the perfect adaptation to purpose, the individually vanished and yet persisting pattern which is now hopping on some other hill. I will wonder, as always, in what manner "particles" pursue such devious plans and symmetries. I will ask once more in what way it is managed, that the simple dust takes on a history and begins to weave these unique and never recurring apparitions in the stream of time. I shall wonder what strange forces at the heart of matter regulate the tiny beating of a rabbit's heart or the dim dream that builds a milkweed pod.

It is said by men who know about these things that the smallest living cell probably contains over a quarter of a million protein molecules engaged in the multitudinous coördinated activities which make up the phenomenon of life. At the instant of death, whether of man or microbe, that ordered, incredible spinning passes away in an almost furious haste of those same particles to get themselves back into the chaotic, unplanned earth.

I do not think, if someone finally twists the key successfully in the tiniest and most humble house of life, that many of these questions will be answered, or that the dark forces which create lights in the deep sea and living batteries in the waters of tropical swamps, or the dread cycles of parasites, or the most noble workings of the human brain, will be much if at all revealed. Rather, I would say that if "dead" matter has reared up this curious landscape of fiddling crickets, song sparrows, and wondering men, it must be plain even to the most devoted materialist that the matter of which he speaks contains amazing, if not dreadful powers, and may not impossibly be, as Hardy has suggested, "but one mask of many worn by the Great Face behind."

Questions To Consider

Did Pasteur prove that spontaneous generation can never occur?

Do you agree with Eiseley that if we create life in a test tube we will have proven nothing? Will we have demonstrated a natural rather than a supernatural origin of life? Will the mystery still remain?

How could Judaeo-Christian religion take both sides of the argument about spontaneous generation?

Why do we consider the theory of the origin of life from non-living matter more materialistic than the theory that life was separately created?

Is the problem of the origin of life a suitable subject for scientific investigation?

What are the differences in method between the biological and the physical sciences?

Suggestions for Further Reading

° Adler, Irving: *How Life Began*, Signet Science, The New American Library, Inc., 1959. An elementary introduction to organic chemistry and biochemistry. Reviews contemporary theories on the nature and origin of life.

° Dubos, René: *Pasteur and Modern Science*, Anchor Books, Doubleday & Co., Inc., 1960. This Science Study Series book reviews the development of Pasteur's genius with special emphasis on the philosophical and social factors that determined the problems on which he worked. The selection on Pasteur in Part 5 came from this book.

Gamow, George: *Matter, Earth, and Sky*, Prentice-Hall, Inc., 1958. Chapter 11 explains the basic principles of organic chemistry.

Moore, Ruth: *The Coil of Life*, Alfred A. Knopf, 1960. Chapters IV through VII describe in biographical form the early work on organic chemistry, the discovery of the cell, and Pasteur's experiments.

Oparin, A. I.: *Life: Its Nature, Origin, and Development*, Academic Press, Inc., New York, 1961. A somewhat technical presentation of the author's own views of the biochemical basis of life.

° Ovenden, Michael: *Life in the Universe*, Anchor Books, Doubleday & Co., Inc., 1962. A speculative scientific discussion on the possibilities of the existence of life on other planets. Includes a description of environmental conditions on the several planets. A Science Study Series book.

Shapley, Harlow: *Of Stars and Men*, Washington Square, Affiliated Publishers, Inc., 1960. The author discusses the probability of other life in the universe and reviews the origin and evolution of life on earth.

° Paperback edition

7

Is Living Matter Immortal?

The two great nineteenth-century discoveries in biology —evolution of the species through natural selection and the laws of heredity—throw new light on some age-old problems: the inevitability of death, the deeper meaning of sex and reproduction, and the immortality of the stream of life.

Is Living Matter Immortal?

Introduction

THERE COULD hardly be a more striking contrast between two scientific theories than between the two great biological discoveries of the late nineteenth century. The theory of evolution by natural selection was in the air at the time Darwin conceived it. The idea of living things evolving gradually from one species into another had been suggested by a number of other writers, among them Charles Darwin's own grandfather. The suggestion of the mechanism by which this evolution might occur came to Darwin from the work of a contemporary writer, Thomas Malthus, who pointed out that human populations are in constant competition for the means of subsistence. Darwin's original genius lay in synthesizing these two current ideas to create a plausible explanation for the origin of the different species. The same synthesis of ideas occurred almost simultaneously to another world traveler, Alfred Wallace. But Darwin's idea was eloquently set forth and buttressed by a vast store of evidence gleaned from his travels, and so, although Wallace's treatise and a letter summarizing Darwin's views appeared at the same time, Darwin received the major share of the credit for this theory. It was received with great interest and aroused heated controversy. The public was quick to realize that here was a scientific theory which had a very significant bearing on man's understanding of himself and his place in nature.

Gregor Mendel, on the other hand, conceived and worked out his laws of heredity entirely alone in a monastery garden. His research was unusual in that it did not build on the work of other scientists, and when it was presented to the world, couched in dry and cautious language, it hardly caused a ripple on the thought of the time. The concept was too original, too unrelated to the work of contemporary biologists. Fortunately, the record was preserved in an obscure scientific journal and was brought to light thirty-five years later when the time was ripe for it.

Mendel's work has many other interesting aspects. While Darwin's theory was completely non-mathematical, Mendel introduced the quantitative approach into genetics. From the discovery of simple numerical relationships in the inheritance of characteristics, he postulated the presence of indivisible hereditary units which were passed on from generation to generation. In this way his theory was the biological parallel to Dalton's theory that the constant ratios in which elements combine to form compounds could be explained on the basis of indivisible units of matter. Mendel's research was conducted with the very simplest of experimental equipment. His laboratory was a small plot in the monastery garden. His tools were calico bags and a camel's-hair brush. Because of the simplicity and unity of his work it provides an excellent example of scientific method, showing how theory and experiment both contribute to the discovery of a basic scientific law.

The two great biological theories described in these readings form the basis of our modern understanding of the nature of living matter and open up implications of great significance for mankind. The question of man's animal origin which was the flaming issue several generations ago has become an accepted part of biological theory today. Other implications of deeper import have made this argument seem trivial. Our modern theory has a great deal to say about immortality, death, the process of reproduction, and the passing on of the stream of life from one generation to another. Is the individual unimportant in the scheme of things? Or is he as necessary to the process of evolution as the continuing germ-plasm itself? Questions like these show how deeply the theories of Darwin, Mendel, Morgan, and other great biologists have affected man's view of himself and his relationship to the rest of the natural world.

Figure 7–1. Left, Charles Robert Darwin (1809–82). Right, (Johann) Gregor Mendel (1822–84). (Photographs courtesy of the Bettmann Archive.)

Evolution and Reproduction

The Science of Life *

by H. G. Wells, J. Huxley, and G. P. Wells (1934)

THE CHIEF THEORIES OF EVOLUTION

Until a century or so ago it was commonly believed that the world as we know it to-day had begun suddenly. It had been created, with man and all the species of beings as we know them to-day. Great numbers of people, including most educated people, held to the view with great tenacity. They had adjusted their moral and religious ideas to that view, and they did not realize that these ideas were not inseparably dependent upon it. All of us are prone to resist changes in our fundamental ideas. We feel instinctively that it may mean a disturbance of our way of living and the abandonment and change of objectives; it is a threat to our peace of mind and our satisfaction with our lives. The idea of the earth's going round the sun was considered to be just as impious in its time of novelty as was the idea of Evolution by the Fundamentalist of the backward States to-day.

Then steadily and more and more abundantly came evidence to show that the existing forms of life were not all the forms of life, and that there had been a great variety of animals and plants which had passed away, a greater variety and multitude indeed than that which still exists. The science of geology became a new region of intellectual activity, and in the study of the earth's crust the traces of a past infinitely longer than men had hitherto suspected were unfolded. Varied and wonderful as was the present spectacle of life, the series of faunas and floras that had preceded it and passed away was found to be more wonderful. Life had a past, a stupendous past. So far from it being a thing of yesterday, the creation of a few thousand years ago, it had a history of enormous variety and infinite fascination. We can still imagine something of the excitement of our grandfathers when the fantastic and marvellous dinosaurs, the vege-

* From H. G. Wells, J. Huxley, and G. P. Wells, *The Science of Life,* Doubleday and Co., New York. Copyright 1934 by H. G. Wells, J. Huxley, and G. P. Wells. Reprinted by permission.

tation of the coal measures, the flying dragons of the Mesozoic Period were revealed to them. Continually now that once incredible catalogue is expanded. Every year the palaeontologist, the seeker and student of fossils, adds fresh details to this history of living forms. . . .

These ancient forms were not so strange and incredible as they seemed. Life had produced them on its way to its present state. Generation by generation it had changed from the wonder it was to the wonder it is. There had been no Creation since the beginning of life. Life had unfolded —or, to latinize unfold, it had been "evolved"—from some remote and very simple beginning. . . .

Life has come to its present variety through the modification year by year, and age by age, of simpler and less various ancestral species. In making this declaration we are denying a belief, formerly very prevalent, the belief that animal species, as they are now, came into being suddenly, through some abrupt act of Creation. That belief has now become impossible in the face of an assemblage of countless known and established facts. On the other hand all these contributing facts build themselves up into the comprehensive vision of Evolution . . . as well-established now as the roundness of the earth or the relative immensity of the sun. All these . . . facts have been disputed in the past. To-day controversy about any of them is dead.

Equally dead [as we have just seen] is the older and really more plausible belief that life has had numerous origins and, even now, can at times be created afresh. That, it seems, is not so. *Life is one thing.* Every living thing is related through a common descent to all the rest of life. There is no reason a priori why this should be so. But all the evidence is that it is so.

In all the three instances we have given—the round earth, the larger sun, and the evolution of life, men have disputed these great generalizations because they had started in life with contrary assumptions and found the shock of the new idea too great. They had intermingled their moral and religious ideas with the notion of a special creation of each kind of animal at a certain date, or with the notion of a flat earth, or with the notion of a small subservient sun going about our planet, and it seemed to them that if these notions were destroyed their very heavens would fall. But new generations have followed them, have accepted the new ideas and found the heavens of religious feeling and moral impulse none the worse for a broadened and enlightened outlook. To-day there is no denial of the fact of organic evolution except on the part of manifestly ignorant, prejudiced and superstitious minds.

But here we enter upon a less certain and established region of biological study. . . . we are going to discuss *how* individual development is carried out, and, further, *how* Evolution has occurred. There we find active and intelligent minds still differing very widely. What are the relations of individual development to the development of the species? There is no question any longer that Evolution has occurred, but our question is now, what has been its method? Or its methods?

This is a field where the débris and glow of recent controversies are still evident and where wide and often flaming differences of opinion are still found. . . . What are the Theories of Evolution between which we are asked to decide?

The fact of vital Evolution has gleamed upon intelligent minds at various phases in the world's history, but the modern revival of biological science had been going on for some time before it rose again to recognition. Linnaeus (1707–78) seems to have had no doubts of the fixity of species. It was only towards the close of the eighteenth century and with the increasing study of comparative anatomy and fossils that the fixity of species began to be questioned.

At first the fact of Evolution was seen piecemeal, as a possible change of one species into another within the boundaries of this or that restricted group of allied forms. It was not apprehended as a process comprehending all living things. Perhaps all the carnivores were genetically related, for example, or all the horned cattle. It was then generally called Transformism. The word Evolution came later. And the question whether the process included man was either not raised, or plainly or tacitly answered in the negative.

The first attempt to explain Transformism was to ascribe it to the effort of the living being to adapt itself to the often difficult conditions under which it had to live. The French naturalist Lamarck (1744–1829) pointed out that the individual was responsive to its circumstances, that it used and developed this organ and made little use of and therefore did not greatly develop that, that within limits need and exercise called forth structure; and he supposed that these individual adaptations were in a measure inherited. The three-toed horse—if we may use an example unkonwn to Lamarck—which under changing conditions was always scampering on firm prairies and scarcely ever going on soft ground, made no use of its once useful side-toes and so they were not stimulated to develop, while the business toe got all the work and all the benefit. The foals, according to the Lamarckian idea, inherited the enhanced main toe and the reduced side ones. This line of argument was made exceedingly plausible by the known fact that we all develop best the organs we use most; the rower his biceps, the singer his chest. The weakness of the Lamarckian case, or at least the unproven assumption of it, was that the individual development was in any degree inherited.

In ordinary biological discussion the individual development is called an "acquired characteristic": the size of the rower's biceps, for instance. Lamarck assumed the inheritance of acquired characteristics and found in that a partial explanation of Transformism. To this day the belief in the inheritance of acquired characters is called Lamarckism. With the inclusion of an involuntary response to the environment (such as the response of growing corals to currents or of the darkening of some birds' feathers when they are reared in a warm and humid atmosphere) and the inheritance of this response, it is called Neo-Lamarckism—Lamarckism modernized.

Lamarck's realisation of at least a limited evolution of species, Transformism, was based on an infinitely smaller knowledge of fact than we have to-day. He relied chiefly on fossil shells, rudimentary structures, and the manifest anatomical resemblances of animals for his belief that Evolution occurred. It was only later (1828) that Geoffroy St. Hilaire called attention to the embryological evidence for Evolution.

Several distinguished living biologists are Neo-Lamarckians.[1] And the view has appealed to many people because of the moral attractiveness of the idea of effort achieving enduring consequences. Master what you can of mathematics and your child will compute with greater ease; be merciful and your children will find it less difficult to practise mercy. One likes to think in that fashion. And with various additions and improvements Lamarckism is to be found vigorously paralleled in much modern thought outside the world of biological specialists. There has been added to the individual effort the idea of an upward driving force of a general sort. Bergson finds an *élan vital*, George Bernard Shaw a *life-force*, both mystical drives towards adaptation, coming from or active through the organism. Both owe something, no doubt, to Schopenhauer's idea of a driving Will in things. Whether such an hypothesis is necessary or even harmonious with the facts of the case we shall leave the reader to judge . . . We give it here as a second theory, which must be treated with respect, the theory of an upward *drive* in life.

Now, while Lamarck was elaborating his transformist ideas, an English clergyman, Dr. Malthus (1766–1834) was developing certain views that did not at first sight seem to have any bearing upon natural history and Transformism at all. His preoccupations seem to have been purely social. He was struck by the rapid increase of the human population about him —and he lived in a prolific age. It was increasing, he thought, much faster than was the food-supply. Consequently there was already a harsh

1. When this book was written, Neo-Lamarckism was officially supported by the U.S.S.R. and championed by Lysenko. For an excellent discussion of this policy see Julian Huxley's, *Heredity, East and West*. Ed.

struggle for subsistence going on. Mankind was breeding its way towards starvation; the weakest would go to the wall. Famine and the check of pestilence were the natural counters to this drift towards over-population and an unendurable poverty, and he urged his fellow-creatures to avoid such miseries by restraining their increase through late marriage and through continence. The artificial interference with conception known as birth-control or Neo-Malthusianism, we may note, had no place in his philosophy. That was as far as he got; he betrayed no consciousness of the bearing of his observations upon the ideas of Transformism, of which indeed he may have been quite unaware.

It happened, however, that his writings were read by two scientific travellers and naturalists who were both coming to believe in the fact of Evolution but by no means satisfied with Lamarckism as an explanation of it ("Creative Evolution" with its *élan vital* was still to come). These were Charles Darwin (1809–82) and Alfred Russel Wallace (1823–1913).

It is well to note here that Darwin did not "discover" Evolution, as many people suppose. Evolution is not Darwinism and Darwinism is not Evolution. The idea of Evolution is not only at least as old in modern thought as Lamarck, but adumbrations of it are clearly traceable in such ancient writers as Lucretius and Empedocles. But in the minds of Darwin and Wallace, looking for operating causes for the evolutionary process, the phrase of Malthus, "the struggle for subsistence," found a fruitful soil. Both realized a second great fact—for fact it is—in the general conditions of life, namely Natural Selection. Every living species is continually producing a multitude of individuals, many more than can all survive, varying more or less among themselves, and all competing against each other for food and a place in the sun. On the whole, Nature will let the better fitted ones live more abundantly and she will kill off the less happily constituted. The weaker will go to the wall; they will not breed so much; the stronger and their offspring will prevail. Assuming that weakness and strength and, in general, fitness and unfitness are hereditable qualities—and that is the general persuasion—a species must be always on the grindstone, having its unsuitable strains eliminated and its suitable strains left in possession.

Now, let us be quite clear here; speaking with precision, Natural Selection we say is not a theory but a fact. But does it, in connexion with the small differences that occur between every individual and its peers and the distinctive resemblance of parent and child, suffice to account for the whole spectacle of Evolution? With or without that element of effort and hereditable acquirement which Lamarckism asserts? There we come to speculative matter, to theories. Darwin thought it did. He did not contradict the Lamarckian hypothesis, but he added a new factor in the process, which factor he drew from Malthus. In 1859 he published a book which made an immense stir in the world, and he called it *The Origin of Species by Means of Natural Selection.* We have insisted that Natural Selection is not a theory. But, on the other hand, this appeal to the fact of Natural Selection and the fact of hereditable variations as giving between them a full and sufficient explanation of the fact of Evolution, is a theory; it is the Darwinian Theory. To the majority of even highly educated people at that period, educated for the most part upon lines of a narrow religious orthodoxy, it brought home for the first time the neglected and repudiated fact of Evolution, and made it seem credible. Explanatory theory and fact to be explained appeared together in their minds, and so to this day, in common talk, Evolution, Darwinism, and Natural Selection are hopelessly mixed and muddled. It became the custom to speak of the Darwinian Theory, the Theory of Natural Selection, and the Theory of Evolution indifferently.

Moreover, Darwin and his associates drew attention to the particular aspect of the question of Evolution that had hitherto been in the background. He followed up his *Origin of Species* by a book upon *The Descent of Man.* He insisted that man was an animal and that if the facts of Evolution were true they applied to man. If other living things had not been specially created but evolved, so, too, man must have been evolved. To do this was to challenge and bring into the discussion the whole world of contemporary theology. What had been a field of interesting speculation for naturalists became an arena of intense interest to the ordinary man.

Darwin's publication was followed by furious controversies, in which Thomas Henry Huxley (1825–95) and Ernst Haeckel (1834–1919) played notable parts in championing the evolutionary cause and defending Darwin and his views from misrepresentation. Huxley liked to call himself "Darwin's bull-dog." But the controversies did much to darken counsel in these matters. The fact of Evolution had to be proved to most people, and many were only too eager to suppose that the defeat or qualification of the theory would abolish the fact. To many of them to the end of their days it remained a theory, and an unsound one at that. All sorts of secondary considerations have played their part in these disputes. There is, for example, a real dislike of the fact of Natural Selection on the part of such a fine and sympathetic nature as Mr. G. B. Shaw's. It seems to him unchivalrous and vile for science to recognize that the weakest do go to the wall. It is hitting the fellow who is down. In the philosophy of a wilful life-force it is natural the wish should be father to the thought. He wishes things were not so, and therefore he declares they are not so, and he does it with great charm, confidence, and conviction. It pleases Mr. Shaw to tell the world at regular intervals that Natural Selection has been "exploded," and it does not hamper the operation of Natural Selection in the very least that he should do this. But Natural Selection has been no more "exploded" by recent research than the rejection of underweight coins at the Mint has been exploded by the doctrine of relativity. Wherever there are favourable or unfavourable hereditable variations Natural Selection must be at work.

Nearly three-quarters of a century have passed since the controversial cataclysms of the mid-Victorian period, and Darwinism has been criticized in every conceivable way. It cannot be said that it has been destroyed, but it has undergone restatement in certain respects.

The modification of a species by the natural selection of variations is still an undefeated theory. That idea from Darwin's writings lives and flourishes. The remoulding of Darwinism has concerned the part of it which deals with the mechanism of heredity and the intimate nature of variations. For in Darwin's time hardly anything was definitely known about the inheritance of individual differences. The chromosomes to be presently described had not yet been seen; the essential facts of fertilization were unknown; most important of all, experimental breeding had not drawn a clear distinction between variations which are inherited and those which are not. . . .

SEXLESS REPRODUCTION THE ORIGINAL METHOD

Among most of the higher animals reproduction, the origination of new individuals, is inseparable from sex. It takes two to make any addition to the race. But that is by no means true of life generally. Nearly all living things have some kind of sexual process, but most of them have also sexless ways of increasing their kind. In biological language, reproduction is often *asexual*. Our own strict adherence to a single generative technique is in fact to be regarded as the exceptional thing.

The most primitive way of multiplying, the method used by the smallest and simplest creatures, is by splitting the whole body into two halves, each of which grows into a complete new individual. This is known as *binary fission*. In such cases the offspring is not merely a detached part of the parent; the whole substance of the parent becomes offspring. The parent leaves no corpse. It ceases to exist; but for it there is no death—only duplication.

This reproduction by splitting, this multiplication of substance passed on into ever new individuals, is most spectacular in the bacteria. A simple bacterium in a congenial nutrient soup may easily accomplish its whole span of individual existence in half an hour. At zero hour, we have one specimen; in half an hour, two specimens—five hours, a thousand and twenty-four—ten hours, over a million—twenty-four hours (if the food holds out) hundreds of billions.

When the dividing animal has a complex structure, remarkable rearrangements must occur at each act of fission. Thus the complicated protozoan Stylonychia, although it is only a single cell, has a definite shape, with special bristles which act like legs, and a gullet armed with vibratile plates. During fission, many of the old organs disappear, new organs appear in each future individual, and, while division is being effected, develop into their definitive forms and migrate to their definitive stations.

Binary fission, we may note, is by no means unknown in many-celled animals. Not only do many sea-anemones reproduce by splitting themselves slowly through from the mouth downwards, but this longitudinal fission is one of the main methods by which the huge colonies of corals are built up from a single original polyp. Transverse division, on the other hand, occurs in various worms, especially Planarians.

From this method, two other main methods of asexual reproduction have been derived. One is multiple fission. In this, the single individual divides into many small ones, either by a series of binary fissions following immediately one upon the other without time for any growth between, or, more frequently in single-celled forms, the central nucleus alone divides repeatedly, and the cell as a whole then splits up simultaneously into as many miniature cells as there are nuclei. The parent individual becomes a mass of smaller cells. This method is frequent with single-celled creatures which grow to a—comparatively speaking—large size, such as Foraminifera, or the common large Amoeba, and is found also in the malarial parasite.

The other method consists in making the two products of division unequal. Sometimes, as in various Flatworms and Annelid worms, reproduction is by transverse division, but the hinder individual is at first small and unformed, and only gradually grows and develops. This method has the biological advantage that the original individual retains its individuality, its head and general alertness, while giving rise to a new specimen from the less specialized tissues of its hinder parts.

Sometimes we find this process several times repeated, and then whole chains of incompletely developed individuals may arise behind the original head, trailing after it until growth has developed them far enough to be detached. . . .

SEX IS A COMPLICATION OF REPRODUCTION

We come now to a difficult and fascinating problem, the problem of sex. What has sex to do with this reproductive process? Why, if creatures can multiply by mere division, should the complication of sex intrude into the life-cycle?

If we trace very briefly its evolution, and show how it presents itself among the simpler forms of life, we shall discover a fact which to us vertebrates seems startling—that essentially sex is not reproductive. *It is a different thing from reproduction.*

In the bacteria there is no sex. There is simply sexless proliferation. The creatures divide and divide by binary fission, by tearing themselves into halves, and as far as we can see they get on perfectly well without any form of sexual union. Thus the simplest living things to-day; and thus, presumably, life began.

Among the microscopic single-celled animals and plants we see the beginnings of sexual union. We see it appearing as a new intrusive process, perfectly distinct from reproductive proliferation, interrupting and delaying the latter and in its essence antagonistic to it. In the simplest flagellates, for example, the organisms multiply by binary fission just as bacteria do, but their life-history is complicated by a contrary tendency. Occasionally, if we are watching the creatures through a microscope, two individuals may be seen to come together and to melt completely into one. It is, of course, a much rarer event than normal fission—otherwise the species would not increase—and the individuals taking part in conjugation, as this union is called, often come from different and not very closely related stocks. And it is as obviously unrelated to reproduction as are feeding or excretion.

In other kinds of protozoa the process is varied in divers ways. In the highly organized Ciliates, for example, two individuals come to lie side by side and then exchange bits of their nuclei. Here the fusion does not involve the whole organism, but, nevertheless, there is a definite mixing of material from different strains. Here also the process is anti-reproductive, because it occupies time which might be spent in the normal rhythm of growth and fission; actually the act of union takes about as long as would three generations of ordinary fission.

In the simpler many-celled animals and plants—the slime-fungi, for example, or the seaweeds—the gradual entanglement of sex with reproduction can be seen. They reproduce by liberating clusters of tiny dancing flagellated cells whose business is to grow into new individuals. But before they do so these cells generally come together in pairs and melt into one. Here then the business of sexual conjugation is relegated to the reproductive cells. Their reproductive value is evidently diminished by this process which halves their number; but it has another compensating purpose, for the members of conjugating pairs are usually from different parents, and so it affords a method for the actual blending of living material from different stocks.

From these lowly plants we can trace a series of stages leading up to the state of affairs that is found in ourselves. In all the higher animals and plants the essence of the process is the same—the reproductive cells have to melt together before they can give rise to new individuals; they are called, therefore, *gametes,* or marrying cells. These gametes are usually of two kinds—active smaller male gametes or sperm-cells and passive larger female gametes or egg-cells. There is every gradation in this inequality. We may have quite equal cells conjugating or we may find very considerable inequality in the size of the conjugating cells. Thus, in the simplest phase of the sexual process there is neither male nor female; there is a sexual process without distinction of sex.

But as a further development of the appearance of the differentiation of the conjugating elements into larger and smaller there presently appears a differentiation of the parent bodies into those producing active and those producing larger conjugating cells. These are the incipient phases of sexual differentiation.

In plants, and in the lowest animals in which sex is thus entangled with reproduction, the sexual method exists, as an alternative to asexual, but in higher forms such as vertebrata reproduction is exclusively sex-ridden. Before we can produce new individuals there has to be this actual mixing of the substance of two parents. Even in our own species this is plainly an anti-reproductive thing, for if we could proliferate asexually it would take only one to do what now needs two, and we could multiply twice as fast. Thus, in the course of Evolution the two originally distinct and antagonistic processes have come together and become inseparably blended.

Evidently there is a riddle here, and one of very profound importance. There must be something very important about this sexual process, this mixing of the stuff of different stocks. What it is we shall presently discover, when the basal principles of heredity have been set forth.

SOME EVASIONS AND REPLACEMENTS OF SEXUALITY

In most of the higher animals, as we have noted, reproduction becomes inseparably entangled with sex. But Nature is a tricky worker; as living things have evolved she has vacillated and often enough she has changed her mind and gone back on her previous acts. A certain number of animals are curious in that they have returned to sexless methods of reproduction; evolved from purely sexual stocks, they have found ways of dodging the entanglement.

In many species there exist females which produce eggs as if for sexual reproduction, but nevertheless dispense with males. The eggs develop without fusion with a sperm; the offspring are fatherless. This "virgin reproduction" or *parthenogenesis* is found in a number of organisms, such as greenfly, water-fleas, rotifers, and occasionally flowering plants. . . .

Moreover, the human experimenter has found ways of getting round the need for sexual fusion. One of the most striking discoveries of modern biology was that of Jacques Loeb in 1899, that eggs which normally needed to be fertilized could be made to develop by substituting some man-devised treatment for the natural stimulus of the sperm. In other words, he caused artificial parthenogenesis. Artificial parthenogenesis was first induced by chemical treatment of sea-urchin eggs; later it was found that almost any eggs which are easily accessible to the experimenter by being laid into the water—including those of sea-urchins, starfish, worms, snails, and even frogs—can be made to develop unfertilized; and that the fatherless young thus produced can be as healthy as those arising in the ordinary course of Nature—fatherless starfish and sea-urchins and tadpoles have been reared to the adult stage. The agencies needed to lift the ban from the unfertilized egg and make it develop differ from animal to animal. Heat or shaking will do it in the starfish, while pricking with a needle dipped in blood (a recipe reminiscent of magic!) is needed for frogs.

In mammals the ovum is inaccessible to the experimenter, so that we do not know whether artificial parthenogenesis is possible. There is no reason to suppose that it is not. Surgery and experimental technique are advancing rapidly, so probably we shall find out very soon.

From these strange facts an important point emerges. It is that a spermatozoon does two things to the egg-cell when it fertilizes it. First of all it *activates* the egg-cell and makes development possible; this is the step that Loeb and his followers can imitate. Secondly, it, or part of it, blends physically with the egg, contributing material from another stock and so, as we shall learn, affording a basis for father-to-child heredity. The second is the essential sexual process. The first is simply a trick, devised by Nature for *preventing* reproduction until this all-important fusion shall have taken place. Once more it becomes evident to us that sex is imposed upon reproduction, and is in its essence a different thing.

WHAT IS MEANT BY THE GERM-PLASM

It is evident from what has gone before that, whether reproduction is sexual or whether it is not, there is material continuity between one generation and the next. The individual is a detached bit of its parent.

Weismann, the great German zoologist, pointed out in the latter half of the last century that that part of a man which grew into his children generally survived the rest of him. And a small part of him, growing into his grandchildren, survived still longer. Indeed, unless a man is childless, he does not wholly die. A bit of him, part of his living substance, is handed on, generation after generation, for ever.

For this immortal bit of the organism, that is to live on after the rest is done with, Weismann coined the phrase *germ-plasm.* He set it in contrast to the *soma,* which is the mortal remainder. More than 99.9 per cent by weight of the reader is soma; a fraction of an ounce of material in his testes or her ovaries is germ-plasm. The soma is the individual, who will live and die; the germ-plasm may go on indefinitely.

The germ-plasm is potentially immortal. Generation after generation it lives on, sprouting out bodies to house it and feed it and keep it warm, driving them with strange appetites and lusts so that it may get release from them and start again. Clearly it is the germ-plasm which evolves, not the ephemeral individual bodies that it throws out. The horse evolution was a slow modification of equine germ-plasm; the Micraster [2] evolution a steady change in sea-urchin germ-plasm; man's rise from the apes is also a stir in the germ-plasm.

For in a sense there is only one germ-plasm. Presumably life had a single origin; the living things we know to-day are divergent branches of one stock, twigs of one tree of germ-plasm. In the frame of space-time there is actual material continuity between Mr. Everyman, his wife, his cat, and his aspidistra.

On the workings of this germ-plasm we must for a while concentrate our attention.

THE MECHANISM OF INHERITANCE

We are now going down into almost ultra-microscopic mysteries. We are dealing with things quite outside and quite unlike the ordinary experiences of Mr. Everyman. Any analogies we can draw from the incidents of daily life are likely to be misleading. And yet what we have to tell here

2. A type of sea-urchin. Ed.

is among the most fundamental stuff of Mr. Everyman's life. All his innate character, all that much of his personal destiny, is determined by these hidden, microscopic, inhuman interactions we shall now detail. What we have to set forth, indeed, takes the place in modern knowledge of the dark spinning of the Fates. It is impossible to grasp modern concepts of the development and destiny of life unless a broad understanding of this, the fundamental texture of the life-process, is attained.

We have already made it clear that all living things take their origin in pieces of living substance detached from the bodies of other living things. This can now be extended by another statement—that every living cell arises from a pre-existing cell.

There are a few organisms, it is true, such as the slime-fungi and some seaweeds, in which cell-boundaries are lost or never developed. They form an exception to the statement, but an exception more logical than real. In the overwhelming majority of organisms, reproduction results from a continued division and growth of cells. Each of us originated, as most of the living things we know originated, from a single living egg-cell. That cell divided itself into two, and then into four, and then into eight, and so on until every one of the millions of cells in our bodies was produced. Cells are never generated independently, never (as was once imagined) arise spontaneously out of some formless matrix, any more than whole animals or plants arise spontaneously from formless slime or decaying corpses. That is why, in order to understand growth and reproduction, we have to think in terms of cells, and to study their methods of multiplication.

Principles of Heredity

Units of Living Matter *

by Ruth Moore (1961)

THE DISCOVERY OF THE CELL

Until the last years of the sixteenth century there was no way to look below the surface or beneath the structures laid bare by the scalpel. Only then did the Dutch spectacle-makers find that they could adjust two lenses in such a way as to enlarge an object under observation.

The microscope, with its ingenious arrangement of lenses and its ability to "overcome the infirmities of the senses," was exactly the kind of device to interest Robert Hooke (1635–1703).

In 1662, when the Royal Society was chartered, Hooke was named its curator. It was his duty to produce "three or four considerable experiments" for each of the weekly meetings.

For one of them the hard-worked curator brought in his own, improved compound microscope. To twentieth-century eyes it resembles a small fire-extinguisher. A nozzle-like lens was attached to a cylinder elaborately ornamented with scrollwork. To light an object under examination, a candle was set up nearby and its light concentrated on the object by means of a reflector and a small convex-plano lens.

"By the help of the microscope," Hooke told the royal fellows, "there is nothing so small as to escape our inquiry."

He predicted to his willing though skeptical audience that it was probable, or at least not improbable, that by working with the microscope science might discover the composition of bodies, the various textures of "their matter," and perhaps even the manner of their "inward motion."

Hooke beamed his candle on the stinging hairs of a nettle, on the head of a fly, on the tufted gnat, on the edge of a knife, on the beard of a wild oat, and on hundreds of other specimens.

Among them was cork—common enough, certainly, and yet remarkably

* From Ruth Moore, *The Coil of Life*, Alfred A. Knopf, New York. Copyright 1960 by Ruth Moore. Reprinted by permission. Revised for this edition.

354

able to hold air in a bottle "without suffering the least bubble to pass" and quite "unapt to suck or drink in water."

One day Hooke sharpened his penknife until it was "as keen as a razor" and cut a very thin slice from the surface. The sliver seemed quite white, so he put it on a black object plate. "And casting the light on it with a deep plano-convex glass," said Hooke, "I could exceedingly plainly perceive it all to be perforated and porous, much like a Honeycomb."

The pores that sprang into view were regular and yet not completely regular; they also varied about as those in the honeycomb did. The similarity went even further. The cork had "very little solid substance in comparison to the empty cavity that was contain'd between the *Interstitia* (or walls, as I may so call them). The walls or partitions were near as thin in proportion to their pores as those thin films of wax in a honeycomb are to theirs." (Figure 7–2.)

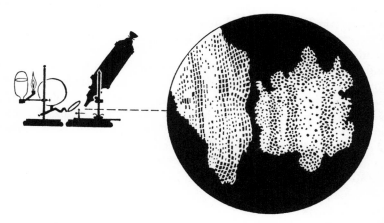

Figure 7–2. Discovery of the cell. When Hooke placed thin slices of cork under his microscope, he saw that they were made up of "an infinite company of small Boxes or Bladders of Air"—cells.

"Next," said Hooke, naming for all time the fundamental unit of living matter, the cork was like honeycomb "in that those pores, or *cells*, were not deep but consisted of a great many little Boxes. . . .

"I no sooner discern'd these (which were indeed the first microscopic pores I ever saw, and perhaps that were ever seen, for I had not met with any Writer or Person, that had made any mention of them before this) but me thought I had with the discovery of them, presently hinted to me the true and intelligible reason of all the *Phaenomena of Cork*."

If Hooke did not foresee the full implication of his epochal discovery, he understood well that it was important and promising.

THE DISCOVERY OF UNITS OF HEREDITY

The next insight into what lay below the largely impenetrable surface of life, came from another investigator working on a totally different problem.

Gregor Johann Mendel was born on July 22, 1822, into a long-settled peasant family living in the tiny village of Heinzendorf in what was then Austrian Silesia and is now Czechoslovakia. As a boy he aided his father in the grafting of trees and in cultivating the garden that was a part of "peasant holding no. fifty-eight." He received additional training in horticulture and beekeeping at the village school. Johann did so well in this work and in his academic studies that his teachers urged that he be sent on to the high school at Troppau. Mendel never lost his love of growing things as he struggled to make his way at Troppau and later at the Philosophical Institute at Olmütz. Gradually this early interest turned into a wider interest in science, although little science was included in the institute's course.

Mendel finished his two years at Olmütz with a fine record, but in a state of physical exhaustion. His parents had tried valiantly to help their promising son through school, even turning over to him the dowry of one of his sisters. They simply did not have the funds to take care of even the extremely modest cost of his education. Through most of his years at school Mendel was on "half-rations" so meager that he was constantly hungry and scarcely had the energy for his studies and the tutoring that he was always forced to do. As he finished the two-year institute course, he knew that he could no longer go on. The university was out of the question. In desperation, Mendel appealed to one of his teachers for advice.

Many years later in a third-person autobiographical note he wrote: "It had become impossible for him to continue such strenuous exertions. It was incumbent on him to enter a profession in which he would be spared perpetual anxiety about a means of livelihood."

The teacher understood. He suggested that Mendel enter the Augustinian monastery at Brünn. It was noted for the learning of its monks, and there Mendel would have an opportunity, free of the pressure of earning a living, to go on with the studies that he loved. His teacher would be happy to recommend him. Mendel gratefully accepted. A letter went to the monastery calling attention to Mendel's "most exceptional" reports at the institute and to his "very solid character." And so it came about that on October 9, 1843, Mendel was admitted to the monastery as a novice. He assumed the name of Gregor.

The young monk was appointed a "supply" teacher in the high school at Znaim in southern Moravia. As he did not have a teacher's certificate, he could not be given a full appointment. Mendel could not have been happier with this turn in his life, and he at once took to teaching, as he had to life in the monastery, "with pleasure and love."

Mendel was so excellent a teacher that the head of the school confidently urged him to try for a teacher's certificate. Mendel wrote the necessary essay and presented himself in Vienna for the oral examinations in the natural history and physics that he wanted to teach. He failed to pass the examination, partly, it seemed, because he lacked certain formal knowledge of his subjects. In part his failure may have been due to the conviction of the friendly chief examiner that the unusual young teacher should be given an opportunity for "higher scientific training" at the University of Vienna.

The abbot of the monastery agreed, and Mendel went to the university for four terms. At the end, he returned to teach in the Brünn "Modern School."

Soon after entering the monastery Mendel began trying to develop new colors in flowers. He also took up the breeding of gray and white mice. Although the latter experiments were dropped after a while, probably at a hint of ecclesiastical disapproval, they were a certain indication that the work with flowers was not a fancy but the first approach of a serious scientist to a fundamental problem.

Mendel's own account of how he happened to begin his studies is a simple one. As he tried to produce new colors in his flowers, he acquired considerable experience in artificial fertilization. His interest was aroused by the surprising and unaccountable results that he sometimes obtained. Whenever he crossed certain species, the same hybrid forms cropped up with striking regularity. But when he crossed one of his hybrids with another, some very different characters sometimes appeared among their progeny.

These phenomena sent Mendel to the literature. He searched all the books available in the monastery and elsewhere in Brünn. A number of scientists were working with the problem of hybrids, but no one had discovered any law governing their formation—if, indeed, anyone could conceive of a law capable of explaining the infinitude of forms in the multitude of plants. Inheritance in all its profusion seemed beyond any nailing down.

Mendel nevertheless had seen certain forms appearing with regularity. Others too had noted this phenomenon. They had not, as far as Mendel could find, counted the forms and classified them. Nor had anyone arranged hybrids according to their generations or worked out their statistical relationships. Mendel, in his remote Austrian town, did not realize that even his concept of counting and figuring the mathematical relationships of hybrid plants was original and entirely his own.

To study heredity properly, Mendel saw, a large number of generations would have to be bred. He also recognized that many plants would have to be included in each generation. A few might produce a misleading picture. "It indeed required some courage to undertake such far-reaching labors," Mendel wrote later in the introduction to one of his monographs. "It appears, however, to be the only way in which we can finally reach the solution of a problem which is of great importance in the evolution of organic forms."

The year was 1854. Many people were asking how the great number of species could have arisen, and yet Charles Darwin would not publish *The Origin of Species* for another five years. It seems unlikely that the Austrian monk was planning a direct study of the great problem of evolution. His interest was concentrated on heredity and how traits could be handed on from parent to offspring. Nevertheless, as his words show, Mendel was well aware of the evolutionary significance of the work he was about to launch.

Mendel planned the big experiment with care and foresight. His first requirement was a plant with varied characters, each of which bred true to form. If a plant produced green peas, he had to be sure that it would go on producing green peas if crossed with another green-pea plant. Mendel also had to have a plant that could be protected from foreign pollen during its flowering period. If even one bee carried in some pollen other than that he would dust on, the whole experiment would be upset. Equally important, the characters had to be easily observable and countable. It was a huge task Mendel was laying out for himself.

The patient monk did not hurry. He tried out enough plants to see that the common pea would best meet his specifications for an experimental plant. His next job was to make sure of his material.

Mendel obtained thirty-four more or less distinct varieties of peas from seedsmen and planted them in his monastery garden. With the exception of one whose seeds quite evidently had been mistakenly mixed, each variety yielded offspring exactly like itself. He repeated the plantings during a second year. The results were the same.

His seeds, then, were reliable; he had his raw material. From the thirty-four varieties Mendel selected twenty-two, and from these, seeds with seven sharply contrasting pairs of characters. As he wanted to make no fine-line decisions about whether or not a part of a plant had changed, he selected the following clear-cut differences with which to work:

1. The form of the ripe seeds—round or wrinkled;
2. The color of the peas (the seed)—yellow or intense green;
3. The color of the transparent seed cover or skin—white or grayish;
4. The form of the ripe pods—inflated or constricted between the peas;
5. The color of the unripe pods—green or yellow;
6. The position of the flowers—distributed along the stem or bunched at the top: in other words, axial or terminal;
7. The length of the stem—tall (six or seven feet) or dwarf (three-fourths to one and a half feet).

Each kind of seed went into its own jar—to await the spring of 1856.

Mendel was at last ready to launch his experiment proper. In one section of his long narrow garden he planted round seeds, and in the next section, wrinkled ones. In other sections went the yellow and the green, and, in their own places, all of the others. Keeping the characters that he wanted to compare next to one another would simplify the work that lay ahead.

The peas did well in the warm, gentle Austrian spring and soon were ready to blossom. Mendel then had to work rapidly, for timing mattered. He opened some of the pretty flower buds of his wrinkled plants, removed the keel from each, and pinched off the stamen to prevent the peas from fertilizing themselves in the normal manner. Then he tied a little paper or calico bag around each one to protect the exposed stigma.

As soon as the pollen had ripened in the adjoining round peas, Mendel collected a bit on a fine camel's-hair brush and, removing the bags on the wrinkled peas, dusted it on their stigmas. The little bags then were tied on again to keep away the bees and other pollen-carrying insects. To make certain that his experiments were not affected by which plant served as the seed parent, Mendel also reversed his fertilization procedure. Some of the pollen from the wrinkled peas was deposited on the prepared stigmas of the round.

The same meticulous process was repeated in each of the other special plots. Altogether Mendel made 287 cross-fertilizations on seventy plants. It was a good growing summer and the peas flourished in what the monks called Mendel's "pea plantation."

Mendel was in the garden early and late, watching over the maturing plants. His first indication of what was happening would come when the pods formed in the "unripe pod color" section of his garden. As the pods appeared and filled out and grew longer, Mendel saw with elation that all of them were green. Whether they grew in the "yellow" half of the plot and came from parents that had produced yellow pods or in the "green" half and sprang from parents with green pods, all of them hung green on the vines. Yellow and green parents alike had produced green offspring. Mendel searched his plants. He could not find a single yellow among the unripe pods. [Figure 7-3.]

Confirmation of this striking result came as the summer drew to a close and the pods dried on the vines. Mendel had to let the pods in the "ripe pod form" section dry thoroughly, for only then were the shape of the pods and the color of the peas they contained completely "set." As the pods turned dry and brownish, there could be no doubt. All of them were inflated. It was as though the "constriction" of half of the parents had never existed.

All of this foretold the outcome of his other experiments, and yet Mendel did not dare to be sure. He tremblingly prepared to open the first pod in the "seed color" section. Would the peas so snugly contained in it, invisible until the moment of opening, show only one color? Here was the final, the critical test. In an instant's glance he saw that there was no question. The peas so nicely ranged against the sere brown of the pod were an unmistakable bright orangey yellow. Mendel harvested his other pods and opened them one by one. Each was filled with yellow peas alone. Not a pea was green or displayed even a trace of its half-green ancestry. If the peas had been pure gold, they could not have looked better to the happy monk.

It was the same when Mendel opened the peas from his "seed form" plot. All of them were round. This time it was the wrinkling of half of the parents which had disappeared.

During the winter, as he studied his jars of peas and the way all had completely taken on the character of one parent, it was evident that one characteristic in each pair had been entirely "dominant" over the other. Mendel decided to designate the hereditary trait that prevailed as a "dominant." Later he named the other factor, the one lost to sight, a "recessive."

Only the first step had been completed in the big experiment. The next, the crossing of hybrid with hybrid, had to await another spring. As the sun grew warm and the spring rains fell, Mendel planted his hybrid seeds. Each carefully marked group went into its own plot, but this time his procedure would be different. He would not operate on the buds. He would permit the peas to fertilize themselves in the natural way, and thus would obtain a cross of two identical hybrids.

The plantation was again filled with pea vines, and Mendel waited as patiently as he could for the pods and peas to form and dry.

As the young pods grew, Mendel saw a few yellows appearing among the greens. He counted both colors and entered the figures in his notebooks. When the pods dried in the "pod form" plot, some were crinkled

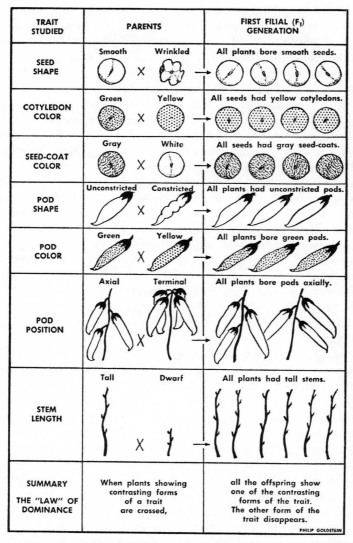

TRAIT STUDIED	PARENTS		FIRST FILIAL (F₁) GENERATION
SEED SHAPE	Smooth X	Wrinkled	All plants bore smooth seeds.
COTYLEDON COLOR	Green X	Yellow	All seeds had yellow cotyledons.
SEED-COAT COLOR	Gray X	White	All seeds had gray seed-coats.
POD SHAPE	Unconstricted X	Constricted	All plants had unconstricted pods.
POD COLOR	Green X	Yellow	All plants bore green pods.
POD POSITION	Axial X	Terminal	All plants bore pods axially.
STEM LENGTH	Tall X	Dwarf	All plants had tall stems.
SUMMARY THE "LAW" OF DOMINANCE	When plants showing contrasting forms of a trait are crossed,		all the offspring show one of the contrasting forms of the trait. The other form of the trait disappears.

PHILIP GOLDSTEIN

Figure 7–3. Results of Mendel's "first set of experiments." (From Philip Gold-stein, Genetics Is Easy, *Lantern Press, 1955. Copyright 1955 by Lantern Press. Reprinted by permission.)*

around the peas they contained; they were, in the terms he was using, constricted. The others were inflated. Again Mendel counted both types, and again he reserved judgment.

At last the day came when the pods could be gathered. Mendel opened the first pod from the "seed color" beds and looked upon a remarkable sight. In the pod with four bright yellow peas was one of green. It seemed to glow against the yellow and the honey tones of the pods. The green was no accident. Most of the pods contained both green and yellow peas. The green of the grandparents was reappearing, and it was as sharp, as clear, as unequivocal as though it had never been associated with the yellow through one entire generation. Mendel no longer had to question. The green had not been lost. Somehow this heritage from the grandparents had persisted and had come forth again.

Mendel began his tally, the tally that he was relying on to explain the relationships to which the yellow and green peas testified. From his 258 plants he obtained 8023 peas. Exactly 6022 were yellow and 2001 green. It was immediately evident, when the score was kept in this way, that three fourths were yellow and one fourth green. The ratio was 3 to 1, the same ratio he had seen in the color of the unripe pods and in the form of the ripe ones. [Figure 7–4.]

Mendel went on to his computation on seed form. The 253 hybrid plants in the "seed form" experiment produced 7324 peas, of which 5474 were round and 1850 wrinkled. Therefore the ratio was 2.96 to 1, or virtually the same 3 to 1.

The same significant ratio turned up in all the other crossings of hybrid with hybrid: 3.15 to 1 on the color of the seed coat, 2.95 to 1 on the form of the pod, and within this range for all the others. The average for the entire group was 3 to 1. Here was no chance combination of numbers, but a regularly occurring phenomenon, a revelation of the long-hidden workings of heredity.

Mendel continued his plantings through six or seven generations in all cases. As he did so, he learned that the 3-to-1 ratio applied to the appearance of the peas only. When Mendel planted the hybrid parents, they produced both round and wrinkled seeds. One fourth were pure rounds and, as long as they were planted, would yield only round peas. Two fourths were round in appearance, but were actually hybrids and in the next generation would produce round and wrinkled peas in a steady 3-to-1 ratio. The wrinkled peas from the union were again pure wrinkled and never would yield anything but their own kind. The wrinkled peas from the first hybrids yielded only wrinkled peas and continued to produce only wrinkled as long as he planted them and permitted them to fertilize themselves. They were pure recessives also. (Figure 7–5.)

TRAIT STUDIED	F₁ HYBRIDS SHOW	F₂ GENERATION PRODUCED BY SELFING THE F₁ HYBRIDS.		RATIO
		SHOWING THE DOMINANT	SHOWING THE RECESSIVE	DOMINANT TO RECESSIVE
SEED SHAPE	Smooth	Smooth → 5,474	Wrinkled + 1,850	2.96:1
COTYLEDON COLOR	Yellow	Yellow → 6,022	Green + 2,001	3.01:1
SEED-COAT COLOR	Gray	Gray → 705	White + 224	3.15:1
POD SHAPE	Unconstricted	Unconstricted → 882	Constricted + 299	2.95:1
POD COLOR	Green	Green → 428	Yellow + 152	2.82:1
POD POSITION	Axial	Axial → 651	Terminal + 207	3.14:1
STEM LENGTH	Tall	Tall → 787	Dwarf + 277	2.84:1
✱ ✱ ✱	TOTALS	14,949 Show the dominant	5,010 Show the recessive	2.98:1
SUMMARY PHILIP GOLDSTEIN	When an F₁ hybrid is selfed	some of the F₂ plants show the DOMINANT TRAIT, and some show the RECESSIVE TRAIT.		in the ratio of approximately 3:1

Figure 7–4. Results of Mendel's "second set of experiments." (From Philip Goldstein, Genetics Is Easy.)

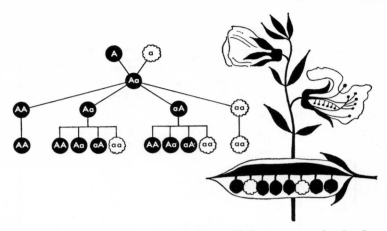

Figure 7–5. The crossing of round and wrinkled peas reveals the laws of heredity. All of the first generation were round. But when two round hybrids were crossed, the wrinkling of one of the grandparents reappeared, in the ratio of one to three. Another generation reveals the true nature of the hybrids.

"It can be seen," said Mendel, "how rash it may be to draw from the external resemblances conclusions as to their internal nature."

Appearance meant little or nothing. It was not surprising that human beings had eternally been bewildered when they tried to understand heredity. The surface differences of offspring were legion in themselves, and yet below the surface lay still other differences and possibilities for variation.

With the clarity and simplicity of genius, Mendel labeled the "dominant" in the union with a capital *A*, and the recessive with a small *a*. A constant dominant thus would be formed by the coming together of two *A*'s, and it would be described as *AA;* a hybrid by either *Aa* or *aA;* and a recessive by *aa*.

With this understanding, it was possible for him to chart this coming together and separation and the clear-cut results that it produced. Mendel drew, and the world has since followed, his chart of heredity.

In initiating his work Mendel had kept his attention fixed on a single pair of characters. He inevitably had to ask whether the same laws of development would apply if several diverse characters were united. Suppose the parents differed in two characteristics.

Mendel crossed peas with round yellow seeds with those bearing wrinkled greens. As roundness and yellowness were dominant, he expected that all of the peas from the union would be round and yellow. And so they turned out to be.

The next year Mendel let the round yellow hybrids fertilize themselves. When the peas were ripe, some of the monks and others interested in science gathered around for the opening of the first pods. Tension mounted as Mendel cracked open the dry pods. And then even the un-initiated were startled. In the one pod lay four different kinds of peas: round and yellow, wrinkled and yellow, round and green, and wrinkled and green. It was almost overwhelming to see Nature, supposedly un-predictable Nature, responding with such precision to an experimental test.

Mendel eagerly counted the 556 peas borne by the fifteen double-hybrid plants he had grown. He had 315 round and yellow peas, 101 wrinkled and yellow, 108 round and green, and 32 wrinkled and green. When two pairs of characteristics were crossed, the ratio was no longer 3 to 1; it was 9:3:3:1. [Figure 7–6.]

Charles Darwin also had experimented with peas and had noticed that the hybrid divided 3 to 1, but Darwin was no mathematician and did not pursue this revealing indication of order in heredity. Mendel, on the other hand, was an excellent mathematician. The new experiment confirmed what he had already glimpsed in his first experiments. He was simply obtaining every combination that could be formed by the separate factors present. If A and a were combined, only one combination could be formed: Aa. If Aa and Aa came together, four combinations could be made: AA, Aa, aA, aa. And this was exactly what had happened.

And if two series were united—$AA + 2\,Aa + aa$ and $BB + 2\,Bb + bb$, sixteen different groupings could be produced. And as the dominants would determine the appearance of each group, the result would be 9 AB, 3 Ab, 3 aB, and 1 ab.

Mendel now felt virtually certain of the principle that lay behind all the different forms of nature. He felt, though, that his tests should be carried at least one step further, for these were strange and unheard-of laws that he was working out. Mendel decided to study three differing traits.

This was the most difficult of all his experiments. Round yellow peas with grayish seed coats were crossed with pollen from plants bearing wrinkled, green, white-skinned peas. It took "time and trouble," Mendel noted, but the twenty-seven groupings that his calculations showed should result did come from the union. He obtained all the combinations that could be made by putting together three series, $AA + 2\,Aa + aa$, $BB + 2\,Bb + bb$, and $CC + 2\,Cc + cc$. Again Mendel could see how it went. With one pair of hybrids, three kinds of offspring; with two, nine; with three, twenty-seven. The combinations piled up, three times three times three.

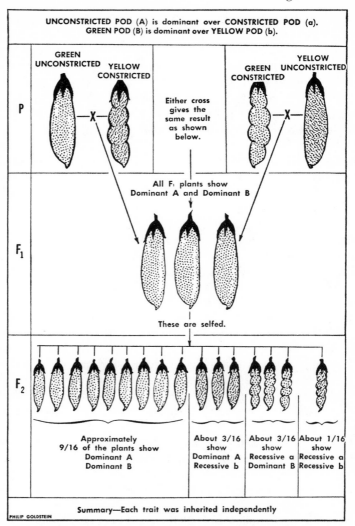

Figure 7–6. The inheritance of two traits simultaneously as demonstrated by Mendel's experiment. (From Philip Goldstein, Genetics Is Easy.)

Mendel had no way to look into the egg and pollen cells to search for the hereditary factors whose existence he inferred from his experiments. His results, however, were explainable in no other way. Just as Mendel had grasped the secrets of the combinations of these factors, so did he reason out the biological basis that had to underlie them. He formulated three laws of inheritance:

1. All living things are a complex of a large number of independent heritable units.

2. When each parent contributes the same kind of factor and the two come together in the offspring, a constant character is produced. But if one parent contributes one kind of factor, say *A*, and the other another, say *a*, a hybrid results. When the hybrid forms reproductive cells, the two differentiating elements "liberate themselves" again and thus are free to form new combinations in the next union.

3. The factors are unaffected by their long association in the individual. They emerge from the union as distinct as when they entered it.

In a letter to a fellow scientist Mendel enlarged upon this radical idea: "The course of development consists simply in this: that in each successive generation the two primal characters issue distinct and unadulterated out of the hybridized pair, there being nothing whatever to show that either of them had inherited or taken over anything from the others."

This was Mendel's ultimately famous law of the purity of the gametes, or reproductive cells. Mendel regarded it only as a hypothesis, and felt that he must subject it to additional tests.

If the hereditary factors separated and re-combined as his work indicated, there were two ways to prove it. He would fertilize the hybrid *AaBb*, a plant having round yellow seeds, with pollen from the parent plant *AB*, which also had round yellow seeds. As far as the eye could see, both were exactly alike. Actually the hybrid would have four factor pairs —*AB, Ab, aB, ab*—and the parent plant only *AB*. Mendel figured out all the combinations that could result if these pairs were combined. There were four: *AABB, AABb, AaBB,* and *AaBb*. And as each pair would contain a dominant, all should have round yellow seeds.

Mendel made his proposed cross-fertilization. As the young plants matured, he again watched anxiously, knowing once more exactly what results he should obtain if his theory was correct. At last the pods were ripe and dry. They contained ninety-eight peas, and every single pea was round and yellow.

Mendel's second test was a "back cross with the recessive parent." The hybrid again had the egg cells *AB, Ab, aB, ab,* and the green wrinkled parent, *ab*. In his notebook Mendel noted the combinations that should result: *AaBb* (round and yellow), *Aabb* (round and green), *aaBb* (wrinkled and yellow), and *aabb* (wrinkled green), and all of them should appear in equal numbers.

His plants in due time produced 31 round yellow peas, 28 round and green, 27 wrinkled and yellow, and 26 wrinkled and green. If enough plants had been raised, the slight variation in numbers would have disappeared. The peas developed as Mendel's theory had forecast and in the ratio he had predicted—1:1:1:1. "In all the experiments," said Mendel, "there appeared all the forms which the proposed theory demands."

At last the time had come to report on his eight years of unremitting work. During the fall and early winter of 1864 Mendel checked and rechecked his findings. In his fine copperplate script he wrote the paper that eventually would explain to the world the all-important phenomenon of heredity.

The Brünn Society for the Study of Natural Science was holding its February 1865 meeting at the Modern School, the school in which Mendel taught. The night was cold and snowy, but most of the forty members came to hear Mendel report on the work he had so long been carrying on at the monastery. Curiosity about it was keen.

As Mendel read, this curiosity gave way to incomprehension. The several botanists in the society were as much confused by the report on invariable hereditary ratios in peas as were the other members—a chemist, an astronomer, a geologist, and an authority on cryptograms. Mendel spoke for the hour allotted to him, and then announced that at the next meeting he would explain why the peculiar and regular segregation of characteristics occurred.

The next month, as Mendel presented his algebraic equations, attention wavered. The combination of mathematics and botany which Mendel was expounding was unheard of. And the idea that lay behind it, that heredity was a giant shuffling and reshuffling of separate and invisible hereditary factors, stood in such diametrical contrast to all that had been taught that it probably could not be grasped. No one rose to ask a question. The minutes recorded no discussion.

A number of the members spoke to Mendel afterward about his experimental work. "I encountered various views," Mendel told his friends. "No one undertook a repetition of the experiment."

The editor of the *Proceedings* of the society extended the usual invitation to Mendel to prepare his paper for publication in the society's journal. "I agreed to do so," said Mendel, "after I had once more looked through my notes relating to the various years of the experiment without being able to discover any sort of mistake."

Mendel's monograph—*Versuche uber Pflanzenhybriden*—appeared in 1866. According to the society's custom, copies of the *Proceedings* in which it was included were sent to Vienna, Berlin, Rome, St. Petersburg, and Uppsala. But the brief paper that could have altered all ideas of heredity, and at a time when Darwin was still at work on the role of heredity in evolution, attracted no attention.[1] It sat all but unread on library shelves.

Experiments in Plant Hybridization *—(The "Lost Paper")
by Gregor Mendel (1865)

Experience of artificial fertilization, such as is effected with ornamental plants in order to obtain new variations in color, has led to the experiments which will here be discussed. The striking regularity with which the same hybrid forms always reappeared whenever fertilization took place between the same species induced further experiments to be undertaken, the object of which was to follow up the developments of the hybrids in their progeny.

To this object numerous careful observers, such as Kölreuter, Gärtner, Herbert, Lecoq, Wichura, and others, have devoted a part of their lives with inexhaustible perseverance. Gärtner especially, in his work "The Production of Hybrids in the Vegetable Kingdom," has recorded very valuable observations; and quite recently Wichura published the results of some profound investigations into the hybrids of the willow. That, so far, no generally applicable law governing the formation and development of hybrids has been successfully formulated can hardly be wondered at by anyone who is acquainted with the extent of the task and can appreciate the difficulties with which experiments of this class have to contend. A final decision can only be arrived at when we shall have before us the results of detailed experiments made on plants belonging to the most diverse orders.

Those who survey the work done in this department will arrive at the conviction that, among all the numerous experiments made, not one has been carried out to such an extent and in such a way as to make it possible to determine the number of different forms under which the offspring of hybrids appear, or to arrange these forms with certainty according to their separate generations, or definitely to ascertain their statistical relations.

1. *The Origin of Species* had been published in 1859, only seven years earlier, and Darwin was at work on his book on *Variations in Animals and Plants under Domestication.*

* Selections from the original paper published in the *"Verh. naturf. Ver. in Brünn," Abhandlung iv.* 1865 ("Proceedings of the Natural History Society of Brünn," Vol. IV, 1865), actually issued in 1866. The English translation was made by the Royal Horticultural Society of London with minor revisions by Bateson.

It requires indeed some courage to undertake a labor of such far-reaching extent; this appears, however, to be the only right way by which we can finally reach the solution of a question, the importance of which cannot be overestimated in connection with the history of the evolution of organic forms.

The paper now presented records the results of such a detailed experiment. This experiment was practically confined to a small plant group and is now, after eight years' pursuit, concluded in all essentials. Whether the plan upon which the separate experiments were conducted and carried out was the best suited to attain the desired end is left to the friendly decision of the reader.

SELECTION OF THE EXPERIMENTAL PLANTS

The value and utility of any experiment are determined by the fitness of the material to the purpose for which it is used, and thus in the case before us it cannot be immaterial what plants are subjected to experiment and in what manner such experiments are conducted.

The selection of the plant group which shall serve for experiments of this kind must be made with all possible care if it be desired to avoid from the outset every risk of questionable results.

The experimental plants must necessarily—

1. Possess constant differentiating characters.

2. The hybrids of such plants must, during the flowering period, be protected from the influence of all foreign pollen or be easily capable of such protection.

The hybrids and their offspring should suffer no marked disturbance in their fertility in the successive generations.

Accidental impregnation by foreign pollen, if it occurred during the experiments and were not recognized, would lead to entirely erroneous conclusions. Reduced fertility or entire sterility of certain forms, such as occurs in the offspring of many hybrids, would render the experiments very difficult or entirely frustrate them. In order to discover the relations in which the hybrid forms stand toward each other and also toward their progenitors, it appears to be necessary that all members of the series developed in each successive generation should be, without exception, subjected to observation.

At the very outset special attention was devoted to the *Leguminosae* on account of their peculiar floral structure. Experiments which were made with several members of this family led to the result that the genus *Pisum* was found to possess the necessary qualifications.

Some thoroughly distinct forms of this genus possess characters which are constant, and easily and certainly recognizable, and when their hybrids are mutually crossed they yield perfectly fertile progeny. Furthermore, a disturbance through foreign pollen cannot easily occur, since the fertilizing organs are closely packed inside the keel and the anther bursts within the bud, so that the stigma becomes covered with pollen even before the flower opens. This circumstance is of special importance. As additional advantages worth mentioning, there may be cited the easy culture of these plants in the open ground and in pots, and also their relatively short period of growth. Artificial fertilization is certainly a somewhat elaborate process, but nearly always succeeds. For this purpose the bud is opened before it is perfectly developed, the keel is removed, and each stamen carefully extracted by means of forceps, after which the stigma can at once be dusted over with the foreign pollen.

In all, thirty-four more or less distinct varieties of peas were obtained from several seedsmen and subjected to a two-years' trial. In the case of one variety there were noticed, among a larger number of plants all alike, a few forms which were markedly different. These, however, did not vary in the following year, and agreed entirely with another variety obtained from the same seedsman; the seeds were therefore doubtless merely accidentally mixed. All the other varieties yielded perfectly constant and similar offspring; at any rate, no essential difference was observed during two trial years. For fertilization twenty-two of these were selected and cultivated during the whole period of the experiments. They remained constant without any exception. . . .

DIVISION AND ARRANGEMENT OF THE EXPERIMENTS

If two plants which differ constantly in one or several characters be crossed, numerous experiments have demonstrated that the common characters are transmitted unchanged to the hybrids and their progeny; but each pair of differentiating characters, on the other hand, unite in the hybrid to form a new character, which in the progeny of the hybrid is usually variable. The object of the experiment was to observe these variations in the case of each pair of differentiating characters, and to deduce the law according to which they appear in the successive generations. The experiment resolves itself, therefore, into just as many separate experiments as there are constantly differentiating characters presented in the experimental plants. . . .

Units of Change *

by Ruth Moore (1961)

> Much of what we know about man is derived from
> the study of sweet peas and vinegar flies.
>
> Author unknown

MUTATIONS AND THE REDISCOVERY OF MENDEL

Mendel's experiments with peas seemed to have been entirely forgotten
except by the few who knew of them personally. No one thought to preserve his papers and records; they were destroyed.

As the years passed and men continued to work at the basic problem of
how the characteristics of the parent are passed along to the offspring,
others sought some of the answers by studying hybrids. They drew closer
to Mendel's work. W. O. Focke, one of the scientists studying heredity,
somehow came upon a reference to Mendel's work. He told Hugo Iltis,
Mendel's fellow townsman who devoted many years to writing a biography of the monk, that he did not know what had drawn his attention to
Mendel's work and led him to look up his writings. Focke failed to see
that Mendel had discovered the answers that he and other students of
heredity were seeking, but he was sufficiently impressed to list the Mendel
monographs in his own book on hybrids.

Thirty-five years after Mendel had completed his work, his monographs
at last were read by a man who could appreciate their significance. Continuing research had prepared the way. Hugo De Vries (1848–1935),
professor of botany at the University of Amsterdam, was a reverent
admirer of the work of Charles Darwin and an advocate of the theory of
evolution. But he was troubled about one major difficulty in the theory
which had persisted even into the 1880's. It seemed to De Vries that there
could be no question about Darwin's basic theory that "descent with
modification is the main law of nature in the organic world," and yet how
did the modification come about? Could natural selection acting only on
the infinitude of small variations that occur in all individuals account for
the wide differences between species and for the diversity of the living
world?

As a botanist, De Vries knew that breeders could go only so far in
working with individual variations. There was a limit to how pink a
rose, how tall a plant, how hardy a bulb they could develop by crossing

* From Ruth Moore, *The Coil of Life.*

two varieties. They could never obtain anything new until some new and different character appeared in Nature to give them the material with which to work. Darwin himself, though not all of his followers, had emphasized the importance of the wholly new—the sport, as he called it —that sometimes appears. If the problem were to be understood, De Vries thought, Nature should be studied in the act of changing. He decided to seek for evidence of large natural changes. They would most likely be found, he was sure, in some place where plants were multiplying rapidly in a new setting. He found it where some primrose plants had escaped from a garden into an abandoned potato field.

During the next twenty years De Vries observed and raised 53,509 primrose plants, and among them found eight new species.[1] The new forms in every case appeared full-blown, without gradation, without step-by-step change. And, once established, a new form maintained itself intact. All the while the other plants went on year after year repeating themselves with only the usual small variations.

As he completed his prodigious experiment, De Vries could formulate some of the laws of mutability which underlay the spectacle of the yellow flowers. He saw that each character—each differently formed leaf, each varied petal, each height—varied by itself. A new red-veined leaf could appear without any change occurring in most other parts of the plant. One character, or at most a small group of characters, mutated at one time. There was never an over-all change in all parts of the plant.

"Attributes of organisms consist of distinct, separate, and independent units," said De Vries. "These units can be associated in groups, and we find in allied species the same units and groups of units."

A mutation, then, was a change in a hereditary unit that was later to be called a *gene*. The idea was a radical one that ran counter to the prevailing and traditional concepts of an over-all becoming, an over-all molding to a new environment. De Vries searched the literature for other evidence of an independent unit of heredity.

In a work on hybridization by a German scientist, W. O. Focke, he found a reference to some hybridization experiments by an Austrian monk, Gregor Mendel. Focke noted: "Mendel believed he had found constant numerical ratios among the types produced by hybridization."

Numerical ratios. That interested De Vries, and he tracked down the reference. In a publication issued in 1866 by the Brünn Society for the Study of Natural History he found a monograph by Gregor Johann Mendel. De Vries knew at once that Mendel had discovered the long-sought secret of heredity, and that the honor of solving one of the most

1. Some of the changes that De Vries considered new species were later found to be only modifications.

fundamental of all problems belonged to the obscure Austrian monk. The Dutch botanist did not hesitate to call full attention to Mendel, although he had thought until he opened the long-unknown monographs that the credit for the all-important insight and discovery was to be his own.

In a paper that he read before the German Botanical Society on March 24, 1900, De Vries told of the events that had led him to Mendel.

"My experiments led me to formulate the two following propositions," he said.

"1. Of the two antagonistic qualities, the hybrid always exhibits one only and that in full development.

"2. During the formation of the pollen cells and ovules the two antagonistic qualities separate from each other.

"These two propositions were, in their essentials, formulated long ago by Mendel for a special case. They fell into oblivion, however, and were misunderstood. According to my own experiments, they are generally valid for true hybrids. . . . This important monograph [of Mendel's] is so rarely quoted that I myself did not become acquainted with it until I had concluded most of my experiments and had independently deduced the above propositions."

On April 24, one month after De Vries had reported his discovery of Mendel's work, a German scientist, Karl Correns, went before the same society to tell how he too had come upon Mendel's discovery. He had been experimenting with peas and maize and had found the constant ratios that he thought were his own discovery until he found Mendel's reports.

"In noting the regular succession of phenomena and finding an explanation for them I believed myself, as De Vries obviously believed himself, to be an innovator," said Correns. "Subsequently, however, I found that in Brünn during the sixties the Abbot Gregor Mendel, devoting many years to the most extensive experiments on peas, not only had obtained the same results as De Vries and myself, but had actually given the same explanation, in so far as this was possible in the year 1866. . . . This paper of Mendel's to which Focke refers (though without ever doing full justice to its importance) is among the best works ever written on the subject of hybrids."

A third scientist, the Viennese botanist Erich Tschermak, had come to the same discovery at the same moment.

Tschermak had decided to repeat Darwin's experiments on the hybridization of the pea. In the first generation, all the seeds resembled the dominant parent. In the second generation they split three to one.

On June 24, exactly two months after Correns's report and three months after De Vries's, Tschermak reported to the same society how he too had discovered Mendel: "Correns' recent report shows that his experiments, like mine, confirm the Menedelian doctrine. The simultaneous discovery of Mendel by Correns, De Vries, and myself seems to me particularly gratifying. I too, as late as the second year of my experiment, believed that I had happened upon something entirely new."

The dramatic triple discovery of the work of Mendel by a Dutch, a German, and an Austrian scientist and their simultaneous confirmation of his brilliant findings caught world-wide attention. The years of oblivion suddenly were ended. At last there was recognition of a great scientist, and understanding that heredity was not a matter of chance or an unfathomable chaos. One of man's oldest desires, to know how the distinctiveness and the very form of living things are passed along from parents to progeny, was at long last satisfied.

Mendel's brief monographs were reissued, and biology was thereby revolutionized. A whole new approach to an understanding of living things and to the natural law that underlay the surface was opened.

The sudden world acclaim of Gregor Mendel came as an almost inconceivable surprise to the town of Brünn. At first the local contributions for a statue came in slowly, but gradually the realization grew of how momentous were the findings made in the monastery garden more than a third of a century earlier, and a fine monument was erected. Dedicated in 1911, it shows Mendel, a kindly solid figure, standing against a background of his pea and bean vines. Its inscription reads simply: "To the investigator P. Gregor Mendel, 1822–1884."

When 1922 brought the hundredth anniversary of Mendel's birth, a centenary festival was held in Brünn. World War I had come to a bitter close only four years before, and normal communications had not been restored between the scientists of central Europe and the rest of the world. But Mendel belonged to all. To honor the man who had explained so much of how men came to be as they are, German, Czech, English, and French scientists joined in the ceremonies before the Mendel monument in Brünn. The animosities of a world war were laid aside to commemorate the universal discoveries of Gregor Mendel.

THE LINE-UP OF HEREDITY

It was 1910 and Thomas Hunt Morgan had been engaged for about a year in what was to be the great work of his life—the study of heredity with Drosophila melanogaster, the little fruit flies that buzz so persistently around overripe fruit. The time was right for it. . . .

With his interests and background, Morgan had eagerly followed the rediscovery of the Mendelian laws a few years earlier, in 1900, and the rush of experiment it prompted. Morgan was skeptical, though, about some of the Mendelian findings. It seemed impossible to him that two hereditary units would not be affected by their association in one individual.

Mendel had emphasized that no matter how often he crossed green with yellow, the two colors emerged in the next generation as sharp and distinctive as though they had never been together. This, Morgan thought, could not possibly apply to all heredity. Mendel himself had found that crossing red and white flowers produced pink and a range of shades.

"Once crossed," Morgan argued in 1905, "always contaminated." He also endorsed an attack by the scientist Oscar Riddle on the Mendelian law of the purity of the gametes. Riddle scoffed at the idea of "hypothetical particles . . . packed with unthinkable precision, order, and potentiality . . ."

The whole matter needed study and investigation, and Morgan wanted to get into it. As he discussed the possibilities, a friend, F. E. Lutz, called his attention to Drosophila as experimental material. The common little flies grew from egg to maturity in twelve days and showed clearly marked characteristics. They would be a great improvement over Mendel's peas. Morgan decided upon an experiment.

Drosophila soon proved even better than Lutz had said. The flies bred rapidly in the great numbers that Morgan knew would be necessary if valid findings were to be made. And they could be readily studied and tallied.

Morgan had been running one "pedigree culture" for about a year when among the flies there suddenly appeared one with white eyes. The eyes of the fly normally are red. Morgan realized at once that the odd, white-eyed fly would give him exactly the marked material, the tag, that he needed.

He bred the lone white-eyed fly to one of the red-eyed females. In a very short order he had 1237 red-eyed offspring. They were hybrids, exhibiting only the dominant red eye color in accordance with Mendel's laws. The test would come when the hybrids were mated.

Again Morgan did not have long to wait. The red-eyed hybrids produced 2459 red-eyed females, 1011 red-eyed males, and 782 white-eyed males. There was not a single white-eyed female among them. This was no quirk of heredity—not with 782 white-eyed males and not even one white-eyed female. It was another revelation of heredity's working.

Somehow in certain cases heredity was linked to sex. Somehow white eyes had been transmitted to the grandsons only. A facet of the laws of heredity was being revealed as strikingly as when Mendel broke open his first hybrid pea pod and saw one bright-green pea nestling among three yellows.

Morgan at once began to seek for an explanation of his remarkable results. As he did so, he was led into full agreement with Mendel and into territory Mendel had not entered.

Mendel had seen that the roundness, the wrinkling, the yellowness and greenness, and other characters that he studied must have their bases in some kind of physical unit that could be passed along from parent to offspring. He did not attempt to face up to the question of where this unit could be found in the living cell. It was, however, a question that could not long be avoided. Where were the units, and how could the coming together and separating, the assortment and reassortment indicated by the appearance of the peas and other living things take place? Where was the mechanism?

It would, in fact, have been impossible for Mendel to grapple with the big question of mechanism. In the 1850's and 1860's not enough was known of the inner structure of the cell to permit even a start.

By 1910, when Morgan was confronted by the strange linkage of white eyes and sex in Drosophila and by the Mendelian ratios, the situation was entirely different. During the half-century in between, scientists had found that the nucleus of every cell contains a number of tiny threadlike structures. The twisting threads took dye very readily and, when they had been colored, could easily be seen under the microscope. Because of their staining propensities they were called chromosomes (*chromo* for color, *somes* for bodies—thus, "colored bodies").

Every single cell in a living body, it was learned, contains the number of chromosomes characteristic of its species—the human, forty-six; Drosophila, eight; the mouse, twenty; Mendel's garden peas, fourteen.

Close microscopic observation also revealed that the chromosomes move about in the nucleus, going through a process of division and a series of maneuvers startling and awe-inspiring in its order, complexity, and rapidity. The maneuvers could be seen as distinctly as those of troops on a parade ground.

Before they began, the cell appeared to be in a resting period. The chromosomal material seemed to be broken into bits and dotted all through the nucleus. As the resting period came to an end, the bits came together in a long curling strand. Soon it split in two longitudinally, and two long strands lay side by side. The double thread then thickened and pulled apart into separate pairs of chromosomes—much as though two lengths of string had been snipped into pieces of varied lengths. The two chromosomes of each pair sometimes still lay parallel, but sometimes they loosely twisted about each other.

By this time the wall of the nucleus had broken and the chromosomes began to move toward the nuclear center or equator. With the microscope—and later with a movie camera—it was easy to watch them arranging themselves there in an orderly array.

Soon afterward one member of each pair of chromosomes was dragged —almost, it seemed, by the scruff of the neck—to the two poles of the nucleus. [Figure 7–7.] A wall then grew between the two polar clusters. Shortly—in human beings the time is about eighty minutes—there were two cells where before there had been only one.

The precise dance of division had endowed each new cell with an exact duplicate of the chromosomes of the cell from which it came. Each cell was guaranteed the same genetic constitution as nearly all the other cells of the body. And as this division was repeated millions upon millions of times, the human being, or any other living thing, grew from a single cell into a full-size adult. The same process constantly replaced older worn-out cells with new ones.

This ordered, shuttling process of cell divsion varied only in one case: the formation of the germ cells, the egg and the sperm. When an egg or a sperm was to be produced—in contrast to a body cell—the chromosomes did not split longitudinally. They broke only into the separate chromosome lengths, and two lengths came together to form a pair. When the pairs collected at the cell's equator and then pulled apart, each cell received only half the full complement of chromosomes.

The way thus was prepared for the new individual. With each egg and sperm contributing half the full quota, the new individual created by the union of the germ cells acquired the full and proper number of chromosomes for his species. And half his hereditary equipment came from the mother and half from the father. Life could be carried on in its eternal pattern.

By 1900, when Mendel's work was discovered, this remarkable process and mechanism of cell reproduction was understood in its essentials at least.

Only two years later W. S. Sutton put two and two together. He suggested that the chromosomes might be the bearers of Mendel's hereditary traits. In their coming together and separating, the chromosomes supplied almost exactly the kind of mechanism required to produce Mendel's results. Mendel had demonstrated that when tall green peas were crossed with dwarf yellow the offspring might include tall-yellow and dwarf-green as well as tall-green and dwarf-yellow. Tallness did not necessarily go with green seeds, or shortness with yellow. In the same way, said Sutton, the movement of one pair of chromosomes is probably inde-

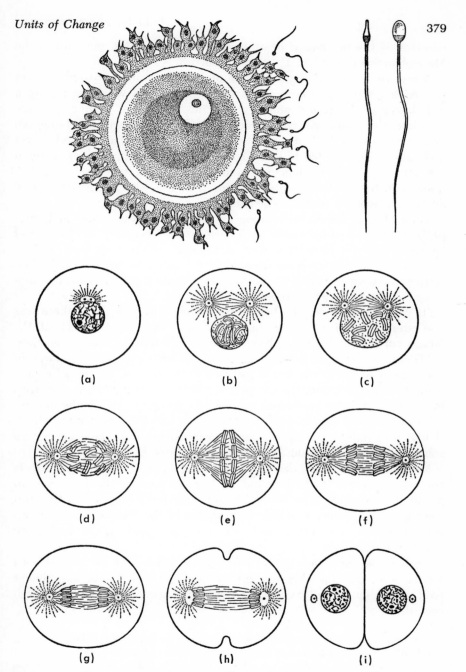

Figure 7–7. Human egg and sperm cells (top). Division of a cell by mitosis. (From Isaac Asimov, The Intelligent Man's Guide to Science.)

pendent of the movement of other pairs. Here was the mechanism the Mendelian theory needed. The two matched.

A few years later William Bateson and R. C. Punnett crossed a sweet pea having a purple flower and a long pollen grain with one having a red flower and a round pollen grain. But instead of getting the free assortment of characters which Mendel had obtained with his tall-green and yellow-dwarf peas, Bateson and Punnett found that the red flower and round grain tended to stay together. Other investigators came upon the same puzzling tendency: certain traits stayed together more frequently in the wider hereditary shuffle than they did in Mendel's peas. Some traits seemed, in fact, to be coupled.

Then Morgan found the relation of whiteness and maleness in Drosophila. It seemed to be similar in nature to the "coupling" of "long" and "purple" in sweet peas. It looked as though certain traits were linked. Perhaps such traits all were situated in the same chromosomes. If they were in the same chromosome, they would remain together as the chromosome went through its divisions.

"It was obvious from the beginning," Morgan argued, "that there was one essential requirement for the chromosome view, namely, that all the factors carried by the same chromosome should tend to remain together.

"Therefore since the number of inheritable characters may be large in comparison with the number of pairs of chromosomes, we would expect actually to find not only the independent behavior of pairs, but also cases in which characters are linked together in groups in their inheritance."

Drosophila had four pairs of chromosomes, and if Morgan was right, it should be possible to map the factors carried by each. The theory was subject to proof. It would, however, take a huge experiment.

Morgan always succeeded in surrounding himself with able students and collaborators. With their aid he began breeding the little flies in prodigious numbers. The assortment of milk bottles in which the flies were kept filled every available square inch of the "fly room" at Columbia University. The eight desks of the "fly squad" could barely be crowded in.[2]

Each of the thousands upon thousands of flies had to be studied with a hand lens. But the laborious scrutiny and the scale of the experiment paid off; other mutations, the raw material needed for the work, appeared. . . .

2. In the summer the fly squad moved en masse to Woods Hole, Massachusetts. The bottles of flies—each marked with scraps of paper torn from the envelopes that had enclosed Morgan's mail—were shipped in barrels. The other animals of the laboratory—a fine assortment of chickens, pigeons, mice, and rats—were carried by hand on the Fall River Line.

In a relatively short time the Morgan laboratory studied the inheritance of more than a hundred characters. There was no doubt that
characters in Drosophila were inherited not only in linked pairs, but also
in linked groups. (Figure 7–8.)

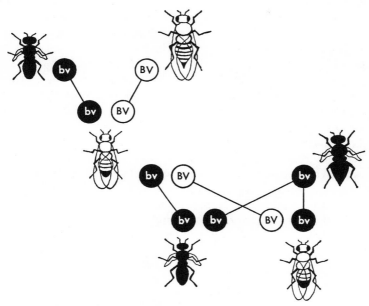

*Figure 7–8. Linkage. The traits "black" and "short wings" were inherited to-
gether, as were the color "gray" and "long wings." Not a single black fly with
long wings or gray with vestigial wings was produced in this mating. The
reason: the hereditary material for the two linked traits was carried by the
same chromosome. The two went together.*

One large group of characters always went along with either the male
or female. It was quite clear that they were carried by one of the Drosophila sex chromosomes. Two other large groups of characters also
remained together. One of the groups was made up of "brown," "chubby,"
"flipper," "fringed," "narrow," "telescope," and more than fifty others.
Thus, when a fly was brown, it was also chubby and had all the other
linked traits.

And then a characteristic appeared which did not go with the sex group
or either of the other two. A year later still another characteristic cropped
up which was linked to the last one, but was inherited independently of
all the others. Every other trait singled out after this belonged to one or
another of the four groups.

The four carefully charted groups indicated four chromosomes as certainly as did the sight of the four chromosomes under the microscope. Any remaining doubts dissolved. The site of the hereditary units whose existence Mendel had deduced had been found. Morgan's work and the investigations of others all pointed to the same locus—the chromosome.

Understanding of the mystery of life had advanced again. The search for the explanation and cause of the form, the diversity, and the functioning of life had moved from the organs to the tissues, to the cell, and now to the twisting little chromosome threads within the cell. As the search went deeper, it came to the smaller and smaller, and yet each time it penetrated below the previously known appearance of things, order was found and explanation of much that had been obscure. At the same time, another cause always lay deeper still. The search did not reach its end.

One of Drosophila's pairs of chromosomes was small; it seemed to consist of little more than two dots. The other three pairs were many times larger. One of the large pairs had something of the bent shape of a boomerang. Another large pair, in the female, was made up of two more or less straight threads; when diagrammed, they resembled two broad strokes with a stub-pointed pen. But in the male, the microscope showed, the two members of the pair differed. One of the chromosomes resembled the straight threads of the female pair; the other had a hooked end. (Figure 7–9.)

Figure 7–9. The chromosomes of the fruit fly. Here is the hereditary material of Drosophila. Left: the female. Right: the male.

As the relative size of the chromosomes was determined, another most enlightening fact stood forth. Their sizes corresponded to the sizes of the four groups of hereditary characters Morgan had discovered. Morgan had two large groups of characters that stayed together, a very small group, and a fourth sizable group linked to the sex of the flies. Here was added confirmation that the hereditary units were grouped in the chromosomes. These units were later called *genes*.

The difference in the sex chromosomes had to be investigated. The three straight sex chromosomes, the two in the female and the one in the male, were soon named the X chromosomes. The male chromosome with the hooked end was called the Y.

Peering through his microscope and working on "the problem of the three chromosomes," Morgan could trace the maneuvers of the two pairs, the four individual sex chromosomes. As he did so, he and others working along the same lines solved one of the most ancient of human mysteries.

When egg cells were formed in the female Drosophila, each received one of the X chromosomes. In the male, half of the sperm came to have the male's X, and half had his Y chromosome. The remainder of the process was not difficult to figure out. If the Y-endowed sperm fertilized an egg, an XY individual, a male, resulted.

If, on the other hand, the egg with its X chromosome was fertilized by the X sperm, an XX individual, a female, was produced.

For the first time the inheritance of sex could be understood. The riddle of why an approximately even number of males and females are born into the world was at last solved, and it was all a matter of a simple Mendelian assortment of hereditary units. Given the three like and the one unlike chromosomes, there was only one way in which it could work out, if sufficient numbers were taken into consideration. The mechanism was simple and certain. (Figure 7–10.)

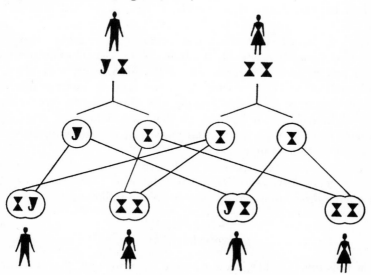

Figure 7–10. Solution of an ancient mystery—the approximate equality of the sexes. With the male bearing an XY chromosome and the female XX, it is inevitable that approximately equal numbers of males and females will be produced.

"The old view that sex is determined by external conditions is entirely disproved," said Morgan. "We have discovered an internal mechanism by means of which the equality of the sexes is attained. We see the results are automatically reached, even if we cannot entirely understand the details of the process."

This work with the sex chromosomes explained the production of the red-eyed flies and the white-eyed male in Morgan's earlier work. He could now work out the whole course of genetic events that had produced the odd white-eyed male and the other, red-eyed flies. Each egg of a red-eyed mother would have an X chromosome bearing the factor for red eyes (R).

The red factor was quite certainly placed in the X chromosome, but its presence there could be confirmed by additional experiments. Morgan made them all. Short of some disarrangement, the transmission of XR together worked out as certainly as though two were being multiplied by two. It was exactly the pattern of inheritance of color-blindness in the human. Heredity was a very satisfying problem with which to work; predictions could be exactly confirmed with living material.

Occasionally, however, Morgan found instances in which whole blocks of genes from one chromosome had shifted to the corresponding chromosome of the pair. Certain changed groupings of characteristics indicated what had happened almost as clearly as though he had seen it taking place.

Morgan could interpret what had occurred, and many later experiments were to substantiate his analysis. When two chromosomes come together just prior to the formation of the germ cells, they often twist around each other. The twisting has been seen in innumerable microscopic photographs. If, in this twining, the chromosomes break, sections of the two may be interchanged. In that case, when the chromosomes again part, as they do in the normal process of cell division, each carries away a new section. [Figure 7–11.]

Morgan jotted down a pattern to illustrate. If one chromosome originally bore genes *ABCDEFGHIJKL* and the other bore the corresponding genes *abcdefghijkl*, they would line up in the following way:

ABCDEFGHIJKL
abcdefghijkl

If, in twisting together, sections were interchanged, the chromosomes on parting might well have the following make-up:

ABCDEFghijkl
abcdefGHIJKL

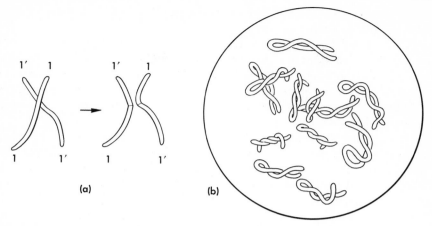

Figure 7–11. (a) *Crossing-over. Left: the two homologous chromosomes in contact. Right: after exchange and separation.* (b) *Twelve paired chromosomes in a pollen mother-cell of a lily,* Fritillaria chitralensis. *The points where the loops meet mark the positions of crossing-over between the partners. (After a photograph,* ×1600. *From Erwin Schrödinger,* What Is Life?)

All of this pointed unmistakably to one conclusion: the genes are arranged in linear order in the chromosome. Ultimately Morgan and many other workers in the field were able, by studying crossing-over, to map the positions of certain genes in the chromosomes.

In their book *The Mechanism of Mendelian Heredity,* Morgan and his principal associates in the work, A. H. Sturtevant, H. J. Muller, and C. B. Bridges, used a map of Drosophila's chromosomes as the frontispiece. It was a most unusual map.

On the straight lines representing one of Drosophila's chromosomes, the scientists marked the places of "yellow," "white," "echinus," "cross-veinless," "cut," "tan," "vermilion," "miniature," "sable," "garnet," "forked," "bar," "cleft," and "bobbed"—their colorful and descriptive names for the genes.

It was also a curiously made map. Not one gene locus had been determined by direct measurement; each place had been fixed by studying certain evidences—say, garnet eyes—by calculating what they must represent, and then by proving the calculation by breeding new generations of the buzzing little fruit flies. In one sense, the map resembled the maps of unseen ocean bottoms made by bounding unseen sound waves against the elevations and depressions of the ocean floor.

And yet, using it, the scientists could predict how much crossing-over there would be and what traits would appear in the offspring of any cross, and then see the flies born with the predicted kind of wings or eyes or color. It was almost uncanny.

"Given the distance between any two factors on the map, the per cent of crossing-over between them can always be calculated from the distance," said the scientists in their book. "This shows that the amount of crossing over is an expression of their position in a *linear series*. This striking fact is a strong argument that the factors are actually arranged in line in the chromosomes."

Photographs showing the chromosomes as strings made up of what seemed to be a series of disks or flattish beads merely confirmed the linearity of the hereditary material already established by Morgan's calculations, his tabulation of eye color, wing shape, and other characteristics of thousands of swarming laboratory flies. [Figure 7–12.]

For seventeen years the Morgan fly squad bred fruit flies. "There can have been few times and places in scientific laboratories with such an atmosphere of excitement and such a record of sustained enthusiasm," Sturtevant wrote many years later. The spirit was in large part traceable to the enthusiasm, the open-mindedness, and the sense of humor of "The Boss," as the squad called Morgan, their bearded, energetic, but never dictatorial chief.

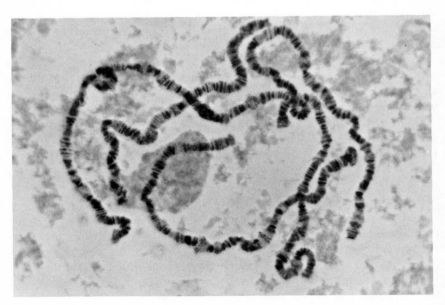

Figure 7–12. Giant chromosomes in salivary gland of Drosophila, the fruit fly.
(Photograph courtesy of the General Biological Supply House, Inc., Chicago.)

The results were well worth the effort, and many honors came to the man whose work with fruit flies was showing men that their very identities were shaped by the orderly maneuvering of bits of matter in the nucleus of the cell.

But what were these threads of heredity? How could an all but invisible bit of matter carry the specifications for making living things what they are? Somehow this fleck of matter had to be studied. But how?

Scientists tried subjecting plants and animals to heat, to cold, to chemicals, in an effort to change the hereditary material and thus to gain some clues to its nature. But the genes, well protected in the heart of the cell, were unaffected.

Only when H. J. Muller bombarded fruit flies with X-rays did change occur. After an X-raying of the parents, flies were born with bulging eyes, with changed wings and no wings. [Figure 7–13.]

Figure 7–13. Genetic changes in fruit flies caused by radiation. Drosophila sired by males exposed to radiation exhibit genetic changes (mutations). Radiation affected the reproductive cells in such a way that offspring grew rudimentary, rather than normal, wings. This characteristic also appeared in subsequent generations, thus proving to be a true mutation. (Photograph courtesy of the Brookhaven National Laboratory.)

They were a motley throng, Muller reported. The roots of life, he said, had "indeed been struck and they had yielded." X-rays, penetrating into the cell, had produced changes that could not be brought about by a gross agent. By thus artificially producing mutations science had gained a way to study the hereditary material.

Significance of the Theory of Heredity

Why do biologists throughout the world today agree that Mendel's discovery is one of first rank? A great deal might be said in this connection. What is essential may be said in a few words. Biology had been, and is still, largely a descriptive and speculative science. Mendel showed by experimental proof that heredity could be explained by a simple mechanism. His discovery has been exceedingly fruitful. Science begins with naïve, often mystic conceptions of its problems. It reaches its goal whenever it can replace its early guessing by verifiable hypotheses and predictable results. This is what Mendel's law did for heredity.

Thomas Hunt Morgan
A Critique of the Theory of Evolution (1916)

Probing the Unseen with Logic *
by Garrett Hardin (1959)

Two of the greatest intellectual achievements of the nineteenth century were the discovery of the invisible: in physics, the discovery of atoms; in biology, of genes. There are many parallels between these two achievements. If one will accept mere ideas without experimental evidence, both concepts can be found crudely expressed at least as far back as in the writings of the Roman poet Lucretius (first century B.C.). But ideas are cheap (and mostly wrong) and no one treasured these, surrounded as they were by a multitude of other, and quite erroneous, speculations of armchair philosophers. When these ideas were brought up again, with evidence and arguments, in the nineteenth century, they quite naturally met considerable resistance among the scientific fraternity. The idea of atoms, for instance—what right did it have to ask for credence? Particles so tiny that we should never expect to see them—and yet we are to believe they really exist—what is this, the Emperor's New Clothes?

No, says the scientific philosopher: I don't know what you mean by "really exist," and it probably will not be profitable to try to find out.

* From Garrett Hardin, *Nature and Man's Fate*, The New American Library. Copyright 1959 by Garrett Hardin. Reprinted by permission.

But, operationally, the situation is of this sort. We begin with a "model" —say a concept of atoms as indivisible, discrete particles, in constant motion and reacting from encounters with perfect elasticity, and from this model we make predictions that can be experimentally checked. If the experiments turn out as predicted, we say the model has been confirmed. Then, a little later, we think of some other experiments that should turn out a certain way if the model is correct: if they do, we say the model has been confirmed still further. And so on. It is not quite as simple as this, of course: sometimes experiments don't come out exactly as we had expected them to (e.g., atoms prove to be destructible), and then we modify the model slightly to fit the new facts, as well as all the old ones. This leads to new predictions that must be tested. And thus, by an organic process, our models—our ideas, our theories—grow, until from many successes and long familiarity, they become as real to us as the cows and trees and tables with which we have (we suppose) direct contact. The idea of atoms, viewed with skepticism by a few good physicists as late as the end of the nineteenth century, had become so real to us before the middle of the twentieth, that we gambled two billion

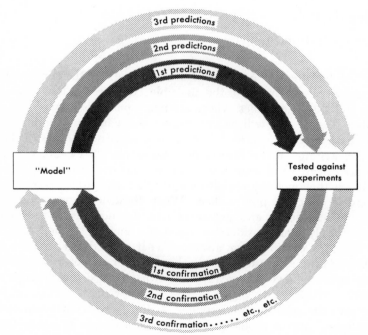

Figure 7–14. The idea of a "model." By thus bypassing the difficult question, "What is truth?" scientists get on with the work that needs to be done.

dollars on one of its predictions. The successful verification of the model, in the atomic bomb, was so spectacular that no thoughtful person seriously asks any more, "Are there *really* atoms?" We cannot see them, but confidence in our logic makes us feel that the existence of these invisible entities is at least as certain as the one-time existence of a man named Julius Caesar. The probability can hardly be less. (Figure 7–14.)

The history of the acceptance of the gene concept repeated, in rough outline, that of the atomic-molecular theory. As usual, however, biology trailed physical science in time. The role of the unappreciated Mendel was played earlier in physical science by the unappreciated Avogadro (1811). General acceptance of the gene theory by scientists came about a half century after the scientific acceptance of the atomic-molecular picture of matter. And if a crude generalization of a very complex situation is acceptable, we may say that the "public" acceptance of both theories took still another half century. Curiously, the very phenomenon which brought final public conviction in the truth of the atom—namely, the atomic bomb—promises ultimately to induce public belief in that other great intellectual creation, the gene. As the biological consequences of high-energy radiation become clearer, it will become more and more difficult for anyone to ask seriously, "Are there *really* genes?"

Natural Selection *

by H. G. Wells, J. Huxley, and G. P. Wells (1934)

THE SIGNIFICANCE OF SEX

Here we can at last tackle a problem that presented itself in the first [selection of Part 7], and has been running like a counter subject of a fugue beneath our argument. What is the advantage of sex? We saw that reproduction is primarily a sexless thing; that living creatures can proliferate and multiply actively without sex. The origin and purpose of conjugation (of which sex is a special case) are still mysterious.

Sex intrudes, an essentially anti-reproductive process, and forces itself on the life-cycle; it entangles itself more and more closely with reproduction until in ourselves the two are inseparable. In the single-celled protozoa two individuals sometimes come together and blend into one. But this conjugation is not essential in these forms. It happens occasionally, but it appears from the results of experiment that strains can be

---

* From H. G. Wells, J. Huxley, and G. P. Wells, *The Science of Life.*

kept going indefinitely, proliferating sexlessly without conjugation, if they are carefully tended. In ourselves this blending of the substance of two individuals is made compulsory; we cannot reproduce without it. This is the rule with the higher animals. In the higher plants also sex is closely entangled with reproduction. But even in these cases there are exceptions—there are parthenogenetic insects, and there are flowers which normally and regularly fertilize themselves. To summarize the situation, sexual union seems to be an eminently desirable thing from the point of view of the species, and yet not absolutely necessary; at a pinch, in exceptional cases, it is dispensed with. Now why should all this be?

We are beginning to see in this [section] how living things evolve. They are not adaptively moulded by their surroundings. They produce mutations at random; their germ-plasm gropes about in the dark and makes experiments, trying now this innovation and now that. And the formative agent, which acts upon these chance mutations and builds out of them the progressive changes of evolution, is . . . Natural Selection. Natural Selection is like a sifting machine and the mutations are the raw proposals that come to it for consideration, rejection, or justification. Undesirable variations are sifted out and thrown aside; successful ones get through and continue in the germ-plasm of the race.

It is clear enough that a race will stand a better chance of evolving and adapting itself if it supplies plenty of variations to the mill of selection. The more numerous and diverse its varieties the better it will get on. So it pays a species to exert itself and keep the mill well-fed.

Now for the secret. Imagine two allied species of plant, each producing mutations at about the same rate. One normally fertilizes itself, . . . so that it tends to sort out into pure lines. The other is regularly cross-fertilized. It is obvious enough that the mutations will be shuffled about and recombined in the second species. Suppose that two good mutations appear in different individual plants. If they belong to the first species they will always stay apart. If they belong to the second they will stand a chance of being combined together in one of the next generations, and of meeting any other mutations that may be about. If, for instance, in a given space of time each species has thrown up ten mutations, then the self-fertilized species will be in possession just of these ten new types and no more, while its cross-fertilized rival will have the possibility of over a thousand new types built out of the recombinations of the ten.

In a word, sexual union is good in plants and animals alike, because it affords a method of variation. By shuffling about the mutations that appear, by combining them in various ways and presenting the results to Natural Selection, it lends efficiency and speed to the evolutionary process.

Sexual union is essentially the pooling of the mutation-experience of two lines of descent. A useful mutation is a precious event, not too frequent; the sex-machinery keeps up a continual mixing and interweaving of germ-plasm strands so that these treasures can be preserved and combined to the best possible advantage.

Such seems to be the clue to our riddle. Sex is forced upon organisms because they reproduce so fast, because of that Malthusian population-pressure that compels them . . . to compete and seize every advantage. Moreover, it is precisely because mutation is a casual random process that the continual juggling machinery of sex is so important. It allows the race to get the most out of its mutations. That is why conjugation interrupts the normal proliferation of protozoa every now and then. That is why in large and elaborately organized individuals like ourselves, which reproduce themselves comparatively infrequently, sexual union is entangled with every reproductive act. . . .

Let us be perfectly clear, even at the risk of repeating one or two things already said, what this phrase "the struggle for existence" means. The essential fact on which it lays stress is that the power of living things to multiply is so great that every living species is constantly tending to press upon its means of subsistence. The daily life of man and mouse alike . . . is primarily a food-hunt. In that food-hunt, the less capable, the less well-equipped hunters are pushed to the wall. They are pushed out of the game, they fail and die, and their sort dies with them.

Every animal and every plant produces offspring in such numbers that many must die if the numbers of the species are not to increase in every generation. The elephant is the slowest breeder among animals; Darwin estimated that an average pair produces only six young in ninety years of reproductive life. But even so, if all the young survived, a single original pair would in five hundred years become fifteen million. Most animals and plants produce their eggs and seeds by the hundreds or thousands, and yet their average numbers remain steady throughout the generations. This can only happen if, out of all the offspring produced by each couple, on the average only two survive to reproduce their kind again. All the rest must die—it is a question of the simplest arithmetic.

The numbers which must normally die are vividly brought home to us when we see a species temporarily released from pressing on its means of subsistence, by being imported into a new country where it happens to thrive. In a few years it fills the whole area. The Canadian water-weed was accidentally introduced into England in the middle of the last century. Within ten years it was clogging the waterways and holding up canal traffic all over the country. The English sparrow is to-day as common and as much of a pest in America as it is in England, but it filled the United States to saturation point in the geologically negligible time of less than a century.

The struggle may act at any period of life; it affects every department of existence. There may be a struggle within the womb; in most mammals more eggs are fertilized than there can be young born. Under every forest tree there is a struggle among the seedlings—a struggle for air, for light, for nourishment from the soil. There is a struggle between closely related species: the brown rat when it invaded Europe almost exterminated the black rat. There is a never-ending struggle between eater and eaten: among the eaten to escape, among the eaters to secure enough prey. There is a struggle among plants to escape being browsed out of existence, a struggle among seeds for wide dissemination. There is a struggle against the forces of nature: of the migrating bird to survive the gale, of the flower not to go under in the rain-squall, of the reindeer not to be frozen in the arctic winter. There is a constant struggle against disease and against parasites. There is a struggle for mates and breeding-places in animals, a struggle for cross-fertilization in flowering plants.

The struggle for existence, as Darwin was careful to point out, is in a sense a metaphorical struggle. It is rarely a conscious effort; there is automatic competition, and some competitors are automatically crowded out. The fast-growing embryo in the womb does not know that it is causing the death of its less-favoured brother-embryo. The black rat was not engaged in conscious warfare with the brown rat, but it simply throve less well and multiplied less rapidly. The bird knows that it is being beaten down by the wind or caught by the hawk; but the true struggle in Darwin's sense lies between it and its stronger or swifter congeners that weather the storm and escape their enemy, and of this the bird knows nothing. But if the struggle is metaphorical in this sense, its results are real enough. The better-equipped survive, the worse-equipped die: that is no metaphor.

Without variation, however, the struggle would bear no fruit for life. If all individuals in a species were exactly alike, then it must be a mere question of luck which failed, and the struggle for existence could not alter the characteristics of the species. Or if they differed but their differences were not inherited, it would not matter from the evolutionary point of view which went under. But since many differences of an advantageous or disadvantageous sort exist and are inherited, the struggle for existence acts on a species like a filter or a sieve. It selects types of success and failure, sets a premium on advantageous variations and continually removes a large majority of the disadvantageous ones, so that the average of the species moves in the advantageous direction.

To picture this selection, this combined effect of struggle and variation, at its work, let us go back in thought to the fir-trees in a forest, each letting fall its thousands of winged seeds. Many fall under their parent; many others just outside its shelter; others are carried farther. Everywhere in the forest and for some distance beyond its boundaries the ground is strewn with seeds every season. The struggle begins at once. There is much purely accidental destruction; as in the parable, some fall on stony ground and cannot germinate, some where they are choked by other plants. But there is a selective struggle, too. An old tree has fallen; there is a vacant spot in the forest. This, too, is covered with seeds. But some germinate faster or better, and so gain a start. Among the horde of seedlings some send leaves up or push roots down more slowly; they will invariably lag and be overshadowed and killed out by their brothers. Some will have less green chlorophyll; some will have leaves less well arranged to catch the light. Some will be particularly efficient at drawing water and salts out of the soil, others at turning the raw materials into new substances for growth. The net result is that some grow faster than others. "From him that hath not shall be taken away," and those that are backward become still more handicapped as their competitors overtop them; the disproportion in growth increases and the innate vigour of the new finally involves the death of the less well-equipped many. There is struggle, there is variation—and so there is selection.

We may perhaps quote Darwin himself to show how he envisaged the struggle and its results in one of the higher animals.

Let us take the case of a wolf, which preys on various animals, securing some by craft, some by strength, and some by fleetness; and let us suppose that the fleetest prey—a deer, for instance—had from any change in the country increased in numbers, or that other prey had decreased in numbers, during that season of the year when the wolf was hardest pressed for food. Under such circumstances the swiftest and slimmest wolves would have the best chance of surviving and so be preserved or selected—provided always that they retained strength to master their prey at this or some other period of the year, when they were compelled to prey on other animals. I can see no more reason to doubt that this would be the result than that man should be able to improve the fleetness of his greyhounds by careful and methodical selection, or by that kind of unconscious selection which follows from each man trying to keep the best dogs without any thought of modifying the breed.

It was this sifting of variations—the automatic preservation of the favourable and elimination of the unfavourable—which Darwin meant by Natural Selection. It would be quite inoperative without inherited variations. But given that, it explains the process of Evolution with a completeness approached by no other explanation. . . .

NATURAL SELECTION AS A CONSERVATIVE FORCE

We are apt to speak and write of the factors of the evolutionary process as though they were driving us on to incessant fresh developments, new things and strange things, but that is by no means always the case. The action of Natural Selection is probably on the whole conservative, except during periods of marked change in the meteorological or biological environment. It has no bias for wild-eyed novelty. It is just as effective in keeping things in their places.

We have compared it to a filter. But it is, we may say, a directive filter. And the direction in which variation is guided by selection is determined by the environment. While that remains stable, selection will be a stabilizing force, a conservative influence. If a species is well adapted to its rôle in life, Natural Selection will be busy pruning the variants that depart too far in any direction from the temporary ideal. But the environment may change; and it may offer inducements to responsive change. This revolutionizes the selective policy: and Natural Selection in such a changing environment becomes a radical influence in the politics of life. It is now all for new ideas. . . .

The pruning effect of selection is also exerted in another way. Whether change or stability is being encouraged, the organism must be kept up to the mark. Wherever mutations have been studied, many of them are found to be deleterious. Mutations are random changes, and random changes in such complex machinery as that of life will often inevitably be changes for the worse. Natural Selection will always be occupied in ousting these from the germ-plasm of the species. Drosophila keeps on throwing mutations with striking effects; often the same one is repeated again and again, yet they are scarcely ever found in Nature—the reduced vigour which they entail leads to their automatic elimination. They fail at the Natural Selection entrance tests. . . .

The germ-plasm is like a garden, and Natural Selection in many respects like its gardener. Weeds are always cropping up in it, and threatening to swamp the cultivated plants. Selection, as well as sometimes helping in the creation of new types of flowers or fruit, is forever busy with the humbler task of weeding. But there are gardeners and gardeners; some have not the time or energy for weeding of a professional standard; others may even prefer an untidy garden. Thus, dropping our metaphor, sheltered conditions often allow variations to persist which more rigorous selection would eliminate. It is commonly believed that this applies particularly to human heredity. Modern civilization is said to be lightening the severity of the selective process upon our race. It is also commonly believed by the same people—but usually at different hours of the day—that modern civilization is more exacting upon nerves and health than any previous state of society.

NATURAL SELECTION UNDER CHANGING CONDITIONS

But now passing from the consideration of natural selection as a species-conserving and species-regulating influence, let us look at it in operation as a fosterer of variations and so as adapting species to new conditions. Here is a case we quote from J. B. S. Haldane's admirable *Possible Worlds.*

The assertion is still sometimes made that no one has ever seen Natural Selection at work. It is therefore perhaps worth giving in some detail a case recently described by Harrison. About 1800 a large wood in the Cleveland district of Yorkshire containing pine and birch was divided into two by a stretch of heath. In 1885 the pines in one division were replaced by birches, while in the other the birches were almost entirely ousted by pines. In consequence the moth *Oporabia autumnata*, which inhabits both woods, has been placed in two different environments. In both woods a light and a dark variety occur, but in the pine wood over 96 per cent are dark, in the birch wood only 15 per cent. This is not due to the direct effect of the environment, for the dark pine-wood race became no lighter after feeding the caterpillars on birch-trees in captivity for three generations, nor can the light form be darkened by placing this variety on pines. The reason for the difference was discovered on collecting the wings of moths found lying about in the pine wood, whose owners had been eaten by owls, bats, and night-jars. Although there were more than twenty-five dark living moths to each light one, a majority of the wings found were light-coloured. The whiter moths, which show up against the dark pines, are being exterminated, and in a few more years Natural Selection will have done its work and the pine wood will be inhabited entirely by dark-coloured insects.

There is a simple and pretty instance of the role of Natural Selection in bringing about adaptation. . . .

Even though mutations be rare, yet selection in a given direction acts as an automatic trap for all mutations whose effects are in the same direction; thus, if it continues for a long stretch, it may accumulate plenty of these rare visitors, and so in time wholly alter the racial constitution. If mutations go on appearing, the amount of change that can be wrought is unlimited. In a word, it gives an explanation for the steady change of a race in a given direction—and that is precisely the sort of thing that the fossil record shows.

There are many who cannot bring themselves to believe that such trifling alterations, even if accumulated over the generations, can ever give rise to the broad and striking changes of large-scale evolution. They forget the extreme slowness of the change revealed whenever we trace

Evolution in action. Only because palaeontologists are thinking on a different scale of time from ordinary mortals can they speak of bursts of rapid evolution and the like. During such periods, change may be faster than at other times; but judged by our ordinary standards it is still of an appalling slowness. . . .

Thus, to sum up, the power of living things to change is definitely restricted. Sometimes it is restricted through the limitation of variation: one germ-plasm may be much more stable than another, or one type of constitution may readily produce variations in some directions, but be debarred by its own nature from producing them easily or even at all in others. Sometimes it is restricted by the mere fact of previous evolution; for specialization, without necessarily restricting the supply of variations, automatically makes the great majority of them less advantageous. The specialized animal is committed to a certain line of advance: variations that would take it along other lines can only be useful if it can manage to destroy or modify the plan it has already built up; and even to its advance along its own chosen line a term is eventually set—it reaches the limit of efficiency prescribed by mechanical or chemical laws.

But when all is said, the liberty of change open to evolving life is much more impressive than its restrictions. Here a door is shut, there a limit imposed, but the range of variety and height of attainment is prodigious. When one kind of creature goes under and becomes extinct, it is often, perhaps usually, because another has varied in new and more successful ways. The single type pursuing a particular direction of specialized advance is restricted, but the group of which it forms part is evolving in many and diverse directions. This or that line of advance, this or that change has been barred; but life as a whole has never ceased to experiment and discover. . . .

Our main conclusion is that the chief agency of evolutionary change is the sifting action of Natural Selection upon practically random variation of the germ-plasm. Lamarckism will not work, because neither the direct effects of the environment, nor those of conscious or unconscious effort are normally inherited; and orthogenesis is, in most cases at least, a quite unnecessary hypothesis. But the theory of Natural Selection provides an adequate explanation for the great majority of the facts of Evolution; it can explain the detailed adaptations of animals and plants and their long-continued trends of specialization, the rise of new types and the extinction of old, the progress of life, its retrogressions and degenerations, and much at least of its variety. The implications of this are far-reaching. Without constant struggle and competition, Evolution could not have occurred; without the failure and death of innumerable individuals, there could have been no gradual perfection of the type; without the extinction of great groups, there could have been no advance of life as a whole. . . .

The result of Evolution and Natural Selection is a constant increase in fitness. But there are limitations to the perfection of fit attained. Trial-and-error is a rough-and-ready method. What it produces is something that will work, by no means necessarily something that will work perfectly. The creatures that exist are those that happen to have survived: taken together they represent an equilibrium which manages to be more or less stable, rather than life's best possible way of utilizing and sharing out the resources of earth.

But . . . as far as we can see, the variations which alone make evolution possible are random variations. That is not to say that they may not be limited in quantity and quality; but that from the point of view of evolution they are at random. In every organism they take place in many directions; the environment, acting through struggle and selection, picks out those that are headed in one particular direction. The identical variation that is selected and kept in one environment may be rejected in another. To take but one example. So long as great swamps abounded and the amphibians that lived in them had not evolved to their limit of size and power, variations making for the capacity of living and reproducing on dry land would be of less value than those promoting success in the ample watery environment. But once this environment began to shrink and dry, those same variations would go up in biological value and would be selected, and so impetus be given to the evolution of reptiles.

Variation is at random; selection sifts and guides it, as nearly as possible, into the direction prescribed by the particular conditions of environment.

Aspects of Immortality, Death, and Reproduction

By the reproduction of cells, life thwarts time. Under the best circumstances the life span of individual cells is measured in days, weeks, months—at most in decades; the slope of time is the declivity of aging. But time can be reversed, with 100 per cent profit to boot, by the reproduction of a cell.

Each cell may begin its individual existence endowed with all the potentialities of its parent and may annihilate its individual existence in the production of two cells that inherit those potentialities unaged and undiluted. The daughters of these daughters may do the same and so on to immortality.

Daniel Mazia
How Cells Divide (1961)

Immortality at the Lower Levels of Life *

by Edmund W. Sinnott (1957)

In the days when almost every housewife had geraniums blossoming through the winter in her south windows, there came a time in spring when the plants had grown too tall and "leggy" to be attractive any longer. Before throwing them out she started from them a new lot of "slips." The process is simple and familiar. With a sharp knife the tip of a vigorous young shoot was cut off, and the base of it was put into water or damp sand. Before many days a circle of root tips began to appear at the cut end, and soon a well-rooted plant became established. A dozen such might thus be grown from one old plant—its offspring by this simple, sexless process of vegetative propagation. . . . The art of rooting cuttings reaches back to the dawn of horticulture and was known even before Theophrastus, the father of botany, practiced it in Aristotle's well-stocked Athenian garden many centuries ago.

Unlike plants grown from seeds, which are the results of sexual mixing and scrambling of traits, such vegetative offspring are rigidly true to type since each is a part, though many times removed, of its first ancestor. All the Concord grapevines in the world are far-flung pieces of that prom-

* From Edmund W. Sinnott, *The Biology of the Spirit*, Viking Press, New York. Copyright 1957 by Edmund Sinnott. Reprinted by permission.

ising seedling Ephraim Bull nurtured so carefully in his Concord garden more than a century ago. Every Burbank potato, likewise, is a faithful replica of the potatoes borne by the plant which the immortal Luther, with his uncanny power to distinguish the superior from the common-place, had selected among hundreds growing on his farm in Lunenburg.

So far as we can tell, such a perennially propagated group of plants, all members one of another, can live forever. Its youthful vigor is renewed each time a shoot is set apart as a new individual. The decrepitude of age cannot affect it as a whole. Cuttings from the ancient Washington elm, taken before it finally toppled over in the fullness of its years, made trees as vigorous and youthful as their parent must have been two centuries before. Senescence seems not to be inevitable in plants like this. It is the price that highly developed organisms like ourselves must pay for their complexity. Life at a lower level is potentially immortal.

Immortality of the Stream of Life *

by Henri Bergson (1907)

We must no longer speak of *life in general* as an abstraction, or as a mere heading under which all living beings are inscribed. At a certain moment, in certain points of space, a visible current has taken rise; this current of life, traversing the bodies it has organized one after another, passing from generation to generation, has become divided amongst species and distributed amongst individuals without losing anything of its force, rather intensifying in proportion to its advance. It is well known that, on the theory of the "continuity of the germ-plasm," maintained by Weismann, the sexual elements of the generating organism pass on their properties directly to the sexual elements of the organisms engendered. . . . Regarded from this point of view, *life is like a current passing from germ to germ through the medium of a developed organism.* It is as if the organism itself were only an excrescence, a bud caused to sprout by the former germ endeavoring to continue itself in a new germ. The essential thing is the *continuous progress* indefinitely pursued, an invisible progress, on which each visible organism rides during the short interval of time given it to live.

Death is Nature's expert device for assuring abundance of life.
Goethe

* From Henri Bergson, *Creative Evolution*, translated by Arthur Mitchell (1911), Henry Holt and Company. Copyright 1911 by Henry Holt and Company. Reprinted by permission.

Are Life and Death Two Aspects of the Same Process? *

by J. S. Haldane (1935)

Living organisms not only tend to maintain and reproduce themselves, but so far as is definitely known they also normally die after a certain period of life, although if they reproduce themselves their life is thus carried on indefinitely. We must, I think, regard this normal death as a feature characteristic of life. Normal death is sometimes regarded as a wearing out of the machinery of life; but this is evidently a quite unsuitable metaphor, since living structure, when we consider it closely, can easily be seen to be constantly renewing itself, so that it cannot be regarded as mere machinery which necessarily wears out. Normal death must apparently be regarded from the biological standpoint as a means by which room is made for further more definite development of life. When we consider the phenomena of life as a whole, including what the geological records reveal, we find life pushing itself forward into fresh forms which are on the whole more and more definitely characterized as regards either structure or life-history. . . .

We can thus consider life as continuously evolving, though from the standpoint of biology alone there is no meaning in discussing whether evolving forms of life are in any way better or more beautiful, since values have no meaning for biology. Normal death may be regarded as just an expression of the nature of life, and from this standpoint normal death becomes biologically intelligible when considered in conjunction with reproduction. Sexual reproduction can perhaps be regarded as a means of securing that a distinct, but only limited difference will exist between parent and offspring.

A consideration of . . . methods of reproduction leads to some interesting and important generalizations.

It is evident in the first place that reproduction is essentially nothing more than a special kind of growth. It is growth accompanied by detachment. A bit of the parent-body is split off; a piece of living substance, instead of growing on as a part, grows into a new whole. Reproduction is not, in any strict sense of the word, creation. Nothing is suddenly called into being. It is simply a separation and a remodelling of part of the parent organism.

H. G. Wells, J. Huxley, and G. P. Wells
The Science of Life

Is the Power To Replicate the One Clear Distinction Between Living and Non-Living Matter? *

by Michael Ovenden (1962)

Surely the ability to reproduce itself is peculiar to a living organism? But it must be remembered that an organism must obtain material from its surroundings in order to reproduce, and we can imagine a set of circumstances (unlikely in nature, it is true, but not impossible) whereby a star might reproduce itself. Suppose we begin with a rapidly rotating star, which is still in the process of contraction. As it contracts, the star will rotate more and more rapidly, and, if the original rotation is rapid enough, it may break up into two smaller stars. If the double star that it has now become should then move into a cloud of interstellar matter, the gravitational pull of the stars would attract some of the interstellar matter. The stars would then grow by *accretion,* and could grow into two stars as large as the original single star, the extra material being provided from outside the original star.

Doubtless such examples could be multiplied, but enough has been said to cast strong doubts on the view that living things are in some ways different *in kind* (and not merely in complexity) from non-living things. Rather is it more likely that the division between the living and the non-living is not sharp, but that the simplest living things differ only imperceptibly from complex non-living things.

I know nothing which to a man well trained in scientific knowledge and method brings so vivid a realisation of our ignorance of the nature of life as the mystery of cell-division. . . . It is this power of spontaneous division which most sharply distinguishes the living from the non-living. . . . The greatest advance I can conceive in biology would be the discovery of the instability which leads to the continued division of the cell. When I look at a dividing cell I feel as an astronomer might do if he beheld the formation of a double star: that an original act of creation is taking place before me.

William Bateson

* From Michael Ovenden, *Life in the Universe.* Anchor Books, Doubleday and Company, Inc., Garden City, New York. Copyright 1962 by Educational Services, Inc. Reprinted by permission.

Questions To Consider

Does reproduction make living matter immortal?

Are the amoeba and the Concord grapevine true examples of immortality?

Are old age and death of the individual necessary to the process of evolution?

From the point of view of biological evolution how important is the individual?

How did the discovery of the laws of heredity illustrate the search for an order in nature?

Mendel's work on heredity has been compared with Dalton's work on atomic theory. Was there anything similar about the methods they used? Was there anything similar about the results they obtained?

Is living matter atomic?

Suggestions for Further Reading

* Eiseley, Loren: *Darwin's Century*, Anchor Books, Doubleday & Co., Inc., 1960. A perceptive account of the discoveries which paved the way for Darwin's theory, the impact of the theory itself, and the reaction to it in subsequent years.

————: *The Firmament of Time*, Atheneum, 1962. A poetic description of the way the theory of evolution became accepted and how it has affected man's view of himself and his place in nature.

* ————: *The Immense Journey*, Vintage Books, Random House, Inc., 1957. A series of imaginative and beautifully written essays on the implications of the theory of evolution. The last selection in Part 6 was taken from this collection.

Evolution, Life Science Library, Time Inc., New York. An attractively illustrated book with text by Ruth Moore introducing the layman to basic ideas in evolution and genetics.

* Goldstein, Philip: *Genetics Is Easy*, Explorer Books, The Viking Press, Inc., 1961. A simplified introduction to genetics.

* Huxley, Julian: *Evolution in Action*, Mentor Books, The New American Library, Inc., 1957. An excellent survey for the layman of the evolutionary process from the one-celled organism through the human phase and its implications for man's future.

* Simpson, George Gaylord: *The Meaning of Evolution*, Yale University Press, 1960. A study of the history of life and its significance for man.

* Paperback edition

8

Does Order Arise from Disorder?

The laws of probability upon which a large part of
modern physics is based and the tendency toward increasing disorder expressed in the Second Law of Thermodynamics are contrasted in these readings with the
high degree of orderliness found in the living molecule.
Does the order which we find in nature come from the
statistical laws of chance or is it derived from pre-existing order?

Does Order Arise from Disorder?

Introduction

ORDER IS all around us. We see it in the snow crystal and the rainbow's arch, in the steady march of the seasons and the wheeling of constellations in annual patterns across the sky. We have found it in the harmonic frequencies of atomic wave forms and in the precise patterns of the protein molecule. The discovery and revelation of the order in nature has been the deepest motivation of scientists across the centuries. As Alfred North Whitehead says: "There can be no living science unless there is a widespread instinctive conviction in the existence of an Order of Things." [1]

However many crucial questions concerning the nature of this order still remain unanswered: Is it an objective attribute of nature or is it a reflection of our own minds? [2] If it is an attribute of nature, does it result from an averaging out of enormous numbers of small random factors, or does it come from an underlying ordering principle, building order on order? Surprising as it may seem, physics supports the former principle although "To the unprepared mind," as Schrödinger says, "the second principle appears to be much simpler, much more plausible. No doubt it is. That is why physicists were so proud to have fallen in with the other one, the order-from-disorder principle."

The readings in this part describe the reasons that have led physicists to this conclusion: the discovery of the statistical nature of physical laws and the Second Law of Thermodynamics which shows that all energy differences are averaging out. The quantity known as "entropy," a mathematical term for molecular disorder, increases in all spontaneous changes. This irreversible process would eventually lead to a completely undifferentiated, inert state where no events would occur.

These conclusions may come as a surprise to the reader who has just followed the chemical evolution of matter from the simplest atomic configurations up to the complex stage of organization which we recognize as essential ingredients of living matter. In Part 9 we will see in greater detail how the intricate molecular structure of the gene determines the form and development of the entire organism and how it passes on this form with amazing precision from generation to generation. How can this degree of organization be reconciled with the order-from-disorder principle embodied in the statistical laws of nature?

1. From Alfred North Whitehead, *Science and the Modern World*, The Macmillan Company, 1925.
2. For a discussion of this question, see *Exploring the Universe*, Parts 3 and 6.

In the selection *What is Life?* Erwin Schrödinger, renowned physicist and father of wave mechanics, steps out of his own field to discuss this problem in relation to the field of genetics. Does life operate on a different principle for non-living matter, after all, or is there some way in which these two descriptions can be reconciled? The answer to this paradox, Schrödinger finds, lies in the quantum nature of matter. The fact that matter and energy are not infinitely divisible protects the molecular organization from random energy disturbances. This solution brings us back almost full circle to the place where we started with the discovery that nature is discontinuous.

The reader can judge for himself whether the solution suggested by Schrödinger resolves the paradox and explains the existence of two kinds of natural change, entropy and evolution, which appear to be going in opposite directions, the one toward a random and disorderly universe, the other toward states of increasing complexity and organization.

Some writers have been profoundly depressed by the picture of the universe as "a blindly running flux of disintegrating energy." Huston Smith considers that the acceptance of reality as unordered in any objective way is the distinctive feature and the major source of insecurity in the contemporary mind. Other writers have found in it a new kind of freedom and a new optimism.

Order from Disorder

The Law of Disorder *
by George Gamow (1947)

THERMAL DISORDER

If you pour a glass of water and look at it, you will see a clear uniform fluid with no trace of any internal structure or motion in it whatsoever (provided, of course, you do not shake the glass). We know, however, that the uniformity of water is only apparent and that if the water is magnified a few million times, there will be revealed a strongly expressed granular structure formed by a large number of separate molecules closely packed together.

Under the same magnification it is also apparent that the water is far from still, and that its molecules are in a state of violent agitation moving around and pushing one another as though they were people in a highly excited crowd. This irregular motion of water molecules, or the molecules of any other material substance, is known as *heat* (or *thermal*) *motion,* for the simple reason that it is responsible for the phenomenon of heat. For, although molecular motion as well as molecules themselves are not directly discernible to the human eye, it is molecular motion that produces a certain irritation in the nervous fibers of the human organism and produces the sensation that we call heat. For those organisms that are much smaller than human beings, such as, for example, small bacteria suspended in a water drop, the effect of thermal motion is much more pronounced, and these poor creatures are incessantly kicked, pushed, and tossed around by the restless molecules that attack them from all sides and give them no rest (Figure 8–1). This amusing phenomenon, known as *Brownian motion,* named after the English botanist Robert Brown, who first noticed it more than a century ago in a study of tiny plant spores, is of quite general nature and can be observed in the study of any kind of sufficiently small particles suspended in any kind of liquid, or of microscopic particles of smoke and dust floating in the air.

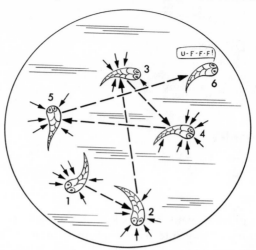

Figure 8–1. *Six consecutive positions of a bacterium which is being tossed around by molecular impacts* (*physically correct; bacteriologically not quite so*).

If we heat the liquid the wild dance of tiny particles suspended in it becomes more violent; with cooling the intensity of the motion noticeably subsides. This leaves no doubt that we are actually watching here the effect of the hidden thermal motion of matter, and that what we usually call temperature is nothing else but a measurement of the degree of molecular agitation. By studying the dependence of Brownian motion on temperature, it was found that at the temperature of $-273°$ C or $-459°$ F, thermal agitation of matter completely ceases, and all its molecules come to rest. This apparently is the lowest temperature and it has received the name of *absolute zero*. It would be an absurdity to speak about still lower temperatures since apparently there is no motion slower than absolute rest!

Near the absolute zero temperature the molecules of any substance have so little energy that the cohesive forces acting upon them cement them together into one solid block, and all they can do is only quiver slightly in their frozen state. . . .

This thermal quivering or vibration of molecules forming a solid body can be easily observed in X-ray photographs . . . since taking a picture of molecules in a crystal lattice requires a considerable time, it is essential that they should not move away from their fixed positions during the exposure. But a constant quivering around the fixed position is not conducive to good photography, and results in a somewhat blurred picture. This effect is shown in the molecular photograph which is reproduced in Figure 8–3. To obtain sharper pictures one must cool the crystals as much

Absolute zero

Room temperature

Melting point

Figure 8–2.

as possible. This is sometimes accomplished by dipping them in liquid air. If, on the other hand, one warms up the crystal to be photographed, the picture becomes more and more blurred, and, at the melting point the pattern completely vanishes, owing to the fact that the molecules leave their places and begin to move in an irregular way through the melted substance. . . .

The breaking up of the beautiful crystalline structure of solid bodies

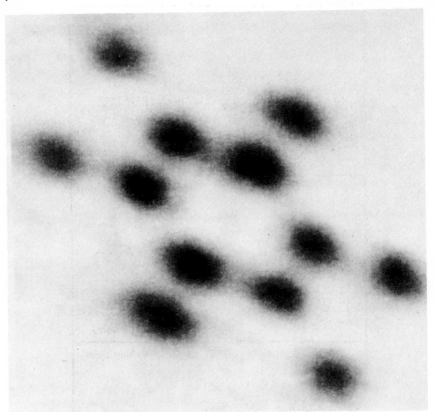

Figure 8–3. Hexamethylbenzine molecule magnified about 300,000,000 times. (Photograph by Dr. Maurice L. Huggins at Kodak Research Laboratories using X-ray data by Brockway and Robertson. Reprinted by permission.)

forces the molecules first to crawl around one another like a pack of worms, and then to fly apart as though they were a flock of frightened birds. But this latter phenomenon still does not represent the limit of the destructive power of increasing thermal motion. If the temperature rises still farther the very existence of the molecules is threatened, since the ever increasing violence of intermolecular collisions is capable of breaking them up into separate atoms. This *thermal dissociation,* as it is called, depends on the relative strength of the molecules subjected to it. The molecules of some organic substances will break up into separate atoms or atomic groups at temperatures as low as a few hundred degrees. Other more sturdily built molecules, such as those of water, will require a temperature of over a thousand degrees to be destroyed. But when the temperature rises to several thousand degrees no molecules will be left and the matter will be a gaseous mixture of pure chemical elements.

This is the situation on the surface of our sun where the temperature ranges up to 6000° C. On the other hand, in the comparatively cooler atmospheres of the red stars, some of the molecules are still present, a fact that has been demonstrated by the methods of spectral analysis.

The violence of thermal collisions at high temperatures not only breaks up the molecules into their constituent atoms, but also damages the atoms themselves by chipping off their outer electrons. This *thermal ionization* becomes more and more pronounced when the temperature rises into tens and hundreds of thousands of degrees, and reaches completion at a few million degrees above zero. At these tremendously hot temperatures, which are high above everything that we can produce in our laboratories but which are common in the interiors of stars and in particular inside our sun, the atoms as such cease to exist. All electronic shells are completely stripped off, and the matter becomes a mixture of bare nuclei and free electrons rushing wildly through space and colliding with one another with tremendous force.[1] However, in spite of the complete wreckage of atomic bodies, the matter still retains its fundamental chemical characteristics, inasmuch as atomic nuclei remain intact. If the temperature drops, the nuclei will recapture their electrons and the integrity of atoms will be reestablished.

In order to attain complete thermal dissociation of matter, that is to break up the nuclei themselves into the separate nucleons (protons and neutrons) the temperature must go up to at least several billion degrees. Even inside the hottest stars we do not find such high temperatures, though it seems very likely that temperatures of that magnitude did exist several billion years ago when our universe was still young. . . . (Figure 8-4.)

Thus we see that the effect of thermal agitation is to destroy step by step the elaborate architecture of matter based on the law of quantum, and to turn this magnificent building into a mess of widely moving particles rushing around and colliding with one another without any apparent law or regularity.

HOW CAN ONE DESCRIBE DISORDERLY MOTION?

It would be, however, a grave mistake to think that because of the irregularity of thermal motion it must remain outside the scope of any possible physical description. Indeed the fact itself that thermal motion

---

1. Matter in this state is known as "plasma." Ed.

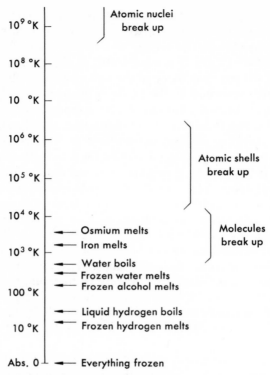

$10^9 \, °\text{K}$

$10^8 \, °\text{K}$

$10 \, °\text{K}$

$10^6 \, °\text{K}$

$10^5 \, °\text{K}$

$10^4 \, °\text{K}$

$10^3 \, °\text{K}$

$100 \, °\text{K}$

$10 \, °\text{K}$

Abs. 0

Atomic nuclei
break up

Atomic shells
break up

Molecules
break up

Osmium melts
Iron melts
Water boils
Frozen water melts
Frozen alcohol melts
Liquid hydrogen boils
Frozen hydrogen melts
Everything frozen

Figure 8–4. The destructive effect of temperature.

is *completely irregular* makes it subject to a new kind of law, the *Law of Disorder* better known as the *Law of Statistical Behavior*. In order to understand the above statement let us turn our attention to the famous problem of a "Drunkard's Walk." Suppose we watch a drunkard who has been leaning against a lamp post in the middle of a large paved city square (nobody knows how or when he got there) and then has suddenly decided to go nowhere in particular. Thus off he goes, making a few steps in one direction, then some more steps in another, and so on and so on, changing his course every few steps in an entirely unpredictable way (Figure 8–5). How far will be our drunkard from the lamp post after he has executed, say, a hundred phases of his irregular zigzag journey? One would at first think that, because of the unpredictability of each turn, there is no way of answering this question. If, however, we consider the problem a little more attentively we will find that, although we really cannot tell where the drunkard will be at the end of his walk, we can answer the question about his most probable distance from the lamp post after a given large

Figure 8–5. Drunkard's walk. (After George Gamow.)

number of turns. . . . [A simple algebraic analysis shows that] *the most probable distance of our drunkard from the lamp post after a certain large number of irregular turns is equal to the average length of each straight track that he walks, times the square root of their number.* [$R = L \cdot \sqrt{N}$ (See Figure 8–5).]

Thus if our drunkard goes one yard each time before he turns (at an unpredictable angle!), he will most probably be only ten yards from the lamp post after walking a grand total of a hundred yards. If he had not turned, but had gone straight, he would be a hundred yards away—which shows that it is definitely advantageous to be sober when taking a walk.

The statistical nature of the above example is revealed by the fact that we refer here only to the *most probable* distance and not to the exact distance in each individual case. In the case of an individual drunkard it may happen, though this is not very probable, that he does not make any turns at all and thus goes far away from the lamp post along the straight line. It may also happen, that he turns each time by, say, 180 degrees thus returning to the lamp post after every second turn. But if a large number of drunkards all start from the same lamp post walking in different zigzag paths and not interfering with one another you will find after a sufficiently long time that they are spread over a certain area around the lamp post in such a way that their *average distance* from the post may be calculated by the above rule. An example of such spreading due to irregular motion is given in Figure 8–6, where we consider six walking drunkards. It goes without saying that the larger the number of drunkards, and the larger the number of turns they make in their disorderly walk, the more accurate is the rule.

Now substitute for the drunkards some microscopic bodies such as plant spores or bacteria suspended in liquid, and you will have exactly the picture that the botanist Brown saw in his microscope. True the spores and bacteria are not drunk, but, as we have said above, they are being incessantly kicked in all possible directions by the surrounding molecules involved in thermal motion, and are therefore forced to follow exactly the same irregular zigzag trajectories as a person who has completely lost his sense of direction under the influence of alcohol.

If you look through a microscope at the Brownian motion of a large number of small particles suspended in a drop of water, you will concentrate your attention on a certain group of them that are at the moment concentrated in a given small region (near the "lamp post"). You will notice that in the course of time they become gradually dispersed all over the field of vision, and that their average distance from the origin increases in proportion to the square root of the time interval as required

Figure 8–6. Statistical distribution of six walking drunkards around the lamp post. (After George Gamow.)

by the mathematical law by which we calculated the distance of the drunkard's walk.

The same law of motion pertains, of course, to each separate molecule in our drop of water; but you cannot see separate molecules, and even if you could, you wouldn't be able to distinguish between them. To make such motion visible one must use two different kinds of molecules distinguishable for example by their different colors. Thus we can fill one half of a chemical test tube with a water solution of potassium permanganate, which will give to the water a beautiful purple tint. If we now pour on the top of it some clear fresh water, being careful not to mix up the two layers, we shall notice that the color gradually penetrates the clear water. If you wait sufficiently long you will find that all the water from the bottom to the surface becomes uniformly colored. This phenomenon, familiar to everybody, is known as *diffusion* and is due to the irregular thermal motion of the molecules of dye among the water molecules. We must imagine each molecule of potassium permanganate as a little drunkard who is driven to and fro by the incessant impacts received from other molecules. Since in water the molecules are packed rather tightly (in contrast to the arrangement of those in a gas) the average free path of each molecule between two successive collisions is very short, being only about one hundred millionth of an inch. Since on the other hand the molecules at room temperature move with the speed of about one tenth of a mile per second, it takes only one million-millionth part of a second for a molecule to go from one collision to another. Thus in the course of a single second each dye molecule will be engaged in about a million million consecutive collisions and will change its direction of motion as many times. The average distance covered during the first second will be one hundred millionth of an inch (the length of free path) times the square root of a million millions. This gives the average diffusion speed of only one hundredth of an inch per second; a rather slow process considering that if it were not deflected by collisions, the same molecule would be a tenth of a mile away! If you wait 100 sec, the molecule will have struggled through 10 times ($\sqrt{100} = 10$) as great a distance, and in 10,000 sec, that is, about 3 hr, the diffusion will have carried the coloring 100 times farther ($\sqrt{10000} = 100$), that is, about 1 in. away. Yes, diffusion is a rather slow process; when you put a lump of sugar into your cup of tea you had better stir it rather than wait until the sugar molecules have been spread throughout by their own motion.

Just to give another example of the process of diffusion, . . . we shall take an entirely different case of cosmic importance. . . . The energy of our sun is produced deep in its interior by the alchemic transformation of chemical elements. This energy is liberated in the form of intensive radiation, and the "particles of light," or the light quanta, begin their long journey through the body of the sun toward its surface. Since light moves at a speed of 300,000 km per second, and the radius of the sun is only 700,000 km it would take a light quantum only slightly over two seconds to come out provided it moved without any deviations from a straight line. However, this is far from being the case; on their way out the light quanta undergo innumerable collisions with the atoms and electrons in the material of the sun. The free pass of a light quantum in solar matter is about a centimeter (much longer than a free pass of a molecule!) and since the radius of the sun is 70,000,000,000 cm, our light quantum must make $(7 \cdot 10^{10})^2$ or $5 \cdot 10^{21}$ drunkard's steps to reach the surface. Since each step requires $\dfrac{1}{3 \cdot 10^{10}}$ or $3 \cdot 10^{-11}$ sec, the entire time of travel is $3 \times 10^{-11} \times 5 \times 10^{21} = 1.5 \times 10^{11}$ sec or about 5000 yr! Here again we see how slow the process of diffusion is. It takes light 50 centuries to travel from the center of the sun to its surface, whereas after coming into empty interplanetary space and traveling along a straight line it covers the entire distance from the sun to the earth in only eight minutes!

COUNTING PROBABILITIES

This case of diffusion represents only one simple example of the application of the statistical law of probability to the problem of molecular motion. Before we go farther with that discussion, and make the attempt to understand the all-important *Law of Entropy*, which rules the thermal behavior of every material body, be it a tiny droplet of some liquid or the giant universe of stars, we have first to learn more about the ways in which the probability of different simple or complicated events can be calculated.

By far the simplest problem of probability calculus arises when you toss a coin. Everybody knows that in this case (without cheating) there are equal chances to get heads or tails. One usually says that there is a *fifty-fifty chance* for heads or tails, but it is more customary in mathematics to say that the chances are *half and half*. If you add the chances of getting heads and getting tails you get $\frac{1}{2} + \frac{1}{2} = 1$. Unity in the theory of probability means a certainty; you are in fact quite certain that in tossing a coin you get either heads or tails, unless it rolls under the sofa and vanishes tracelessly.

Suppose now you drop the coin twice in succession or, what is the same, you drop 2 coins simultaneously. It is easy to see that you have here 4 different possibilities shown in Figure 8–7.

Figure 8–7. Four possible combinations in tossing coins.

In the first case you get heads twice, in the last case tails twice, whereas the two intermediate cases lead to the same result since it does not matter to you in which order (or in which coin) heads or tails appear. Thus you say that the chances of getting heads twice are 1 out of 4 or $\frac{1}{4}$, the chances of getting tails twice are also $\frac{1}{4}$, whereas the chances of heads once and tails once are 2 out of 4 or $\frac{1}{2}$. Here again $\frac{1}{4} + \frac{1}{4} + \frac{1}{2} = 1$, meaning that you are certain to get one of the 3 possible combinations. Let us see now what happens if we toss the coin 3 times. There are altogether 8 possibilities summarized in the following table:

First tossing	h	h	h	h	t	t	t	t
Second	h	h	t	t	h	h	t	t
Third	h	t	h	t	h	t	h	t
	I	II	II	III	II	III	III	IV

If you inspect this table you find that there is 1 chance out of 8 of getting heads three times, and the same of getting tails three times. The remaining possibilities are equally divided between heads twice and tails once, or heads once and tails twice, with the probability three eighths for each event.

Our table of different possibilities is growing rather rapidly, but let us take one more step by tossing 4 times. Now we have the following 16 possibilities:

First tossing	h	h	h	h	h	h	h	h	t	t	t	t	t	t	t	t
Second	h	h	h	h	t	t	t	t	h	h	h	h	t	t	t	t
Third	h	h	t	t	h	h	t	t	h	h	t	t	h	h	t	t
Fourth	h	t	h	t	h	t	h	t	h	t	h	t	h	t	h	t
	I	II	II	III	II	III	III	IV	II	III	III	IV	III	IV	IV	V

Here we have $\frac{1}{16}$ for the probability of heads four times, and exactly the same for tails four times. The mixed cases of heads three times and

tails once or tails three times and heads once have the probabilities of
$\frac{4}{16}$ or $\frac{1}{4}$ each, whereas the chances of heads and tails the same number
of times are $\frac{6}{16}$ or $\frac{3}{8}$.

If you try to continue in a similar way for larger numbers of tosses the
table becomes so long that you will soon run out of paper; thus for ex-
ample for ten tosses you have 1024 different possibilities (i.e., $2 \times 2 \times 2 \times$
$2 \times 2 \times 2 \times 2 \times 2 \times 2 \times 2$). But it is not at all necessary to construct
such long tables since the simple laws of probability can be observed in
those simple examples that we already have cited and then used directly
in more complicated cases.

First of all you see that the probability of getting heads twice is equal
to the product of the probabilities of getting it separately in the first and
in the second tossing; in fact $\frac{1}{4} = \frac{1}{2} \times \frac{1}{2}$. Similarly the probability of
getting heads three or four times in succession is the product of prob-
abilities of getting it separately in each tossing ($\frac{1}{8} = \frac{1}{2} \times \frac{1}{2} \times \frac{1}{2}$;
$\frac{1}{16} = \frac{1}{2} \times \frac{1}{2} \times \frac{1}{2} \times \frac{1}{2}$). Thus if somebody asks you what the chances
are of getting heads each time in ten tossings you can easily give the
answer by multiplying $\frac{1}{2} \times \frac{1}{2}$ ten times. The result will be .00098, indicating that the chances are very low indeed: about one chance out of a
thousand! Here we have the rule of "multiplication of probabilities," which
states that *if you want several different things, you may determine the
mathematical probability of getting them by multiplying the mathematical probabilities of getting the several individual ones.* If there are many
things you want, and each of them is not particularly probable, the
chances that you get them *all* are discouragingly low!

There is also another rule, that of the "addition of probabilities," which
states that *if you want only one of several things (no matter which one),
the mathematical probability of getting it is the sum of mathematical
probabilities of getting individual items on your list.*

This can be easily illustrated in the example of getting an equal division
between heads and tails in tossing a coin twice. What you actually want
here is *either* "heads once, tails once" or "tails once, heads once." The
probability of each of the above combinations is $\frac{1}{4}$, and the probability
of getting either one of them is $\frac{1}{4}$ plus $\frac{1}{4}$ or $\frac{1}{2}$. Thus: If you want "that,
and that, *and* that . . ." you *multiply* the individual mathematical proba-
bilities of different items. If, however, you want "that, *or* that, *or* that"
you *add* the probabilities.

In the first case your chances of getting everything you ask for will
decrease as the number of desired items increases. In the second case,
when you want only one out of several items your chances of being
satisfied increase as the list of items from which to choose becomes
longer.

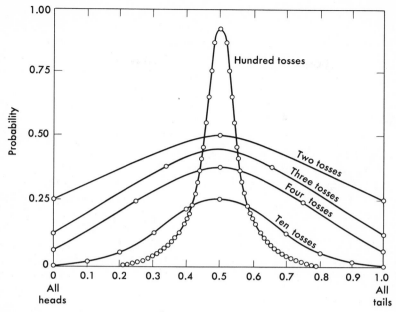

Figure 8–8. Relative number of tails and heads.

The experiments with tossing coins furnish a fine example of what is meant by saying that the laws of probability become more exact when you deal with a large number of trials. This is illustrated in Figure 8–8, which represents the probabilities of getting a different relative number of heads and tails for two, three, four, ten, and a hundred tossings. You see that with the increasing number of tossings the probability curve becomes sharper and sharper and the maximum at fifty-fifty ratio of heads and tails becomes more and more pronounced.

Thus whereas for 2 or 3, or even 4 tosses, the chances to have heads each time or tails each time are still quite appreciable, in 10 tosses even 90 per cent of heads or tails is very improbable. For a still larger number of tosses, say 100 or 1000, the probability curve becomes as sharp as a needle, and the chances of getting even a small deviation from fifty-fifty distribution becomes practically nil. . . .

[An] interesting example of probability calculation, an example that leads to a quite unexpected answer, is the problem of "Coinciding Birthdays." Try to remember whether you have ever been invited to two different birthday parties on the same day. You will probably say that the chances of such double invitations are very small since you have only about 24 friends who are likely to invite you, and there are 365 days in the year on which their birthdays may fall. Thus, with so many possible dates to choose from, there must be very little chance that any 2 of your 24 friends will have to cut their birthday cakes on the same day.

However, unbelievable as it may sound, your judgment here is quite wrong. The truth is that there is a rather high probability that in a company of 24 people there are a pair, or even several pairs, with coinciding birthdays. As a matter of fact, there are more chances that there is such a coincidence than that there is not.

You can verify that fact by making a birthday list including about 24 persons, or more simply, by comparing the birth dates of 24 persons whose names appear consecutively on any pages of some such reference book as "Who's Who in America," opened at random. Or the probabilities can be ascertained by using the simple rules of probability calculus with which we have become acquainted in the problems of coin tossing . . .

Suppose we try first to calculate the chances that in a company of twenty-four persons everyone has a different birth date. Let us ask the first person in the group what is his birth date; of course this can be any of the 365 days of the year. Now, what is the chance that the birth date of the second person we approach is *different* from that of the first? Since this (second) person could have been born on any day of the year, there is one chance out of 365 that his birth date coincides with that of the first one, and 364 chances out of 365 (i.e., the probability of 364/365) that it does not. Similarly, the probability that the third person has a birth date different from that of either the first or second is 363/365, since two days of the year have been excluded. The probabilities that the next persons we ask have different birth dates from the ones we have approached before are then: 362/365, 361/365, 360/365 and so on up to the last person for whom the probability is $\frac{(365-23)}{365}$ or $\frac{342}{365}$. Since we are trying to learn what the probability is that one of these coincidences of birth dates exists, we have to multiply all the above fractions, thus obtaining for the probability of all the persons having different birth dates the value:

$$\frac{364}{365} \times \frac{363}{365} \times \frac{362}{365} \times \cdots \frac{342}{365}$$

One can arrive at the product in a few minutes by using certain methods of higher mathematics, but if you don't know them you can do it the hard way by direct multiplication, which would not take so very much time. The result is 0.46, indicating that the probability that there will be no coinciding birthdays is slightly less than one half. In other words there are only 46 chances in 100 that no two of your two dozen friends will have birthdays on the same day, and 54 chances in 100 that two or more will.

Thus if you have 25 or more friends, and have never been invited to two birthday parties on the same date you may conclude with a high degree of probability that either most of your friends do not organize their birthday parties, or that they do not invite you to them!

The problem of coincident birthdays represents a very fine example of how a common-sense judgment concerning the probabilities of complex events can be entirely wrong. The author has put this question to a great many people, including many prominent scientists, and in all cases except one was offered bets ranging from 2 to 1 to 15 to 1 that no such coincidence will occur. If he had accepted all these bets he would be a rich man by now!

It cannot be repeated too often that if we calculate the probabilities of different events according to the given rules and pick out the most probable of them, we are not at all sure that this is exactly what is going to happen. Unless the number of tests we are making runs into thousands, millions or still better into billions, the predicted results are only "likely" and not at all "certain." . . .

THE "MYSTERIOUS" ENTROPY

From the above examples of probability calculus, all of them pertaining to ordinary life, we have learned that predictions of that sort, being often disappointing when small numbers are involved, become better and better when we go to really large numbers. This makes these laws particularly applicable to the description of the almost innumerable quantities of atoms or molecules that form even the smallest piece of matter we can conveniently handle. Thus, whereas the statistical law of Drunkard's Walk can give us only approximate results when applied to a half-dozen drunkards who make perhaps two dozen turns each, its application to billions of dye molecules undergoing billions of collisions every second leads to the most rigorous physical law of diffusion. We can also say that the dye that was originally dissolved in only one half of the water in the test tube tends through the process of diffusion to spread uniformly through the entire liquid, because, such uniform distribution is *more probable* than the original one.

For exactly the same reason the room in which you sit reading this book is filled uniformly by air from wall to wall and from floor to ceiling, and it never even occurs to you that the air in the room can unexpectedly collect itself in a far corner, leaving you to suffocate in your chair. However, *this horrifying event is not at all physically impossible, but only highly improbable.* . . . The waiting time for the right combination is $10^{299,999,999,999,999,999,999,999,998}$ sec as compared with only 10^{17} sec representing the total age of the universe! Thus you may go on quietly reading your book without being afraid of being suffocated by chance.

To take another example, let us consider a glass of water standing on the table. We know that the molecules of water, being involved in the irregular thermal motion, are moving at high speed in all possible directions, being, however, prevented from flying apart by the cohesive forces between them.

Since the direction of motion of each separate molecule is governed entirely by the law of chance, we may consider the possibility that at a certain moment the velocities of one half of the molecules, namely those in the upper part of the glass, will all be directed upward, whereas the other half, in the lower part of the glass, will move downwards. In such a case, the cohesive forces acting along the horizontal plane dividing two groups of molecules will not be able to oppose their "unified desire for parting," and we shall observe the unusual physical phenomenon of half the water from the glass being spontaneously shot up with the speed of a bullet toward the ceiling!

Another possibility is that the total energy of thermal motion of water molecules will be concentrated by chance in those located in the upper part of the glass, in which case the water near the bottom suddenly freezes, whereas its upper layers begin to boil violently. Why have you never seen such things happen? Not because they are absolutely impossible, but only because they are extremely improbable. In fact, if you try to calculate the probability that molecular velocities, originally distributed at random in all directions, will by pure chance assume the distribution described above, you arrive at a figure that is just about as small as the probability that the molecules of air will collect in one corner. In a similar way, the chance that, because of mutual collisions, some of the molecules will lose most of their kinetic energy, while the other part gets a considerable excess of it, is also negligibly small. Here again the distribution of velocities that corresponds to the usually observed case is the one that possesses the largest probability.

If now we start with a case that does not correspond to the most probable arrangement of molecular positions or velocities, by letting out some gas in one corner of the room, or by pouring some hot water on top of the cold, a sequence of physical changes will take place that will bring our system from this less probable to a most probable state. The gas will diffuse through the room until it fills it up uniformly, and the heat from the top of the glass will flow toward the bottom until all the water assumes an equal temperature. Thus we may say that *all physical processes depending on the irregular motion of molecules go in the direction of increasing probability* and *the state of equilibrium, when nothing more happens, corresponds to the maximum of probability.* Since . . . the probabilities of various molecular distributions are often expressed by inconveniently small numbers, it is customary to refer to their logarithms instead. This quantity is known by the name of *entropy*, and plays a prominent role in all questions connected with the irregular thermal motion of matter. The foregoing statement concerning the probability changes in physical processes can be now rewritten in the form: *Any spontaneous changes in a physical system occur in the direction of increasing entropy, and the final state of equilibrium corresponds to the maximum possible value of the entropy.*

This is the famous *Law of Entropy*, also known as the Second Law of Thermodynamics (the First Law being the Law of Conservation of Energy), and as you see there is nothing in it to frighten you.

The Law of Entropy can also be called the *Law of Increasing Disorder* since, as we have seen in all the examples given above, the entropy reaches its maximum when the position and velocities of molecules are distributed completely at random so that any attempt to introduce some order in their motion would lead to the decrease of the entropy. Still another, more practical, formulation of the Law of Entropy can be obtained by reference to the problem of turning the heat into mechanical motion. Remembering that the heat is actually the disorderly mechanical motion of molecules, it is easy to understand that the complete trans- formation of the heat content of a given material body into mechanical energy of large-scale motion is equivalent to the task of forcing all molecules of that body to move in the same direction. However, in the example of the glass of water that might spontaneously shoot one half of its contents toward the ceiling, we have seen that such a phenomenon is sufficiently improbable to be considered as being practically impossible. Thus, *although the energy of mechanical motion can go completely over into heat (for example, through friction), the heat energy can never go completely into mechanical motion.* This rules out the possibility of the so-called "perpetual motion motor of the second kind," [2] which would extract the heat from the material bodies at normal temperature, thus cooling them down and utilizing for doing mechanical work the energy so obtained. For example, it is impossible to build a steamship in the boiler of which steam is generated not by burning coal but by extracting the heat from the ocean water, which is first pumped into the engine room, and then thrown back overboard in the form of ice cubes after the heat is extracted from it.

But how then do the ordinary steam-engines turn the heat into motion

2. Called so in contrast to the "perpetual motion motor of the first kind" which violates the law of conservation of energy working without any energy supply.

without violating the Law of Entropy? The trick is made possible by the fact that in the steam engine *only a part of the heat liberated by burning fuel is actually turned into energy*, another larger part being thrown out into the air in the form of exhaust steam, or absorbed by the specially arranged steam coolers. In this case we have two opposite changes of entropy in our system: (1) the decrease of entropy corresponding to the transformation of a part of the heat into mechanical energy of the pistons, and (2) the increase of entropy resulting from the flow of another part of the heat from the hot-water boilers into the coolers. The Law of Entropy requires only that *the total amount* of entropy of the system increase, and this can be easily arranged by making the second factor larger than the first. The situation can probably be understood somewhat better by considering an example of a 5 lb weight placed on a shelf 6 ft above the floor. According to the Law of Conservation of Energy, it is quite impossible that this weight will spontaneously and without any external help rise toward the ceiling. On the other hand it is possible to drop one part of this weight to the floor and use the energy thus released to raise another part upward.

In a similar way we can decrease the entropy in one part of our system if there is a compensating increase of entropy in its other part. In other words *considering a disorderly motion of molecules we can bring some order in one region, if we do not mind the fact that this will make the motion in other parts still more disorderly*. And in many practical cases, as in all kinds of heat engines, we do not mind it.

STATISTICAL FLUCTUATION

The discussion of the previous section must have made it clear to you that the Law of Entropy and all its consequences are based entirely on the fact that in large-scale physics we are always dealing with an immensely large number of separate molecules, so that any prediction based on probability considerations becomes almost an absolute certainty. However, this kind of prediction becomes considerably less certain when we consider very small amounts of matter. . . .

Thus, on a small scale, the distribution of molecules in the air is far from being uniform. If we could use sufficient magnification, we should notice the small concentration of molecules being instantaneously formed at various points of the gas, only to be dissolved again, and be replaced by other similar concentrations appearing at other points. This effect is known as *fluctuation of density* and plays an important role in many physical phenomena. Thus, for example, when the rays of the sun pass through the atmosphere these inhomogeneities cause the scattering of blue rays of the spectrum, giving to the sky its familiar color and making the sun look redder than it actually is. This effect of reddening is especially pronounced during the sunset, when the sun rays must pass through the thicker layer of air. Were these fluctuations of density not present the sky would always look completely black and the stars could be seen during the day.

Similar, though less pronounced, fluctuations of density and pressure also take place in ordinary liquids, and another way of describing the cause of Brownian motion is by saying that the tiny particles suspended in the water are pushed to and fro because of rapidly varying changes of pressure acting on their opposite sides. When the liquid is heated until it is close to its boiling point, the fluctuations of density become more pronounced and cause a slight opalescence.

We can ask ourselves now whether the Law of Entropy applies to such small objects as those to which the statistical fluctuations become of primary importance. Certainly a bacterium, which through all its life is tossed around by molecular impacts, will sneer at the statement that heat cannot go over into mechanical motion! But it would be more correct to say in this case that the Law of Entropy loses its sense, rather than to say that it is violated. In fact all that this law says is that molecular motion cannot be transformed completely into the motion of large objects containing immense numbers of separate molecules. For a bacterium, which is not *much* larger than the molecules themselves, the difference between the thermal and mechanical motion has practically disappeared, and it would consider the molecular collisions tossing it around in the same way as we would consider the kicks we get from our fellow citizens in an excited crowd. If we were bacteria, we should be able to build a perpetual motion motor of the second kind by simply tying ourselves to a flying wheel, but then we should not have the brains to use it to our advantage. Thus there is actually no reason for being sorry that we are not bacteria!

Maxwell's Little Demon *

by Isaac Asimov (1962)

The difference between an invariable flow and a flow that deviates immeasurably from being invariable is all-important philosophically but seems so insignificant in any practical sense that Maxwell felt the need to dramatize it somehow. He therefore pictured a tiny being at a stop-cock between two containers of gas, that were at equal temperatures to begin with. This being behaved in the following fashion: When a fast-moving molecule in the right-hand container approached he let it through the stopcock, while rejecting all the slow-moving molecules. On the other hand, when a slow-moving molecule in the left-hand container approached he let that through the stopcock, while rejecting all the fast-moving molecules. In this way the left-hand container would accumu-late fast-moving molecules and grow warmer, while the right-hand con-tainer would accumulate slow-moving molecules and grow cooler. Heat would continue to flow from the cold body to the hot body, a situation inconceivable by the old theory but conceivable by the new one. "Max-well's demon," as the imaginary being was called, has been famous ever since as the ideal entropy-reverser. [Figure 8–9.]

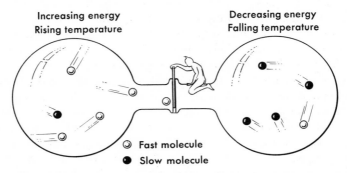

Figure 8–9. Maxwell's demon. (After Hyman Levy, Modern Science, *Alfred Knopf, 1939. Reprinted by permission.)*

> . . . *Chaos umpire sits*
> *And by decision more*
> *embroils the fray*
> *By which he reigns: next*
> *him high arbiter*
> *Chance governs all.*
> John Milton

The Law *

by Robert M. Coates (1947)

The first intimation that things were getting out of hand came one
early-fall evening in the late nineteen-forties. What happened, simply,
was that between seven and nine o'clock on that evening the Triborough
Bridge had the heaviest concentration of outbound traffic in its entire
history.

This was odd, for it was a weekday evening (to be precise, a Wednesday), and though the weather was agreeably mild and clear, with a moon
that was close enough to being full to lure a certain number of motorists
out of the city, these facts alone were not enough to explain the phenomenon. No other bridge or main highway was affected, and though
the two preceding nights had been equally balmy and moonlit, on both
of these the bridge traffic had run close to normal.

The bridge personnel, at any rate, was caught entirely unprepared. A
main artery of traffic, like the Triborough, operates under fairly predictable conditions. Motor travel, like most other large-scale human
activities, obeys the Law of Averages—that great, ancient rule that states
that the actions of people in the mass will always follow consistent patterns—and on the basis of past experience it had always been possible to
foretell, almost to the last digit, the number of cars that would cross the
bridge at any given hour of the day or night. In this case, though, all
rules were broken.

The hours from seven till nearly midnight are normally quiet ones on
the bridge. But on that night it was as if all the motorists in the city,
or at any rate a staggering proportion of them, had conspired together
to upset tradition. Beginning almost exactly at seven o'clock, cars poured
onto the bridge in such numbers and with such rapidity that the staff
at the toll booths was overwhelmed almost from the start. It was soon
apparent that this was no momentary congestion, and as it became more
and more obvious that the traffic jam promised to be one of truly monu-
mental proportions, added details of police were rushed to the scene to
help handle it.

Cars streamed in from all directions—from the Bronx approach and the
Manhattan one, from 125th Street and the East River Drive. (At the
peak of the crush, about eight-fifteen, observers on the bridge reported

that the drive was a solid line of car headlights as far south as the bend at Eighty-ninth Street, while the congestion crosstown in Manhattan disrupted traffic as far west as Amsterdam Avenue.) And perhaps the most confusing thing about the whole manifestation was that there seemed to be no reason for it.

Now and then, as the harried toll-booth attendants made change for the seemingly endless stream of cars, they would question the occupants, and it soon became clear that the very participants in the monstrous tieup were as ignorant of its cause as anyone else was. A report made by Sergeant Alfonse O'Toole, who commanded the detail in charge of the Bronx approach, is typical. "I kept askin' them," he said, " 'Is there night football somewhere that we don't know about? Is it the races you're goin' to?' But the funny thing was half the time they'd be askin' *me*. 'What's the crowd for, Mac?' they would say. And I'd just look at them. There was one guy I mind, in a Ford convertible with a girl in the seat beside him, and when he asked me, I said to him, 'Hell, you're *in* the crowd, ain't you?' I said. 'What brings *you* here?' And the dummy just looked at me. 'Me?' he says. 'I just come out for a drive in the moonlight. But if I'd known there'd be a crowd like this . . .' he says. And then he asks me, 'Is there any place I can turn around and get out of this?' " As the *Herald Tribune* summed things up in its story next morning, it "just looked as if everybody in Manhattan who owned a motorcar had decided to drive out on Long Island that evening."

The incident was unusual enough to make all the front pages next morning, and because of this, many similar events, which might otherwise have gone unnoticed, received attention. The proprietor of the Aramis Theatre, on Eighth Avenue, reported that on several nights in the recent past his auditorium had been practically empty, while on others it had been jammed to suffocation. Luncheon owners noted that increasingly their patrons were developing a habit of making runs on specific items; one day it would be the roast shoulder of veal with pan gravy that was ordered almost exclusively, while the next everyone would be taking the Vienna loaf, and the roast veal went begging. A man who ran a small notions store in Bayside revealed that over a period of four days two hundred and seventy-four successive customers had entered his shop and asked for a spool of pink thread.

These were news items that would ordinarily have gone into the papers as fillers or in the sections reserved for oddities. Now, however, they seemed to have a more serious significance. It was apparent at last that something decidedly strange was happening to people's habits, and it was as unsettling as those occasional moments on excursion boats when the passengers are moved, all at once, to rush to one side or the other of the vessel. It was not till one day in December when, almost incredibly, the Twentieth Century Limited left New York for Chicago with just three passengers aboard that business leaders discovered how disastrous the new trend could be, too.

Until then, the New York Central, for instance, could operate confidently on the assumption that although there might be several thousand men in New York who had business relations in Chicago, on any single day no more—and no less—than some hundreds of them would have occasion to go there. The play producer could be sure that his patronage would sort itself out and that roughly as many persons would want to see the performance on Thursday as there had been on Tuesday or Wednesday. Now they couldn't be sure of anything. The Law of Averages had gone by the board, and if the effect on business promised to be catastrophic, it was also singularly unnerving for the general customer.

The lady starting downtown for a day of shopping, for example, could never be sure whether she would find Macy's department store a seething mob of other shoppers or a wilderness of empty, echoing aisles and unoccupied salesgirls. And the uncertainty produced a strange sort of jitteriness in the individual when faced with any impulse to action. "Shall we do it or shan't we?" people kept asking themselves, knowing that if they did it, it might turn out that thousands of other individuals had decided similarly; knowing, too, that if they *didn't*, they might miss the one glorious chance of all chances to have Jones Beach, say, practically to themselves. Business languished, and a sort of desperate uncertainty rode everyone.

At this juncture, it was inevitable that Congress should be called on for action. In fact, Congress called on itself, and it must be said that it rose nobly to the occasion. A committee was appointed, drawn from both Houses and headed by Senator J. Wing Slooper (R.), of Indiana, and though after considerable investigation the committee was forced reluctantly to conclude that there was no evidence of Communist instigation, the unconscious subversiveness of the people's present conduct was obvious at a glance. The problem was what to do about it. You can't indict a whole nation, particularly on such vague grounds as these were. But, as Senator Slooper boldly pointed out, "You can control it," and in the end a system of reëducation and reform was decided upon, designed to lead people back to—again we quote Senator Slooper—"the basic regularities, the homely averageness of the American way of life."

In the course of the committee's investigations, it had been discovered, to everyone's dismay, that the Law of Averages had never been incorporated into the body of federal jurisprudence, and though the upholders of States' Rights rebelled violently, the oversight was at once corrected, both by Constitutional amendment and by a law—the Hills-Slooper Act—implementing it. According to the Act, people were *required* to be average, and, as the simplest way of assuring it, they were divided alphabetically and their permissible activities catalogued accordingly. Thus, by the plan, a person whose name began with "G," "N," or "U," for example, could attend the theatre only on Tuesdays, and he could go to baseball games only on Thursdays, whereas his visits to a haberdashery were confined to the hours between ten o'clock and noon on Mondays.

The law, of course, had its disadvantages. It had a crippling effect on theatre parties, among other social functions, and the cost of enforcing it was unbelievably heavy. In the end, too, so many amendments had to be added to it—such as the one permitting gentlemen to take their fiancées (if accredited) along with them to various events and functions no matter what letter the said fiancées' names began with—that the courts were frequently at a loss to interpret it when confronted with violations.

In its way, though, the law did serve its purpose, for it did induce—rather mechanically, it is true, but still adequately—a return to that average existence that Senator Slooper desired. All, indeed, would have been well if a year or so later disquieting reports had not begun to seep in from the backwoods. It seemed that there, in what had hitherto been considered to be marginal areas, a strange wave of prosperity was making itself felt. Tennessee mountaineers were buying Packard convertibles, and Sears, Roebuck reported that in the Ozarks their sales of luxury items had gone up nine hundred per cent. In the scrub sections of Vermont, men who formerly had barely been able to scratch a living from their rock-strewn acres were now sending their daughters to Europe and ordering expensive cigars from New York. It appeared that the Law of Diminishing Returns was going haywire, too.

Order from Order

What Is Life? [*]

by Erwin Schrödinger (1944)

To-day, thanks to the ingenious work of biologists, mainly of geneticists, during the last thirty or forty years, enough is known about the actual material structure of organisms and about their functioning to state that, and to tell precisely why, present-day physics and chemistry could not possibly account for what happens in space and time within a living organism.

The arrangements of the atoms in the most vital parts of an organism and the interplay of these arrangements differ in a fundamental way from all those arrangements of atoms which physicists and chemists have hitherto made the object of their experimental and theoretical research. Yet the difference which I have just termed fundamental is of such a kind that it might easily appear slight to anyone except a physicist who is thoroughly imbued with the knowledge that the laws of physics and chemistry are statistical throughout.[1] For it is in relation to the statistical point of view that the structure of the vital parts of living organisms differs so entirely from that of any piece of matter that we physicists and chemists have ever handled physically in our laboratories or mentally at our writing desks. It is well-nigh unthinkable that the laws and regularities thus discovered should happen to apply immediately to the behaviour of systems which do not exhibit the structure on which those laws and regularities are based.

The non-physicist cannot be expected even to grasp—let alone to appreciate the relevance of—the difference in "statistical structure" stated in terms so abstract as I have just used. To give the statement life and colour, let me anticipate what will be explained in much more detail later, namely, that the most essential part of a living cell—the chromo-

---

[*] From Erwin Schrödinger, *What Is Life? and Other Scientific Essays*, Anchor Books, Doubleday & Co., Garden City, New York, 1956. Reprinted by permission of Doubleday & Co.

1. This contention may appear a little too general. The discussion must be deferred to the end of [this article].

some fibre [2]—may suitably be called an *aperiodic crystal*. In physics we have dealt hitherto only with *periodic crystals*. To a humble physicist's mind, these are very interesting and complicated objects; they constitute one of the most fascinating and complex material structures by which inanimate nature puzzles his wits. Yet, compared with the aperiodic crystal, they are rather plain and dull. The difference in structure is of the same kind as that between an ordinary wallpaper in which the same pattern is repeated again and again in regular periodicity and a masterpiece of embroidery, say a Raphael tapestry, which shows no dull repetition, but an elaborate, coherent, meaningful design traced by the great master.

In calling the periodic crystal one of the most complex objects of his research, I had in mind the physicist proper. Organic chemistry, indeed, in investigating more and more complicated molecules, has come very much nearer to that "aperiodic crystal" which, in my opinion, is the material carrier of life. And therefore it is small wonder that the organic chemist has already made large and important contributions to the problem of life, whereas the physicist has made next to none.

THE $\sqrt{n}$ RULE

If I tell you that a certain gas under certain conditions of pressure and temperature has a certain density, and if I expressed this by saying that within a certain volume (of a size relevant for some experiment) there are under these conditions just n molecules of the gas, then you might be sure that if you could test my statement in a particular moment of time, you would find it inaccurate, the departure being of the order of $\sqrt{n}$. Hence if the number $n = 100$, you would find a departure of about 10, thus relative error $= 10\%$. But if $n = 1$ million, you would be likely to find a departure of about 1000, thus relative error $= \frac{1}{10}\%$. Now, roughly speaking, this statistical law is quite general. The laws of physics and physical chemistry are inaccurate within a probable relative error of the order of $1/\sqrt{n}$, where n is the number of molecules that co-operate to bring about that law—to produce its validity within such regions of space or time (or both) that matter, for some considerations or for some particular experiment.

You see from this again that an organism must have a comparatively gross structure in order to enjoy the benefit of fairly accurate laws, both for its internal life and for its interplay with the external world. For otherwise the number of co-operating particles would be too small, the

2. The molecules of DNA and RNA which are now considered to be the fundamental molecules of living matter will be discussed in Part 9. Ed.

"law" too inaccurate. The particularly exigent demand is the square root. For though a million is a reasonably large number, an accuracy of just 1 in 1000 is not overwhelmingly good, if a thing claims the dignity of being a "Law of Nature."

THE CLASSICAL PHYSICIST'S EXPECTATION, FAR FROM BEING TRIVIAL, IS WRONG

Thus we have come to the conclusion that an organism and all the biologically relevant processes that it experiences must have an extremely "many-atomic" structure and must be safeguarded against haphazard, "single-atomic" events attaining too great importance. That, the "naïve physicist" tells us, is essential, so that the organism may, so to speak, have sufficiently accurate physical laws on which to draw for setting up its marvellously regular and well-ordered working. How do these conclusions, reached, biologically speaking, *a priori* (that is, from the purely physical point of view), fit in with actual biological facts? . . .

To-day, we know that this opinion would have been a mistake. As we shall presently see, incredibly small groups of atoms, much too small to display exact statistical laws, do play a dominating role in the very orderly and lawful events within a living organism. They have control of the observable large-scale features which the organism acquires in the course of its development, they determine important characteristics of its functioning; and in all this very sharp and very strict biological laws are displayed. . . .

PERMANENCE UNEXPLAINABLE BY CLASSICAL PHYSICS

Aided by the marvellously subtle instrument of X-rays (which, as the physicist remembers, revealed thirty years ago the detailed atomic lattice structures of crystals), the united efforts of biologists and physicists have of late succeeded in reducing the upper limit for the size of the microscopic structure, being responsible for a definite large-scale feature of the individual—the "size of a gene"— . . . We are now seriously faced with the question: How can we, from the point of view of statistical physics, reconcile the facts that the gene structure seems to involve only a comparatively small number of atoms (of the order of 1000 and possibly much less), and that nevertheless it displays a most regular and lawful activity—with a durability or permanence that borders upon the miraculous?

Let me throw the truly amazing situation into relief once again. Several members of the Habsburg dynasty have a peculiar disfigurement of the lower lip ("Habsburger Lippe"). Its inheritance has been studied care-

fully and published, complete with historical portraits, by the Imperial
Academy of Vienna, under the auspices of the family. The feature proves
to be a genuinely Mendelian "allele" [3] to the normal form of the lip. Fixing our attention on the portraits of a member of the family in the sixteenth century and of his descendant, living in the nineteenth, we may
safely assume that the material gene structure responsible for the abnormal feature has been carried on from generation to generation through
the centuries, faithfully reproduced at every one of the not very numerous
cell divisions that lie between. Moreover, the number of atoms involved
in the responsible gene structure is likely to be of the same order of
magnitude as in the cases tested by X-rays. The gene has been kept at
a temperature around 98° F. during all that time. How are we to understand that it has remained unperturbed by the disordering tendency of
the heat motion for centuries?

A physicist at the end of the last century would have been at a loss to
answer this question, if he was prepared to draw only on those laws of
Nature which he could explain and which he really understood. Perhaps,
indeed, after a short reflection on the statistical situation he would have
answered (correctly, as we shall see): These material structures can
only be molecules. Of the existence, and sometimes very high stability,
of these associations of atoms, chemistry had already acquired a widespread knowledge at the time. But the knowledge was purely empirical.
The nature of a molecule was not understood—the strong mutual bond
of the atoms which keeps a molecule in shape was a complete conundrum
to everybody. Actually, the answer proves to be correct. But it is of
limited value as long as the enigmatic biological stability is traced back
only to an equally enigmatic chemical stability. The evidence that two
features, similar in appearance, are based on the same principle, is always
precarious as long as the principle itself is unknown.

EXPLICABLE BY QUANTUM THEORY

In this case it is supplied by quantum theory. In the light of present
knowledge, the mechanism of heredity is closely related to, nay, founded
on, the very basis of quantum theory. This theory was discovered by Max
Planck in 1900. Modern genetics can be dated from the rediscovery of
Mendel's paper by de Vries, Correns and Tschermak (1900) and from
de Vries's paper on mutations (1901–03). Thus the births of the two great
theories nearly coincide, and it is small wonder that both of them had to

3. In Mendelian inheritance, contrasting pairs of characters such as smooth and
wrinkled, or the contrasting genes which produce them, are known as alleles. Ed.

reach a certain maturity before the connection could emerge. On the side of quantum theory it took more than a quarter of a century till in 1926–27 the quantum theory of the chemical bond was outlined in its general principles by W. Heitler and F. London. The Heitler-London theory involves the most subtle and intricate conceptions of the latest development of quantum theory (called "quantum mechanics" or "wave mechanics"). A presentation without the use of calculus is well-nigh impossible or would at least require another little volume like this. But fortunately, now that all work has been done and has served to clarify our thinking, it seems to be possible to point out in a more direct manner the connection between "quantum jumps" and mutations, to pick out at the moment the most conspicuous item. That is what we attempt here.

QUANTUM THEORY—DISCRETE STATES—QUANTUM JUMPS

The great revelation of quantum theory was that features of discreteness were discovered in the Book of Nature, in a context in which anything other than continuity seemed to be absurd according to the views held until then.

The first case of this kind concerned energy. A body on the large scale changes its energy continuously. A pendulum, for instance, that is set swinging is gradually slowed down by the resistance of the air. Strangely enough, it proves necessary to admit that a system of the order of the atomic scale behaves differently. On grounds upon which we cannot enter here, we have to assume that a small system can by its very nature possess only certain discrete amounts of energy, called its peculiar energy levels. The transition from one state to another is a rather mysterious event, which is usually called a "quantum jump."

But energy is not the only characteristic of a system. Take again our pendulum, but think of one that can perform different kinds of movement, a heavy ball suspended by a string from the ceiling. It can be made to swing in a north-south or east-west or any other direction or in a circle or in an ellipse. By gently blowing the ball with a bellows, it can be made to pass continuously from one state of motion to any other.

For small-scale systems most of these or similar characteristics—we cannot enter into details—change discontinuously. They are "quantized," just as the energy is.

The result is that a number of atomic nuclei, including their body-guards of electrons, when they find themselves close to each other, forming "a system," are unable by their vary nature to adopt any arbitrary configuration we might think of. Their very nature leaves them only a very numerous but discrete series of "states" to choose from.[4] We usually call them levels or energy levels, because the energy is a very relevant part of the characteristic. But it must be understood that the complete description includes much more than just the energy. It is virtually correct to think of a state as meaning a definite configuration of all the corpuscles.

The transition from one of these configurations to another is a quantum jump. If the second one has the greater energy ("is a higher level"), the system must be supplied from outside with at least the difference of the two energies to make the transition possible. To a lower level it can change spontaneously, spending the surplus of energy in radiation.

MOLECULES

Among the discrete set of states of a given selection of atoms there need not necessarily but there may be a lowest level, implying a close approach of the nuclei to each other. Atoms in such a state form a molecule. The point to stress here is that the molecule will of necessity have a certain stability; the configuration cannot change unless at least the energy difference necessary to "lift" it to the next higher level is supplied from outside. Hence this level difference, which is a well-defined quantity, determines quantitatively the degree of stability of the molecule. It will be observed how intimately this fact is linked with the very basis of quantum theory, viz. with the discreteness of the level scheme.

I must beg the reader to take it for granted that this order of ideas has been thoroughly checked by chemical facts; and that it has proved successful in explaining the basic fact of chemical valency and many details about the structure of molecules, their binding-energies, their stabilities at different temperatures, and so on. I am speaking of the Heitler-London theory, which, as I said, cannot be examined in detail here.

THEIR STABILITY DEPENDENT ON TEMPERATURE

We must content ourselves with examining the point which is of paramount interest for our biological question, namely, the stability of a molecule at different temperatures. Take our system of atoms at first to be actually in its state of lowest energy. The physicist would call it a molecule at the absolute zero of temperature. To lift it to the next higher

4. I am adopting the version which is usually given in popular treatment and which suffices for our present purpose. But I have the bad conscience of one who perpetuates a convenient error. The true story is much more complicated, inasmuch as it includes the occasional indeterminateness with regard to the state the system is in.

state or level a definite supply of energy is required. The simplest way of trying to supply it is to "heat up" your molecule. You bring it into an environment of higher temperature ("heat bath"), thus allowing other systems (atoms, molecules) to impinge upon it. Considering the entire irregularity of heat motion, there is no sharp temperature limit at which the "lift" will be brought about with certainty and immediately. Rather, at any temperature (different from absolute zero) there is a certain smaller or greater chance for the lift to occur, the chance increasing of course with the temperature of the heat bath. The best way to express this chance is to indicate the average time you will have to wait until the lift takes place, the "time of expectation."

From an investigation, due to M. Polanyi and E. Wigner,[5] the "time of expectation" largely depends on the ratio of two energies, one being just the energy difference itself that is required to effect the lift (let us write W for it), the other one characterizing the intensity of the heat motion at the temperature in question (let us write T for the absolute temperature and kT for the characteristic energy).[6] It stands to reason that the chance for effecting the lift is smaller, and hence that the time of expectation is longer, the higher the lift itself compared with the average heat energy, that is to say, the greater the ratio W/kT. What is amazing is how enormously the time of expectation depends on comparatively small changes of the ratio W/kT. To give an example (following Delbrück): for W thirty times kT the time of expectation might be as short as $\frac{1}{10}$ sec., but would rise to 16 months when W is 50 times kT, and to 30,000 years when W is 60 times kT!

FIRST AMENDMENT

In offering these considerations as a theory of the stability of the molecule it has been tacitly assumed that the quantum jump which we call the "lift" leads, if not to a complete disintegration, at least to an essentially different configuration of the same atoms—an isomeric molecule, as the chemist would say, that is, a molecule composed of the same atoms in a different arrangement (in the application to biology it is going to represent a different "allele" in the same "locus" and the quantum jump will represent a mutation).

To allow of this interpretation two points must be amended in our story, which I purposely simplified to make it at all intelligible. From the

5. *Zeitschrift für Physik*, Chemie (A), Haber-Band, 1928, p. 439.
6. k is a numerically known constant, called Boltzmann's constant; $3/2\ kT$ is the average kinetic energy of a gas atom at temperature T.

way I told it, it might be imagined that only in its very lowest state does our group of atoms form what we call a molecule and that already the next higher state is "something else." That is not so. Actually the lowest level is followed by a crowded series of levels which do not involve any appreciable change in the configuration as a whole, but only correspond to those small vibrations among the atoms which we have mentioned [Figure 8–3]. They, too, are "quantized," but with comparatively small steps from one level to the next. Hence the impacts of the particles of the "heat bath" may suffice to set them up already at fairly low temperature. If the molecule is an extended structure, you may conceive these vibrations as high-frequency sound waves, crossing the molecule without doing it any harm.

So the first amendment is not very serious: we have to disregard the "vibrational fine-structure" of the level scheme. The term "next higher level" has to be understood as meaning the next level that corresponds to a relevant change of configuration.

SECOND AMENDMENT

The second amendment is far more difficult to explain, because it is concerned with certain vital, but rather complicated, features of the scheme of relevantly different levels. The free passage between two of them may be obstructed, quite apart from the required energy supply; in fact, it may be obstructed even from the higher to the lower state.

Let us start from the empirical facts. It is known to the chemist that the same group of atoms can unite in more than one way to form a molecule. Such molecules are called isomeric ("consisting of the same parts"; *isos* = same, *méros* = part). Isomerism is not an exception, it is the rule. The larger the molecule, the more isomeric alternatives are offered. Figure 8–10 shows one of the simplest cases, the two kinds of propyl-alcohol, both consisting of 3 carbons (C), 8 hydrogens (H), 1 oxygen (O). The oxygen can be interposed between any hydrogen and its carbon, but only the two cases shown in our figure are different substances. And they really are. All their physical and chemical constants are

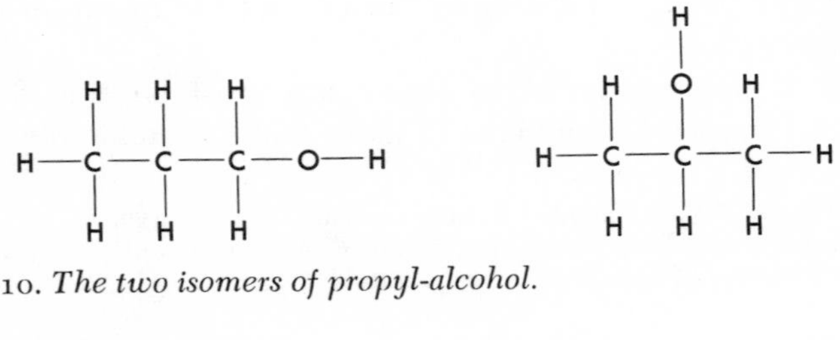

Figure 8–10. The two isomers of propyl-alcohol.

distinctly different. Also their energies are different, they represent "different levels."

The remarkable fact is that both molecules are perfectly stable, both behave as though they were "lowest states." There are no spontaneous transitions from either state towards the other.

The reason is that the two configurations are not neighbouring configurations. The transition from one to the other can only take place over intermediate configurations which have a greater energy than either of them. To put it crudely, the oxygen has to be extracted from one position and has to be inserted into the other. There does not seem to be a way of doing that without passing through configurations of considerably higher energy. The state of affairs is sometimes figuratively pictured as in Figure 8–11, in which 1 and 2 represent the two isomers, 3 the "threshold" between them, and the two arrows indicate the "lifts," that is to say, the energy supplies required to produce the transition from state 1 to state 2 or from state 2 to state 1, respectively.

Now we can give our "second amendment," which is that transitions of this "isomeric" kind are the only ones in which we shall be interested in our biological application. It was these we had in mind when explaining "stability." . . . The "quantum jump" which we mean is the transition from one relatively stable molecular configuration to another. The energy supply required for the transition (the quantity denoted by W) is not the actual level difference, but the step from the initial level up to the threshold (see the arrows in Figure 8–11).

Transitions with no threshold interposed between the initial and the

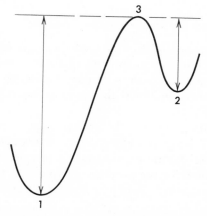

Figure 8–11. Energy threshold (3) between the isomeric levels (1) and (2). The arrows indicate the minimum energies required for transition.

final state are entirely uninteresting, and that not only in our biological application. They have actually nothing to contribute to the chemical stability of the molecule. Why? They have no lasting effect, they remain unnoticed. For, when they occur, they are almost immediately followed by a relapse into the initial state, since nothing prevents their return.

THE GENERAL PICTURE OF THE HEREDITARY SUBSTANCE

From these facts emerges a very simple answer to our question, namely: Are these structures, composed of comparatively few atoms, capable of withstanding for long periods the disturbing influence of heat motion to which the hereditary substance is continually exposed? We shall assume the structure of a gene to be that of a huge molecule, capable only of discontinuous change, which consists in a rearrangement of the atoms and leads to an isomeric [7] molecule. The rearrangement may affect only a small region of the gene, and a vast number of different rearrangements may be possible. The energy thresholds, separating the actual configuration from any possible isomeric ones, have to be high enough (compared with the average heat energy of an atom) to make the change-over a rare event. These rare events we shall identify with spontaneous mutations.

The later parts of this article will be devoted to putting this general picture of a gene and of mutation (due mainly to the German physicist M. Delbrück) to the test, by comparing it in detail with genetical facts. Before doing so, we may fittingly make some comment on the foundation and general nature of the theory.

THE UNIQUENESS OF THE PICTURE

Was it absolutely essential for the biological question to dig up the deepest roots and found the picture on quantum mechanics? The conjecture that a gene is a molecule is to-day, I dare say, a commonplace. Few biologists, whether familiar with quantum theory or not, would disagree with it. . . .

Quantum mechanics is the first theoretical aspect which accounts from first principles for all kinds of aggregates of atoms actually encountered in Nature. The Heitler-London bondage is a unique, singular feature of the theory, not invented for the purpose of explaining the chemical bond. It comes in quite by itself, in a highly interesting and puzzling manner,

7. For convenience I shall continue to call it an isomeric transition, though it would be absurd to exclude the possibility of any exchange with the environment.

being forced upon us by entirely different considerations. It proves to correspond exactly with the observed chemical facts, and, as I said, it is a unique feature, well enough understood to tell with reasonable certainty that "such a thing could not happen again" in the further development of quantum theory.

Consequently, we may safely assert that there is no alternative to the molecular explanation of the hereditary substance. The physical aspect leaves no other possibility to account for its permanence. . . .

SOME TRADITIONAL MISCONCEPTIONS

But it may be asked: Are there really no other endurable structures composed of atoms except molecules? Does not a gold coin, for example, buried in a tomb for a couple of thousand years, preserve the traits of the portrait stamped on it? It is true that the coin consists of an enormous number of atoms, but surely we are in this case not inclined to attribute the mere preservation of shape to the statistics of large numbers. The same remark applies to a neatly developed batch of crystals we find embedded in a rock, where it must have been for geological periods without changing.

That leads us to the second point I want to elucidate. The cases of a molecule, a solid, a crystal, are not really different. In the light of present knowledge they are virtually the same. . . .

The reason for this is that the atoms forming a molecule, whether there be few or many of them, are united by forces of exactly the same nature as the numerous atoms which build up a true solid, a crystal. The molecule presents the same solidity of structure as a crystal. Remember that it is precisely this solidity on which we draw to account for the permanence of the gene!

The distinction that is really important in the structure of matter is whether atoms are bound together by those "solidifying" Heitler-London forces or whether they are not. In a solid and in a molecule they all are. In a gas of single atoms (as, e.g., mercury vapour) they are not. In a gas composed of molecules, only the atoms within every molecule are linked in this way.

THE APERIODIC SOLID

A small molecule might be called "the germ of a solid." Starting from such a small solid germ, there seem to be two different ways of building up larger and larger associations. One is the comparatively dull way of repeating the same structure in three directions again and again. That is the way followed in a growing crystal. Once the periodicity is established, there is no definite limit to the size of the aggregate. The other way is that of building up a more and more extended aggregate without the dull device of repetition. That is the case of the more and more complicated organic molecule in which every atom, and every group of atoms, plays an individual role, not entirely equivalent to that of many others (as is the case in a periodic structure). We might quite properly call that an aperiodic crystal or solid and express our hypothesis by saying: We believe a gene—or perhaps the whole chromosome fibre [8]— to be an aperiodic solid.

THE VARIETY OF CONTENTS COMPRESSED IN THE MINIATURE CODE

It has often been asked how this tiny speck of material, the nucleus of the fertilized egg, could contain an elaborate code-script involving all the future development of the organism? A well-ordered association of atoms, endowed with sufficient resistivity to keep its order permanently, appears to be the only conceivable material structure that offers a variety of possible ("isomeric") arrangements sufficiently large to embody a complicated system of "determinations" within a small spatial boundary. . . .

COMPARISON WITH FACTS: DEGREE OF STABILITY; DISCONTINUITY OF MUTATIONS

Now let us at last proceed to compare the theoretical picture with the biological facts. The first question obviously is, whether it can really account for the high degree of permanence we observe. Are threshold values of the required amount—high multiples of the average heat energy kT—reasonable, are they within the range known from ordinary chemistry? That question is trivial; it can be answered in the affirmative without inspecting tables. The molecules of any substance which the chemist is able to isolate at a given temperature must at that temperature have a lifetime of at least minutes. (That is putting it mildly; as a rule they have much more.) Thus the threshold values the chemist encounters are of necessity precisely of the order of magnitude required to account for practically any degree of permanence the biologist may encounter; for we recall from page 439 that thresholds varying within a range of about 1:2 will account for lifetimes ranging from a fraction of a second to tens of thousands of years.

---

8. That it is highly flexible is no objection; so is a thin copper wire.

But let me mention figures, for future reference. The ratios W/kT mentioned by way of example on page 439, viz.

$$\frac{W}{kT} = 30, 50, 60,$$

producing lifetimes of

$\frac{1}{10}$ sec., 16 months, 30,000 years,

respectively, correspond at room temperature with threshold values of

0.9, 1.5, 1.8 electron-volts.

We must explain the unit "electron-volt," which is rather convenient for the physicist, because it can be visualized. For example, the third number (1.8) means that an electron, accelerated by a voltage of about 2 volts, would have acquired just sufficient energy to effect the transition by impact. (For comparison, the battery of an ordinary pocket flashlight has 3 volts.)

These considerations make it conceivable that an isomeric change of configuration in some part of our molecule, produced by a chance fluctuation of the vibrational energy, can actually be a sufficiently rare event to be interpreted as a spontaneous mutation. Thus we account, by the very principles of quantum mechanics, for the most amazing fact about mutations, the fact by which they first attracted de Vries's attention, namely, that they are "jumping" variations, no intermediate forms occurring.

STABILITY OF NATURALLY SELECTED GENES

Granted that we have to account for the rare natural mutations by chance fluctuations of the heat motion, we must not be very much astonished that Nature has succeeded in making such a subtle choice of threshold values as is necessary to make mutation rare. For we have, earlier . . . arrived at the conclusion that frequent mutations are detrimental to evolution. Individuals which, by mutation, acquire a gene configuration of insufficient stability, will have little chance of seeing their "ultra-radical," rapidly mutating, descendancy survive long. The species will be freed of them and will thus collect stable genes by natural selection.

THE SOMETIMES LOWER STABILITY OF MUTANTS

But, of course, as regards the mutants which occur in our breeding experiments and which we select, *qua* mutants, for studying their offspring, there is no reason to expect that they should all show that very high stability. For they have not yet been "tried out"—or, if they have, they have been "rejected" in the wild breeds—possibly for too high muta-bility. At any rate, we are not at all astonished to learn that actually some of these mutants do show a much higher mutability than the nor-mal "wild" genes.

A REMARKABLE GENERAL CONCLUSION FROM THE MODEL

From Delbrück's general picture of the hereditary substance it emerges that living matter, while not eluding the "laws of physics" as established up to date, is likely to involve "other laws of physics" hitherto unknown, which, however, once they have been revealed, will form just as integral a part of this science as the former.

ORDER BASED ON ORDER

This is a rather subtle line of thought, open to misconception in more than one respect. . . . A preliminary insight, rough but not altogether erroneous, may be found in the following considerations:

It has been explained . . . that the laws of physics, as we know them, are statistical laws.[9] They have a lot to do with the natural tendency of things to go over into disorder.

But, to reconcile the high durability of the hereditary substance with its minute size, we had to evade the tendency to disorder by "inventing the molecule," in fact, an unusually large molecule, which has to be a masterpiece of highly differentiated order, safeguarded by the conjuring rod of quantum theory. The laws of chance are not invalidated by this "invention," but their outcome is modified. The physicist is familiar with the fact that the classical laws of physics are modified by quantum theory, especially at low temperature. There are many instances of this. Life seems to be one of them, a particularly striking one. Life seems to be orderly and lawful behaviour of matter, not based exclusively on its tendency to go over from order to disorder, but based partly on existing order that is kept up.

To the physicist—but only to him—I could hope to make my view clearer by saying: The living organism seems to be a macroscopic system which in part of its behaviour approaches to that purely mechanical (as contrasted with thermodynamical) conduct to which all systems tend, as the temperature approaches the absolute zero and the molecular disorder is removed.

9. To state this in complete generality about "the laws of physics" is perhaps challengeable. The point will be discussed [later].

The non-physicist finds it hard to believe that really the ordinary laws of physics, which he regards as the prototype of inviolable precision, should be based on the statistical tendency of matter to go over into disorder. . . . The general principle involved is the famous Second Law of Thermodynamics (entropy principle) and its equally famous statistical foundation. . . . I will try to sketch the bearing of the entropy principle on the large-scale behaviour of a living organism—forgetting at the moment all that is known about chromosomes, inheritance, and so on.

LIVING MATTER EVADES THE DECAY TO EQUILIBRIUM

What is the characteristic feature of life? When is a piece of matter said to be alive? When it goes on "doing something," moving, exchanging material with its environment, and so forth, and that for a much longer period than we would expect an inanimate piece of matter to "keep going" under similar circumstances. When a system that is not alive is isolated or placed in a uniform environment, all motion usually comes to a standstill very soon as a result of various kinds of friction; differences of electric or chemical potential are equalized, substances which tend to form a chemical compound do so, temperature becomes uniform by heat conduction. After that the whole system fades away into a dead, inert lump of matter. A permanent state is reached, in which no observable events occur. The physicist calls this the state of thermodynamical equilibrium, or of "maximum entropy."

Practically, a state of this kind is usually reached very rapidly. Theoretically, it is very often not yet an absolute equilibrium, not yet the true maximum of entropy. But then the final approach to equilibrium is very slow. It could take anything between hours, years, centuries, . . . To give an example—one in which the approach is still fairly rapid: if a glass filled with pure water and a second one filled with sugared water are placed together in a hermetically closed case at constant temperature, it appears at first that nothing happens, and the impression of complete equilibrium is created. But after a day or so it is noticed that the pure water, owing to its higher vapour pressure, slowly evaporates and condenses on the solution. The latter overflows. Only after the pure water has totally evaporated has the sugar reached its aim of being equally distributed among all the liquid water available.

These ultimate slow approaches to equilibrium could never be mistaken for life, and we may disregard them here. I have referred to them in order to clear myself of a charge of inaccuracy.

IT FEEDS ON "NEGATIVE ENTROPY"

It is by avoiding the rapid decay into the inert state of "equilibrium," that an organism appears so enigmatic; so much so, that from the earliest times of human thought some special non-physical or supernatural force (*vis viva*, entelechy) was claimed to be operative in the organism, and in some quarters is still claimed.

How does the living organism avoid decay? The obvious answer is: By eating, drinking, breathing and (in the case of plants) assimilating. The technical term is *metabolism*. The Greek word (*metabállein*) means change or exchange. Exchange of what? Originally the underlying idea is, no doubt, exchange of material. (E.g. the German for metabolism is Stoffwechsel.) That the exchange of material should be the essential thing is absurd. Any atom of nitrogen, oxygen, sulphur, etc., is as good as any other of its kind: what could be gained by exchanging them? . . .

What then is that precious something contained in our food which keeps us from death? That is easily answered. Every process, event, happening—call it what you will; in a word, everything that is going on in Nature means an increase of the entropy of the part of the world where it is going on. Thus a living organism continually increases its entropy—or, as you may say, produces positive entropy—and thus tends to approach the dangerous state of maximum entropy, which is death. It can only keep aloof from it, i.e. alive, by continually drawing from its environment negative entropy—which is something very positive as we shall immediately see. What an organism feeds upon is negative entropy. Or, to put it less paradoxically, the essential thing in metabolism is that the organism succeeds in freeing itself from all the entropy it cannot help producing while alive.

WHAT IS ENTROPY?

What is entropy? Let me first emphasize that it is not a hazy concept or idea, but a measurable physical quantity just like the length of a rod, the temperature at any point of a body, the heat of fusion of a given crystal or the specific heat of any given substance. At the absolute zero point of temperature (roughly $-273°$ C.) the entropy of any substance is zero. When you bring the substance into any other state by slow, reversible little steps (even if thereby the substance changes its physical or chemical nature or splits up into two or more parts of different physical or chemical nature) the entropy increases by an amount which is computed by dividing every little portion of heat you had to supply in that procedure by the absolute temperature at which it was supplied—and by summing up all these small contributions. To give an example, when you melt a solid, its entropy increases by the amount of the heat of fusion divided by the temperature at the melting-point. You see from this, that the unit in which entropy is measured is calories/degree C. (just as the calorie is the unit of heat or the centimetre the unit of length).

THE STATISTICAL MEANING OF ENTROPY

I have mentioned this technical definition simply in order to remove entropy from the atmosphere of hazy mystery that frequently veils it. Much more important for us here is the bearing on the statistical concept of order and disorder, a connection that was revealed by the investigations of Boltzmann and Gibbs in statistical physics. This too is an exact quantitative connection, and is expressed by

$$\text{entropy} = k \log D,$$

where k is the so-called Boltzmann constant $(= 3.2983 \times 10^{-24}$ calories/degree C.), and D a quantitative measure of the atomistic disorder of the body in question. To give an exact explanation of this quantity D in brief non-technical terms is well-nigh impossible. The disorder it indicates is partly that of heat motion, partly that which consists in different kinds of atoms or molecules being mixed at random, instead of being neatly separated, e.g. the sugar and water molecules in the example quoted above. Boltzmann's equation is well illustrated by that example. The gradual "spreading out" of the sugar over all the water available increases the disorder D, and hence (since the logarithm of D increases with D) the entropy. It is also pretty clear that any supply of heat increases the turmoil of heat motion, that is to say increases D and thus increases the entropy; it is particularly clear that this should be so when you melt a crystal, since you thereby destroy the neat and permanent arrangement of the atoms or molecules and turn the crystal lattice into a continually changing random distribution.

An isolated system or a system in a uniform environment (which for the present consideration we do best to include as a part of the system we contemplate) increases its entropy and more or less rapidly approaches the inert state of maximum entropy. We now recognize this fundamental law of physics to be just the natural tendency of things to approach the chaotic state (the same tendency that the books of a library or the piles of papers and manuscripts on a writing desk display) unless we obviate it. (The analogue of irregular heat motion, in this case, is our handling those objects now and again without troubling to put them back in their proper places.)

How would we express in terms of the statistical theory the marvellous faculty of a living organism by which it delays the decay into thermo-dynamical equilibrium (death)? We said before: "It feeds upon negative entropy," attracting, as it were, a stream of negative entropy upon itself, to compensate the entropy increase it produces by living and thus to maintain itself on a stationary and fairly low entropy level.

If D is a measure of disorder, its reciprocal, $1/D$, can be regarded as a direct measure of order. Since the logarithm of $1/D$ is just minus the logarithm of D, we can write Boltzmann's equation thus:

$$- (\text{entropy}) = k \log (1/D).$$

Hence the awkward expression "negative entropy" can be replaced by a better one: entropy, taken with the negative sign, is itself a measure of order. Thus the device by which an organism maintains itself stationary at a fairly high level of orderliness (= fairly low level of entropy) really consists in continually sucking orderliness from its environment. This conclusion is less paradoxical than it appears at first sight. Rather could it be blamed for triviality. Indeed, in the case of higher animals we know the kind of orderliness they feed upon well enough, viz. the extremely well-ordered state of matter in more or less complicated organic com-pounds, which serve them as foodstuffs. After utilizing it they return it in a very much degraded form—not entirely degraded, however, for plants can still make use of it. (These, of course, have their most powerful supply of "negative entropy" in the sunlight.)

What I wish to make clear . . . is, in short, that from all we have learnt about the structure of living matter, we must be prepared to find it work-ing in a manner that cannot be reduced to the ordinary laws of physics. And that not on the ground that there is any "new force" or what not, directing the behaviour of the single atoms within a living organism, but because the construction is different from anything we have yet tested in the physical laboratory. To put it crudely, an engineer familiar with heat engines only will, after inspecting the construction of an electric motor, be prepared to find it working along principles which he does not yet understand. He finds the copper familiar to him in kettles used here in the form of long, long wires wound in coils; the iron familiar to him in levers and bars and steam cylinders is here filling the interior of those coils of copper wire. He will be convinced that it is the same copper and the same iron, subject to the same laws of Nature, and he is right in that. The difference in construction is enough to prepare him for an entirely different way of functioning. He will not suspect that an electric motor is driven by a ghost because it is set spinning by the turn of a switch, without boiler and steam.

REVIEWING THE BIOLOGICAL SITUATION

The unfolding of events in the life cycle of an organism exhibits an admirable regularity and orderliness, unrivalled by anything we meet with in inanimate matter. We find it controlled by a supremely well-ordered group of atoms, which represent only a very small fraction of the sum total in every cell. Moreover, from the view we have formed of the mechanism of mutation we conclude that the dislocation of just a few atoms within the group of "governing atoms" of the germ cell suffices to bring about a well-defined change in the large-scale hereditary characteristics of the organism.

These facts are easily the most interesting that science has revealed in our day. We may be inclined to find them, after all, not wholly unacceptable. An organism's astonishing gift of concentrating a "stream of order" on itself and thus escaping the decay into atomic chaos—of "drinking orderliness" from a suitable environment—seems to be connected with the presence of the "aperiodic solids," the chromosome molecules, which doubtless represent the highest degree of well-ordered atomic association we know of—much higher than the ordinary periodic crystal—in virtue of the individual role every atom and every radical is playing here.

To put it briefly, we witness the event that existing order displays the power of maintaining itself and of producing orderly events. That sounds plausible enough, though in finding it plausible we, no doubt, draw on experience concerning social organization and other events which involve the activity of organisms. And so it might seem that something like a vicious circle is implied.

SUMMARIZING THE PHYSICAL SITUATION

However that may be, the point to emphasize again and again is that to the physicist the state of affairs is not only not plausible but most exciting, because it is unprecedented. Contrary to the common belief, the regular course of events, governed by the laws of physics, is never the consequence of one well-ordered configuration of atoms—not unless that configuration of atoms repeats itself a great number of times, either as in the periodic crystal or as in a liquid or in a gas composed of a great number of identical molecules.

Even when the chemist handles a very complicated molecule *in vitro* he is always faced with an enormous number of like molecules. To them his laws apply. He might tell you, for example, that one minute after he has started some particular reaction half of the molecules will have reacted, and after a second minute three-quarters of them will have done so. But whether any particular molecule, supposing you could follow its course, will be among those which have reacted or among those which are still untouched, he could not predict. That is a matter of pure chance.

This is not a purely theoretical conjecture. It is not that we can never observe the fate of a single small group of atoms or even of a single atom. We can, occasionally. But whenever we do, we find complete irregularity, co-operating to produce regularity only on the average. . . . The Brownian movement of a small particle suspended in a liquid is completely irregular. But if there are many similar particles, they will by their irregular movement give rise to the regular phenomenon of diffusion. . . .

THE STRIKING CONTRAST

In biology we are faced with an entirely different situation. A single group of atoms existing only in one copy produces orderly events, marvellously tuned in with each other and with the environment according to most subtle laws. I said, existing only in one copy, for after all we have the example of the egg and of the unicellular organism. In the following stages of a higher organism the copies are multiplied, that is true. But to what extent? Something like 10^{14} in a grown mammal, I understand. What is that! Only a millionth of the number of molecules in one cubic inch of air. Though comparatively bulky, by coalescing they would form but a tiny drop of liquid. And look at the way they are actually distributed. Every cell harbours just one of them (or two, . . .). Since we know the power this tiny central office has in the isolated cell, do they not resemble stations of local government dispersed through the body, communicating with each other with great ease, thanks to the code that is common to all of them?

Well, this is a fantastic description, perhaps less becoming a scientist than a poet. However, it needs no poetical imagination but only clear and sober scientific reflection to recognize that we are here obviously faced with events whose regular and lawful unfolding is guided by a "mechanism" entirely different from the "probability mechanism" of physics. For it is simply a fact of observation that the guiding principle in every cell is embodied in a single atomic association existing only in one copy (or sometimes two)—and a fact of observation that it results in producing events which are a paragon of orderliness. Whether we find it astonishing or whether we find it quite plausible, that a small but highly organized group of atoms be capable of acting in this manner, the situation is unprecedented, it is unknown anywhere else except in living matter. The physicist and the chemist, investigating inanimate matter, have never witnessed phenomena which they had to interpret in this way. The case did not arise and so our theory does not cover it—our beautiful statistical theory of which we were so justly proud because it allowed us to look behind the curtain, to watch the magnificent order of exact physical law coming forth from atomic and molecular disorder; because it revealed that the most important, the most general, the all-embracing, law of entropy increase could be understood without a special assumption *ad hoc,* for it is nothing but molecular disorder itself.

TWO WAYS OF PRODUCING ORDERLINESS

The orderliness encountered in the unfolding of life springs from a different source. It appears that there are two different "mechanisms" by which orderly events can be produced: the "statistical mechanism" which produces "order from disorder" and the new one, producing "order from order." To the unprejudiced mind the second principle appears to be much simpler, much more plausible. No doubt it is. That is why physicists were so proud to have fallen in with the other one, the "order-from-disorder" principle, which is actually followed in Nature and which alone conveys an understanding of the great line of natural events, in the first place of their irreversibility. But we cannot expect that the "laws of physics" derived from it suffice straightaway to explain the behaviour of living matter, whose most striking features are visibly based to a large extent on the "order-from-order" principle. You would not expect two entirely different mechanisms to bring about the same type of law—you would not expect your latch-key to open your neighbour's door as well.

We must therefore not be discouraged by the difficulty of interpreting life by the ordinary laws of physics. For that is just what is to be expected from the knowledge we have gained of the structure of living matter. We must be prepared to find a new type of physical law prevailing in it. Or are we to term it a non-physical, not to say a super-physical, law?

THE NEW PRINCIPLE IS NOT ALIEN TO PHYSICS

No. I do not think that. For the new principle that is involved is a genuinely physical one: it is, in my opinion, nothing else than the principle of quantum theory over again. To explain this, we have to go to some length, including a refinement, not to say an amendment, of the assertion previously made, namely, that all physical laws are based on statistics.

This assertion, made again and again, could not fail to arouse contradiction. For, indeed, there are phenomena whose conspicuous features are visibly based directly on the "order-from-order" principle and appear to have nothing to do with statistics or molecular disorder.

The order of the solar system, the motion of the planets, is maintained for an almost indefinite time. The constellation of this moment is directly connected with the constellation at any particular moment in the times of the Pyramids; it can be traced back to it, or vice versa. Historical eclipses have been calculated and have been found in close agreement with historical records or have even in some cases served to correct the accepted chronology. These calculations do not imply any statistics, they are based solely on Newton's law of universal attraction.

Nor does the regular motion of a good clock or of any similar mechanism appear to have anything to do with statistics. In short, all purely mechanical events seem to follow distinctly and directly the "order-from-order" principle. And if we say "mechanical," the term must be taken in a wide sense. A very useful kind of clock is, as you know, based on the regular transmission of electric pulses from the power station.

I remember an interesting little paper by Max Planck on the topic "The Dynamical and the Statistical Type of Law" ("Dynamische und Statistische Gesetzmässigkeit"). The distinction is precisely the one we have here labelled as "order from order" and "order from disorder." The object of that paper was to show how the interesting statistical type of law, controlling large-scale events, is constituted from the "dynamical" laws supposed to govern the small-scale events, the interaction of the single atoms and molecules. The latter type is illustrated by large-scale mechanical phenomena, as the motion of the planets or of a clock, etc.

Thus it would appear that the "new principle," the order-from-order principle, to which we have pointed with great solemnity as being the real clue to the understanding of life, is not at all new to physics. Planck's attitude even vindicates priority for it. We seem to arrive at the ridiculous conclusion that the clue to the understanding of life is that it is based on a pure mechanism, a "clock-work" in the sense of Planck's paper. The conclusion is not ridiculous and is, in my opinion, not entirely wrong, but it has to be taken "with a very big grain of salt."

THE MOTION OF A CLOCK

Let us analyse the motion of a real clock accurately. It is not at all a purely mechanical phenomenon. A purely mechanical clock would need no spring, no winding. Once set in motion, it would go on for ever. A real clock without a spring stops after a few beats of the pendulum, its mechanical energy is turned into heat. This is an infinitely complicated atomistic process. The general picture the physicist forms of it compels him to admit that the inverse process is not entirely impossible: A spring-less clock might suddenly begin to move, at the expense of the heat energy of its own cog wheels and of the environment. The physicist would have to say: The clock experiences an exceptionally intense fit of Brownian movement. . . . with a very sensitive torsional balance (electrometer or galvanometer) that sort of thing happens all the time. In the case of a clock it is, of course, infinitely unlikely.

Whether the motion of a clock is to be assigned to the dynamical or to the statistical type of lawful events (to use Planck's expressions) depends on our attitude. In calling it a dynamical phenomenon we fix attention on the regular going that can be secured by a comparatively weak spring, which overcomes the small disturbances by heat motion, so that we may disregard them. But if we remember that without a spring the clock is gradually slowed down by friction, we find that this process can only be understood as a statistical phenomenon.

However insignificant the frictional and heating effects in a clock may be from the practical point of view, there can be no doubt that the second attitude, which does not neglect them, is the more fundamental one, even when we are faced with the regular motion of a clock that is driven by a spring. For it must not be believed that the driving mechanism really does away with the statistical nature of the process. The true physical picture includes the possibility that even a regularly going clock should all at once invert its motion and, working backward, rewind its own spring—at the expense of the heat of the environment. The event is just "still a little less likely" than a "Brownian fit" of a clock without driving mechanism.

CLOCK-WORK AFTER ALL STATISTICAL

Let us now review the situation. The "simple" case we have analysed is representative of many others—in fact of all such as appear to evade the all-embracing principle of molecular statistics. Clock-works made of real physical matter (in contrast to imagination) are not true "clock-works." The element of chance may be more or less reduced, the likelihood of the clock suddenly going altogether wrong may be infinitesimal, but it always remains in the background. Even in the motion of the celestial bodies irreversible fractional and thermal influences are not wanting. Thus the rotation of the earth is slowly diminished by tidal friction, and along with this reduction the moon gradually recedes from the earth, which would not happen if the earth were a completely rigid rotating sphere.

Nevertheless the fact remains that "physical clock-works" visibly display very prominent "order-from-order" features—the type that aroused the physicist's excitement when he encountered them in the organism. It seems likely that the two cases have after all something in common. It remains to be seen what this is and what is the striking difference which makes the case of the organism after all novel and unprecedented.

NERNST'S THEOREM

When does a physical system—any kind of association of atoms—display "dynamical law" (in Planck's meaning) or "clock-work features"? Quantum theory has a very short answer to this question, viz. at the absolute zero of temperature. As zero temperature is approached the molecular disorder ceases to have any bearing on physical events. This fact was, by the way, not discovered by theory, but by carefully investigating chemical reactions over a wide range of temperatures and extrapolating the results to zero temperature—which cannot actually be reached. This is Walther Nernst's famous "Heat-Theorem," which is sometimes, and not unduly, given the proud name of the "Third Law of Thermodynamics" (the first being the energy principle, the second the entropy principle).

Quantum theory provides the rational foundation of Nernst's empirical law, and also enables us to estimate how closely a system must approach to the absolute zero in order to display an approximately "dynamical" behaviour. What temperature is in any particular case already practically equivalent to zero?

Now you must not believe that this always has to be a very low temperature. Indeed, Nernst's discovery was induced by the fact that even at room temperature entropy plays an astonishingly insignificant role in many chemical reactions. (Let me recall that entropy is a direct measure of molecular disorder, viz. its logarithm.)

THE PENDULUM CLOCK IS VIRTUALLY AT ZERO TEMPERATURE

What about a pendulum clock? For a pendulum clock room temperature is practically equivalent to zero. That is the reason why it works "dynamically." It will continue to work as it does if you cool it (provided that you have removed all traces of oil!). But it does not continue to work if you heat it above room temperature, for it will eventually melt.

THE RELATION BETWEEN CLOCK-WORK AND ORGANISM

That seems very trivial but it does, I think, hit the cardinal point. Clock-works are capable of functioning "dynamically" because they are built of solids, which are kept in shape by London-Heitler forces, strong enough to elude the disorderly tendency of heat motion at ordinary temperature.

Now, I think, few words more are needed to disclose the point of resemblance between a clock-work and an organism. It is simply and solely that the latter also hinges upon a solid—the aperiodic crystal forming the hereditary substance, largely withdrawn from the disorder of heat motion. But please do not accuse me of calling the chromosome fibres just the "cogs of the organic machine"—at least not without a reference to the profound physical theories on which the simile is based.

For, indeed, it needs still less rhetoric to recall the fundamental difference between the two and to justify the epithets novel and unprecedented in the biological case.

The most striking features are: first, the curious distribution of the cogs in a many-celled organism, for which I may refer to the somewhat poetical description on page 452 and secondly, the fact that the single cog is not of coarse human make, but is the finest masterpiece ever achieved along the lines of the Lord's quantum mechanics.

EPILOGUE: ON DETERMINISM AND FREE WILL

As a reward for the serious trouble I have taken to expound the purely scientific aspect of our problem *sine ira et studio*, I beg leave to add my own, necessarily subjective, view of its philosophical implications.

According to the evidence put forward in the preceding pages the space-time events in the body of a living being which correspond to the activity of its mind, to its self-conscious or any other actions, are (considering also their complex structure and the accepted statistical explanation of physico-chemistry) if not strictly deterministic at any rate statisticodeterministic. To the physicist I wish to emphasize that in my opinion, and contrary to the opinion upheld in some quarters, *quantum indeterminacy* plays no biologically relevant role in them, except perhaps by enhancing their purely accidental character in such events as *meiosis*, natural and X-ray-induced mutation, and so on—and this is in any case obvious and well recognized.

For the sake of argument, let me regard this as a fact, as I believe every unbiassed biologist would, if there were not the well-known, unpleasant feeling about "declaring oneself to be a pure mechanism." For it is deemed to contradict Free Will as warranted by direct introspection.

But immediate experiences in themselves, however various and disparate they be, are logically incapable of contradicting each other. So let us see whether we cannot draw the correct, non-contradictory conclusion from the following two premises:

1. My body functions as a pure mechanism according to the Laws of Nature.

2. Yet I know, by incontrovertible direct experience, that I am directing its motions, of which I foresee the effects, that may be fateful and all-important, in which case I feel and take full responsibility for them.

The only possible inference from these two facts is, I think, that I—I in the widest meaning of the word, that is to say, every conscious mind that has ever said or felt "I"—am the person, if any, who controls the "motion of the atoms" according to the Laws of Nature.

Within a cultural milieu (Kulturkreis) where certain conceptions (which once had or still have a wider meaning amongst other peoples) have been limited and specialized, it is daring to give to this conclusion the simple wording that it requires. In Christian terminology to say: "Hence I am God Almighty" sounds both blasphemous and lunatic. But please disregard these connotations for the moment and consider whether the above inference is not the closest a biologist can get to proving God and immortality at one stroke.

In itself, the insight is not new. The earliest records to my knowledge date back some 2500 years or more. From the early great Upanishads the recognition *Athman = Brahman* (the personal self equals the omnipresent, all-comprehending eternal self) was in Indian thought considered, far from being blasphemous, to represent the quintessence of deepest insight into the happenings of the world. The striving of all the scholars of Vedanta was, after having learnt to pronounce with their lips, really to assimilate in their minds this grandest of all thoughts.

Again, the mystics of many centuries, independently, yet in perfect harmony with each other (somewhat like the particles in an ideal gas) have described, each of them, the unique experience of his or her life in terms that can be condensed in the phrase: *Deus Factus Sum* (I have become God).

To Western ideology the thought has remained a stranger, in spite of Schopenhauer and others who stood for it, and in spite of those true lovers who, as they look into each other's eyes, become aware that their thought and their joy are *numerically* one—not merely similar or identical; but they, as a rule, are emotionally too busy to indulge in clear thinking, in which respect they very much resemble the mystic.

Allow me a few further comments. Consciousness is never experienced in the plural, only in the singular. Even in the pathological cases of split consciousness or double personality the two persons alternate, they are never manifest simultaneously. In a dream we do perform several characters at the same time, but not indiscriminately: we *are* one of them; in him we act and speak directly, while we often eagerly await the answer or response of another person, unaware of the fact that it is we who control his movements and his speech just as much as our own.

How does the idea of plurality (so emphatically opposed by the Upanishad writers) arise at all? Consciousness finds itself intimately connected with, and dependent on, the physical state of a limited region of matter, the body. (Consider the changes of mind during the development of the body, as puberty, ageing, dotage, etc., or consider the effects of fever, intoxication, narcosis, lesion of the brain, and so on.) Now, there is a great plurality of similar bodies. Hence the pluralization of consciousnesses or minds seems a very suggestive hypothesis. Probably all simple ingenious people, as well as the great majority of Western philosophers, have accepted it.

It leads almost immediately to the invention of souls, as many as there are bodies, and to the question whether they are mortal as the body is or whether they are immortal and capable of existing by themselves. The former alternative is distasteful, while the latter frankly forgets, ignores, or disowns the facts upon which the plurality hypothesis rests. Much sillier questions have been asked: Do animals also have souls? It has even been questioned whether women, or only men, have souls.

Such consequences, even if only tentative, must make us suspicious of the plurality hypothesis, which is common to all official Western creeds. Are we not inclining to much greater nonsense, if in discarding their gross superstitions we retain their naïve idea of plurality of souls, but "remedy" it by declaring the souls to be perishable, to be annihilated with the respective bodies?

The only possible alternative is simply to keep to the immediate experience that consciousness is a singular of which the plural is unknown; that

460

Does Order Arise from Disorder?

there *is* only one thing and that what seems to be a plurality is merely a series of different aspects of this one thing, produced by a deception (the Indian *Maja*); the same illusion is produced in a gallery of mirrors, and in the same way Gaurisankar and Mt. Everest turned out to be the same peak seen from different valleys.

There are, of course, elaborate ghost-stories fixed in our minds to hamper our acceptance of such simple recognition. E.g. it has been said that there is a tree there outside my window, but I do not really see the tree. By some cunning device of which only the initial, relatively simple, steps are explored, the real tree throws an image of itself into my consciousness, and that is what I perceive. If you stand by my side and look at the same tree, the latter manages to throw an image into your soul as well. I see my tree and you see yours (remarkably like mine), and what the tree in itself is we do not know. For this extravagance Kant is responsible. In the order of ideas which regards consciousness as a *singulare tantum* it is conveniently replaced by the statement that there is obviously only *one* tree and all the image business is a ghost-story.

Yet each of us has the undisputable impression that the sum total of his own experience and memory forms a unit, quite distinct from that of any other person. He refers to it as "I." *What is this "I"?*

If you analyse it closely you will, I think, find that it is just a little bit more than a collection of single data (experiences and memories), namely the canvas *upon which* they are collected. And you will, on close introspection, find that what you really mean by "I" is that ground-stuff upon which they are collected. You may come to a distant country, lose sight of all your friends, may all but forget them; you acquire new friends, you share life with them as intensely as you ever did with your old ones. Less and less important will become the fact that, while living your new life, you still recollect the old one. "The youth that was I," you may come to speak of him in the third person, indeed the protagonist of the novel you are reading is probably nearer to your heart, certainly more intensely alive and better known to you. Yet there has been no intermediate break, no death. And even if a skilled hypnotist succeeded in blotting out entirely all your earlier reminiscences, you would not find that he had killed *you*. In no case is there a loss of personal existence to deplore.

Nor will there ever be.

Chance, Causality, and Free Will

The Law of Chance *

by Erwin Schrödinger (1935)

Let us return to the specific question of causality. Here we are still faced with a dilemma. [On the one hand we] can form the opinion that the real essence, or the intrinsic constitution, of the Laws of Nature has been exhaustively discovered through the revelation of their statistical character, and that consequently the idea of a necessary causal connection between natural occurrences ought to be banished from our world picture, just as the concept of heat as a fluid disappeared from physics the moment it was discovered that heat is nothing more than a random movement of the smallest particles. We shall be especially inclined to sacrifice the causal principle if we follow Hume in recognizing that it is not a necessary feature of our thought, but only a convenient habit, generated by the observation of that regularity in the course of actual occurrences the merely statistical character of which is now clearly perceived.

If, however, we disagree with Hume and hold that the causal principle is something of an *a priori* nature, forming a necessary element in our thought, and inevitably marking every possible experience with its stamp, then we must adopt *the second alternative*, which may be expressed as follows: We shall maintain that the behavior of each atom is in every single event determined by rigid causality. And we shall even contend that strictly causal determinism of the elementary processes, although we cannot observe their details, must necessarily be admitted, in order to allow the mass phenomena, which result from their coöperation, to be treated by the methods of statistics and the probability calculus. From this viewpoint causality would lie at the basis of statistical law.

This second view is the conservative one. The former is extremely revolutionary. And the one is the direct antithesis of the other. According to the revolutionary view, undetermined chance is primary and is not further explicable. Law arises only statistically in mass phenomena owing

* From Erwin Schrödinger, *Science, Theory, and Man,* translated by James Murphy and W. H. Johnston, Dover Publications, Inc., New York, 1957. Reprinted by permission of Dover Publications, Inc., and George Allen & Unwin, Ltd.

to the coöperation of myriads of chances at play in these phenomena. According to the conservative view the compulsion of law is primary and not further explicable, whereas chance is due to the coöperation of innumerable partial causes which cannot be perceived. Therefore chance here is something subjective—only a name for our own inability to discover the detailed action of numerous small component causes.

There is scarcely any possibility of deciding this issue by experiment. For the methods of pure reasoning evidently allow us either to derive chance from law, or law from chance, whichever we prefer. Wherever we are concerned with a law-determined process forming the ultimate *recognizable* structural element in our world picture, a domain of chance behind it can be supposed to produce the law statistically, if anybody desires to suppose this. And in a similar way the champion of the causal principle is justified in thinking that any chance he observes is dependent on the action of uncontrollable changing causes which give rise to this or that effect, but always compulsorily.

The current controversy about the principle of causality is a phase in our changing intellectual outlook, which is paralleled by the problem of the true character of space and time, a question which has arisen anew as a result of Einstein's theories. The old links between philosophy and physical science, after having been temporarily frayed in many places, are being more closely renewed. The farther physical science progresses the less can it dispense with philosophical criticism. But at the same time philosophers are increasingly obliged to become intimately acquainted with the sphere of research, to which they undertake to prescribe the governing laws of knowledge.

The Idea of Chance *

by J. J. Bronowski (1953)

There is of course nothing sacred about the causal form of natural laws. We are accustomed to this form, until it has become our standard of what every natural law ought to look like. If you halve the space which a gas fills, and keep other things constant, then you will double the pressure, we say. If you do such and such, the result will be so and so; and it will always be so and so. And we feel by long habit that it is this "always"

* From J. J. Bronowski, *The Commonsense of Science*, Harvard University Press, Cambridge, Mass., 1953. Reprinted by permission of Harvard University Press and William Heineman, Ltd., London.

which turns the prediction into a law. But of course there is no reason why laws should have this always, all-or-nothing form. If you self-cross the offspring of a pure white and a pure pink garden pea, said Mendel, then on an average one quarter of these grandchildren will be white, and three quarters will be pink. This is as good a law as any other; it says what will happen, in good quantitative terms, and what it says turns out to be true. It is not any less respectable for not making that parade of every-time certainty which the law of gases makes. And indeed, the gas law takes its air of finality only from the accumulation of such chances as Mendel's law makes explicit.

It is important to seize this point. If I say that after a fine week, it *always* rains on Sunday, then this is recognised and respected as a law. But if I say that after a fine week, it rains on Sunday more often than not, then this somehow is felt to be an unsatisfactory statement; and it is taken for granted that I have not really got down to some underlying law which would chime with our habit of wanting science to say decisively either "always" or "never." Even if I say that after a fine week, it rains on seven Sundays out of ten, you may accept this as a statistic, but it does not satisfy you as a law. Somehow it seems to lack the force of law.

Yet this is a mere prejudice. It is nice to have laws which say, This configuration of facts will always be followed by event A, ten times out of ten. But neither taste nor convenience really make this a more essential form of law than one which says, This configuration of facts will be followed by event A seven times out of ten, and by event B three times out of ten. In form the first is a causal law and the second a statistical law. But in content and in application, there is no reason to prefer one to the other. The laws of science have two functions, to be true and to be helpful; probably each of these functions includes the other. If the statistical law does both, that is all that can be asked of it. We may persuade ourselves that it is intellectually less satisfying than a causal law, and fails somehow to give us the same feeling of understanding the process of nature. But this is an illusion of habit. No law ever gave wider satisfaction than the law of gravitation. Yet . . . the explanation it gave of the workings of nature was false, and the understanding we got from it mistaken. What it really did, and did superbly, was to predict the movements of the heavenly bodies to an excellent approximation.

There is, however, a limitation within every law which does not contain the word "always." Bluntly, when I say that a configuration of facts will be followed sometimes by event A and at other times by B, I cannot be certain whether at the next trial A or B will turn up. I may know that A is to turn up seven times and B three times out of ten; but that brings me no nearer at all to knowing which is to turn up on the one occasion I have my eye on next time. Mendel's law is all very fine when you grow peas by the acre; but it does not tell you, and cannot, whether the single second generation seed in your windowbox will flower white or pink. Mendel himself ran into this trouble when he tested his law, because he had to do his experimental work in a rather small monastery garden.

So far, this is obvious enough. It is obvious that if we did know what is to happen precisely next time, then we would at once have not a statistical law, but a law of certainty into which we could write the word "always." . . .

Modern science . . . uses no principle but that of forecasting with as much assurance as possible, but with no more than is possible. That is, it idealises the future from the outset, not as completely determined, but as determined within a defined area of uncertainty. Let me illustrate the kind of uncertainty. We know that the children of two blue-eyed parents will certainly have blue eyes; at least, no exception has ever been found. By contrast, we cannot be certain that all the children of two brown-eyed parents will have brown eyes. And we cannot be certain of it even if they have already had ten children with brown eyes. The reason is that we can never discount a run of luck of the kind which Dr. Johnson once observed when a friend of his was breeding horses. "He has had," said Dr. Johnson, "sixteen fillies without one colt, which is an accident beyond all computation of chances." But what we can do is to compute the *odds* against such a run; this is not as hard as Johnson supposed. And from this we can compute the likelihood that the next child will have brown eyes.[1] That is, we can make a forecast which states our degree of uncertainty in a precise form. Oddly enough, it is just here that Mendel's own account of his work is at fault. He assumed in effect that once a couple has had ten brown-eyed children, the chance that they may yet have blue-eyed children is negligible. But it was not.

This area of uncertainty shrinks very quickly in its proportion if we make our forecasts not about one family but about many. I do not know whether this or that couple will have a child next year; I do not even know whether I shall. But it is easy to estimate the number of children who will be born to the whole population, and to give limits of uncertainty to our estimate. The motives which lead to marriage, the trifles which cause a car to crash, the chanciness of today's sunshine or tomor-

1. The gene for brown eyes is dominant, so a brown-eyed person may carry and pass on the gene for blue eyes. But a truly blue-eyed person cannot carry the gene for brown eyes. See Figure 7-5 for the mechanism of the heredity of dominant and recessive traits. Ed.

row's egg, are local, private and incalculable. Yet, as Kant saw long ago, their totals over the country in a year are remarkably steady; and even their ranges of uncertainty can be predicted.

This is the revolutionary thought in modern science. It replaces the concept of the *inevitable effect* by that of the *probable trend*. Its technique is to separate so far as possible the steady trend from local fluctuations in the past, the greater is the confidence with which we look along the trend into the future. We are not isolating a cause. We are tracing a pattern of nature in its whole setting. We are aware of the uncertainties which that large, flexible setting induces in our pattern. But the world cannot be isolated from itself: the uncertainty *is* the world. The future does not already exist; it can only be predicted. We must be content to map the places into which it may move, and to assign a greater or less likelihood to this or that of its areas of uncertainty.

These are the ideas of chance in science today. They are new ideas: they give chance a kind of order; they re-create it as the life within reality. These ideas have come to science from many sources. Some were invented by Renaissance brokers; some by seventeenth-century gamblers; some by mathematicians who were interested in aiming-errors and in the flow of gases and more recently in radio-activity. The most fruitful have come from biology within little more than the last fifty years. I need not stress again how successful they have been in the last few years, for example in physics: Nagasaki is a monument to that. But we have not yet begun to feel their importance outside science altogether. For example, they make it plain that problems like Free Will or Determinism are simply misunderstandings of history. History is neither determined nor random. At any moment, it moves forward into an area whose general shape is known but whose boundaries are uncertain in a calculable way. A society moves under material pressure like a stream of gas; and on the average, its individuals obey the pressure; but at any instant, any individual may, like an atom of the gas, be moving across or against the stream. The will on the one hand and the compulsion on the other exist and play within these boundaries. In these ideas, the concept of chance has lost its old dry pointlessness and has taken on a new depth and power; it has come to life. Some of these ideas have begun to influence the arts: they can be met vaguely in the novels of the young French writers. In time they will liberate our literature from the pessimism which comes from our divided loyalties: our reverence for machines and, at odds with it, our nostalgia for personality. I am young enough to believe that this union, the union as it were of chance with fate, will give us all a new optimism.

Climates of Opinion *

by Carl L. Becker (1932)

Edit and interpret the conclusions of modern science as tenderly as we like, it is still quite impossible for us to regard man as the child of God for whom the earth was created as a temporary habitation. Rather must we regard him as little more than a chance deposit on the surface of the world, carelessly thrown up between two ice ages by the same forces that rust iron and ripen corn, a sentient organism endowed by some happy or unhappy accident with intelligence indeed, but with an intelligence that is conditioned by the very forces that it seeks to understand and to control. The ultimate cause of this cosmic process of which man is a part, whether God or electricity or a "stress in the ether," we know not. Whatever it may be, if indeed it be anything more than a necessary postulate of thought, it appears in its effects as neither benevolent nor malevolent, as neither kind nor unkind, but merely as indifferent to us. What is man that the electron should be mindful of him! Man is but a foundling in the cosmos, abandoned by the forces that created him. Unparented, unassisted and undirected by omniscient or benevolent authority, he must fend for himself, and with the aid of his own limited intelligence find his way about in an indifferent universe.

Such is the world pattern that determines the character and direction of modern thinking. The pattern has been a long time in the weaving. It has taken eight centuries to replace the conception of existence as divinely composed and purposeful drama by the conception of existence as a blindly running flux of disintegrating energy. But there are signs that the substitution is now fully accomplished; and if we wished to reduce eight centuries of intellectual history to an epigram, we could not do better than to borrow the words of Aristophanes, "Whirl is king, having deposed Zeus."

* From Carl L. Becker, *The Heavenly City of the Eighteenth Century Philosophers*, Yale University Press, New Haven, 1932. Reprinted by permission of Yale University Press.

The Revolution in Western Thought *

by Huston Smith (1959)

The distinctive feature of the contemporary mind as evidenced by frontier thinking in science, philosophy, theology and the arts is its acceptance of reality as unordered in any objective way that man's mind can discern. This acceptance separates the Post-Modern Mind from both the modern mind, which assumed that reality is objectively ordered, and the Christian mind, which assumed it to be regulated by an inscrutable but beneficent will.

It remains only to add my personal suspicion that the change from the vision of reality as ordered to unordered has brought Western man to as sharp a fork in history as he has faced. Either it is possible for man to live indefinitely with his world out of focus, or it is not. I suspect that it is not, that a will-to-order and orientation is rather fundamental in the human make-up. If so, the post-modern period, like all the intellectual epochs that preceded it, will turn out to be a transition to a still different perspective.

But if reality does get reordered for the Western mind, this order is certain to be very different from that which the modern mind envisioned. What it will be like cannot at this juncture be surmised. The most that can be ventured is the abstract prediction that it will be more complicated than the modern mind suspected and that its order will be recognized as partially imposed by man's mind and not just passively mirrored within it. The order will not describe reality as it exists by itself apart from us. Instead it will describe an ellipse in which man in his entirety— his purposes and feelings as well as his intellect—stands as one focus in balance and tension with its complementing focus: the cosmos in which his life is set and against which his destiny must be enacted.

* From Huston Smith, "The Revolution in Western Thought," from the series "Adventures of the Mind," *Saturday Evening Post*, August 26, 1961. Reprinted by permission.

Questions To Consider

In Part 3 we saw how the quantum nature of matter and energy led to a basic uncertainty in describing the position and velocity of an individual photon or electron. Out of this uncertainty grew the statistical interpretation of modern physical laws. But Schrödinger shows here how the quantum nature of energy preserves the orderliness of the living molecule. How can the same aspect of nature lead to both uncertainty and order?

If the situation described by Robert Coates in "The Law" did actually occur would it indicate that the Law of Chance was no longer valid?

Is heredity random or orderly?

Schrödinger says that the methods of pure reasoning "allow us either to derive chance from law or law from chance whichever we prefer." Which view of nature do you prefer?

Suggestions for Further Reading

American Foundation for Continuing Education, Louise B. Young, Editor: *Exploring the Universe*, McGraw-Hill, 1963. Part 3 discusses the discovery of an order in nature, and Part 6 discusses the uncertainty principle and its bearing on man's understanding of nature.

Asimov, Isaac: *Life and Energy*, Doubleday & Co., Inc., 1962. This book is especially recommended for the reader who would like to understand more about the thermodynamics of living matter.

° Born, Max: *The Restless Universe*, Dover Publications, Inc., 1951. The first chapter of this book discusses molecular motion and the laws of chance. (See *Suggestions for Further Reading*, Part 2.)

° Bronowski, J. J.: *The Commonsense of Science*, Random House, Inc., 1953. This little book contains an interesting discussion of the changing ideas of order, chance, and causality. (See *Suggestions for Further Reading*, Part 3.)

Gamow, George: *Matter, Earth, and Sky*, Prentice-Hall, Inc., 1958. The chapter entitled "Restless Molecules" is particularly pertinent in connection with these readings. (See *Suggestions for Further Reading*, Part 6.)

° Schrödinger, Erwin: *What Is Life? and Other Scientific Essays*, Anchor Books, Doubleday & Co., Inc., 1956. Although we have included a long selection from this book we strongly recommend reading this little classic in its entirety. It contains an especially lucid description of the principles of heredity. Other essays discuss the conception of matter, "quantum jumps," and the scientific world view.

° Weaver, Warren: *Lady Luck*, Anchor Books, Doubleday & Co., Inc., 1962. An engaging and thorough discussion of probability and statistics using only elementary mathematics.

° Paperback edition

9

What Is Life?

A study of the modern biochemical theory of the basic living molecule leads to the conclusion that life is a spontaneous, irrepressible manifestation of matter. Can this process be said to take place by chance as the result of the coming together of random elements which then evolved by natural selection? Or is there some other organizing principle which influences the emergence of life from inorganic material?

What Is Life?

Introduction

W E HAVE seen that the same building blocks are used to construct all living matter from the single-celled amoeba to the rational human being. Furthermore these blocks can be broken down to yield common elements that are found in rocks and oceans and spinning galaxies. But just as a building is more than a pile of bricks and mortar, so each different organism that is made from the basic organic building blocks is a distinctive whole and in this sense it is more than the sum of its parts.

The readings in this section describe how biochemists have in recent years begun to decipher the code that determines the precise arrangement of each different form of living matter and how they have discovered some of the mechanisms by which the organism grows and reproduces itself. These discoveries have been made by the analytical methods of scientific research. As Sinnott points out, "The advantage of the analyst is obvious, for to dissect an object is far simpler than to find what formed it. Any youngster can take the mechanism of a clock apart, but to put it together again requires much skill." [1] Is it possible that in breaking matter down into its component parts we have lost something which is an essential property of the whole?

One of the distinctive features of a living organism is its ability to regulate itself. It grows and develops as a single unified entity in accordance with an inner impulse. What are the principles that control the organization of the individual, that preserve the organism against decay, and that build through the evolutionary process ever higher levels of complexity? These principles of integration are hard to define and to study.

Some writers, even some biologists, see in this organizing power a quality which is peculiar to living things. Most scientists, however, believe that the distinctive qualities of life arise as a result of the greater complexity of the molecular organization, that the same principle which organizes the inorganic crystal organizes the DNA molecule on a higher level. They believe that random mutations sifted by natural selection over millions of years have built more and more improbable molecular combinations on increasing levels of complexity. But they do not yet understand just how or why this particular level of complexity endows

1. See p. 538.

matter with the special characteristics of life such as consciousness, thought, and free will.

The statement that life is a manifestation of matter does not necessarily imply a mechanistic explanation of life. Matter, as we have seen, cannot be entirely explained on the basis of mechanical laws. The simplest atomic configurations display properties of individuality, identity, and regeneration. If life is a spontaneous and irrepressible manifestation of matter then the qualities that we attribute to life may be latent in matter itself. This idea seems so mysterious that we are tempted to exclaim with Eiseley, "If 'dead' matter has reared up this curious landscape of fiddling crickets, song sparrows, and wondering men, it must be plain even to the most devoted materialist that the matter of which he speaks contains amazing if not dreadful powers, and may not impossibly be, as Hardy has suggested, 'but one mask of many worn by the Great Face behind.'"[2]

Metaphysical explanations, however, are not useful to science. In the face of unsolved problems, science keeps its faith in the rational approach and believes that these questions will yield to scientific investigation, that they are not different in kind from the questions which science has already answered. Science is a continuing search and the existence of unanswered questions is the incentive that leads it on to further discovery.

2. See Part 6, p. 335.

Definition of Life

What Do We Mean by Life? *

by H. G. Wells, Julian Huxley, and G. P. Wells (1929)

We will begin . . . by asking what is meant by life? What are its distinctive characteristics? . . .

When an ordinary superficial man speaks of life he has a certain group of distinctive points in his mind. Firstly, a living thing moves about. It may not be in movement continuously—many living seeds lie immobile for long periods, but sooner or later they will thrust and stir. Life may move as swiftly as a flying bird, or as slowly as an expanding turnip, but it moves. It moves in response to an inner impulse. It may be stimulated to move, but the driving-force is within. It does not move simply like dust before the wind or sand stirred up by the waves.

And not only does it move of itself, but it feeds. It takes up matter from without into itself, it changes that matter chemically, and from these changes it gathers the energy for movement. Crystals, stalactites, and other non-living things grow, but only by additions, by the laying-on or fitting-in of congenial particles, without any change of chemical nature or release of energy. This process of taking in, assimilating and using matter, is called *metabolism*. Metabolism and spontaneous movement are the primary characteristics of living things.

In addition, life seems always to be produced by pre-existing life. It presents itself as a multitude of individuals which have been produced by division or the detachment of parts from other individuals, and most of which will in their time give rise to another generation. This existence in the form of distinct individuals which directly or indirectly reproduce their kind by a sort of inherent necessity is a third distinction between living and non-living things. Waves in water or wind-ripples in sand may be said to reproduce themselves, but not by a detachment and growth of their own substance; drops of oil or water grow and break up under suitable conditions, but not through any innate disposition to do so. Liv-

---

* From H. G. Wells, Julian Huxley, and G. P. Wells, *The Science of Life.*

ing things display an impulse to reproduce themselves even in adverse circumstances. . . .

Life as we know it flows in a strictly defined stream from its remote and unknown origins, it dissolves and assimilates food, but it receives no living tributaries.

Yet the distinction of what is living and what is not living is by no means easy. Seeds, small worms and microscopic animalcula can be dried up and left totally inert for long periods of time, so that it is impossible to distinguish them from dead organisms; then at the touch of moisture they will resume the recognizable process of life. Do they *live* meanwhile? . . .

Our knowledge of the chemistry and physics of the systems that are found in living tissues has developed rapidly. It has been found possible to imitate a number of the properties of living things by means of artificial models. It is at least possible that the distinctive properties of living things depend simply upon the complexity of their molecular organization.

How Life Began

_____

The Wellsprings of Life *
by Isaac Asimov (1960)

THE IMPORTANCE OF STRUCTURE

As we have already seen [1] chemically all life is one. But if the chemistry of life is so uniform from top to bottom, how is it that, in actual fact, a man is so different from a bacterium? They share the same building blocks, the same chemical abilities.

The answer lies in the fact that, in the earlier articles, there has been deliberate concentration on the building blocks, rather than on the final structures. One might as well ask why Naples differs so from New York in appearance when the structures of both cities are built so largely of stone and brick.

Different proteins are all built of the same amino acids (of which some nineteen are now known to occur generally in the various proteins), connected in the fashion first elucidated by Fischer.[2] However, the amino acids can be arranged in any order, and every different order results in a different protein with different properties.

Each amino acid in the string of amino acids (called a *peptide chain*) making up a protein can be any of the nineteen, without restriction. A peptide chain of, say, five amino acids can, therefore, have any of the nineteen in first place, any of the nineteen in second, and so on. The total number of different peptide chains that can result is $19 \times 19 \times 19 \times 19 \times 19$, or 2,476,099. Two and a half million alternatives, two and a half million different peptide chains with different properties—and only five places are involved.

What if there are 600 amino acids in a protein molecule, as there are, indeed, in a protein with average-sized molecules, such as hemoglobin? The total number would then be so large that to express it we would need

* From Isaac Asimov, *The Wellsprings of Life*.
1. It may be helpful at this time to refer back to the Asimov selections in Part 6, p. 288 and p. 310. Ed.
2. See Part 6, p. 317. Ed.

a one followed by 639 zeroes. Yet even that does not exhaust the possibilities. There are important proteins with thousands and tens of thousands of amino acids in the peptide chain. And there are ways in which proteins can vary in structure and properties even without affecting the actual order of the amino acids. (For instance, the same peptide chain can be wound or coiled in different fashions or linked to other such chains in various ways.)

To all intents and purposes, then, we are safe in saying that the possible number of different protein molecules that can exist is virtually infinite. If every protein molecule ever formed on earth or ever likely to be formed were different, the total number would still form only a completely insignificant fraction of all the different proteins that could theoretically exist.

You might wonder why proteins differ in properties when the amino acid order is changed.

Well, each amino acid has a different side-chain, and when amino acids are combined in the Fischer manner, amine group to acid group, the side-chains are left free and stick out to form the surface of the protein molecule, so to speak.

Now each side-chain has different properties. Some contain few atoms and are small, some contain many and are large. Some carry no electric charge, some a negative electric charge, some a positive. Some are capable of forming certain connecting links with other groups, some are not.

Each different arrangement of amino acids, or each different type of coiling of the same arrangement, results in a molecule with a different surface pattern; one that differs in electric charge pattern, in the manner in which the mechanical projection of groupings is shaped, in the positions where other groups may, or may not, hook on.

These variations in surface can seriously and profoundly affect the organism. Why and how that should be requires some explanation.

THE SURFACE INFLUENCE

In the early days of chemistry, it was noticed that sometimes two substances would react much more quickly in the presence of small quantities of a third substance than in its absence. The third substance, moreover, was not visibly affected by the reaction.

For instance, hydrogen and oxygen will combine with each other so rapidly, when heated, that a mixture of the two gases will explode violently. At room temperature, however, a mixture will stand quietly for indefinite periods without showing any signs of reaction. However, if a bit of finely divided platinum powder is added to the mixture, there will be an explosion even at room temperature. The German chemist Johann Wolfgang Döbereiner discovered this in 1822 and even invented an automatic lighter in which a jet of hydrogen could be directed onto a surface containing powdered platinum, so that it would catch fire spontaneously. (It was a very impressive lighter, but not practical.)

Other such phenomena were discovered, and finally Berzelius, in 1836, discussed all such cases and suggested a name. He proposed calling a substance which, in small quantities, affected the speed of a reaction without itself being affected, a *catalyst,* and the process, *catalysis.* The word comes from Greek words meaning "breaking down," because a catalyst influences the breaking down of other substances.

There is a great temptation to consider catalysis a very mysterious phenomenon, involving some almost supernatural influence of the catalyst upon other substances. Actually, nothing supernatural is involved. A catalyst merely offers a surface upon which a reaction can take place. Such surface influences arise commonly in the ordinary affairs of life and are then taken for granted.

Imagine, for instance, a man with a pencil and paper, and nothing else, standing in the midst of a desert with only soft, shifting sand underfoot. The man wishes to write something upon the paper. He knows how to write, he has something to write with and something to write upon. Nevertheless, he can write only the most fumbling note, one that is very likely to be undecipherable, and he will almost certainly tear the paper in the process.

Now imagine him suddenly endowed with a smooth writing board of polished wood, which will not itself take a pencil mark. In a way, this introduces no change in the situation, since he has no additional knowledge of writing, nothing more to write with, and nothing more on which to write directly.

Yet how different is the situation. Now his message can be written smoothly, clearly and without trouble—all thanks to a writing board, which offers him a surface on which to place the paper so that the writing can take place. The writing board is not itself affected in the process, but remains unchanged. Any number of mesages on separate pieces of paper can be written on it, so that one writing board will suffice, given time enough, for a million messages.

The analogy is a close one. A catalyst, too, offers a surface. Finely divided platinum offers a surface on which hydrogen and oxygen molecules can attach themselves and quietly combine at temperatures which, under ordinary circumstances, yield them insufficient energy to combine. When one set of hydrogen and oxygen molecules has combined, it leaves the surface and another set can take its place. Thus, a small quantity of powdered platinum can (and does) suffice for large quantities of hydrogen and oxygen.

As it turns out, catalysis is crucially intertwined with life.

Reactions do take place in living organisms that do not ordinarily take place in the inanimate world. For instance, food is broken down and digested in the stomach, or putrefied by microorganisms. In the absence of action by life, it remains virtually unchanged for prolonged periods. What is there in life that does to food what platinum does to hydrogen and oxygen?

As long ago as 1752 the French naturalist René A. F. de Réaumur placed meat in little metal tubes with open ends capped by wire mesh and allowed birds of prey to swallow them. Eventually, the tubes were regurgitated by the bird. The metal had protected the food from any mechanical grinding in the stomach, so anything that happened to it was the result of the chemical action of stomach fluids. De Réaumur found the meat gone and only a liquid left behind, so the fluids must have dissolved the meat.

The stomach juices, however, were later found to be acid, and in 1824 the English chemist William Prout showed the acid to be *hydrochloric acid*. This is a strong acid which will act upon meat protein in the test tube and gradually liquefy it. That seemed the answer to Dr. Réaumur's observations and nothing unusual seemed to be involved.

But in 1835, Schwann (the cell theory man) described experiments which showed that hydrochloric acid alone could not explain the manner in which meat was liquefied in the stomach. He maintained that stomach juices, in addition to the acid, contained some unknown substance which hastened the liquefaction; something that belonged to that class of agents which Berzelius, the next year, was to call "catalysts." Schwann called the new substance *pepsin* (from a Greek word meaning "to digest").

This suggestion was at first met with great skepticism, but then saliva was found to break down starch, despite the fact that saliva contained no acid. Furthermore, juice from a gland known as the pancreas was found to break down proteins, starch and fat, although it contained no acid, either.

And in 1857, Louis Pasteur had discovered that the fermentation of fruit juices (producing wine) was caused by the presence of certain varieties of living cells, called yeast. Without the presence of yeast, the proper fermentation would not go on. More and more, it seemed that living tissue could produce certain catalysts, in the presence of which various reactions, characteristic of life, could proceed.

Because the fermentation reaction was the longest known and best studied of these reactions, it became customary to speak of these life catalysts as *ferments*. Two types of ferments were recognized. One existed outside the cell, the digestive catalysts being examples. If pancreatic juice (filtered and perfectly clear of cells) were removed from the body and placed in a test tube, it would still digest various foodstuffs. Its contents were examples of *unorganized ferments*.

Then there was the kind of catalyst that caused the fermentation of sugar to alcohol. This, it was thought, would proceed only in the presence of intact yeast cells. This was a catalyst that was inseparably bound to life itself and would not exist in the absence of life, and was called an *organized ferment*. (This was a kind of revival, in weakened form, of "vitalism.")

In 1876, the German physiologist Willy Kühne suggested that unorganized ferments be called *enzymes* (from Greek words meaning "in yeast"), to reinforce the notion that they resembled substances in yeast, but to restrict the term "ferment" to the catalysts actually within cells.

In 1897, however, the German chemist Eduard Buchner ground up yeast cells with sand until not one intact cell was left. He filtered off the dead, cell-free juice and showed that it would bring about the fermentation of sugar as well as would the original cells. It was at once obvious that there was no real difference between organized and unorganized ferments and that all catalysts formed by living tissue, in or out of the cell, were merely chemicals and had no mysterious connection with any sort of "vital force." From then on, all body catalysts were included under the name of "enzyme." For this service to science, among others, Buchner received the Nobel prize for chemistry in 1907.

But what were enzymes? What was the structure of their molecules?

The trouble was that enzymes, although essential to the working of living tissue, occurred in such small quantities that it was difficult to isolate them in quantities large enough to study. (Any other substance which is needed by the body in only small quantities, such as the vitamins and certain minerals, are, as is now known, involved in enzyme action, and are therefore vital to life, although necessary only in traces.)

There was evidence indicating that enzymes were protein in nature, but it was all indirect and many biochemists refused to be convinced. Then, in 1926, the American biochemist James B. Sumner obtained small crystals of some substance from a solution of jack bean flour, and these crystals proved to be a pure enzyme named *urease*. It was a catalyst that hastened the breakdown of urea to carbon dioxide and ammonia. (Again, as in Wöhler's day, urea was involved in a major scientific advance.) When Sumner subjected these crystals of urease to various tests, there could be no doubt that they were protein.

The example was followed. In 1930, another American biochemist, John H. Northrop, crystallized pepsin. He and his research colleagues followed this by the crystallization of still other enzymes.

There are now nearly a hundred enzymes that have been crystallized and all, without exception, have proven to be proteins. It is generally accepted, now, that the thousands of other enzymes that have been studied but not yet crystallized are also proteins. In fact, the word "enzyme" can be defined most simply now as "a catalytic protein," or, if you prefer, "a protein catalyst."

No two enzymes are exactly alike in either function or structure. This is not surprising in view of the virtually infinite possibilities of protein structure variations.

The most natural view of the function of enzymes, once they are known to be proteins and once the infinite variability of the protein molecule is understood, is that they serve as surfaces on which particular reactions may take place. There are many thousands of different reactions going on constantly in all cells, and for each one of those reactions there is a special enzyme, with an amino acid arrangement so designed that its surface is just suitable for the hastening of that particular reaction and few, if any, others.

In general, almost none of the reactions that go on in living cells would proceed at room temperature except with imperceptible speed. The enzymes are, therefore, powerful directors of the chemical machinery. A particular compound might, if left to itself, react very slowly in each of a dozen different ways. Some molecules would follow each of the dozen paths. In the presence of an enzyme, however, which catalyzes only one of those paths, virtually all the molecules would hasten in that catalyzed direction, while virtually none would have a chance to react in the non-catalyzed ways.

The chemistry of a cell is, therefore, the reflection of the type of enzymes it contains, of the quantity of each, and of the position of each within the cell.

For instance, there are small bodies in the cell cytoplasm [Figure 9–1], called *mitochondria* (from Greek words meaning "cartilage threads," because of their appearance, although they are definitely not composed of cartilage). These mitochondria contain a number of enzymes which serve as catalysts for one step or another of the many reactions that, together, will convert glucose to carbon dioxide and water, liberating energy in the process. It is possible to imagine a glucose molecule as entering the mitochondrion at one end and being passed from enzyme to enzyme, each catalyzing the next reaction until carbon dioxide and water come out the other end, leaving behind, in the mitochondrion, a number

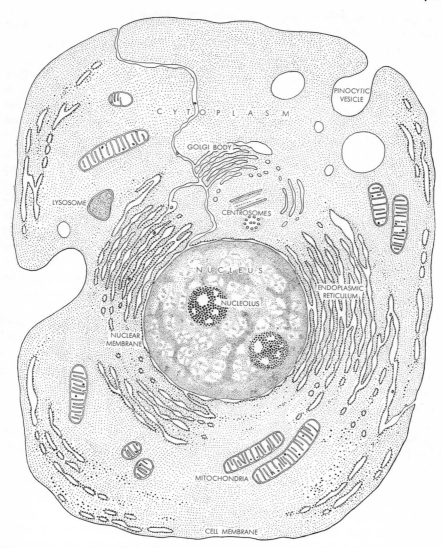

Figure 9–1. Modern diagram of a typical cell is based on what is seen in electron microscope. The mitochondria are the sites of the oxidative reactions that provide the cell with energy. The dots that line the endoplasmic reticulum are ribosomes: the sites of protein synthesis. In cell division the pair of centrosomes, one shown in longitudinal sections (rods), the other in cross section (circles), part to form poles of apparatus that separate two duplicate sets of chromosomes. (From Scientific American, September, 1961. *Reprinted by permission.)*

of special energy-containing compounds which can be called upon by the cell at any time to liberate energy and thus make life processes possible. (The picture is rather that of an assembly line, in which each enzyme is a worker with a specific function.)

Any interference with any of these enzymes would seriously impair the capacity of the cell to maintain life. In fact, a number of common substances do interfere with one enzyme or another of the mitochondrion and small quantities of these are poisons for that reason. Potassium cyanide is the most familiar example.

It is also possible for an enzyme to be destroyed, without entailing death for the cell or organism, but nevertheless bringing about some radical change.

For instance, most animals have the capacity to form a brownish-black pigment called melanin. In human beings, it is melanin that is responsible for brown or black hair, for brown eyes and for swarthiness of skin. Some individuals are rich in melanin, rich enough to have dark-brown skin. Others are poorer in it and have merely olive complexions. Others are poorer still in melanin and are fair-skinned, blue-eyed and blonde-haired. Even the fairest normal human being, however, has the capacity to form at least some melanin.

Now melanin is produced from tyrosine (the amino acid first isolated in cheese) as the result of a number of successive chemical reactions, each of which is catalyzed by some appropriate enzyme. One of these enzymes (the one catalyzing the first step in the process, as a matter of fact) is called *tyrosinase*. Occasionally, a human being (or other organism) is born without the ability to form tyrosinase. Without tyrosinase, the entire series of reactions forming melanin comes to a halt.

An individual without tyrosinase, therefore, has white hair and skin, and eyes that are colorless except for the color of blood showing through. Such individuals are albinos (from a Latin word for "white") and the change from the normal condition is most striking, considering that it has come about through the loss of but a single one of the many thousands of enzymes present in human beings.

To be born an albino can be the result of a mutation, just as being born a hemophiliac may be. The parents of albinos may be quite normally pigmented individuals. They may even be Negroes.

In view of cases such as this, it was inevitable that sooner or later geneticists would turn their attention to the inheritance of enzymes. Beginning about 1941, the American geneticist George W. Beadle did just this. He worked with a pink bread mold called Neurospora, which ordinarily requires nothing more than some sugar and minerals (plus one vitamin) to live on. Naturally, it makes use of all the usual amino acids in its proteins but it manufactures these in all necessary quantities out of the sugar and minerals.

Beadle exposed the Neurospora to ultraviolet radiation and to X-rays to encourage mutations and, sure enough, he obtained a spore which would not grow in the sugar-mineral solution. It might, however, grow if he added, say, a particular amino acid to the nutrient mixture. Once the spore started growing, its appearance was no different from that of a normal mold specimen. Nevertheless, it was a mutant, since it lacked some enzyme that served to synthesize the amino acid in normal specimens. Without the ability to synthesize it, the mutant had to have the amino acid supplied it ready-made and would not grow without it.

By this method, Beadle could follow mutations involving Neurospora enzymes as well as Muller could follow mutations involving Drosophila wing shapes.

Beadle could even gain knowledge about enzymes that was available to biochemists in no other way. For instance, he would try to grow a mutant Neurospora spore on various compounds resembling the amino acid it required. If we call these precursors (that is, compounds that might be formed by the organism on the way to the formation of the amino acid) A, B, C, and D, it might turn out that the mutant would grow on C and D, but not on A and B. The conclusion would be that the mutant possessed enzymes that would convert C and D to the amino acid but not A and B. If B resembled C closely and if biochemical experience indicated that the type of change involved in going from B to C usually required a single enzyme, then it would be possible to say that the Neurospora lacked the enzyme catalyzing the conversion of B to C.

A second mutant, also requiring the same amino acid in the diet, might be able to grow on B as well as on C and D, showing that Neurospora could indeed have the B-to-C enzyme. However, this second mutant might not be able to live on A, indicating the loss of an A-to-B enzyme.

By the study of many such mutations, it was possible to work out detailed schemes for the synthesis routes of many amino acids, vitamins and other compounds of biochemical importance. It was also possible to show definitely that the presence or absence of enzymes was a gene-controlled characteristic, following the ordinary laws of genetics.

In fact, geneticists now more or less accept the fact that genes exert their influence through the enzymes they cause to be formed (or fail to cause to be formed). The enzyme pattern of a particular organism gives rise to its various physical characteristics. Sometimes the connection can be traced, as in the case of albinism; much more often, the connection is obscure. But, obscure or not, the connection is there.

But if the enzyme pattern is controlled by the gene pattern, the obvious question is: how?

How does a particular gene supervise the formation of a particular enzyme (or a particular group of enzymes, perhaps) and not any other enzyme out of all the infinite number possible?

To answer that question it is necessary to consider a type of substance quite different from any of those yet discussed.

THE LIVING MOLECULE

In 1869, a German chemist named Friedrich Miescher was working with pus (broken-down white blood cells) and obtained from it a material which was neither carbohydrate, lipid nor protein. It was made up of carbon, hydrogen, oxygen and nitrogen, as proteins were, but in addition contained phosphorus. Because white blood cells usually have very prominent nuclei and because Miescher suspected this new substance came from those nuclei, he called it *nuclein*.

Nuclein showed definite acid properties, however, and by 1889, it became customary to speak of it as *nucleic acid* and that has been its name ever since. It was also found that within the cells nucleic acid was associated with protein and the two together formed a substance which was called *nucleoprotein*.

Biochemists were at the time most interested in protein, and investigation of the nucleic acid portion of nucleoprotein molecules proceeded slowly. It was found that nucleic acid broke down on treatment with acid to yield smaller building blocks, just as was true of other large molecules in living tissue. In the case of the nucleic acids, the building blocks were called *nucleotides*.

The nucleotides, themselves, could be broken down further; and each was found to consist, in its turn, of three parts. One part was phosphate (the phosphorus-containing portion), another a sugar, and the third a nitrogen-containing compound of a rather unusual type.

The chief investigator of nucleic acids in the early days was a Russian-born American chemist, Phoebus Aaron Levene. In 1911, he showed that the sugar contained in the nucleotides of one type of nucleic acid was *ribose*. This sugar had been synthesized by Emil Fischer back in 1901 and he had invented the name "ribose" for it, without its having any particular meaning. It was considered a laboratory sugar that did not occur in nature, until Levene showed otherwise. Levene also found a second type of nucleic acid with nucleotides containing a sugar similar to ribose but with one oxygen atom missing. This he called *deoxyribose*. The formulas for the two sugars follow in Figure 9–2.

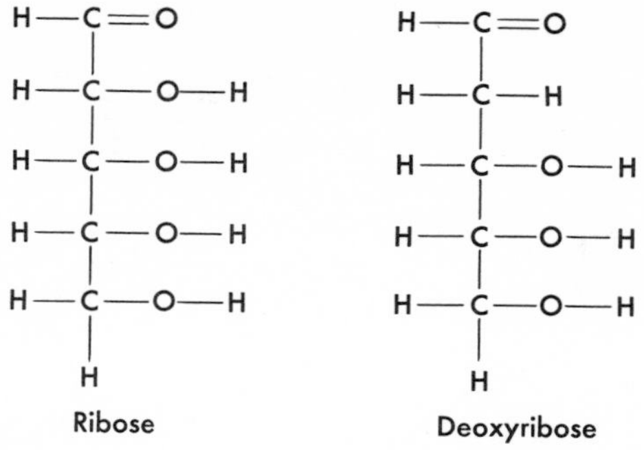

Figure 9–2.

If you were to compare these formulas with that for glucose given earlier in the book [3] you would see that these differ mainly in that they have one less carbon atom.

In any particular nucleic acid, the nucleotides are always identical with respect to the sugar component; either they all contain ribose, or they all contain deoxyribose. Nucleic acids are divided into two species, so to speak, for that reason; they are called *ribosenucleic acid* and *deoxyribosenucleic acid*. For the sake of convenience, these names are usually abbreviated (like government agencies) and are spoken of as, respectively, RNA and DNA.

Eventually, it was discovered that RNA occurred chiefly in the cytoplasm of the cell [Figure 9–1], with only minor quantities present in the nucleus. DNA, however, was present only in the nucleus, and never in the cytoplasm. (In the case of RNA, "nucleic acid" is obviously a misnomer, but the name sticks.)

The third component of the nucleotides, the nitrogen-containing compounds, was found to vary in structure. The atoms composing the molecules of these compounds are arranged in distinctive rings, sometimes in a double, sometimes in a single, ring.

The double-ring variety belongs to that class of compounds known as *purines*.

The two purine compounds present in nucleic acids are *adenine* and *guanine*. Their structural formulas, showing the double ring of atoms, follow in Figure 9–3.

The single-ring compounds are *pyrimidines*. Molecules of DNA contain two different pyrimidines, *cytosine* and *thymine*. Their structural formulas follow in Figure 9–4.

3. See p. 316. Ed.

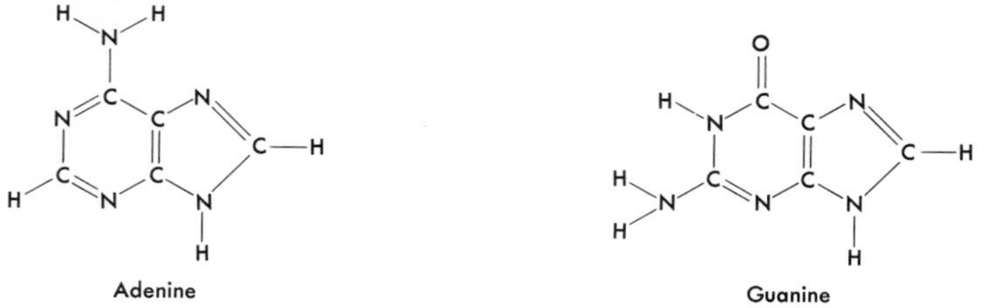

Adenine

Guanine

Figure 9–3.

Cytosine

Thymine

Figure 9–4.

Molecules of RNA do not contain thymine. Instead, they contain a very similar pyrimidine called *uracil* (Figure 9–5).

The manner in which nucleotides are hooked together to form nucleic acids took far longer to work out than did the similar problem of amino acids hooked together to form proteins. It now appears that in the individual nucleotide the nitrogenous compound (N) is connected to the sugar (S), which is connected to the phosphate (P). The phosphate group of each nucleotide is connected also to the sugar of the neighboring nucleotide, and that internucleotide link holds the nucleic acid together. A schematic diagram can be made of what a nucleic acid molecule must look like, as in Figure 9–6.

In any given nucleic acid molecule, the phosphate group is the same all down the line of nucleotides. So is the sugar group, being either ribose (in RNA) or deoxyribose (in DNA). The nitrogenous compounds can vary, however, being any one of four, and each of the four occurring at different places down the line of nucleotides.

Levene, in fact, considered the nucleic acid molecule to be made up of just four nucleotides, one containing each of the nitrogenous compounds. This would make the nucleic acid molecule rather smaller than that of a lipid and much smaller than those of starch and proteins. This view was held well into the 1930's.

However, beginning in 1939, studies of nucleic acids extracted from tissue in a very gentle manner (so that the molecules would not break down into fragments in the very process of extraction) showed that more

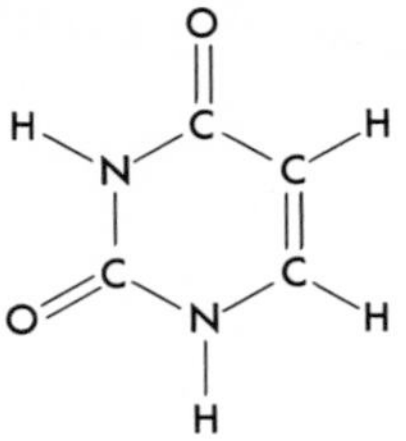

Uracil

Figure 9–5.

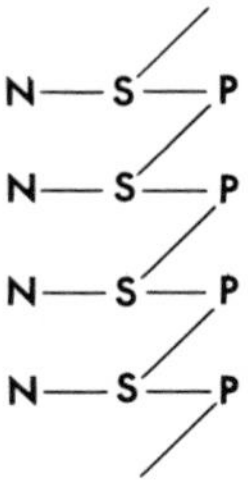

Nucleic acid (schematic)

Figure 9–6.

than four nucleotides must be present per nucleic acid molecule. First dozens of nucleotides were reported per molecule, then hundreds, then thousands.

By the 1950's, it was generally accepted (rather to the surprise of most biochemists) that in its natural state within the cell the molecule of nucleic acid was as large as any protein molecule, and larger than most. It could be made up of a thousand or more nucleotide units strung together.

Slowly the unique importance of nucleoproteins began to be realized by biochemists. As stated earlier, staining methods had been developed to color some parts of cells and not others, and the importance of chromosomes were first understood through the use of such stains. But the stains that colored chromosomes also colored nucleoproteins!

Several lines of evidence all began to converge toward the view that the chromosomes were nucleoprotein in nature. About 1936, the matter was virtually settled when a Swedish biochemist, T. Caspersson, devised a method for taking microphotographs of a cell illuminated by ultraviolet light. The purines and pyrimidines in nucleic acids absorbed such light, while most of the other cell constituents did not. Regions containing nucleic acids, therefore, showed up white against a black background. It turned out that both chromosomes in the nucleus and mitochondria in the cytoplasm contained nucleic acids. The nucleic acid in the chromosomes was almost entirely DNA; that in the mitochondria, entirely RNA.

The thought then arose that the genes, which until then had been rather mysterious units whose existence was only deduced from genetic data, might be definite chemical compounds; that they might, in fact, be merely complex nucleoprotein molecules.

A second and completely independent line of investigation also pointed to the nucleoprotein molecule as being chiefly implicated in inheritance.

Louis Pasteur, in 1862, first published his germ theory of disease, which stated that infectious diseases were caused by the parasitic activity of microscopic organisms within the human body. The first great advances in the control of infectious diseases came in the decades following the establishment of Pasteur's theory, as physicians learned to isolate the bacteria causing a particular disease and then found some way to fight them, by means of a chemical, vaccine or serum.

Yet bacteria were not always found that could be associated with a particular disease. Pasteur himself studied the disease hydrophobia, and produced a vaccine against it, yet could find no microscopic agent that caused it. Pasteur was too confident of his theory to allow this one fact to overthrow it. He simply pointed out that the causative agent of hydrophobia was probably too small to be seen by a microscope.

Another disease with no visible causative agent was "tobacco mosaic disease," an infectious condition in which the leaves of tobacco plants grew mottled. In 1889, a Dutch bacteriologist, Martinus Willem Beijerinck, referred to whatever invisible agent or poison carried that disease as a *virus*, a word which in Latin means simply "poison."

In 1892, the Russian botanist D. Ivanovski made a mash of leaves from tobacco plants suffering from the disease and passed the liquid from the mash through filters so fine that even bacteria could not pass through. The bacteria-free liquid that emerged could, however, still pass the disease on to healthy tobacco plants. The agent was, therefore, a filterable virus.

In 1916, the American bacteriologist H. A. Allard used a finer filter which would hold back even some particles too small to be seen under the microscope. Liquid passing through such a filter did not cause the disease. The virus, then, was a particle too small to be seen by ordinary microscopes but larger than the protein molecules which could pass through Allard's filter.

Then, in 1935, the American biochemist Wendell M. Stanley separated out pure tobacco mosaic virus and crystallized it. Once this was done, viruses could be studied as substances that could be weighed and subjected to definite chemical tests. It was found at once that tobacco mosaic virus was nucleoprotein in nature. It contained RNA.

Later on, when other viruses were crystallized, all were found to be nucleoprotein in nature. Some contained only RNA, some only DNA, some both.

Because of this work, Stanley shared the 1946 Nobel prize for chemistry, along with Sumner and Northrop, the crystallizers of enzymes.

Viruses come in all sizes and complexities, but all have this property in common: they cannot grow and reproduce independently, they can do so only within some living cell. It is as though they are themselves incomplete cells.

It is tempting to suppose that viruses may have grown incomplete as a result of their turning to parasitism. Higher organisms which turn to parasitism specialize by losing structures and organs they no longer need as parasites. Perhaps cells that have turned to parasitism also lose various cellular structures and chemical abilities.

This cellular degeneration can be seen in stages. For instance, there are a group of microorganisms called Rickettsia (named after the American pathologist Howard Taylor Ricketts, who first discovered them) which cause such diseases as typhus fever, psittacosis and Rocky Mountain spotted fever. The Rickettsia are sufficiently large to be seen in the microscope but they are smaller than ordinary cells and are apparently incomplete. At least they can only grow and reproduce within the cells they parasitize.

Below the Rickettsia are the viruses proper, which have abandoned more and more of their cellular properties. There are large viruses, like vaccinia (which cause smallpox) and bacteriophage (which infest bacteria) which still retain substances in the fashion of possible free-living ancestors. They possess, for instance, certain phosphorus-containing fat-like compounds called phospholipids, and even some enzymes and vitamins.

As viruses grow smaller and smaller, however, more and more of this extraneous material is abandoned until the tiniest viruses (like the tobacco mosaic virus) are nucleoprotein only. It is as though life had finally gotten down to the bare chromosome; as though the smallest viruses were nothing more than collections of "wild genes" ready to invade cells and impose their own will upon them over and above the supervision of the cell's own genes.

(A variation on this theme is the fact that certain filterable particles were discovered which could pass on some forms of cancer from one organism to another of the same species. The first example was discovered in 1911 by Peyton Rous. Others have been discovered since. These are called tumor viruses, and are also nucleoprotein in nature. A tumor virus might be looked upon as a "mutated gene," and a cancerous one, that can be transmitted from cell to cell.)

All of this made it look as though it was nucleoprotein that was the essential of life, and that all else was merely commentary. The other substances in the cell were the machinery, so to speak, with which the nucleoprotein worked; it was the nucleoprotein that did the working. The converging evidence that both gene and virus were nucleoprotein seemed to make that plain.

But why nucleoprotein rather than any other kind of protein? There seemed, for many decades, no particular importance of the nucleic acid prosthetic group over other types of prosthetic groups. Even when, in 1939 and thereafter, it turned out that nucleic acid molecules were very large, biochemists were not unduly impressed. Mere size is not all-important. Starch molecules can be extremely large, but they are made up of only one type of building block, glucose. Their properties lack the flexibility and versatility of the protein molecule, which is built up of nineteen building blocks, the various amino acids. Nucleic acids, built up of four building blocks (two nucleotides containing purines and two containing pyrimidines) might be more versatile than starch, but must be far less so, almost infinitely less so, than proteins. Or so it seemed.

Yet evidence piled upon evidence to show that nucleic acids were important, far more so than they seemed to be.

The first bit of evidence came from the sperm cell. The history of that evidence dates back to the very beginning of nucleic acid chemistry.

It was Miescher himself (the discoverer of nucleic acids) who first isolated nucleic acid in the sperm cells of fish. (This in itself was really the first indication that chromosomes are nucleoprotein in nature, since sperm cells are little more than tiny bags of compressed chromosomes.) Along with the nucleic acid, sperm cells always contained one of two proteins.

But here arose an odd point. These proteins are rather simple proteins, considerably simpler than most cell proteins.

This seemed difficult to understand. The sperm cell carries all the genes necessary to transmit all the inherited characteristics. It must follow, then, that unusually simple proteins, ridiculously simple proteins, suffice to contain within their structure all the supremely complicated paraphernalia of inheritance.

Biochemists retained for a long time the notion that (in order to save weight, perhaps, so that the sperm cell might be more maneuverable and be quicker to reach the waiting egg cell) all but the absolutely necessary portion of the protein molecule was discarded in sperm-cell formation. Just enough was carried along to serve as a foundation upon which the rest of the gene could be built up within the fertilized egg. (The protein that is associated with nucleic acid in the chromosomes of ordinary cells is, as it eventually turned out, a fully complicated one.)

However, once the true size of the nucleic acid was understood, it became plain that, despite any necessity for weight reduction, all sperm cells carried along a set of nucleic acid molecules in full size, as complex as any in ordinary tissue. There was no simplification whatsoever. It was as though sperm cells could afford to skimp on protein, but not on nucleic acid. Or perhaps (and this thought must have started occurring to some biochemists in the early 1940's) it was the nucleic acid portion of the nucleoprotein molecule that carried the genetic information and not the protein portion.

A stronger hint next came in the study of bacteria. A particular species of bacteria (or virus) can exist in several strains, that is, in several varieties distinguished from each other by their appearance, virulence, infectivity, or any other measurable characteristic. New strains continually arise through mutations.

In the case of the pneumococcus (a bacterium causing pneumonia), two strains are called "smooth" and "rough" because the first variety possesses a complex carbohydrate capsule as enclosure, which gives the bacteria a smooth appearance under the microscope. The second variety, not possessing this capsule, appears rough.

Experimenters discovered that an extract of the smooth variety could be prepared which, if added to the rough variety, converted the rough variety into a smooth one, indistinguishable from the ordinary smooth variety. It was as though the rough strain lacked a certain gene, which could be mechanically added from the smooth strain that possessed it. Once the gene was added, the rough strain became, and remained, smooth, passing the gene on to its descendant cells until such time as a mutation, involving the loss of the gene, once again gave rise to a rough strain.

In 1944, a group of American biochemists, including O. T. Avery, showed that the chemical in the extract that changed the strains was DNA. It was pure nucleic acid, with no protein whatever in the extract. The DNA behaved like a gene without the help of any protein. DNA was carrying genetic information, all right; it contained within its structure the ability to supervise the formation of some enzyme that made it possible to construct the capsule of the smooth variety.

For the first time, biochemists found themselves forced to consider nucleic acid as material that might possibly be even more important than protein.

Decisive evidence in this same direction came in connection with the study of viruses, which has been proceeding with great vigor in the 1950's.

In 1955, for instance, the biochemist H. Fraenkel-Conrat reported that he had treated tobacco-mosaic virus in such a way that it was separated into a nucleic acid portion and a protein portion, neither of which was too badly damaged. Although the tobacco-mosaic virus had been infective before, neither fraction separately was infective. Neither protein alone nor nucleic acid alone seemed capable of giving the disease to the tobacco plant.

If the two fractions of the original virus were then mixed, a certain amount of infectivity, about one per cent of the original, was restored. Apparently, the nucleic acid rejoins the protein in the mixture but usually in an incorrect and useless manner. One out of a hundred reunions, however, clicks into place correctly and the intact virus molecule is restored.

In one respect, however, things are not quite so simple. Actually some infectivity remained in the nucleic acid portion of the virus molecule. It was very small in amount, and at first it seemed it must be due to the nucleic acid portion being impure. There must be, it seemed, a small quantity of intact virus hanging on.

But no amount of purification of the nucleic acid seemed to remove the small residual infectivity, and doubts grew. Was the nucleic acid infective on its own but just having trouble getting into the cell? The nucleic acid from the virus was injected into cells and, sure enough, there it multiplied.

The situation with respect to nucleic acid and protein within a virus would seem to be analogous to that of a man and an automobile. The man is alive and can travel from city to city by himself, but slowly and with difficulty. With the aid of a nonliving automobile he can do the job easily and quickly. The nonliving automobile cannot do the job by itself at all.

This shows itself (with respect to a virus) even more plainly in the case of bacteriophage, the bacteria-infesting virus. (Bacteriophage was discovered by the Canadian bacteriologist Felix Hubert D'Hérelle in 1915, when he found that certain cell-free liquids apparently dissolved bacterial cultures and wiped them out.)

Under the electron miscroscope bacteriophage proved to be a comparatively large virus. The most common strains of the virus are shaped like tiny tadpoles, with a polyhedral head and a distinct, stubby tail.

Bacteriophage was studied by X-ray diffraction; that is, by aiming a beam of X-rays at it and observing the manner in which this beam was turned from its path. It was also bombarded with various subatomic particles to see how and in what manner the virus particles were damaged. From such studies (using techniques that were unknown and unheard of a short generation ago) the American bacteriologist Ernest C. Pollard drew a picture of the virus in the mid-1950's that is now generally accepted.

The protein of the bacteriophage forms a hollow shell on the outside of the virus. Inside the hollow is coiled the nucleic acid. When a bacteriophage molecule encounters a bacterial cell, the end of the bacteriophage tail is attracted strongly to a specific spot on the bacterial cell surface. (Probably the pattern of electric charge on the virus tail-tip just matches, in reverse—for unlike charges attract—the pattern of electric charge on the surface spot.)

In any case, the virus makes contact and sticks. A digestive enzyme at the tip of the bacteriophage tail now catalyzes the dissolution of that portion of the bacterial cell surface with which it is in contact.

That, you see, is the essential service performed by the protein of the virus. It takes the nucleic acid to the cell interior, as the automobile takes the man to the next city. But once man and automobile arrive, it is the man, and not the automobile, who must fulfill the purpose of the trip; this also holds for the nucleic acid protein. After arrival at the cell interior, it is the nucleic acid that takes over.

The nucleic acid moves into the bacterium. Only the nucleic acid moves inside; the protein shell of the virus remains outside!

This startling turn of affairs is a conclusion that is deduced from several converging lines of evidence. For one thing, the protein of the virus can be so treated as to incorporate into its structure atoms of radioactive sulfur, while the nucleic acid of the virus is made to incorporate atoms of radioactive phosphorus. Both types of radioactive atoms can be easily and unmistakably detected and distinguished by modern instruments. After bacteria have been infected with the bacteriophage, the radioactive phosphorus is found within the bacterial cell; it cannot be removed without completely disintegrating the cell. The radioactive sulfur, on the other hand, remains on the outside of the cell. It can be washed off, or even shaken off, while leaving the cells intact and unbroken.

Within the bacterial cell, the nucleic acid of the bacteriophage acts as though it were a foreign gene that has successfully invaded and conquered the cell. It takes over the duties of the cell's own genes. It is the invading nucleic acid that now supervises the chemical machinery of the cell. Under the forced rule of the invader, the cell machinery turns out replicas of the virus nucleic acid, and not replicas of the nucleic acid molecules of the bacterium itself, as should be the customary task of the cell.

Not only that, but the bacteriophage nucleic acid also forces the bacterial cell machinery to form bacteriophage protein as well. When the process is complete and the sucked-dry bacterial cell dissolves into shreds, there are present hundreds upon hundreds of complete bacteriophage molecules, each with its deadly nucleic acid coiled within its protein shell.

There seems little doubt now that the nucleic acid, rather than the nucleoprotein, is the irreducible (as far as we can tell) essential of life. Nucleic acid, in its natural state, is what might be called a living molecule. All else, including all protein, is but the machinery it works with.

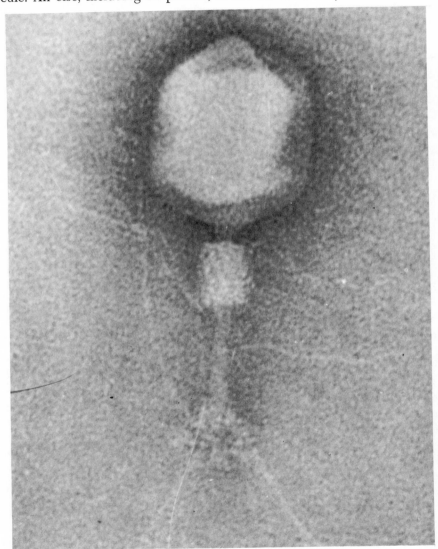

Figure 9–7A. Electron micrograph of triggered T_2 *bacteriophage virus (magnified* $\times 500,000$ *). Virus has polyhedral head and a curious pronged device at the end of its tail. Exposure to a specific bacterial substance causes contraction of the tail sheath and discharge of viral genes.*

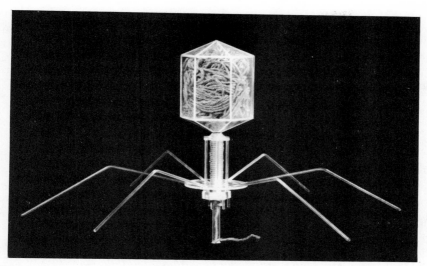

Figure 9–7B. *Model of T₂ bacteriophage virus. (Photographs by R. W. Horne and S. Brenner, University of Cambridge. Reprinted by permission of Academic Press.)*

Is It Alive? *

by George W. Gray (1937)

A virus can be crystallized, a property that we think of as purely inanimate and wholly chemical. . . . it has not been cultured in a test tube. This would seem to say that it is not a bacterium. A few bacteria placed in a nutrient soup will rapidly multiply into uncounted millions, but the crystalline protein shows no growth behavior in a glass vessel, no metabolism, no reproduction.

And yet, observe what happens when it comes in contact with the inner tissue of a tobacco plant or other vegetable host. Instantly the molecules begin to multiply. An almost imperceptible particle of a crystal will infect a plant, and in a few days the disease will spread through a field, producing an amount of virus millions of times that of the original. It exhibits a fecund ability to propagate itself, to extend its occupancy of space and

* From George W. Gray, *The Advancing Front of Science.* Copyright 1937 by McGraw-Hill Book Co., Inc. Reprinted by permission.

time at the expense of its environment. Is not this a characteristic of living things?

Perhaps the virus is a molecule of double personality, alive and yet not alive—animated by its environment when that environment is specific to its nature, but passive in any other environment. The discovery of this substance and the elucidation of its properties is one of the most important biological advances of our century.

Passing On the Information °

by Isaac Asimov (1962)

When Levene first worked out his theory of the structure of nucleic acid (that is, that it was made up of one of each of the four different nucleotides), one of his reasons for doing so was that analysis seemed to show that equal quantities of each nucleotide could be isolated from nucleic acids. In the late 1940's, using *paper chromatography*, a technique unknown in Levene's time, this was proved to be not quite so.

(In paper chromatography a small quantity of a mixture of similar compounds is placed at one end of a sheet of filter paper and is allowed to dry there. [See Figure 9–8.] An appropriate liquid is allowed to creep up the paper, past the spot and beyond. As the liquid creeps on, it drags the components of the mixture with it, but each component is dragged at its own characteristic rate. After a while, the individual components have separated, like runners in a race who begin abreast but, because of their differing speeds, end in single file. Each of the components, which may be the individual nucleotides of a nucleic acid, may be removed from the paper separately and its quantity determined. This technique, developed in 1944 by a group of British biochemists, including A. J. P. Martin, is now the most important single technique in biochemistry. It is hard to think of any branch of biochemical research that does not use it or how the science could progress further without it.)

Paper chromatography in the hands of such biochemists as Erwin Chargaff showed, by 1949, that the four nucleotides were never present in quite equal proportions in nucleic acids. However, some regularities did show up. The total number of purines seemed always to be roughly equal to the total number of pyrimidines. That meant that adenine plus

° From Isaac Asimov, *The Wellsprings of Life,* and from *The Genetic Code,* The Orion Press, Inc., 1962. Copyright 1962 by Isaac Asimov. Revised for this edition.

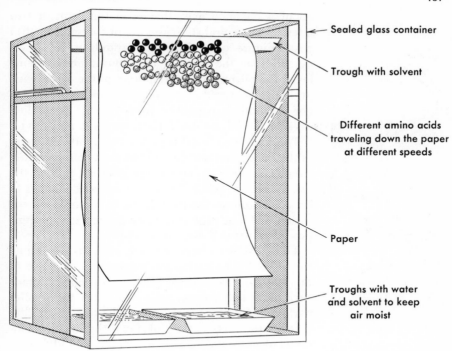

Sealed glass container

Trough with solvent

Different amino acids traveling down the paper at different speeds

Paper

Troughs with water and solvent to keep air moist

Figure 9–8. *Paper chromatography.* (*From Isaac Asimov,* The Intelligent Man's Guide to Science.)

guanine was equal to thymine plus cytosine in DNA (or to uracil plus cytosine in RNA). Furthermore, the number of adenine nucleotides was roughly equal to the number of thymine (or uracil) nucleotides and the number of guanine nucleotides equal to the number of cytosine nucleotides.

Furthermore, by breaking down nucleic acids carefully and observing the makeup of the fragments, it became clear in the early 1950's that there was no set order or periodicity to the arrangement of the nucleotides. Just as amino acids can (and do) occur in any order in proteins, so nucleotides can (and do) occur in any order in nucleic acids. For the same reason that no two proteins need be alike, so no two nucleic acids need be alike.

In 1953, two biochemists at Cambridge University, F. H. C. Crick and J. D. Watson, using X-ray diffraction data, deduced that molecules of nucleic acids in viruses (and presumably elsewhere) consisted not of one, but of two nucleotide strands. This double strand was arranged in a helix

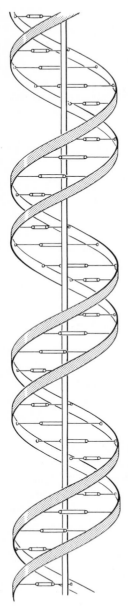

about a common axis; that is in the form of two interlocking, spiral staircases about the same central post [Figure 9–9]. The two strands were so arranged that the purines and pyrimidines of one faced the purines and pyrimidines of the other, each purine (or pyrimidine) being attached to the purine (or pyrimidine) opposite by a type of weak link called a *hydrogen bond* (Figures 9–10 and 9–11).

The hydrogen bond is only a twentieth as strong as the bonds that usually hold atoms together within a molecule. It is strong enough, even so, to hold the two strands in place. Yet it is also weak enough to break and allow the two chains to separate on occasion, without requiring more energy for the purpose than the cell can easily supply.

The distance between the strands is equal throughout. The gap is too narrow to allow two of the comparatively large purine molecules to face each other and yet too wide for two of the smaller pyrimidines to face each other. The only possibility that fits the facts is that all down the line of thousands of nucleotides, a purine on one strand faces a pyrimidine on the other and vice versa. This would at once account for the observation that the total number of purines in nucleic acids seems to equal the total number of pyrimidines.

Furthermore, if it is assumed that an adenine on one strand is invariably faced with a thymine on the other strand, while a guanine on one strand is invariably faced with a cytosine on the other strand, that would account for the additional observation that the number of adenines in the nucleic acids seem to equal the number of thymines, while the number of guanines seem to equal the number of cytosines.

None of this interferes with the randomness of the nucleic acid structure. Each strand, taken by itself, can have any arrangement of nucleotides. It is only with respect to each other that the strands

Figure 9–9. The nucleic acid double-helix. (From Ruth Moore, The Coil of Life.)

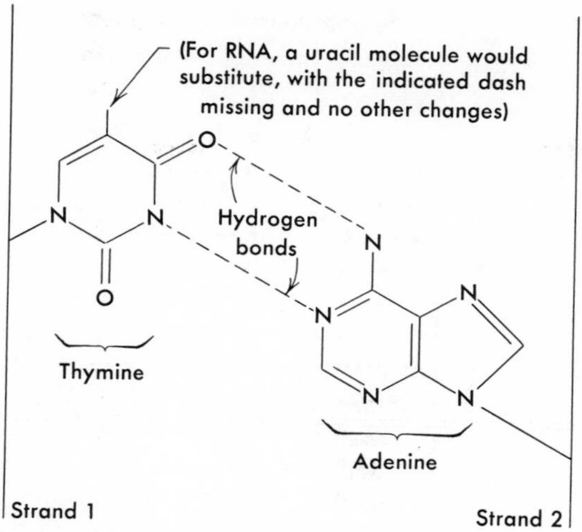

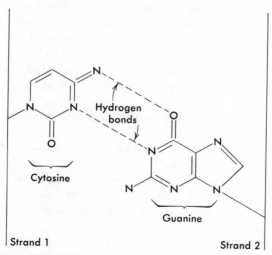

Figure 9–10. *The adenine-thymine combination.* (*From Isaac Asimov,* The Genetic Code.)

show anything other than randomness. The structure of one strand determines the structure of the other; they fit together like a plug and a socket or one jigsaw piece and its neighbor.

If we want to simplify the Watson-Crick picture to the fullest, we can let adenine be represented by *A* and thymine (or uracil, in RNA), its

Figure 9–11. *The guanine-cytosine combination.* (*From Isaac Asimov,* The Genetic Code.)

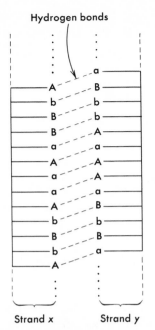

Figure 9–12. The double strand of nucleic acid (schematic).

invariable partner, by *a*; guanine by *B* and cytosine, its partner, by *b*. Now the double-stranded nucleic acid can be schematically represented, as you see in Figure 9–12, in which the helical shape is straightened out for the sake of convenience and the hydrogen bonds are represented by slanted, rather than horizontal, lines. Notice that the hydrogen bonds invariably connect an *A* with an *a* and a *B* with a *b*, but that the order of *A, a, B,* and *b* down either one of the strands is as random as I could make it.

The problem of replication of the nucleic acid now lends itself to a dramatic solution.

Suppose that conditions within the cell are such that the weak hydrogen bonds are broken and that the double helix of the nucleic acid separates into two single strands. Suppose, further, that each separate strand is surrounded by cell fluid which contains (as it does) a plentiful supply of individual nucleotides, or material out of which nucleotides can be formed on short notice.

These individual nucleotides are always (by blind movement) striking against the single nucleotide strands. If a thymine nucleotide strikes a section of the strand carrying an adenine nucleotide, it attaches itself by a hydrogen bond. If it strikes any other section, the hydrogen bond does not form. Similarly, a cytosine nucleotide will attach itself to a guanine nucleotide. The same is true in reverse in both cases.

In other words, A will fit itself to *a, a* to A; B to *b;* and *b* to B. When all the nucleotides are lined up, each to its natural mate, they are combined into a chain by the action of appropriate enzymes.

In short, strand *x* acts as a mold for the formation of an adjoining strand just like the strand *y* that left it. Similarly, strand *y* acts as a mold for the formation of an adjoining strand *x*. Each is the basis for a new double strand and the result is that two (each exactly like the first) exist afterward where only one double strand existed before.

Clear as this picture is, it is not without its problems. For instance, just how do the two nucleotide strands manage to separate? On a molecular scale, they make up a long and intimate union and it is not easy to see how there could be enough time for the two strands to get completely disentangled before starting to replicate. Furthermore, once loose, the individual strands ought easily to get twisted and fail to behave as proper molds.

A suggested possibility designed to get around this difficulty is that as the chains start separating at one end, the proper nucleotides start hooking on at once. The new joinings proceed down the line as the separation continues, and replication is complete the moment the disentanglement is. It is as though you imagined a slide-fastener opening and, as it opened, a new row of teeth joining to each of the separating halves so that when you completed the opening you found, not one open slide-fastener, but two identical closed ones.

Even this, however, does not answer the question of what it is that spurs the strands of the double helix into a separation in the first place when mitosis is beginning and not at other times. I know of no suggested answer to this question, but then how dull science would become if all questions had answers already known. Fortunately, on that basis, science will never be dull.

Using the Watson-Crick model of replication, one can see how a nucleotide strand might, on occasion, fail to replicate itself perfectly. For instance, A, rather than B, might just happen to wedge itself next to *b* and be built into a strand in that place before it could bounce away. The result would be a double strand with an unusual *b*–A combination in place of the ancestral *b*–B.

At the next replication, the *b* of the first strand would attach itself to a B as it should and become a double strand of the ancestral type. However, the interloping A of the other strand would attach itself to an *a*, forming an *a*–A double strand that would be unlike the ancestral type and which would replicate itself thereafter as an *a—A* until such time as another imperfect replication would involve it.

At any given point of the double strand, such imperfect replications would happen rarely. However, there are thousands of nucleotide pairs along the strand, and for an imperfection to take place somewhere among the thousands is perhaps not so rare.

Each imperfect replication would produce a slightly different nucleic acid. The slightly different nucleic acid would produce in its turn a slightly different enzyme which would introduce a slight difference into cell chemistry which, in the long run, might produce some deviation from the normal great enough to be seen by eye. An imperfection during nucleic acid replication would through a chain of circumstances, in other words, result in a mutation.

Another way of looking at it is to suppose that actually any nucleotide could join to any other, but that there is a minimum of energy that the body needs to supply to cause *A* and *a* to join, and *B* and *b* to join. In that case, a new strand in which *a* and *A* join and *b* and *B* join all down the line requires the least energy and is the most probable situation. Imperfectly matched strands require more energy to form, are therefore less probable, but can nevertheless be formed. The more imperfect the matching, the less probable it is, and the more infrequent the occurrence.

If, then, extraneous energy is supplied to the cell so that there is more energy available, imperfect matches (which are energy-consuming) are now more likely to take place. A supply of energy, in the form of elevated temperature, ultraviolet light, X-rays, radioactive particles, and so on, could, therefore, bring about an increase in the number of imperfect replications and, consequently, increase the rate of mutations.

Specific enzymes that are involved in the process of nucleic acid replication have been isolated. In 1955, the Spanish-born American biochemist, Severo Ochoa, isolated one (from a bacterium) which was involved in the formation of RNA from nucleotides.

By supplying such an enzyme with a particular nucleotide as raw material, Ochoa found he could form synthetic RNA made up entirely of nucleotides containing uracil groups or adenine groups and so on. He could even build up synthetic nucleic acids containing different nucleotides.

The next year, 1956, the American biochemist Arthur Kornberg did the equivalent with DNA. He isolated an enzyme that would form long nucleotide chains when the four different kinds of nucleotides which compose DNA were all present in solution. What's more, DNA was only formed when a sample of long-chain DNA was already present in the solution.

Apparently, the formation of the two varieties of nucleic acid proceeded in different fashion in the test tube. RNA was formed by the addition of one nucleotide to another, without the necessity of any guiding model. DNA, however, seemed to be formed by replication even in the test tube.

This seems reasonable, since it is DNA, not RNA, that is the characteristic nucleic acid of the genes and chromosomes. It is DNA, not RNA, that is *the* replicating material in cells.

This is not to say that the RNA molecule cannot engage in replication, for it can. The proof of this is simply that a number of the simpler viruses contain only RNA, and no DNA at all. One example of this is the well-known tobacco-mosaic virus, the first virus to be crystallized. When a tobacco-mosaic virus infests a cell of the tobacco leaf, it multiplies within that cell, and new virus molecules by the hundreds are formed. Each new molecule contains an RNA molecule different from any of the RNA molecules in tobacco but identical with the RNA of the original invading virus. The new RNA molecules could only have been formed by replication.

Nevertheless, life based upon RNA replication is evidently not as successful as life based upon DNA replication. Only the simpler viruses are examples of the former; the more complicated viruses and all cellular life, without known exception, are based upon DNA replication.

And yet all cellular life retains RNA, in addition to DNA, and every species has characteristic varieties of RNA. How are specific RNA molecules built up and preserved through generations without replication?

The answer seems to be that RNA molecules can be built up by using DNA as a model.

In that case, why is RNA needed at all? If it is merely a "copy-cat," what is it there for? Let's consider that next.

THE MESSENGER FROM THE NUCLEUS

The importance of RNA was certainly not underestimated in the days before the Watson-Crick model, even though it was known not to be the major component of chromosomes. If anything, it was overestimated because of the clear connection between RNA and protein synthesis.

The DNA concentration in the different cells of a particular organism seems to be a constant. Every cell, whether it is growing or not, whether it is constantly secreting material or not, has the same quantity of DNA. This is not surprising, since every cell has the same set of chromosomes, and it is there that the DNA is located. In fact, the sole exceptions are the egg cells and the sperm cells. They have only one of each pair of chromosomes, a half-set in other words, and to no one's surprise they contain only half the quantity of DNA contained in ordinary cells.

The RNA concentration in the different cells of a particular organism, however, varies over a wide range. Experiments dating back to the early 1940's have shown invariably that RNA concentration is higher where the rate of protein synthesis is higher. Growing cells are richer in RNA than are resting cells; a growing cell, after all, has to double its protein content between the time it is formed and the time when it is ready to divide again. When part of a tissue is growing and part is not, the RNA concentration is higher in the growing part.

Put all this evidence together and there seems to be no doubt that RNA is deeply involved in protein synthesis.

Since protein synthesis takes place principally in the cytoplasm [Figure 9–1], RNA should be found there, and indeed it is. In fact, the major portion of cellular RNA is in the cytoplasm, although no DNA at all is present there. This means that RNA must be passed out of the nucleus and into the cytoplasm as it is formed. Studies with the electron microscope have actually photographed material bulging out from the nucleus and being pinched off in the cytoplasm, and these "blebs" (as they have been uneuphoniously named) contain RNA.

RNA, then, picks up the genetic code from the DNA of the chromosome and carries the message into the cytoplasm, where it supervises the formation of protein. Earlier, I said that it looked as if the only function of any particular gene was to form a particular enzyme. This is still true, but it must not be thought that this takes place in a single stage. Rather, the particular gene (DNA) forms a particular RNA, which in turn forms the particular enzyme. This last step was also found to involve several stages.

THE SITE OF SYNTHESIS

The cytoplasm is by no means a smooth and homogeneous fluid; it is a complex system, containing thousands upon thousands of small bodies of various sizes, shapes, and functions.

The best known of these small bodies are called *mitochondria*, which we have already mentioned. There are also smaller particulates called *microsomes*, from Greek words meaning "little bodies," that are each about $\frac{1}{10,000}$ the size of mitochondria.

RNA turned out to be located in the microsomes, which proved rich in nucleic acid. In view of their RNA content, might they not be the site of protein synthesis?

This hypothesis was borne out by experimental evidence. Cells supplied with radioactive amino acids incorporated the acids into poly-peptide chains, so that the protein thereafter formed within the cell will turn out to be radioactive. If the cell is allowed to remain in contact with the radioactive amino acids for only a very short time and then immediately searched for radioactivity, only the proteins at the immediate site of protein formation should have been able to pick up the radioactivity. When this search was carried through, radioactivity was, in fact, found only in the microsomal fraction. The microsomes were therefore clearly the protein-factories of the cell.

The electron miscroscope now began to be focused on the microsomes. In 1953, the Romanian-born American biochemist George E. Palade found tiny particles densely distributed on the network of membranes associated with the microsomal fraction. By 1956, he had isolated these tiny particles (each about $\frac{1}{10,000,000}$ the size of a mitochondrion, and perhaps not much larger than an individual gene), and found that they contained just about all of the RNA in the microsomal fraction. In fact, as much as 90 per cent of the RNA in some cells is found in these numerous particulates, which are made up of RNA and protein, in about a 50-50 ratio. They came to be known as *ribosomes*.

RNA AT THE SITE

In the late 1950's, biochemists enthusiastically thought that in the ribosomes they had the important clue to the problem of protein synthesis. It was believed that each gene produced RNA by a Watson-Crick replication and that this RNA, after traveling into the cytoplasm, collected to form individual ribosomes.

This would mean that each different enzyme of the cell would be produced by some specific ribosome that had been formed by some specific gene. However the RNA molecules making up the ribosomes had a peculiar composition that weakened the whole idea.

DNA molecules, you see, vary markedly from species to species. Some species have DNA molecules that are rich in adenine but poor in guanine, the ratio being as high as 3 to 1; others have DNA molecules that are poor in adenine but rich in guanine, the ratio being as low as 1 to 3.

If the ribosomal-RNA is formed by the DNA of the chromosomes, it certainly ought to reflect these differences in base ratio—that is, if the Watson-Crick model of replication is correct. However, ribosomal-RNA does *not* reflect the varying ratio from species to species. In ribosomal-RNA, the four nucleotides are pretty evenly distributed, and so it was discovered in all the species of organisms tested.

Was the Watson-Crick model of replication wrong? Biochemists couldn't bring themselves to believe that. They sought the explanation, and by 1960 they had found it.

Ribosomes are the site of protein manufacture all right, but ribosomal-RNA is not the means by which this is done. Ribosomal-RNA does not carry the genetic code; it merely serves as the structural backbone of the ribosomes. It is something like a "key-blank," which can be made to fit any lock, provided it is ground into the proper shape.

There must then be another variety of RNA: one which *is* formed by Watson-Crick replication from the gene; one which *does* carry the genetic code; one which travels from the gene to the ribosome with the gene's "message."

This second variety of RNA is called, appropriately enough, *messenger-RNA*. (It is sometimes called *template-RNA*, a "template" being a mold which serves as the guide for the production of some specific shape.)

SETTING UP THE KEY

If the cell is tagged with radioactive carbon-14 atoms, they show up at once in messenger-RNA. Then, after a brief time, the radioactive atoms appear, scattered elsewhere, in the cell. From this, it can be deduced that the messenger-RNA, once formed, is quickly broken down into individual nucleotides, which are then put to a variety of uses in the cell.

Here, then, is the picture as it now stands:

1. The DNA of a particular gene manufactures a molecule of messenger-RNA by Watson-Crick replication. The messenger-RNA possesses a complement of the order of nucleotides in the DNA (except that there is uracil in all those places where thymine exists in DNA). Messenger-RNA, made up of perhaps as many as 1500 nucleotides, thus carries the genetic code of the gene that made it.

2. The messenger-RNA molecule travels into the cytoplasm and attaches itself to an unoccupied ribosome. The "blank" of the ribosomal-RNA, now combined with messenger-RNA, is "keyed in" and becomes capable of manufacturing a specific protein.

3. After a few protein molecules have been formed (or perhaps even after only one has been formed), the messenger-RNA breaks down, leaving the ribosome blank once again, ready to be "keyed in" for another protein, perhaps the same one as before, perhaps a different one. [Figure 9–13.]

BREAKING THE CODE—THE TRIPLETS

How does one go from a specific messenger-RNA to a specific polypeptide chain? At first glance, getting at the solution to this problem seems to be obscured by the same formidable obstacle referred to earlier. The nucleic-acid molecule is a "sentence" made up of four different "words," the nucleotides. The protein molecule is another "sentence" made up of twenty-two different "words," the amino acids. How can information carried by four different items suffice to explain what must be done by twenty-two different items?

This difficulty, which bothered many at first, is really no difficulty at all. That the thought even arises is only evidence that we are used to thinking of those codes in which a particular letter stands for some different letter, as in the cryptogram puzzles one finds in some newspapers. Thus, if in a particular cryptogram each letter were represented by the next letter in the alphabet, the word *protein* would be encoded as *qspufjo*.

And yet the most common codes we have by no means work in this fashion. We have, for instance, exactly 26 letters in the English alphabet. These 26 letters are sufficient to encode the more than 450,000 words in Webster's Third New International Dictionary (Unabridged). The ten symbols used in constructing numbers (nine digits and zero) are enough to encode an infinite set of numbers; in fact, two symbols, 1 and 0, would be enough to serve that same purpose, and do so in computers.

To make this possible, it is only necessary to agree to make use of the coding symbols, the letters of the alphabet or the numerals, in groups.

There are only 26 letters to be sure, but there are 26 x 26 or 676 possible two-letter combinations, 26 x 26 x 26 or 17,576 possible three-letter combinations, and so on. In the same way, there are only 9 possible one-digit numbers but 90 possible two-digit numbers, 900 possible three-digit numbers, and so on.

In passing from nucleotides to amino acids, therefore, we must abandon all thought of a one-to-one correspondence and take the nucleotides in multiple units. There are only 4 different nucleotides in messenger-RNA (or in the DNA of the gene), but there are 4 x 4 or 16 different dinucleotide combinations ("twins"), and 4 x 4 x 4 or 64 different trinucleotide combinations ("triplets"). These are all shown in Figure 9–14, where the four nucleotides are represented by their initials: U for uridylic acid, C for cytidylic acid, A for adenylic acid, and G for guanylic acid.

This at once raises a new problem. There are too few dinucleotides to account for the different amino acids, but too many trinucleotides. We simply can't do with too few, so that we have no choice but to go at least as far as the triplets.

That leaves us, however, with 64 triplets for 22 amino acids. Two possible ways out still remain. Perhaps 42 different triplets are "blanks," and are therefore to be ignored in the general coding. Or it may be that two

508

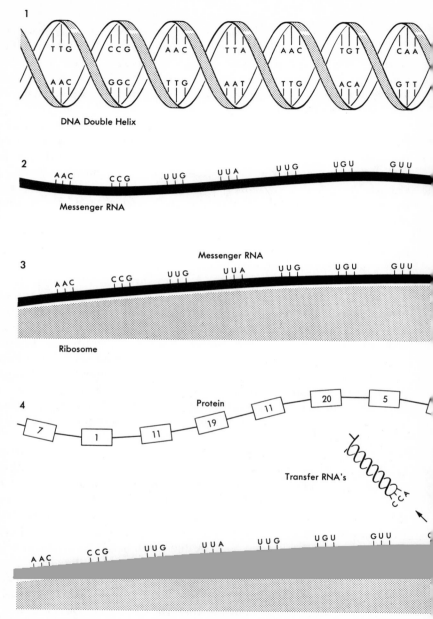

Figure 9–13. *Synthesis of protein begins with the genetic code embodied in DNA (1). The code is transcribed into messenger RNA (2). In the diagram it is assumed that the message has been derived from the DNA strand which begins at the far upper left of the diagram. The messenger RNA finds its way to a ribosome (3), the site of protein synthesis. Amino acids, indicated by num-*

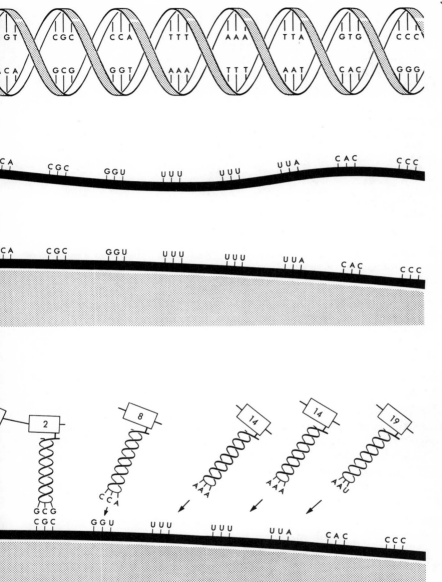

bered rectangles, are carried to proper sites on the messenger RNA by molecules of transfer RNA (small helical molecules). Bases are actually equidistant, not grouped in triplets, and mechanism of recognition between transfer RNA and messenger RNA is hypothetical. Linkage of amino acid subunits creates a protein molecule.

A		G		C		U	

4 nucleotides

AA	AC	GA	GC	CA	CC	UA	UC
AG	AU	GG	GU	CG	CU	UG	UU

16 dinucleotides ("twins")

AAA	ACA	GAA	GCA	CAA	CCA	UAA	UCA
AAG	ACG	GAG	GCG	CAG	CCG	UAG	UCG
AAC	ACC	GAC	GCC	CAC	CCC	UAC	UCC
AAU	ACU	GAU	GCU	CAU	CCU	UAU	UCU
AGA	AUA	GGA	GUA	CGA	CUA	UGA	UUA
AGG	AUG	GGG	GUG	CGG	CUG	UGG	UUG
AGC	AUC	GGC	GUC	CGC	CUC	UGC	UUC
AGU	AUU	GGU	GUU	CGU	CUU	UGU	UUU

64 trinucleotides ("triplets")

Figure 9–14. *Nucleotide combinations.* (*From John Abelson, "Transfer of Genetic Information,"* Science, *February 22, 1963. Reprinted by permission.*)

or even three different triplets all stand for the same amino acid. Experimental evidence has definitely decided in favor of the second alternative.

THE TRIPLET DICTIONARY

There still remains the question of the actual key of the code: which triplet stands for which amino acid?

The first breakthrough in this direction came in 1961 in what was perhaps the most important advance since the Watson-Crick model was proposed eight years earlier. The breakthrough was the result of an experiment by Marshall W. Nirenberg and J. Heinrich Matthaei at the National Institutes of Health.

They realized that in order to learn the key, it was necessary to start with the simplest possible situation—a nucleic acid made up of a chain of one single variety of nucleotide. Ochoa had already shown how such a chain could be built up with the help of the proper enzyme, so that polyuridylic acid, for instance, could be easily manufactured and used.

Nirenberg and Matthaei therefore added this acid to a system that contained the various amino acids, enzymes, ribosomes, and all the other components necessary to synthesize proteins. Out of that mixture tumbled a protein that was as simple as the RNA they had in the beginning. Just as the nucleic acid was all *uridylic* acid, so the protein was all *phenylalanine*.

This was important. Polyuridylic acid could be represented as UUUUUUUUUUUU. . . . The only possible triplet that can exist in such a chain is, of course, UUU. The only amino acid used in building the polypeptide chain was phenylalanine, although all the different amino acids were present and available in the system. The conclusion that can be drawn from this is that the triplet UUU is equivalent to the amino acid phenylalanine.

The first step had been taken toward the decoding of the genetic code: "UUU means phenylalanine" was the first item in a "triplet dictionary."

The next step was seized upon at once; a number of research groups swung into action, following the lead that had been given them. Suppose a polynucleotide is built up enzymatically out of a solution of uridylic acid to which a little adenylic acid has been added. The chain will consist mostly of U, with an occasional A appearing at random. The chain may then be, for instance, UUUUUUUUUAUUUUUUUUUAUUUUUU-AUUU. . . .

Such a chain would be made up of the following triplets: UUU, UUU, UUU, AUU, UUU, UUU, UAU, UUU, UUA, UUU. . . . The triplets are still for the most part UUU, but occasionally an AUU, UAU, or UUA will creep in. (These are the only three triplets that can be built from two U's and an A.)

Sure enough, the protein formed by such an "impure" polyuridylic acid turned out to be mainly phenylalanine, but with occasional "intrusions" of other amino acids. Three such "intruders" have been detected: leucine, isoleucine, and tyrosine. It seems clear that one of the three triplets AUU, UAU, or UUA stands for leucine, one for isoleucine, and one for tyrosine. Which is which, however, has not, at the moment of writing, been decided.

The best we can do is write UUA in parentheses (UUA), and permit that to signify the three different triplets that can be built from the two U's and an A, without even trying to specify the order. In that case our dictionary could read: "(UUA) means leucine, isoleucine, or tyrosine."

If instead of adenylic acid, a little cytidylic acid or a little guanylic acid is added to the original solution of uridylic acid, polynucleotides are built up containing triplets that are (UUC) and (UUG). Again, the parentheses mean that we are not specifying the exact order of the three nucleotides.

In both these latter cases, leucine can still be detected in the still chiefly phenylalanine protein that is produced. This can only mean that (UUA), (UUG), and (UUC) can all be translated as leucine—an example of several different triplets standing for the same amino acid. [Figure 9–15.]

The amino acid code as determined by researchers at the National Institutes of Health and New York University. [Sequence of nucleotides within code words was not determined experimentally except for tyrosine (AUU) by the New York University group.]

Amino acid	Code word	
	National Institutes of Health	New York University
Alanine	CCG	CUG CAG CCG
Arginine	CGC	GUC GAA GCC
Asparagine *	ACA	UAA CUA CAA
Aspartic acid *	ACA	GUA GCA
Cysteine †	UUG or UGG	GUU
Glutamic acid ‡	ACA AGA AUG	AAG AUG
Glutamine ‡	ACA	AGG ACA
Glycine	UGG	GUG GAG GCG
Histidine	ACC	AUC ACC
Isoleucine	UUA	UUA AAU
Leucine §	GUU CUU AUU (UUU)	UAU UUC UGU
Lysine	AAA AAC AAG AAU	AUA AAA
Methionine	UGA	UGA
Phenylalanine	UUU	UUU UUC
Proline	CCC CCU CCA CCG	CUC CCC CAC
Serine	UCG UUC UCC	CUU CCU ACG
Threonine	CAC CAA	UCA ACA CGC
Tryptophan	UGG	UGG
Tyrosine	UAU	AUU
Valine	UGU	UUG

* The NIH group cannot as yet determine whether ACA represents aspartic acid or asparagine. † It is not clear yet which of these possibilities is correct. ‡ The NIH group cannot as yet determine whether ACA represents glutamic acid or glutamine. § Poly U will serve as a template for leucine in the absence of phenylalanine.

Figure 9–15. The amino acid code as determined by researchers at the National Institutes of Health and New York University. (From John Abelson, "Transfer of Genetic Information," Science, February 22, 1963.)

IMPLICATIONS FOR THE FUTURE

It is possible that all this theoretical concern with the inside of the cell may end by introducing startling changes in man's way of life.

Actually, the practical side of these matters is just beginning to peep out at us. We are reaching the point where we can perhaps begin to turn from molecular hunting to molecular herding.

The human race did something like that, once, on a large scale. Carnivorous man was first a hunter, foraging for what game he could find and going hungry when he could not find it. At some stage, however, he learned that if he kept certain animals behind fences or under guard and fed them and took care of them, they would breed. Instead of going out to search for animals, his tame herds would produce animals for him. Some of these would serve to keep the herd going, while the surplus would serve as food. The food supply was made several times more secure and human civilization took a giant step forward. In the plant world, the same step was taken in passing from picking fruit off wild trees to the point where farmers deliberately planted orchards and fields of grain.

On a molecular scale, however, we are still hunters. If we want insulin, for instance (a protein manufactured by the pancreas which, if injected into the body, will temporarily restore to normal the limping cell machinery of people suffering from diabetes), we must look for it in its native haunt, the pancreas. The pancreases most available are those of slaughtered cattle and swine. However, each steer and each hog has one, and only one, pancreas so that there is an upper limit to the amount of insulin that can be available in a given time.

If we must have more insulin than that, we are out of luck!

But suppose we "tame" the nucleic acid molecules which, in the appropriate pancreas cells, supervise not merely the production of more nucleic acid like itself, *à la* Kornberg, but the manufacture of insulin molecules as well, what then? What if we put these nucleic acid molecules in a test tube at the right temperature and in the right surroundings and feed them amino acids (which can be prepared by the ton, if necessary)? There would then be no theoretical reason why we could not have any amount of insulin prepared for us. Or any other protein, following the same principle. We would be herding protein, not hunting it.

This is just at the edge of being something more than speculation and dream.

In some ways, our situation is analogous now to what it was in, say, 1820. In that year, one might have predicted that chemists would learn how to construct organic compounds; that they would then proceed to construct thousands upon thousands of such compounds that were not found in nature; that they would even construct particular compounds which they knew in advance would have certain uses. In that year, one might have predicted that within a century and a half, synthetic dyes, synthetic fibers, synthetic plastics, synthetic pharmaceuticals, never yet found in nature, and far superior to any natural product for those uses to which they were to be put, would come into common use. Such predictions, however, would have sounded irrationally fantastic.

Now we can predict the same thing, but on the subtler, more intricate, and more wonder-working level of protein chemistry. Is this also irrationally fantastic?

THE ULTIMATE GOAL

The prospects for the future are not only a matter of new chemical industries. Knowledge begets knowledge, and the promise of current research in molecular biology is fabulous.

If a particular messenger-RNA is isolated in quantity, and if the enzyme it controls is identified, that messenger-RNA might then be used to identify the particular DNA molecule that formed it. It would attach itself to that portion of an isolated chromosome which would be its exact complement and to which it could then attach strongly via hydrogen bonds.

The way would then be open for precise "chromosome mapping."

One may speculate about some far future in which individuals will routinely undergo "genic analysis," as nowadays they are routinely vaccinated. This could lead eventually to the development of a rational basis for eugenics—that is, for a course of action designed to remove deleterious genes and encourage the dissemination of desirable genes.

Perhaps massive genic analysis of the population will eventually give us the information that will lead to working out the physical basis for mental disease. We might even work out the gene combinations for such things as high intelligence, artistic creativity, and for all the things that are the essence of humanity in its highest and most idealized form.

Will the day come, then, when we can reach the ultimate goal of directing our own evolution intelligently and purposefully toward the development of a better and more advanced form of human life?

IN THE BEGINNING

These speculations carry us far into the future. But we must go back now to the beginning and finish filling in the picture of the way scientists believe life developed on earth.

From all that has been said concerning the long evolution of matter into the complex chemicals which serve as the building blocks for living matter, it would certainly seem that the one-celled animal is by no means the beginning of life. Primitive though a unicellular creature seems in comparison to a man, or even to an oyster, it must itself be the end product of a long line of evolution, of which no trace has been left.

Is there enough time for that? Astronomers currently believe that the universe is six billion, possibly even twelve billion, years old. The sun, and the solar system generally, is perhaps five billion years old.

These enormous lengths of time are not, however, fully available for the development of life on earth. Life on this planet could only have developed after the earth's solid crust was laid down and after the oceans were formed.

Yet even that limits us to no mean interval of time. The oldest rocks in the earth's crust (as judged by the slow radioactive decay of the uranium they contain) seem to be about three and a half billion years old. The crust (and presumably the ocean) is, therefore, that old at least.

The earliest fossils we know of are not much more than half a billion years old but, to be sure, the multicellular forms of life then existing were already quite advanced. Even if we double the time and allow a full billion years as the time during which multicellular life has been in existence, there would still be a gap of two and a half billion years between the time of the forming of earth's crust and its ocean and the development of multicellular life. Two and a half billion years during which cells might slowly evolve from subcellular life and in which those cells might develop and grow complex! Ample time, in all probability.

Once a nucleic acid molecule was formed, the equivalent of free-living genes (or tiny viruses) were present in the ocean, and they multiplied at the expense of the organic compounds that had been built up all about them by the action of the sun. These original viruses were not parasites, for there was nothing for them to be parasitic upon.

Eventually, an equilibrium was reached, for as the organic compounds which served as food were incorporated into the virus molecules, food concentration became progressively thinner, and it became ever more difficult for the original viruses to multiply. In the long run, the viruses could multiply no faster than the sun could build up a food supply for them; finally their numbers would become stabilized, and the ocean would contain a thin scum of life.

In the process of replication, there would be numerous imperfections, so that eventually there would be many strains of viruses, each with somewhat different capacities. Natural selection would play its role and those viruses which could compete most successfully with their fellows for the thinned food supply would replicate most frequently. Their strains would become predominant, and in this fashion there would be a slow evolution of viruses.

For instance, some viruses might stick together after replication, forming a string of individual nucleoprotein molecules. The individual molecules might specialize as a result of imperfect replications now and again, and pass on their specializations to descendants when the entire group replicated at once. Those groups in which the specializations best fitted, making the most efficient whole, multiplied at the expense of the other, less efficient nucleoprotein groups, and also, of course, at the expense of the individual nucleoprotein molecules. In this way, the equivalent of free-living chromosomes (or large viruses) then swarmed in the ocean.

The pressure of a depleting food supply must have placed a high premium of survival on any virus that managed to store food more efficiently than its neighbors. Some strains may have somehow developed a membrane about themselves through which small molecules like sugar and amino acid could pass, but not large molecules like starch and protein. Such viruses could absorb small molecules and build them up into large molecules which would be trapped within the membrane. They would have succeeded in accumulating a food supply and preserving it for their own exclusive use. They would survive at the expense of the naked, improvident viruses, and thus the ocean would become filled with very primitive cells.

These cells must have put the precellular organisms out of business. It is possible that some subcells survived by giving up the fight for an independent competition for food (so to speak) and turning to parasitism as an out. They let the cells collect the food, then invaded the cells and lived on them. Or, as may be more likely, none of the subcells survived, but some of the less efficient cells found the going too rough in competition with the more efficient ones and themselves turned to parasitism, gradually losing their cellular specializations and forming the whole gamut of parasitic viruses of today, from the Rickettsia on down. In either case, the hypothetical free-living viruses of the primordial ocean were wiped out.

Certain cells then developed chlorophyll, which enabled them to manufacture starch and proteins from the simple molecules all about them (from water, carbon dioxide and some minerals), using sunlight as the source of energy. These were the first plant cells.

Chlorophyll is a green compound (in fact, the name is from Greek words meaning "green leaf") which enables the plant to form carbohydrates, lipids and proteins from carbon dioxide, water and minerals by using the energy of sunlight. Animals cannot do this, because they lack chlorophyll. All green plants possess chlorophyll; all animals lack chlorophyll. Here is an example of a supremely important and apparently arbitrary chemical distinction that divides all life into two groups.

But what is the structure of chlorophyll? It consists of a porphyrin nucleus in which some of the atom groups attached to the ring have been changed somewhat as compared with heme,[1] and in which a magnesium atom replaces the iron atom. In short, chlorophyll is not something that is completely and amazingly different. It is merely a kind of "mutated heme." Some time in the far distant past, we can imagine, a cell in its

---

1. Heme is one of the constituents of hemoglobin. Ed.

manufacture of heme slipped up and manufactured chlorophyll instead, turned it to good use, and from that random occurrence, the plant kingdom developed. There may even have been a series of "pre-chlorophyll" stages in which successively more efficient molecules made use of the energy of sunlight, cells with the more efficient molecules replacing those with the less efficient by the usual forces of natural selection, until modern chlorophyll was developed.

We animals also displayed inventiveness in the same respect. The use of blood (which developed only ages after simple, multicellular life forms had come into being) made it possible to carry oxygen from the outer world to the cells inside the body with new and greater efficiency. For such oxygen transport, a new protein was developed which we call *hemoglobin*. Hemoglobin uses precisely the same prosthetic group, heme (which is named from the Greek word for "blood," by the way), that the cytochromes use. An old compound was thus adapted to a new purpose.

The same line of reasoning which makes it logical to suppose that lions and tigers evolved from a common ancestral species makes it also logical to suppose that the red of blood and the green of leaves evolved from a common ancestral chemical. Plant cells no longer depended on the slow formation of food by ultraviolet radiation, as had the preplants. Instead, plant cells manufactured their own food and could multiply to many times the numbers that had previously been possible. Those cells that did not develop chlorophyll could indirectly benefit also, for instead of scouring the ocean for the thinning supply of organic material, they could let the chlorophyll-containing cells manufacture food and then eat those cells, food and all. The development of chlorophyll, in short, made it possible for the ocean to grow thick with life.

Chlorophyll and the *photosynthesis* ("putting together by light") that it made possible inevitably altered the nature of the atmosphere. When carbon dioxide and water are combined to form starch by the action of chlorophyll, there is oxygen left over which is discharged into the atmosphere as oxygen gas. The carbon dioxide is slowly used up and oxygen takes its place. The growing amount of oxygen combines with the ammonia in the atmosphere and oceans. It combines with the hydrogen atoms in the ammonia molecule particularly, forming water and leaving the nitrogen atoms of the ammonia molecule to combine in pairs to form gaseous nitrogen and remain behind in the atmosphere. The oxygen also combines with any methane present to form carbon dioxide and water, the carbon dioxide being broken down further to oxygen.

The end result is the formation of our present atmosphere of oxygen and nitrogen.

An atmosphere containing free oxygen must have completely revolutionized life, since oxygen is a powerful chemical that requires careful handling. Life forms had to develop cytochromes,[2] for instance, to handle it. The only life forms that exist without cytochromes today are certain *anaerobic bacteria,* which live without oxygen and to which, indeed, oxygen is poisonous (one of the best known of these is the germ causing tetanus, or "lockjaw"). Perhaps the anaerobes are the last remnants of ultraconservative life which succeeded in filling an environmental niche that still resembles what all of the earth must have been like in the days before chlorophyll.

Chlorophyll was described as possibly having arisen from the "mutated heme" of a cytochrome molecule. This is one possible way of looking at the matter since almost all creatures, plant and animal alike, possess cytochromes, while only plants possess chlorophyll. It is the cytochrome that would thus seem more fundamental and the earlier formed.

However, if the oxygen atmosphere is indeed the result of photosynthesis, then perhaps matters are reversed. The heme of cytochromes may be a "mutated chlorophyll." In that case, animals must have developed the heme of cytochromes independently from some molecule (now lost) that was ancestral to both chlorophyll and heme, or else animals must be descended from some primitive plant forms.

In fact, in the last couple of years, the latter suggestion has indeed been made. The most primitive plant forms now existing are the blue-green algae. They are so primitive that they lack a clearly defined nucleus or chromosomes. The only other life forms that are simpler in structure are the bacteria and the viruses. (Sometimes the blue-green algae, bacteria and viruses are put into a separate kingdom on the basis of their primitive structure.)

It has been suggested that all creatures whose cells (whether one or many) possess well-developed nuclei are evolved from the blue-green algae (or from their ancestors, rather). These creatures with well-developed nuclear cells include other forms of algae, plus multicellular plants, plus all animals, whether one-celled or many-celled.

The original animal cells may be looked upon as offshoots of the early blue-green algae. The algae had developed first chlorophyll (which produced the oxygen), then cytochromes (which made use of it). Other plant cells kept both as they developed and specialized the nucleus. The original animal cells also developed the nucleus and kept the cytochromes, but abandoned the chlorophyll.

We may never know the details clearly or exactly how it all happened,

2. Cytochromes are enzymes which catalyze the transfer of hydrogen atoms from certain organic molecules in the cell ultimately to oxygen, leading to the formulation of water. Ed.

but this is one rough and very speculative picture of how it came about that a billion years ago the earth had its present atmosphere, plus an ocean full of cells, both plant and animal, so that the great adventure of multicellularity was ready to begin.

There seems a grim inevitability about the scheme presented in this chapter. Given a planet with the proper kind of chemistry, with a temperature that is neither too high nor too low, with an adequate air supply made up of the right gases, with an ocean, and with a sun of the right type shining down—and, most of all, given enough time!—it would seem that with grand relentlessness, first nucleic acid molecules would form, then cells, then chlorophyll (changing the atmosphere), then multicellular creatures.

Perhaps, if there is no other way of testing this scheme, we can test it by its inevitability. For instance, why does it not keep happening? Why is not life forming constantly? Why is it not forming right now in the ocean?

Ah, conditions have changed. Once nucleoproteins formed, they depleted the food supply and made less likely the independent formation of another series of nucleoproteins later on. Once the first cells appeared, then any single nucleic acid molecule that was miraculously formed was not the progenitor of a new race of life; it merely formed an article of food for some cell that blundered past. Finally, once chlorophyll started its work, oxygen filled the atmosphere, and with oxygen came the ozone layer high in the atmosphere. That meant the ultraviolet light of the sun was cut off, and that put a stop to the driving energy behind the build-up of life.

How Life Began *

by Earl A. Evans, Jr. (1960)

The study of fossils shows the presence of primitive life some 1,000,000,000 years ago. The earth itself was then five times as old. As for the written records of human life, they cover only about 6000 years. The precision of these figures is less important to our study than their relative dimension—time-spans so vast that they are hard to conceive. The transition from the first primitive cell to the nerve cells in the human cerebrum required only a fourth of the time nature took to form life from nonlife. The proudest human pedigree in the Almanach de Gotha can be

* From Earl Evans, Jr., "How Life Began," *Saturday Evening Post*, November 26, 1960. Reprinted by permission.

traced back no more than 100 generations, whereas a complete record would list more than 50,000,000 generations. Thus nature had ample time for the endless experimentation she required to create life. Like Darwinian evolution, the process of chemical evolution involved chance variation followed by selection and survival of forms able to exist in the environment of the moment. . . .

The evolutionary sequence has the beauty of logic. It can be traced through succeeding eras of enormous duration: the oxygen-free, hydrogenous atmosphere of the primitive earth permitting the synthesis and accumulation of organic substances as the precursors of living organisms; the interaction of these to form self-duplicating systems leading to the depletion of the organic molecules in the ocean and to the appearance of photosynthesizing organisms; finally, the emergence of oxygen-requiring organisms—each step irreversible and essential for evolution.

Where does this evidence lead us, if we accept the argument that human life, with its intelligence, its moral sense and spiritual aspirations arose from nonliving materials; that life is a spontaneous, irrepressible manifestation of matter; that, given the right environment, the necessary sources of energy and the suitable building stones, life inevitably results? The question prompts yet another question. What is matter?

Our reluctance to conceive of our physical being as nothing more than the matter of the inanimate world stems primarily from our consciousness of individual existence. We feel we are more than science can analyze. Yet every attempt to separate the psyche from the physical body has failed. If we modify or destroy our molecular fabric, we modify or destroy its psychic properties. The scientist concludes that they are but different aspects of the whole human. That life is a manifestation of matter can be expressed in a variety of vocabularies. No model, no concrete image of the nature of matter exists, and its behavior can be predicted and explained only in terms of mathematical equations. To say that matter is energy, or electricity, or a warpage of space reveals no more than to call it spirit, nature or God. Before such problems, the scientist tends only to retain his faith in reason and rational investigation, and to look for the next approximation rather than the last analysis.

The Effect of Natural Selection *

by Julian Huxley (1953)

"How can a blind and automatic sifting process like selection, operating on a blind and undirected process like mutation, produce organs like the eye or the brain, with their almost incredible complexity and delicacy of adjustment? How can chance produce elaborate design? In a word, are you not asking us to believe too much?" The answer is no: all this is not too much to believe, once one has grasped the way the process operates. Professor R. A. Fisher once summed the matter up in a pithy phrase— "Natural selection is a mechanism for generating an exceedingly high degree of improbability." Of course, this is in a sense a paradox, and the improbability is only an apparent one: but it is a useful shorthand phrase to denote the real improbability of the results having been produced in any other way than by means of natural selection. The clue to the paradox is time. The longer selection operates, the more improbable (in this sense) are its results; and in point of fact it has been operating for a very long time indeed. All living things are equally old—they can all trace their ancestry back some two thousand million years. With that length of time available, little adjustments can easily be made to add up to miraculous adaptations; and the slight shifts of gene frequency between one generation and the next can be multiplied to produce radical improvements and totally new kinds of creatures.

A little calculation demonstrates how incredibly improbable the results of natural selection can be when enough time is available. Following Professor Muller, we can ask what would have been the odds against a higher animal, such as a horse, being produced by chance alone: that is to say by the accidental accumulation of the necessary favorable mutations, *without* the intervention of selection. To calculate these odds, we need to estimate two quantities—the proportion of favorable mutations to useless or harmful ones; and the total number of mutational steps, or successive favorable mutations, needed for the production of a horse from some simple microscopic ancestor. A proportion of favorable mutations of one in a thousand does not sound much, but is probably generous, since so many mutations are lethal, preventing the organism living at all, and the great majority of the rest throw the machinery slightly out of gear. And a total of a million mutational steps sounds a great deal, but is probably an underestimate—after all, that only means one step every two thousand years during biological time as a whole. However, let us take these figures as being reasonable estimates. With this proportion, but without any selection, we should clearly have to breed a thousand strains to get one with one favorable mutation; a million strains (a thousand squared) to get one containing two favorable mutations; and so on, up to a thousand to the millionth power to get one containing a million.

Of course, this could not really happen, but it is a useful way of visualizing the fantastic odds against getting a number of favorable mutations in one strain through pure chance alone. A thousand to the millionth power, when written out, becomes the figure 1 with three million noughts after it: and that would take three large volumes of about five hundred pages each, just to print! Actually this is a meaninglessly large figure, but it shows what a degree of improbability natural selection has to surmount, and can circumvent. One with three million noughts after it is the measure of the unlikeliness of a horse—the odds against it happening at all. No one would bet on anything so improbable happening; and yet it *has* happened. It has happened, thanks to the workings of natural selection and the properties of living substance which make natural selection inevitable.

Let us look at the matter in a more realistic way. What natural selection actually *does* is to take a series of rare and abnormal events, in the shape of favorable mutations, and make them (or strictly speaking, the resultant mutant genes) common and normal. As we have just seen, the proportion of favorable to unfavorable mutations can be taken as one in a thousand. The frequency of mutation itself is much lower. It varies a good deal: for some genes it is as high as one mutation in fifty thousand, for others as low as one in several million. Perhaps we may take an average of one in a hundred thousand—after reproduction has provided a hundred thousand genes, you may expect that one of them will have mutated. So the actual frequency of favorable mutations will average only one in ten million available genes. Nevertheless, once a rare favorable mutation crops up, selection can and does convert it, in the course of a mere few hundreds of generations, into a normal character of the group; and so on with the next and the next.

In actual practice, the existence of sex renders the process enormously speedier; for it makes possible the combination of all the mutant genes that already exist in different individuals of a species, as well as those that may crop up at different times during the evolutionary future. Sex is thus an indispensable ally of selection in the business of effecting evolutionary change, for it enormously increases the possibility of securing favorable combinations of mutant genes; and it is no accident that sexual recombination has only been abandoned in forms for which stability is more immediately advantageous than change.

On the basis of our present knowledge, natural selection is bound to produce genetic adaptations: and genetic adaptations are thus presumptive evidence for the efficacy of natural selection.

We have got used to the idea—which was very disturbing when Lyell first advanced it over a hundred years ago—that the "eternal hills" are not eternal at all, but will all eventually be flattened out, while the materials of which they are made will be deposited to make new rocks elsewhere; and that this all takes place by the accumulation, over a very long lapse of time, of the scarcely perceptible changes that are always going on. We are now getting used to the even more disturbing idea that living nature (including our own nature) is not unchangeable, but can be and is molded into the strangest shapes; and that this takes place by the slow accumulation of the scarcely perceptible changes brought about by natural selection in each generation. In face of this realization, all the objections to a selectionist explanation of evolution that are based on the improbability of its results simply fall to the ground. In fact the shoe is now on the other foot. Improbability is to be *expected* as the result of natural selection; and we have the paradox that an exceedingly high apparent improbability in its products can be taken as evidence for the high degree of its efficacy.

The Thread of Life *

by Loren Eiseley (1960)

Since the first human eye saw a leaf in Devonian sandstone and a puzzled finger reached to touch it, sadness has lain over the heart of man. By this tenuous thread of living protoplasm, stretching backward into time, we are linked forever to lost beaches whose sands have long since hardened into stone. The stars that caught our blind amphibian stare have shifted far or vanished in their courses, but still that naked, glistening thread winds onward. No one knows the secret of its beginning or its end. Its forms are phantoms. The thread alone is real; the thread is life.

"Nevertheless, there is a goal," we seek to console ourselves. "The thread is there, the thread runs to a goal." But the thread has run a tangled maze. There are strange turns in its history, loops and knots and constrictions.

* From Loren Eiseley, *The Firmament of Time*, Atheneum, New York, 1960. Copyright 1960 by Loren Eiseley. Reprinted by permission.

Today the dead beasts decorate the halls of our museums, and that nature of which men spoke so trustingly is known to have created a multitude of forms before the present, played with them, building armor and strange reptilian pleasures, only to let them pass like discarded toys on a play-room floor. Nevertheless, the thread of life ran onward, so that if you look closely you can see the singing reptile in the bird, or some ancient am-phibian fondness for the ooze where the child wades in the mud.

One thing alone life does not appear to do; it never brings back the past. Unlike lifeless matter, it is historical. It seems to have had a single point of origin and to be traveling in a totally unique fashion in the time dimension.

Figure 9–16. *Drawing by Chas. Addams.* © 1963 *The New Yorker Magazine, Inc.*

I am, in point of fact, a particularly haughty and exclusive person, of preadamite ancestral descent. You will understand this when I tell you that I can trace my ancestry back to a protoplasmal primordial atomic globule.

W. S. Gilbert

Is the Whole More than the Sum of Its Parts?

Lines in Dispraise of Dispraise *
by Ogden Nash (1930)

I hereby bequeath to the Bide-a-Wee Home all people who have statistics
    to prove that a human
Is nothing but a combination of iron and water and potash and albumen.
That may very well be the truth
But it's just like saying that a cocktail is nothing but ice and gin and
    vermouth.
People who go around analyzing
Are indeed very tanalizing.
They always want to get at the bottom
Of everything from spring to ottom.
They can't just look at a Rembrandt or a Bartolozzi
And say, Boy! that's pretty hozzi-tozzi!
No, they have to break it up into its component parts
And reconstruct it with blueprints and charts.
My idea is that while after looking around me and even at me
I may not be proud of being a human
I object to having attention called to my iron and water and potash and
    albumen.
In the first place, it's undignified,
And in the second place, nothing by it is signified.
Because it isn't potash etcetera that makes people Republicans or Demo-
    crats or Ghibellines or Guelphs,
It's the natural perversity of the people themselfs.
No, no, you old analysts, away with the whole kit and kaboodle of you.
I wouldn't even make mincemeat to give to a poodle of you.

* From *The Face Is Familiar* by Ogden Nash. Copyright 1931 by Ogden Nash
Reprinted by permission of Little, Brown & Co., and J. M. Dent & Sons, Ltd.

The Problem of Problems *
by George Gaylord Simpson (1949)

What forces have been acting throughout the history of life? This is the problem of problems for evolution and for life itself.

Are these the same forces that act throughout the material universe, different in their results only to the extent that the matter on which they are acting is differently organized? Or do they include forces peculiar to and inherent in life, essentially different from the mechanistic forces of cause and effect in the purely material realm? Or, again, do they involve some principle that transcends both matter and life itself, a force that brings about progression toward foreordained goals, and that not only negates but also reverses materialistic cause and effect so that effect precedes cause?

Each of these questions has been answered affirmatively by one or another scientist or philosopher. They embody the three main possibilities in the solution of the problem of problems and each has its ardent supporters. The first solution is that of the materialist, or mechanist, or causalist—the terms are not synonymous but in this connection they designate roughly congruous philosophical points of view. The second solution is that of the vitalist, the student who maintains basic distinction between the principles and forces reflected in vital and those reflected in material phenomena. Adherents of the third solution are almost always also vitalists in this sense (although in fact there is no logical necessity for them to be such), and this solution has commonly been considered no more than another of the innumerable varieties of vitalism. It adds, however, an alternative that differs from vitalism alone as profoundly as vitalism does from materialism. If life, as the vitalists submit, has its own, nonmaterial forces, it does not necessarily follow that these tend toward a final goal or achieve a transcendental purpose. That life, or that the whole cosmos, does have such a finality is the view of the finalist.

There has been a great deal of misunderstanding and name calling among the materialists, vitalists, and finalists. The vitalists and finalists usually impute to the materialists the views that there is nothing in the universe but pure mechanism and that there is no essential difference between life and nonlife. Some materialists have accepted these imputations and have attempted to defend these propositions. Their purely or merely

* From George Gaylord Simpson, *The Meaning of Evolution.* Copyright 1949, 1951 by Yale University Press. Reprinted by permission.

mechanistic view was more popular a generation or two ago, arising in the first enthusiasm over the great nineteenth-century discoveries in science, than it is today, but it still has able supporters. Others have found this viewpoint indefensible, scientifically or philosophically, and have decided that they were, after all, vitalists rather than materialists, vitalists of some special sort, adherents of "emergent vitalism" or "monistic vitalism."

Now it is merely silly to maintain that there is no essential difference between life and nonlife. The vitalist is naïve indeed who proclaims the discovery of such a difference and concludes that because living organisms operate otherwise than if they were not alive, therefore materialism is wrong and life is a new element or a vital principle or what not. This, the common argument against materialism as it is defined by its opponents, is analogous to claiming that there is a "fire substance" or "fire principle" because fire has properties and phenomena peculiar to it and absent in nonfire. This, indeed, was the theory of our ancestors who gave the name "phlogiston" to the supposed fire element or principle,[1] very much in the same way that some vitalists have given names such as "entelechy" to a hypothetical life element or principle. We know that fire is not such a separate element or principle but that it is a process and organization of matter in which the behavior of matter is different from that in nonfire. Similarly, the materialistic view is not abandoned when life is seen as a process and organization in which the behavior of matter is different from that in its nonliving state.

Granting, as any reasonable person must, that there is an important difference between life and nonlife, you may, if you wish, call the different behavior of matter in life "vitalistic," but this accomplishes nothing and means nothing that was not already obvious. It is an example of the naming fallacy to call this an explanation or a contribution to evolutionary theory. The real issue between materialists and vitalists is not whether life has its own principles and functions, a proposition admitted by most modern materialists and (it sems to me) self-evident. This sort of "emergent" as opposed to "substantive" vitalism[2] is embraced within most of the less crude brands of materialism. A valid issue arises only as regards substantive or dualistic vitalism, the view that there is a life substance or principle which is independent of and in addition to the substances found in inorganic nature and the laws of their behavior. On the other hand, the distinctive claim of materialism is not stupid denial of special attributes

1. This fascinating aberration and the long struggle to correct it are worthy of close study by anyone interested in problems of truth and error. See any good history of science, such as A. Wolf, *A History of Science and Technology,* and *Philosophy in the Eighteenth Century,* Macmillan, New York, 1939.

2. See for example, C. D. Broad, *The Mind and Its Place in Nature,* Harcourt, Brace, New York, 1925.

to life, but the view that the substances and the principles involved in organic evolution are those universal in the material world and that the distinctive attributes and activities of life are inherent in its organization only.

This clarification is essential in the marshaling of evidence that may bear, one way or another, on choice between materialistic and vitalistic interpretation of the history of life. . . . The view of life as mere mechanism or automatism represents one extreme of the general field of materialism, an extreme now rather widely abandoned by materialists. It is compatible with materialism to hold that life and the universe involve more than objective material and mechanism. At one end of the enquiry the origin and nature of the existing materials and mechanisms have no evident materialistic explanation even though, given these as existing, their operation may be purely materialistic. At the other end the possibility is not excluded that, within the unique organization of matter that is life, these operations may develop choice, values, and moral judgment. The existence of these qualities is also a basic tenet of most vitalist theories, which tend, however, to maintain that they are inherent in, rather than developed by, life.

The distinctive finalist belief is that of progression toward a goal or end. The end is not reached, the finalist believes, because of what goes before, but what goes before is but a means for reaching the end. The end, although later in time, is, then, the cause and the preceding course of history is the effect. The history of life is thus to be viewed as purposeful, and (it almost goes without saying) finalists usually consider man as the essential feature of that purpose. Such a view is not necessarily inconsistent with materialism: the forces of history could be materialistic and yet have been instituted as a means for reaching an end. Finalists more commonly, however, hold subsidiary opinions that are vitalistic rather than materialistic. The purposefulness of evolution is considered inherent in, or special to, life, or an essential vital essence is seen as a means of reaching the goal.

Scientists and particularly the professional students of evolution are often accused of a bias toward mechanism or materialism, even though believers in vitalism and in finalism are not lacking among them. Such bias as may exist is inherent in the method of science. The most successful scientific investigation has generally involved treating phenomena *as if* they were purely materialistic, rejecting any metaphysical hypothesis as long as a physical hypothesis seems possible. The method works. The restriction is necessary because science is confined to physical means of subject is not physical and so not susceptible to its methods. Yet few investigation and so it would stultify its own efforts to postulate that its scientists would maintain that the required restrictions of their methods necessarily delimit all truth or that the materialistic nature of their hypotheses imposes materialism on the universe.

Biological Goals *

by Edmund W. Sinnott (1955)

The most difficult problem in biology is to discover how, in the development of an animal or plant, a precisely formed body and not a formless mass is produced.

Every living thing is an organized system, well named an "organism." Each part and function is so closely correlated with the rest that the whole develops in an orderly fashion toward the growth of the mature individual, as if to a "goal." If normal development is blocked or interrupted, the organism, particularly in its early stages and in lower types, shows a strong tendency to restore lost parts and regulate its growth processes so that it still can reach its goal. Each part, at least potentially, is able to restore the whole, so that the whole seems to be immanent in all its parts. . . .

Questions concerned with the familiar processes by which life is maintained—digestion, nutrition, respiration, and other activities in what is called metabolism—are difficult enough, but a direct attack on them through the techniques of chemistry and physics is making most encouraging progress. What guides the development of an animal or plant, however, so that a body is produced and not a formless mass, a body with a characteristic pattern and an organized structure, is far more difficult to understand. The same difficulty is present in such remarkable physiological regulations as those by which constant body temperature, blood sugar, and oxygen levels are maintained.

These problems have been actively considered by many, both biologists and philosophers. At the turn of the century a distinguished German embryologist, Hans Driesch, through the results of his experiments became so impressed with the difficulty of a purely mechanical explanation of developmental processes that he saw no alternative but to support the idea that there is a sort of non-material agent, or entelechy, in the organism, which directs its growth. Such a vitalistic philosophy is now held by few biologists and is quite unorthodox in a day when the whole tendency

* From Edmund W. Sinnott, The Biology of the Spirit.

of the science of life is to explain its facts in terms of the known laws of chemistry and physics. Nevertheless, the serious difficulties in accounting for the phenomena of development and embryology, first emphasized by the experiments and discussions of Driesch, have never been satisfactorily met. Along most other lines of attack on the problems of life, biologists have made notable advances, but this particular bastion has stubbornly resisted their assaults.

In simple terms, the problem is this: Every living thing is an organized system, each part and function closely correlated with all the others. This is evident in many ways, but most conspicuously in the processes of growth and development. A plant or animal grows in an orderly fashion to a precise bodily form characteristic of the particular species to which it belongs, as toward a precise "goal." Growth is so nicely coordinated —faster in some directions, slower in others—that in all parts it keeps step until the final end is reached. Differences within the organism arise in orderly progression. Development is determined, we know, by thousands of inherited genetic units in each cell, but their actions are so nicely coordinated in timing and degree that only rarely do the normal processes become confused. All this is hard enough to understand, but the difficulty is greatly increased by the results of experiments in blocking or interrupting the usual course of development. Under these conditions the organism and its parts show a surprising ability to restore what has been lost, rearrange its normal processes of growth, and produce at last, often by circuitous courses, a whole and typical individual. The whole seems somehow immanent in all its parts. This regulatory capacity is present to a greater degree in some forms than in others, and varies with conditions. It is more evident in early stages of development than in later ones, but it vividly demonstrates the action of a coordinating control of some sort, which guides development to a definite culmination. A living thing is an organized and self-regulating system, well named an "organism." This is a fundamental fact in biology and the basis for regarding the life sciences as distinct from the physical ones.

To explain all this in terms of the sort of mechanism with which physics and chemistry have made us familiar is exceedingly difficult. The biologist refuses to invoke a mystical agent like a psyche or entelechy to account for these puzzling facts, but he has little to offer in its place save a firm faith that something will ultimately be discovered that can give the answer. Sir Charles Sherrington has well expressed this attitude. "Chemistry and physics," says he, "account for so much which the cell does, and for so much to which years ago physical science could at that time offer no clue, that it is justifiable to suppose that the still unexplained residue of the cell's behavior will prove resoluble by chemistry and physics." [1] [Figure 9–17.] Despite our substantial knowledge of the activities that go on in the body, however, it must be admitted that as yet we have not even a plausible working hypothesis that can explain these regulated processes of development. This failure is embarrassing to biologists and is rarely discussed with the frankness it deserves. Nevertheless, at the very center of their science still sits this unsolved problem, a bolus of undigested, unexplained phenomena. . . .

SCRAMBLED SPONGES

Half a century ago an imaginative biologist, Professor H. V. Wilson, studying sponges at a seaside laboratory, performed an experiment simple enough in nature but so astonishing in its implications that it has become a classic in zoology. Sponges are widely varied in character. The familiar ones, which are dedicated to the bath or other cleaning processes, are simply the skeletons of the larger and more complex kinds from which all living tissue has carefully been removed. In the sponge as it grows in nature, the surfaces of this skeleton, inside and out, are covered with layers of living cells. Sponges are simple animals. They have no typical sense organs or muscles or stomachs such as are found in the higher forms of life. Some of them are hardly more than cellular colonies. They are far more complex, however, than single-celled animals like the amoeba, and in them are the beginnings of that organized division of labor that finally makes possible a complex animal like man.

The basic plan of a sponge is a tubular structure into which water is drawn through a multitude of tiny pores, passed along a canal or series of canals, and then forced out of a vent. This is accomplished by thousands of tiny cells that line the canals. Each cell has a little collar and within this a threadlike whip which is waved back and forth, more vigorously toward the vent than in the other direction, and thus draws water in and wafts it along. From this stream of water, as it passes by them, the cells absorb whatever minute bits of food it may contain. In addition to the collar cells there are several other kinds—the ones that compose the skin or epidermis, the ones of the middle layer, and the ones that form the tough skeleton by which the soft body of the sponge is supported.

---

1. *Man on His Nature*, Cambridge University Press, Cambridge, 1941, p. 135.

Figure 9–17. The Upjohn model of a human cell, showing the nucleus with its ropes of chromosomes in the center. The flattened white sacs rising from the nucleus probably carry chemicals from one part to another. The spiked sphere touching them is the centrosome, crucial in cell division. Above the centrosome and also to its right are blimp-shaped mitochondria which turn food into energy. (Courtesy of the Upjohn Co., Kalamazoo, Michigan.)

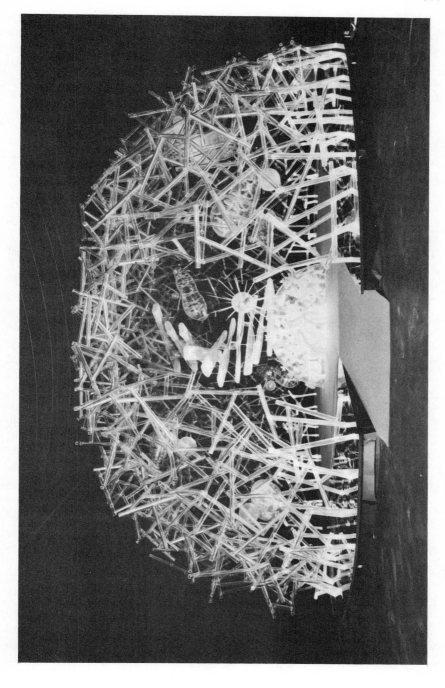

Some sponges have definite bodily forms, but in others the form is rather irregular. All, however, develop the typical cellular organization by which water is kept flowing through the whole. The species on which most of Professor Wilson's experiments were performed belongs to the genus *Microciona,* which makes bright red crustlike masses on the surfaces of stones and other objects covered by shallow water near the shore. The surface of this species is usually thrust up into irregular, thickish lobes.

Most sponges are able to produce new individuals by a process of regeneration, from pieces cut out of the old sponge. This is not surprising, since many simple animals can do so. But just how much cutting up will a sponge stand and still be able to reproduce a normal individual? No one, apparently, had tried to find an answer to this question before Professor Wilson undertook to do so. To break up the sponge as completely as possible without killing it, he first tried to pull it apart with needles. This was not thorough enough, so instead he subjected it to the most drastic physical mauling any living organism could face—he squeezed it through the tiny pores of fine-meshed bolting cloth. About a gram of clean, fresh sponge tissue was placed in a small cloth bag under water and gently jammed together with forceps. The structure of the sponge was thoroughly mashed by this treatment, and the softer portions were pushed out through the cloth's tiny pores. The sieve was so fine that to pass it the tissue had to be broken up into single cells or very small groups of cells. As they came through the bottom of the bag these thousands of minute bits, falling through the water down to the surface of a glass plate, looked like a small, reddish cloud. Surely this was the ultimate in the disintegration of an organism. What expectation could there be that a living thing, its delicate fabric thus so completely disorganized and its tiny cells all rent asunder, could survive?

But a sponge turns out to be an unexpectedly tough animal. Though its delicate structure may be thus drastically disintegrated, the cells that compose it, if the operation is skillfully done, come through alive. They are not closely held together as a plant's cells or those of a higher animal are, and thus slip apart rather easily. When they fall through the water to the plate under the filter bag, most of the cells, now free, begin to behave like tiny amoebae, gliding over the surface and sending out questing protoplasmic strands or filaments. Now comes the most remarkable part of the story. These minute individuals, released from the bonds that once held them together in this simple cellular society, seem not to cherish their newly found independence. When two approach each other and their filaments touch, the cells promptly fuse. The two fused cells in turn soon add a third to their company, and then another and another, until the host of separate cells, simple in character and all much alike, have come together into small roundish masses. All remaining stray cells are soon incorporated into nearby groups. Adjacent masses now fuse, and finally the whole body of cells, once completely separated, may produce a few large groups or even a single one, which finally forms a crust on the surface of the slide. As a school of fish or a flock of birds, scattered by the attack of an enemy, will mobilize into a compact group again, so these disunited cells, in a few hours or days, pull themselves together to form something not unlike the original body of which they all once were members. Soon in this mass the characteristic cellular differences appear —an outer epidermal layer, middle tissue, skeletal cells, and canals with their surfaces covered by collar cells and beating whips.

Whether, as the result of their drastic separation, all the cells revert to a primitive embryonic form from which any type of cell may later arise in the new sponge, or whether some of them may keep their original characters and assume their proper places once again, is not certain, but the new whole is built by the spontaneous assembling of individual units, each of which develops into a cell characteristic for the particular place it happens to occupy. These cells do not come together to form a disorganized throng such as one sees in certain kinds of abnormal plant or animal growth or in cultures of various tissues; but, like soldiers in a well-drilled military unit, when the bugle blows they assemble in orderly formation. In some way the structure of the whole sponge, with its specific pattern and its cellular variety, is immanent in each individual cell. How this is possible is a secret still locked in the innermost structure of protoplasm. Evidently each tiny living unit is a much more complex thing than it appears to be, for it bears within itself an image of the whole organism, the "goal" toward which its development persistently will move. . . .

What is the source of this remarkable trait in living things? For many years this has been the subject of active experiment and speculation. Great progress has been made in a knowledge of just what the changes are in cells and their constituents, in chemical substances and physical relations, which occur as an organism grows, and are especially evident when the course of its normal development is upset. The altering potencies of growing structures and the ways in which differences arise among them have been examined. There are encouraging results from explorations on the roles of many specific agencies and substances involved in embryology; and about some of these, notably genes, hormones, and various stimulators and inhibitors of growth, much is already known. What controls them, however, so that just the right amount is present at the right time and place, what regulates the developing system and holds it together as an organism against the disorganizing tendencies in lifeless matter, is still unknown. Here lies the great enigma of biology. Ingenious hypotheses of many sorts have been proposed, but none has pierced to the center of the problem or won wide acceptance. The organism has been analyzed with increasing precision into even smaller bits and processes, but how from these an organized and living whole arises still eludes us.

SELF-REGULATION AND NATURAL SELECTION

The evolutionist, however, has a suggestion here. Self-regulation, he says, is obviously advantageous. It restores lost or injured parts, maintains the organism's physical equilibrium, and in general keeps it going. Like all such useful traits in living things, it must have arisen through natural selection. Those individuals in which it was best developed had an advantage over their competitors, survived, and passed this trait on to their descendants. There is nothing more mysterious about self-regulation than there is about any other organic character.

This explanation, I think, is open to serious objection. In the first place, ability to regenerate lost parts is difficult to account for through natural selection since in most species a need for it would rarely be met. In nature there are few occasions when the ability of an isolated piece of stem to restore a root system, for example, would be called upon, and it is difficult to believe that this widespread ability has arisen through competitive selection. Furthermore, the most remarkable cases of regeneration, such as the growth of a whole tadpole from one of the first two cells of a frog embryo, or the reintegration of a sponge from its many scrambled cells, could have been discovered only by laboratory experiments and would almost never have occurred in nature.

Another argument against this idea is that the specific shapes of tissue and organ so characteristic of living things, which are the most obvious result of organized and regulated growth, seem rarely to be of value in evolution. In many cases—perhaps most—what favors survival seems rather an inherent toughness and adaptability, or success in producing many offspring. Can we imagine, for example, that the differences in leaf shape among our various species of maples and oaks have a great deal to do with the evolutionary success of these species? This success is rooted in something deeper, but it is these relatively unimportant shape differences that result from the regulated development we have been discussing. Surely natural selection can hardly be invoked to explain such regulation.

It must be recognized, of course, that organization occurs at many levels, and that in the higher ones part of it may be disturbed or even destroyed. In tumors or other types of abnormal growth, for example, the control that holds the organism together as an integrated system has been broken down. This is even more evident in tissue culture, where cells or bits of tissue may be made to grow indefinitely without showing any phenomena of organization above the cellular level. These cells are alive and active, however, though they have lost the capacity to build an organism. This does not mean that the basic organizing control over cellular metabolism and growth at this *lowest* level is not as active as ever. Without it, life would cease. Indeed, some self-regulation, though at different levels and to different degrees and subject to partial loss, seems present everywhere in living things and is an essential characteristic of life itself. Life *is* a state of dynamic equilibrium in which the organism, like a man walking on a tightrope, is continually adjusting itself to external circumstances. The constant physiological conditions it maintains and the precise forms it develops are the result of this. Without regulation life would not be life. In considering the origin of self-regulation, we therefore are not dealing with the sort of trait that has been developed by natural selection —such as a bird's ability to fly or the adaptation of flowers to insect pollination—but with a fundamental quality of all life. . . .

Something there surely is in any living thing which pulls dead, random matter into the form of an organized individual and holds it steadily there through material flux and change. The moment death occurs a radical alteration takes place, for this integrating force is gone and the bodily materials at once begin to break up into randomness again. This organizing power is life's peculiar quality. It never seems to arise spontaneously but is passed along from one organism to its offspring in a kind of apostolic succession, without a break. . . .

ANALYSIS AND SYNTHESIS

The scientist has blazed a wide trail into this tangled jungle of problems, though not into its very depths. His success in learning the secrets of the universe has been due in large measure to the most important of his methods, analysis. He breaks down his material into smaller and smaller pieces and thus divides to conquer. Modern biology began with the discovery that every individual is composed of tiny living units, the cells. Further analysis showed that the essential part of each cell is the nucleus, and within the nucleus were found the chromosomes. In the chromosomes are genes, each apparently a large protein molecule. Molecules are composed of atoms, and in atoms there are various "ultimate" particles—electrons, protons, mesons, and many more. Even energy is broken up into tiny units or quanta.

The continual aimless shuffling of physical particles tends to increase their randomness and to distribute them more evenly. As a result of this, says physics, the universe is steadily "running down"; its complex structures are disintegrating, and it is moving toward a state where all its material will be evenly dispersed and at the same temperature—a static death.

This drift toward disorganization has by no means broken nature down into uniformity, however, for in the world around us there are hosts of objects that are by no means random in their character. The simplest sort are those that show a definite relation between their parts and thus possess a form or pattern. This may be evident in external shape or in internal structure. In all such objects—crystals, clouds, trees, rocks, or animals—form has been impressed on formless, random matter. In the concern of science with analysis and its emphasis on unitary particles and their behavior, it has tended to lose sight of the processes of synthesis that produce form. In its preoccupation with the dancing, shuffling atoms, it has too much neglected how these particles actually behave. There must be forces that counteract the disorganizing ones we have described. Form is everywhere, and its significance has been pondered by thinkers from Aristotle to Goethe, Bergson, and Whitehead. Its importance has recently been emphasized anew by Whyte. "Beneath the apparently haphazard motions of particles," says he, "may lie a formative tendency toward simplicity of form, order and regularity." He suggests that "laws express the changes in whole patterns and cannot be expressed in terms of properties of single parts. . . . The only role of particles may be to mark and anchor patterns." [2] Form makes the particles, not particles the form.

The advantage of the analyst is obvious, for to dissect an object is far simpler than to find what formed it. Any youngster can take the mechanism of a clock apart, but to put it together again requires much skill. For this reason, doubtless, the analyzers, from Democritus and Newton to the atomic physicists of today, have been more successful than the synthesizers. The latter, to be sure, have framed many hypotheses. Whitehead regarded atoms as minute organisms. Karl Heim believes that a "wholeness tendency" must have a position of primacy in our philosophy. Whyte assumes a formativeness in nature. Others read there the designs of Universal Mind. L. J. Henderson believes that organization is a major category in nature, standing beside matter and energy. It is hard to subject such ideas to scientific study. They are difficult to take hold of, to test and measure. . . .

Are *all* forms, it now may be asked, evidence of purposive organization, of goal-seeking, or should we distinguish between inorganic and

2. Lancelot Law Whyte, *Accent on Form*, Harper and Brothers, New York, 1954, pp. 67, 63.

organic ones? Many philosophers are inclined to see a gradual transition between the simple, lifeless patterns of atom and crystal and the more complex ones of living things. A hydrogen atom with its single electron spinning around a nucleus is in a sense an organized system. In atoms with more electrons, the orbit of each has a definite relation to those of the others, and the organization is thus more complex. Whitehead saw no sharp distinction between these simple systems and far more complex ones, and was inclined to regard physics as the science that deals with minute organisms and biology as that which deals with larger ones. Molecules are patterned complexes of atoms, some of which can organize themselves into crystals possessing the most specific and constant forms in nature, almost limitless in number and variety. A crystal grows by the selective addition at its surface of particular kinds of molecules from its environment. It may even repair a broken portion of itself. No wonder that many have compared crystals to living organisms and have seen the same "formative tendency" in both. Some viruses may exist for long periods in "crystalline" form.

If this organic formativeness is essentially like that in living organisms, the basis for purposiveness and mind may exist far down in the lifeless world. *All* objects may thus have within them something of the psychical, as the philosophy of panpsychism maintains.

There is good reason, however, to believe that the sort of formativeness found in living things is really different from that in such lifeless ones as crystals. First, the crystal system is static. Its molecules are at rest. Whatever change there is results from the addition of new molecules along the crystal surface. A living organism, on the contrary, is in a continual state of change. Matter enters it and leaves it in a steady procession, and all sorts of processes go on within its cells. Unlike the rigid crystal, protoplasm is fluid in character. Despite this, the organism maintains its specific form—not as constant, to be sure, as that of a crystal, where all the faces and angles are determined with mathematical exactitude, but still so constant a pattern that each of the million kinds of living things may be recognized by its particular outer form and inner structure. An organism has a sort of fluid form like that of a waterfall, through which water ceaselessly is pouring but which keeps in its descent a definite pattern. The crystal's form results from the way its molecules are fitted tightly together, like pieces in a jigsaw puzzle; an organism's results from forces that control the molecules' fluid interactions and relations.

A second difference between crystal and organism is that crystals, like lifeless patterns generally, are fixed and changeless, whereas living things are changeful and creative. A crystal of sodium chloride two billion years ago was the same in form and structure, we are convinced, as is one today. Meanwhile the living world has arisen to its present high estate. To evolve is a trait of life, not of lifelessness. New things appear in life. Variation is the constant rule of living nature, and thence has come the upward course of evolutionary change with its high promise for the future.

What Is Life? *

by Michael Ovenden (1962)

It has been said that a living organism is different from a non-living body because "the whole is greater than the parts of which it is made." Even if the behavior of an individual cell of a living organism were understood, this would not mean that we could explain the organism as a whole—for example, a living cell cannot live if removed from the body of which it was a part. But a bit of a star cannot shine by itself, for if we took a piece of a star away, it would immediately evaporate into space and grow cold. The generation of energy inside a star depends upon there being the weight of the whole star outside the center. One part of the star interacts with another part. If we took a bit of matter from the center of a star and applied to it the same forces that it was subjected to inside the star, then it would shine; and, in the same way, a cell can be made to live and grow outside its original body if it is put in the right "culture medium," this medium imitating for the cell the conditions that the cell found in the living organism. In fact, the "whole being greater than the parts" is a commonplace of physics; in any physical system we have to consider both the nature of the parts and the interactions between them. In this sense, a watch is more than the sum of the cogs, springs and wheels of which it is made.

Or again, it has been suggested that the ability to heal itself after injury is a peculiar property of a living organism. But what would happen to a star if we removed a part of it? It immediately would resume its original spherical shape, and be a perfectly good star, albeit not as heavy as it was originally. The star would have "healed" itself. The reason that it does this is that the removal of part of the star destroyed the symmetry of internal forces in the star; those parts of the star at the edge of the cut were pushed (by the pressure of the stellar material) *from one side only,* so they moved until the pressure on both sides balanced. Something very similar, although rather more complicated, and more in the realms of

° From Michael Ovenden, *Life in the Universe.*

chemistry than physics, is true of the cells of my finger when I cut it, and this asymmetry of conditions leads to the organism's adjusting itself to a new symmetrical condition—i.e., healing itself. . . .

Yet, when all this has been said, there still remains the feeling that living things, as we find them on Earth, are somehow different from earthly non-living things. Part of this feeling is no doubt associated with the idea of *consciousness*. Consciousness is a very difficult idea to deal with scientifically, for while we have direct experience of our *own* consciousness, we can experience consciousness in other creatures only if we have some means of communication with them. In any case, it is doubtful that it can be said that the simplest undoubtedly living organisms have consciousness at all, so it is probably not a quality that distinguishes life from non-life. But there is more to the feeling of difference than this. I think it is that living things seem to have the ability to resist decay.

Non-living things seem always to tend to change from the more highly arranged state to the less highly arranged. A house of cards will fall down by itself, but if you throw a pack of cards into the air, you would be surprised if it fell down as a house of cards! On the other hand, the pattern or *structure* of a living thing seems to remain, even though the material of which the living thing is made changes. With the important exception of his brain, the matter of which a human being is made is being constantly replaced, yet he remains recognizably the same human being. . . . As an analogy to this property of living things, I have in mind a whirlpool. Water flows into one side of the whirlpool, and out of the other; yet the pattern of the whirlpool remains. Of course, the comparison is only superficial, for the structure of the whirlpool is maintained by forces outside it—the play of wind on water, and the distribution of rock —while a living thing has within its own make-up this ability to keep its structure while the material of which it is made changes.

Life Is a Stage in the Organization of Matter *

by George W. Gray (1937)

Perhaps the nearest we can come to a definition [of living matter] is to say that life is a stage in the organization of matter. The ascent of life is a hierarchy of organizations continually becoming more complex and more versatile. And so with the ascent of matter, from the single electron or proton to the numerous and enormously complicated colony of elec-

* From George W. Gray, *The Advancing Front of Science.*

trical particles which make up the bacterium—it too is a hierarchy of continually increasing complexity, of relationships, of organization.

Protons and neutrons, with their encircling electrons, associate together to form atoms, but their organization is too primitive to permit any behavior recognizable as life. The atoms, in their turn, group to form molecules of simple compounds—water, salts, carbon oxides—but again the grouping is too limited to operate in ways that class as animate. From these simple molecules more complicated ones are synthesized in nature's unresting crucible, sugars and other carbohydrates, fats and more intricate hydrocarbons. And somehow, in the melee, atoms get joined together in the distinctive patterns known as catalysts, of which the enzymes are a special class. The primitive catalysts may fabricate the first amino acids. Out of these essential acids they build the first proteins, simple ones at first. Proteins associate with other proteins, eventually they join as subgroupings of larger molecules to form what we imagine to be the first genes, and chains of these giant molecules line up or interweave and interlink as chromosomes. And so specialization develops, coordination evolves, the ability to duplicate the pattern, to divide, to multiply, to enter into a dynamic equilibrium of continually moving material and forces—life!

The Principle of Organization *

by Loren Eiseley (1946)

Men talk much of matter and energy, of the struggle for existence that molds the shape of life. These things exist, it is true; but more delicate, elusive, quicker than the fins in water, is that mysterious principle known as "organization," which leaves all other mysteries concerned with life stale and insignificant by comparison. For that without organization life does not persist is obvious. Yet this organization itself is not strictly the product of life, nor of selection. Like some dark and passing shadow within matter, it cups out the eyes' small windows or spaces the notes of a meadow lark's song in the interior of a mottled egg. That principle—I am beginning to suspect—was there before the living in the deeps of water.

The temperature has risen. The little stinging needles have given way to huge flakes floating in like white leaves blown from some great tree in open space. In the car, switching on the lights, I examine one intricate crystal on my sleeve before it melts. No utilitarian philosophy explains

* From Loren Eiseley, *The Immense Journey.*

a snow crystal, no doctrine of use or disuse. Water has merely leapt out of vapor and thin nothingness in the night sky to array itself in form. There is no logical reason for the existence of a snowflake any more than there is for evolution. It is an apparition from that mysterious shadow world beyond nature, that final world which contains—if anything contains—the explanation of men and catfish and green leaves.

Questions To Consider

Are viruses alive?

Can a process which is inevitable be said to take place by chance?

Earl Evans asks, "Where does this evidence lead us, if we accept the argument . . . that life is a spontaneous irrepressible manifestation of matter . . . ? The question prompts yet another question. What is matter?"

In Part 3, Victor Weisskopf mentioned three characteristics of atomic configurations: identity, stability, and regeneration. Are these same characteristics demonstrated by living matter?

Looking back we see that many of the questions which were asked in former parts about the nature of matter can be asked again in relation to the nature of life:

Is matter at the level of organization which we call life, substance or form?

Is the scientific explanation of living matter materialistic?

Can the order exhibited in the highly organized living molecule arise from disorder?

Is there any scientific evidence that living matter is organized on a different principle from non-living matter?

Does the emergence of life tell us anything about the nature of matter itself?

Suggestions for Further Reading

* Asimov, Isaac: *The Genetic Code*, The New American Library, 1962. An interesting account of the biochemistry of the cell and the molecular basis of heredity. The selection beginning on p. 496 was partially adapted from this book.

* Bonner, David M.: *Heredity*, Foundations of Modern Biology Series, Prentice-Hall, Inc., 1961. A more detailed and technical account of the biochemical basis of heredity.

* *Scientific American*, Editors of: *The Physics and Chemistry of Life*, Simon and Schuster, 1956. An outstanding collection of articles dealing with physics and chemistry of living matter: protein structure, cellular activities, heredity, photosynthesis, and theories of the origin of life.

* Swanson, Carl P.: *The Cell*, Foundations of Modern Biology Series, Prentice-Hall, Inc., 1961. This book is excellent supplementary reading covering in detail an area which we only had space to mention very briefly in these readings.

* Weidel, Wolfhard: *Virus*, Ann Arbor, 1959. A translation from the German original. Discusses the nature of viruses and their crucial place in solving the puzzle of complicated life processes.

* Paperback edition

10

Will Fallout Affect the Course of Evolution?

Recent experiments indicate that all exposure to X–rays and radioactivity will increase the mutation rate in human beings. Scientists agree that the large majority of mutations are detrimental although the small proportion of advantageous mutations provides the vehicle for evolution. They disagree, however, on the extent and importance of the increased rate from fallout. In the light of our present knowledge what action should be taken about the use of X–rays and testing of nuclear weapons?

Will Fallout Affect the Course of Evolution?

Introduction

IN THE PAST few decades science has caused a great revolution in the human condition. The study of the structure of matter has led to the discovery of vast sources of energy which mankind can release for his own destruction or to improve many aspects of his physical environment. The study of the basic molecules of living matter has led to the possibility of changing and directing man's genetic constitution and perhaps even his evolutionary development. Such powers are wonderful and frightening. The potential good can be turned into a disaster by small errors in judgment. A little mistake can affect the lives of hundreds of thousands of people.

One of the principal factors which contribute to errors in judgment is the great pressure in our society to exploit every scientific advance for practical ends as rapidly as possible. Within the past fifty years such pressure has resulted in a lack of proper caution in the use of X–rays, radium, insecticides, and such drugs as thalidomide.

The readings in this part raise the question of whether nuclear testing is another such mistake. In our haste to exploit the new energy sources are we doing irreparable damage to our genetic constitution and running up a heavy debt of suffering to be paid by future generations? The issue is complicated by political overtones and moral issues. It is further confused by the fact that the experts themselves do not agree on the dangers of speeding up the natural rate of mutation. Edward Teller points out that mutations are the vehicle for the evolutionary process. In the long run they have resulted in the many magnificent creatures which nature has produced. The waste, failure, and suffering which have been an inevitable corollary of this process cannot be eliminated without destroying the process itself. To think that they can be eliminated is a sign of immaturity, says Garrett Hardin, "Out of luxuriant waste, winnowed by selection, come designs more beautiful and in greater variety than ever man could plan." [1] Can we be sure, therefore, that an increase of a few per cent in the mutation rate of man will prove to be evil and destructive? Might it not actually speed the course of evolution?

Linus Pauling, on the other hand, says, "Natural selection is a cruel way, and man has now outgrown it." [2] The problem is not to be solved by increasing the mutation rate and thus increasing the number of defec-

---

1. See Garrett Hardin selection, p. 569.
2. See Linus Pauling selection, p. 578.

tive children born, but rather by finding some acceptable replacement for natural selection. This point of view is also supported by Steven Spencer who questions our moral right to accept the risk of damage to future generations.

In the face of such basic disagreement among the scientists themselves how can the ordinary citizen be expected to make a wise decision on the subject of nuclear testing? [3] In our democratic society the citizen carries the ultimate responsibility for such decisions. His inability to evaluate properly the scientific aspects of important current problems has led to grave concern on the part of many people that he will abdicate his right to self government unless he learns to deal effectively with these problems.

The controversy presented in these readings serves to illustrate the dilemma of the citizen in the new age of science. Does a knowledge of the principles of genetics and atomic science as well as the nature of the scientific process equip him better to deal with the problems of atomic testing than the man who has no such scientific knowledge? Is the real issue a scientific question at all or is it purely a political and moral one? And, finally, are these problems becoming so complex that the citizen has no choice but to leave the decisions up to the experts?

3. In Part 4 we saw a similar divergence of opinion among scientists concerning the use of the atomic bomb against Japan. In this case wartime secrecy prevented the citizen from assuming his normal role in influencing national policy.

Mutation and Natural Selection

Radiation and Human Mutation [*]
by H. J. Muller (1955)

The revolutionary impact on men's minds brought about by the development of ways of manipulating nuclear energy, both for destructive and for constructive purposes, is causing a public awakening in many directions: physical, biological, and social. Among the biological subjects attracting wide interest is the effect of radiation upon the hereditary constitution of mankind. This article will consider the part which may be played by radiation in altering man's biological nature, and also the no less important effects that may be produced on our descendants by certain other pertinent influences under modern civilization.

At the cost of being too elementary for readers who are already well informed on biological matters it must first be explained that each cell of the body contains a great collection—10,000 or more—of diverse hereditary units, called genes, which are strung together in a single-file arrangement to form the tiny threads, visible under the microscope, called chromosomes. [Figure 10–1.] It is by the interactions of the chemical products of these genes that the composition and structure of every living thing is determined. Before any cell divides, each of its genes reproduces itself exactly or, as we say, duplicates itself. Thus each chromosome thread becomes two, both structurally identical. Then when the cell divides, each of the two resulting cells has chromosomes exactly alike. In this way the descendant cells formed by successive divisions, and, finally, the individuals of subsequent generations derived from such cells, tend to inherit genes like those originally present. (Figure 10–2.)

However, the genes are subject to rare chemical accidents, called gene mutations. Mutation usually strikes but one gene at a time. A gene changed by mutation thereafter produces daughter genes having the mutant composition. Thus descendants arise that have some abnormal characteristic. Since each gene is capable of mutating in numerous more

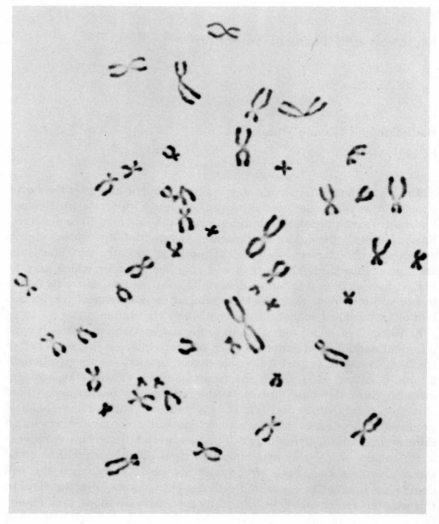

Figure 10–1. A metaphase plate of a cell from a human fibroblast in culture, showing 46 chromosomes. (Photograph courtesy of Dr. T. C. Hsu, M. D. Anderson Hospital and Tumor Institute, Texas Medical Center.)

or less different ways, the mutant characteristics are of many thousands of diverse kinds, chemically at least.

Very rarely a mutant gene happens to have an advantageous effect. This allows the descendants who inherit it to multiply more than other individuals in the population, until finally individuals with that mutant

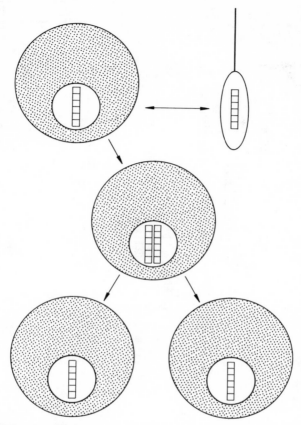

Figure 10–2. Fundamental process of heredity is depicted in highly schematic form. At the upper left is an egg cell: at the upper right, a sperm cell. Each contains a single chromosome bearing only six genes (square segments of chromosome). The chromosomes are paired in the fertilized egg (center), resulting in an organism with a complete set of genes from each parent. When the organism produces its own germ cells (bottom), the chromosomes are separated leaving one set of genes to combine with those of a mate in the new generation. Cells containing single chromosome strands are called haploid *(see top and bottom rows); those containing double strands are called* diploid *(see center cell).*

gene become so numerous as to establish the new type as the normal type, replacing the old. This process, continued step after step, constitutes evolution.

But in more than 99 per cent of cases the mutation of a gene produces some kind of harmful effect, some disturbance of function. This dis-

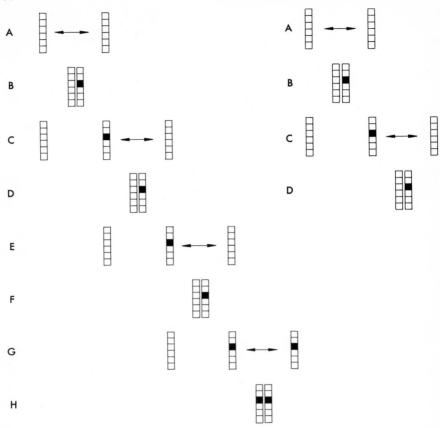

Figure 10–3. (Left) *Harmful recessive mutation may persist for generations before it is fully expressed. This diagram is based on the schematic chromosomes depicted in Figure* 10–2. *In row A the chromosomes of two parents are paired (arrow). In row B a gene of their offspring mutates (black). In row C the mutant gene has been transmitted to the next generation. If the mutant gene is recessive (i.e., if the corresponding gene of the paired chromosome has a dominant effect), it is masked. Here a new set of genes is introduced (second arrow) from another line of descent. In rows D, E, and F the mutant gene is passed along. In row G a mutant gene of the same character is introduced from still another line of descent. In offspring of this union (row H), the harmful effect of the paired recessive genes is expressed.*

Figure 10–4. (Upper right) *Harmful dominant mutation, as opposed to a recessive one, is quickly eliminated. Here the mutation (black) occurs at the same stage as in the diagram in Figure* 10–3. *It occurs in a germ cell, so its effect is not expressed in that generation. When the chromosome bearing the mutant gene is paired with another, however, the mutation is expressed in the offspring of the union.*

turbance is sometimes enough to kill with certainty any individual who has inherited a mutant gene of the same kind from both his parents. Such a mutant gene is called a lethal. More often the effect is not fully lethal but only somewhat detrimental, giving rise to some risk of premature death or failure to reproduce. (Figures 10–3 and 10–4.)

Now in the great majority of cases an individual who receives a mutant gene from one of his parents receives from the other parent a corresponding gene that is "normal." He is said to be heterozygous, in contrast to the homozygous individual who receives like genes from both parents. In a heterozygous individual the normal gene is usually dominant, the mutant gene recessive. That is, the normal gene usually has much more influence than the mutant gene in determining the characteristics of the individual. However, exact studies show that the mutant gene is seldom completely recessive. It does usually have some slight detrimental effect on the heterozygous individual, subjecting him to some risk of premature death or failure to reproduce or, as we may term it, a risk of genetic extinction. This risk is commonly of the order of a few per cent, down to a fraction of 1 per cent.

If a mutant gene causes an average risk of extinction of, for instance, 5 per cent, that means there is one chance in 20 that an individual possessing it will die without passing on the same gene to offspring. Thus such a mutant gene will, on the average, pass down through about 20 generations before the line of descent containing it is extinguished. It is therefore said that the "persistence" of that particular gene is 20 generations. There is some reason to estimate that the average persistence of mutant genes in general may be something like 40 generations, although there are vast differences between genes in this respect.

THE HUMAN STORE OF MUTATIONS

Observations on the frequency of certain mutant characteristics in man, supported by recent more exact observations on mice by W. L. Russell at Oak Ridge, indicate that, on the average, the chance of any given human gene or chromosome region undergoing a mutation of a given type is one in 50,000 to 100,000 per generation. Moreover, studies on the fruit fly *Drosophila* show that for every mutation of a given type there are at least 10,000 times as many other mutations occurring. Now since it is very likely that man is at least as complicated genetically as Drosophila, we must multiply our figure of $\frac{1}{100,000}$, representing our more conservative estimate of the frequency of a given type of mutation, by at least 10,000 to obtain a minimum estimate of the total number of mutations arising in each generation among human germ cells. Thus we find that at least every tenth egg or sperm has a newly arisen mutant gene. Taking the less conservative estimate of $\frac{1}{50,000}$ for the frequency of a given type of mutation, our figure would become two in 10.

Every person, however, arises from both an egg and a sperm and therefore contains twice as many newly arisen mutant genes as the mature germ cells do, so the figure becomes two to four in 10. When we say that the per capita frequency of newly arisen mutations is .2 to .4, we mean that there are, among every 10 of us, some two to four mutant genes which arose among the germ cells of our parents. This is the frequency of so-called spontaneous mutation, which occurs even without exposure to radiation or other special treatment.

Far more frequent than the mutant genes that have newly arisen are those that have been handed down from earlier generations and have not yet been eliminated from the population by causing death or failure to reproduce. The average per capita frequency of all the mutant genes present, new and old, is calculated by multiplying the frequency of newly arisen mutations by the persistence figure.

The greatly simplified diagram (Figure 10–5), in which we suppose the frequency of new mutations in each generation to be .2 and the persistence to be only four generations, shows why this relation holds. We start with 10 individuals. Let us suppose that in this first generation eight persons contain no mutant genes while each of the other two has one newly arisen mutant gene. In the second generation these two mutant genes are passed along and two new ones are added to the group, making the total frequency $\frac{4}{10}$. By the fourth generation the frequency is $\frac{8}{10}$. After that the frequency remains constant because each mutant gene lasts only four generations and is assumed to be replaced by a normal gene.

Of course in any actual case neither the multiplication nor the distribution of mutant genes among individuals is as regular as in this simplified illustration, but the general principle holds. However, as previously mentioned, the persistence of mutant genes is of the order of 40 generations, instead of only four. Thus the equilibrium frequency becomes not $\frac{8}{10}$ but 8. In other words, each person would on the average contain, by this reckoning, an accumulation of about eight detrimental mutant genes.

It happens that this very rough, "conservative" estimate, made by the present writer six years ago, agrees well with the estimate arrived at a few months ago by Herman Slatis, in a study carried out in Montreal by a more direct method. His method was based on the frequency with which homozygous abnormalities appeared among the children of marriages between cousins.

The eight mutations estimated above, it should be understood, do not

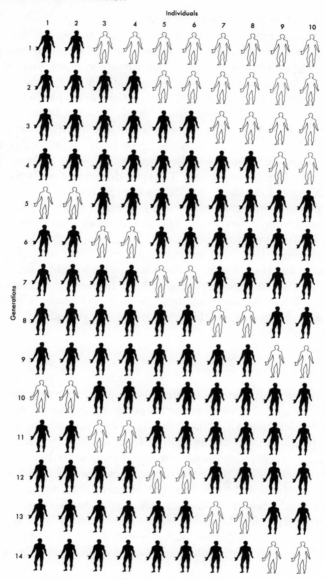

Figure 10–5. *Equilibrium is attained by recessive mutant genes under the conditions assumed here. The first assumption is that in each generation (horizontal rows) two new mutant genes (shaded figures) arise among ten individuals. The second assumption is that each line of descent bearing the mutant gene dies out four generations after the mutation has occurred. In the diagram this extinct line is then replaced by a new one. Thus after three generations the number of individuals bearing a mutant gene is stabilized at eight out of ten.*

include most of the multitude of more or less superficial differences, sometimes conspicuous but very minor in the conduct of life, whereby, in the main, we recognize one another. The latter mutations probably arise relatively seldom yet become inordinately numerous because of their very high persistence. Thus the value that we arrive at for the frequency of mutant genes depends very much upon just where the line is drawn in excluding this mutational "froth." As yet little attention has been given to this point. The number eight, at any rate, includes only mutant genes which when homozygous give rather definite abnormalities. In the great majority of cases these genes are only heterozygous and usually are but slightly expressed. Yet they do become enough expressed to cause, in each individual, his distinctive pattern of functional weaknesses, depending upon which of these mutant genes he contains and what his environment has been. The influence of environment on gene expression is often important.

Even the genes that give only a trace of detrimental effect, or are detrimental only when homozygous, play an important role, because of their high persistence and consequent high frequency. When conditions change, certain combinations of these genes may occasionally happen to be more advantageous than the type previously prevailing, and so tend to become established.

THE EFFECTS OF MUTANT GENES

In general each detrimental mutant gene gives rise to a succession of more or less slight impairments in the generations that carry it. Even if only slightly detrimental, it must finally result in extinction. Moreover, even though an individual suffers less from a slightly detrimental gene than from a markedly detrimental or lethal one, nevertheless the slightly detrimental gene, being passed down to a number of individuals which is inversely proportional to the amount of harm done to each individual, occasions a total amount of damage comparable to that produced by the very detrimental gene. Although each of us may be handicapped very little by any one of our detrimental genes, the sum of all of them causes a noticeable amount of disability, which is usually felt more as we grow older.

The frequency of mutant genes levels off at an equilibrium only when conditions for both mutation frequency and gene elimination have remained stable (or have at any rate fluctuated about a given average) for many generations. During such a period about as many mutations must be eliminated as are arising per generation. If, however, the mutation rate or the average persistence or both changed significantly because of increased radiation or a change in environmental conditions which made mutant genes more or less harmful than previously, then the frequency would move toward a new level. But it would be a long time before the new equilibrium was reached. If the average persistence of mutant genes was 40 generations, the new equilibrium would still be very incompletely attained after 1000 years.

THE EFFECTS OF RADIATION

We may next consider how a given dose of ionizing radiation would affect the population. Such radiation, when absorbed by the germ cells of animals, usually induces mutations which are similar to the spontaneous ones. They are induced at a frequency which is proportional to the total amount of the radiation received, regardless of the duration or time-distribution of the exposure. Russell's data on mice—the nearest experimental object to man that has been used in such studies—show that it would take about 40 roentgen units [1] of radiation to produce mutations in them at a frequency equal to their spontaneous frequency. If the frequency of spontaneous mutations is two new mutations per generation among each 10 individuals, a dose of 40 roentgens, by adding two induced mutations to the two spontaneous ones, would result in a total mutation frequency of four new mutations per generation among 10 individuals. Now assuming the total mutant gene content is eight per individual to begin with, the radiation dose would raise this figure from 8 to 8.2, an increase of only 2.5 per cent. This effect on the population would ordinarily be too small to produce noticeable changes in important characteristics. One must also bear in mind that an actual mean change in a population may be masked by the great genetic differences among individuals and by differences in environment between two groups that are to be compared. These considerations explain why even Hiroshima survivors who had been relatively close to the blast, and who may have absorbed several hundred roentgens, showed no statistically significant increase in genetic defects among their children. However, offspring of U.S. radiologists who (judging by the incidence of leukemia) probably were exposed during their work over a long period to about as much radiation as these Hiroshima survivors, do show a statistically significant increase in congenital abnormalities, as compared with the offspring of other medical specialists. This was recently established in a study by Stanley Mecht and Philip Lawrence.

---

1. A roentgen unit is a measure of the quantity of absorbed radiation as defined by the amount of ionization produced. One roentgen will produce ions carrying one electrostatic unit of electricity in one cubic centimeter of dry air. Ed.

The toll taken by mutant genes upon the descendants of exposed individuals is spread out over more than a thousand years—40 generations. It is too small to be demonstrable in any one generation of descendants. In the first generation of offspring of a population exposed to 40 roentgens, where the induced mutation rate is .2 per individual and the average risk of extinction for any given mutant gene is $\frac{1}{40}$, the frequency of extinctions occasioned by these mutant genes would be $\cdot\frac{2}{40}$ or $\frac{1}{200}$. This would mean, for example, that in a total population of 100 million some 500,000 persons would die prematurely or fail to reproduce as a result of having mutant genes that had been induced in their parents by the exposure. Moreover, a much larger number would be damaged to a lesser extent. The total of induced extinctions in all generations subsequent to the exposure would be .2 times 100 million, or 20 million, and the disabilities short of extinction would be numbered in the hundreds of millions. And yet the amount of genetic deterioration in the population due to the exposure would be small in a relative sense, for the induced mutations would have added only 2.5 per cent to the load of mutant genes already accumulated by spontaneous mutation.

The situation would be very different if the doubling of the mutation frequency by irradiation in each generation were continued for many generations, say for 1500 years. For after 1500 years the mutant gene content would have been raised from eight to nearly 16 per individual. Along with this doubled frequency of detrimental genes there would of course be a corresponding increase in the amount of disability and in the frequency of genetically occasioned extinction of individuals.

It is possible that all this would be ruinous to a modern human population, even though in most kinds of animals it could probably be tolerated. For, in the first place, human beings multiply at a low rate which does not allow nearly as rapid replacement of mutant genes by normal ones as can occur in the great majority of species. Secondly, under modern conditions the rate of human multiplication is reduced much below its potential. Thirdly, the pressure of natural selection toward eliminating detrimental genes is greatly diminished, under present conditions at least, through the artificial saving of lives. Under these circumstances a long-continued doubling of the mutation frequency might eventually mean, if the situation persisted, total extinction of the population. However, we do not now have nearly enough knowledge of the strength of the various factors here involved to pass a quantitative judgment as to how high the critical mutation frequency would have to be, and how low the levels of multiplication and selection, to bring about this denouement. We can only see that danger lies in this direction, and call for further study of the whole matter.

BOMB EFFECTS

In the light of the facts reviewed, we are prepared to come to some conclusions concerning the problem of the genetic effects of nuclear explosions. Let us start with the test explosions. J. Rotblat of London has estimated that the tests of the past year approximately doubled the background radiation for the year, in regions of the earth remote from the explosions. In the U. S. they raised the background radiation from about .1 to about .2 of a roentgen for the year. The natural background radiation of about .1 roentgen per year causes, we estimate, about 5 per cent of the spontaneous mutations in man. Hence a doubling of it would cause a rise of the same amount in the occurrence of new mutant genes. Although this influence, if continued over a generation, would induce an enormous number of mutations—of the order of 20 million in the world population of some two billion—nevertheless the effect, in relation to the already accumulated store of detrimental mutations, would be comparatively small. It would raise the per capita content of mutant genes at most by only a few tenths of 1 per cent.

Much more serious genetic consequences would follow from atomic warfare itself, in the regions subject to the fall-outs of the first few days. As for regions remote from the explosions (say the Southern Hemisphere), Rotblat and Ralph Lapp have reckoned that a hydrogen-uranium bomb like those tested in the Pacific would deliver an effective dose of about .04 roentgen throughout the whole period of radioactive disintegration. Thus, 1500 such bombs would deliver about 60 roentgens—an amount which might somewhat more than double the mutation frequency for one generation. Since there would be relatively little residual radioactivity in these remote regions after the passage of a generation, and since it is scarcely conceivable that such bombing would be repeated in many successive generations, it seems probable that most of the world's inhabitants below about the Tropic of Cancer would escape serious genetic damage. However, they would be likely in the course of centuries to become contaminated by extensive interbreeding with the survivors of the heavy irradiations in the North. For although an attempt might be made to establish a genetic quarantine, this would, for psychological reasons, be unlikely to be maintained with sufficient strictness for the hundreds of years required for the success of such a program.

In the regions subject to the more immediate fall-outs, pattern bombing could have resulted in practically all populous areas receiving several thousand roentgens of gamma radiation. Even persons well protected in shelters during the first week might subsequently be subjected to a pro-

tracted exposure adding up to some 2500 roentgens. Moreover, this estimate fails to take into account the soft radiation from inhaled and
ingested materials which under some circumstances, as yet insufficiently
dealt with in open publications, may become concentrated in the air,
water or food and find fairly permanent lodgment in the body. Now
although some 400 roentgens is the semilethal dose (that killing half its
recipients) if received within a short time, a considerably higher dose
can be tolerated if spread out over a long period. Thus it is quite possible
that a large proportion of those who survive and reproduce will have
received a dose of some 1000 to 1500 roentgens or even more. This
would cause a 12-fold to 40-fold rise in the mutation frequency of that
generation.

Such an increase, assuming that the population was already loaded
with an accumulation of mutant genes amounting to 40 times the annual
spontaneous mutation rate, would at one step cause a 30 to 100 per cent
increase in the mutant gene content. In fact, the detrimental effect would
be considerably greater than that indicated by these figures, because the
newly added mutant genes, unlike those being "stored" at an equilibrium
level, would not yet have been subjected to any selective elimination in
favor of the less detrimental ones. It can be estimated that this circumstance might cause the total detrimental influence to be twice as strong
for each new mutant gene, on the average, as for each old one. Therefore
the increase in detrimental effect would be between 60 and 200 per cent.

Owing to these circumstances, an effect would be produced similar to
that of a doubled accumulation of genes, such as we saw would ensue
from a doubled mutation frequency after about a thousand years of repetition. Thus offspring of the fall-out survivors might have genetic ills twice
or even three times as onerous as ours.

The worst of the matter is that the effects of this enormous sudden
increase in the genetic load would by no means be confined to just one
or two generations. Here is where the inertia of mutant-gene content,
which in the case of a moderately increased mutation frequency works to
spread out and thus to soften its impact, now shows the reverse side of its
nature: its extreme prolongation of the effect. That is, the gene content is
difficult to raise, but once raised, it is equally resistant to being
reduced.

Supposing the average content of markedly, detrimental genes per
person to be only doubled, from 8 to 16, more than 50 per cent of the
population would come to contain a number of these mutant genes (16 or
more) that was as great or greater than that now present in the most
afflicted 1 per cent, . . . When we consider the extent to which we are
already troubled with ills of partly or wholly genetic origin, especially as

we grow older, the prospect of so great an increase in them in the future is far from reassuring.

It is fortunate, in the long run, that sterility and death ensue when the accumulated dose has risen beyond about 1000 to 3000 roentgens. For the frequency of mutations received by the descendants of an exposed population is thereby prevented from rising much beyond the amount which we have here considered. This being the case, it is probable that the offspring of the survivors, even though considerably weakened genetically, would nevertheless—some of them—be able to struggle through and re-establish a population which could continue to survive.

Yet, supposing the population were able to re-establish its stability of numbers within, say, a couple of centuries, what would be the toll among the later generations in terms of premature death and failure to reproduce? If 40 roentgens produce .2 new mutant genes per person, then 1000 roentgens must on the average add five mutant genes to each person's composition. All of these five genes must ultimately lead to genetic extinction. But if, to be conservative, we suppose that two to three genes, on the average, work together in causing extinction, we reach the conclusion that, in a population whose numbers remain stable after the first generation following the exposure, there will ultimately be about two cases of premature death or failure to reproduce for each first-generation offspring of an exposed individual.

If, however, the descendants multiply and re-establish the original population size in a century or two, then the number of extinctions will be multiplied also. Over the long run the number of "genetic deaths" will be approximately twice as large, altogether, as the population total in any one generation. The future extinctions would in this situation be several times as numerous as the deaths that had occurred in the directly exposed generation.

Even though it is probable that mankind would revive ultimately after exposure to radiation, large or small, let us not make the all-too-common mistake of gauging whether or not such an exposure is genetically "permissible" merely by the criterion of whether or not humanity would be completely ruined by it. The instigation of nuclear war, or indeed of any other form of war, can hardly find a valid defense in the proposition, even though true, that it will probably not wipe out the whole of mankind.

RADIATION FROM OTHER SOURCES

It is by the standard of whether individuals are harmed, rather than whether the human race will be wiped out, that we should judge the propriety of everyday practices that may affect the human genetic constitution. We have to consider, for one thing, the amount of radiation which the population should be allowed to receive as a result of the peacetime uses of atomic energy.

How much effort, inconvenience and money are we willing to expend in the avoidance of one genetic extinction, one frustrated life and other partially frustrated lives, not to be beheld by us? Shall we accept the present official view that the "permissible" dose for industrially exposed personnel may be as high as .3 roentgen per week, that is, 300 roentgens in 20 years—a dose which would cause such a worker to transmit somewhere between .5 and 1.5 mutations per offspring conceived after that time?

Exactly the same questions apply in medical practice. A U. S. Public Health survey conducted three years ago showed that at that time Americans were receiving a skin dose of radiation averaging about two roentgens per year per person from diagnostic examinations alone. Of course only a small part of this could have reached the germ cells, but if the relative frequencies of the different types and amounts of exposure were similar to those enumerated in studies recently carried out in British hospitals, we may calculate that the total germ-cell dose was about a thirtieth of the total skin dose, namely, about .06 roentgen per person per year. This is about 12 times as much as the dose that had previously been estimated to reach the reproductive organs of the general population (not the hospital population) in England. However, the U. S. is notoriously riding "the wave of the future" in regard to the employment of X-rays; it is still expanding their use rapidly, while other countries are following as fast as they can.

Now this dose of .06 roentgen per year, the only estimate for the U. S. that we have, is of the same order of magnitude (perhaps twice as large) as the annual dose received in the U. S. over the past four years from all the nuclear test explosions. It seems rather disproportionate that so much furor should be raised about the genetic effects of the latter and so little about the former.

The writer's personal conviction is that, at the present stage of international relations or at least at the stage of the past several years, the tests have been fully justified as warnings and defensive measures against totalitarianism, despite the future sacrifices that they inexorably bring in their train, although it is to be hoped that this stage is now about to become obsolete. On the other hand, it seems impossible to find justification for the large doses to which the germ cells of patients are exposed in medical practice. It would involve comparatively little care or expense to shield the gonads or take other precautions to reduce the dose being received by the reproductive organs and other parts not being examined.

And the deliberate irradiation of the ovaries to induce ovulation, and of the testes to provide an admittedly temporary means of avoiding pregnancies, should be regarded as malpractice.

We must remember that nuclear weapons tests and possibly nuclear warfare may be dangers of our own turbulent times only, whereas physicians will always be with us. It is easier and better to establish salutary policies with regard to any given practice early than late in its development. If we continue neglectful of the genetic damage from medical irradiations, the dose received by the germ cells will tend to creep higher and higher. It will also be joined by a rising dose from industrial uses of radioactivity. For the industrial and administrative powers-that-be will tend to take their cue in such matters from the physicians, not from the biologists, even as they do today. It should be our generation's concern to take note of this situation and to make further efforts to start off the expected age of radiation, if there is to be one, in a rational way as regards protection from this insidious agent, so as to avoid that permanent, significant raising of the mutation frequency which in the course of ages could do even more genetic damage than a nuclear war.

CHEMICAL AGENTS

Radiation is by no means the only agent that is capable of drastically increasing the frequency of mutation. Diverse organic substances, such as the mustard gas group, some peroxides, epoxides, triazene, carbamates, ethyl sulfate, formaldehyde and so forth, can raise the mutation frequency as much as radiation.

The important practical question is: to what extent may man be unwittingly raising his mutation frequency by the ingestion or inhalation of such substances, or of substances which, after entering the body, may induce or result in the formation of mutagens that penetrate to the genes of the germ cells? As yet far too little is known of the extent to which our genes, under modern conditions of exposure to unusual chemicals, are being subjected to such mutagenic influences.

A surprising recent finding by Aaron Novick and Leo Szilard at the University of Chicago is that in coli bacteria the feeding of ordinary purines normal to the organism more than doubled the spontaneous mutation frequency, while methylated purines, and more especially caffeine (as had been found by other workers), had a much stronger mutagenic effect. Thus far, however, caffeine has not proved mutagenic in fruit flies, although it is possible that it is destroyed in their gut. In Novick and Szilard's work compounds of purines with ribose (e.g. adenosine) counteracted the mutagenic effect of the purines. Furthermore, adenosine and guanosine even acted as "antimutagens" when there had been no addition of purines to the nutrient medium, as though a considerable part, about a third, of the spontaneous mutations were being caused by the purines naturally present in the cells. This work, then, indicates both the imminence of the mutagenic risks to which we may be subject and also the fact that means of controlling these risks and, to some extent, even of controlling the processes of spontaneous mutation themselves, are already coming into view.

Other large differences in the frequency of so-called spontaneous mutations were found in my studies in 1946 on the mutation frequencies characterizing different stages in the germ-cell cycle of the fruit fly. Moreover, J. B. S. Haldane, dealing with data of others, adduced some evidence that the germ cells of older men have a much higher frequency of newly arisen mutant genes than those of young men. If this result for man, so different from what we have just noted for fruit flies, should be confirmed, it might prove to be more damaging, genetically, for a human population to have the habit of reproduction at a relatively advanced age than for its members to be exposed regularly to some 50 roentgens of ionizing radiation in each generation.

It is evident from these varied examples that the problem of maintaining the integrity of the genetic constitution is a much wider one than that of avoiding the irradiation of the germ cells, inasmuch as diverse other influences may play a mutagenic role equal to or greater in importance than that of radiation.

The view has been expressed that, since some chemical mutagenesis and even radiation mutagenesis occur naturally, the effects of such normal processes should cause us no great concern. Aside from the fact that not everything that is natural is desirable, we must always be conscious of the hazards added by civilization. Certain civilized practices, such as the use of X-rays and radioactivity (and possibly reproduction at an advanced age or the drinking of coffee and tea), are causing genetic damage to be done at a significantly more rapid rate than in olden times.

RELAXED SELECTION

It is evident that the rate of elimination of mutant genes is just as important as the mutation frequency in the determination of the human genetic constitution. What we really mean here, of course, is "selective" elimination. The importance of this distinction is seen in the fact that in the ancestors of both men and mice much the same mutations must have occurred, but that the different conditions of their existence—the ever more mousy living of the mouse progenitors and the manlier living of the pre-men—caused a different group of genes to become selected from out of their common store.

A very distinctive feature of our modern industrial civilization is the tremendous saving of human lives which would have been sacrificed under primitive conditions. This is accomplished in part by medicine and sanitation but also by the abundant and diverse artificial aids to living supplied by industry and widely disseminated through the operation of modern social practices. The proportion of those who die prematurely is now so small that it must be considerably below the proportion who would have to be eliminated in order to extinguish mutant genes as fast as new ones arise. In other words, many of the saved lives must represent persons who under more primitive conditions would have died as a result of genetic disabilities. Moreover, the genetically less capable survivors apparently do not have a much lower rate of multiplication than the more capable; in fact, there are certain oppositely working tendencies.

It is probably a considerable underestimate to say that half of the detrimental genes which under primitive conditions would have met genetic extinction, today survive and are passed on. On the basis of this conservative estimate we can calculate that in some 10 generations, or 250 to 300 years, the accumulated genetic effect would be much like that from exposure of a population to a sudden heavy dose of 200 to 400 roentgens, such as was received by the most heavily exposed survivors of Hiroshima. If the techniques of saving life in our civilization continue to advance, the accumulation of mutant genes will rise to ever higher levels. After 1000 years the population in all likelihood would be as heavily loaded with mutant genes as though it were descended from the survivors of hydrogen-uranium bomb fall-outs, and the passage of 2000 years would continue the story until the system fell of its own weight or changed.

The process just depicted is a slow, invisible, secular one, like the damage resulting from many generations of exposure to overdoses of diagnostic X-rays. Therefore it is much less likely to gain credence or even attention than the sensational process of being overdosed by fall-outs from bombs. This situation, then, even more than the danger of fall-outs, calls for basic education of the public and publicists, if they are to reshape their deep-rooted attitudes and practices as required.

It is necessary for mankind to realize that a species rises no higher, genetically, and stays no higher, than the pressure of selection forces it to, and that it responds to any relaxation of that pressure by sinking correspondingly. It will in fact take as much rope in sinking as we pay out to it.

The policy of saving all possible genetic defectives for reproduction must, if continued, defeat its own purposes. The reason for this is evident as soon as we consider that when, by artificial devices, a moderately detrimental gene is made less detrimental, its frequency will gradually creep upward toward a new equilibrium level, at which it is finally being eliminated anyway at the same rate as that at which it had been eliminated originally, namely, at the rate at which it arises by mutation. This rate of elimination, being once more just as high as before medicine began, will at the same time reflect the fact that as much suffering and frustration (except insofar as we may deaden them with opiates) will then be existing, in consequence of that detrimental gene, as existed under primitive conditions. Thus, with all our medicine and other techniques, we will be as badly off as when we started out.

Not all genetic disabilities, however, would simply be made less detrimental. Some of them would be rendered not detrimental at all under the circumstances of a highly artificial civilization, in the sense that they were enabled to persist indefinitely and thus to become established as the new norm of our descendants. The number of these disabilities would increase up to such a level that no more of them could be supported and compensated for by the technical means available and by the resources of the social system. The burden of the individual cases, up to that level, would have become largely shifted from the given individuals themselves to the whole community, through its social services (a form of insurance), yet the total cost would be divided among all individuals and that cost would keep on rising as far as it was allowed to rise.

Ultimately, in that Utopia of Inferiority in the direction of which we are at the moment headed, people would be spending all their leisure time in having their ailments nursed, and as much of their working time as possible in providing the means whereby the ailments of people in general were cared for. Thus we should have reached the acme of the benefits of modern medicine, modern industrialization and modern socialization. But, because of the secular time scale of evolutionary change and the inertia which retards changes in gene frequency, this condition would come upon the world with such insensible slowness that, except for a few long-haired cranks who took genetics seriously, and perhaps some archaeologists, no one would be conscious of the transformation. If it were called to their attention, they would be likely to rationalize it off as progress. It is hard to think of such a system not at length collapsing, as people lost the capabilities and the incentives needed to keep it going. Such a collapse could not be into barbarism, however, since the population would have become unable to survive primitive conditions; thus a collapse at this point would mean annihilation.

COUNTERMEASURES

There is an alternative policy, and I am hopeful it will be adopted. The alternative does not by any means abandon modern social techniques or call for a return to the fabulous golden age of noble savages or even of rugged individualism. It makes use of all the science, skills and genuine arts we have, to ameliorate, improve and ennoble human life, and, so far as is consistent with its quality and well-being, to extend its quantity and range. Medicine, especially that of a far-seeing and a promoting kind, seeking actively to foster health, vigor and ability, becomes, on this policy, more developed than ever. Persons who nevertheless had defects would certainly have them treated and compensated for, so as to help them to lead useful, satisfying lives. But—and here is the crux of the matter—those who were relatively heavily loaded with genetic defects would consider it their obligation, even if these defects had been largely counteracted, to refrain from transmitting their genes, except when they also possessed genes of such unusual value that the gain for the descendants was likely to outweigh the loss. Only by the adoption of such an attitude towards genetics and reproduction, an attitude seldom encountered as yet, will it be possible for posterity indefinitely to sustain and extend the benefits of medicine, of technology, of science and of civilization in general.

With advance in realistic education should come a better realization of man's place in the great sweep of evolution, and of the risks and the opportunities, genetic as well as nongenetic, which are increasingly opening up for him.

It is evident from these considerations that the same change in viewpoint that leads to the policy of voluntary elimination of detrimental genes would carry with it the recognition that there is no reason to stop short at the arrested norm of today. For all goods, genetic or otherwise, are relative, and, so far as the genetic side of things is concerned, our own highest fulfillment is attained by enabling the next generation to receive the best possible genetic equipment. What the implementation of this viewpoint involves, by way of techniques on the one hand, and of wisdom in regard to values on the other hand, is too large a matter for treatment here. Nevertheless, certain points regarding the genetic objectives to be more immediately sought do deserve our present notice.

For one thing, the trite assertion that one cannot recognize anything better than oneself, or in imagination rise above oneself, is merely a foolish vanity on the part of the self-complacent. Among the important objectives to be sought for mankind are all-around health and vigor, joy of life and longevity. Yet they are far from the supreme aims. For these aims we must search through the most rational and humane thought of those who have gone before us, and integrate with it thinking based on our present vantage point of knowledge and experience. In the light of such a survey it becomes clear that man's present paramount requirements are, on the one hand, a deeper and more integrated understanding and, on the other hand, a more heartfelt, keener sympathy, that is, a deeper fellow-feeling, leading to a stronger impulse to cooperation—more, in a word, of love.

It is wishful thinking on the part of some psychologists to assert that these qualities result purely from conditioning or education. For although conditioning certainly plays a vital role, nevertheless *Homo sapiens* is both an intelligent and a cooperating animal. It is these two complex genetic characteristics, working in combination and serviced by the deftness of his hands, which above all others have brought man to his present estate. Moreover, there still exist great, diverse and numerous genetic differences in the biological bases of these traits within any human population. Although our means of recognition of these genetic differences are today very faulty and tend to confound differences of genetic origin with those derived from the environment, these means can be improved. Thus we can be enabled to recognize our betters. Yet even today our techniques are doubtless more accurate than the trials and errors whereby, after all, nature did manage to evolve us up to this point where we have become effective in counteracting nature. Certainly then it would be possible, if people once became aware of the genetic road that is open, to bring into existence a population most of whose members were as highly developed in regard to the genetic bases of both intelligence and social behavior as are those scattered individuals of today who stand highest in either separate respect.

If the dread of the misuse of nuclear energy awakens mankind not only to the genetic dangers confronting him but also to the genetic opportunities, then this will have been the greatest peacetime benefit that radioactivity could bestow upon us.

Design Emerges from Blind Waste *
by Garrett Hardin (1959)

CAN GENETIC DAMAGE BE PROVED?

In 1946, shortly after the explosion of the atomic bombs over Hiroshima and Nagasaki, there was appointed one of the most unusual commissions ever to be set up: the Atomic Bomb Casualty Commission, a field agency of the United States National Academy of Sciences. One of the principal jobs of this commission was to try to determine the genetic effects of the bombs. A sensible-enough assignment this appeared to be, on the surface, yet it was a foregone conclusion—known to every geneticist in advance —that: (1) the bombs undoubtedly caused genetic damage, (2) the commission would fail to find evidence of such damage.

These statements raise arresting questions. How do we know Fact 1? How can we be so sure of Fact 2? If Fact 2 is true, is Fact 1 to be relied on? If the assignment was certain to fail, why embark on it?

The last question should perhaps be answered first—it involves only politics. We *had* to appoint the commission. We Americans were the ones who had done the damage, who had subjected civilians to a devastating, destructive force the like of which had never before been known. As a matter of decency we had to at least face what we had done, to study the results as carefully as possible. We had to appoint the commission, even though some of its assignments were doomed to failure. And failure was what its genetic investigations ended in. The commission's reports, issued many years later, when shorn of numerous and justifiable qualifications, add up to just what had been expected: no provable significant genetic effect of the bombing; nevertheless, a firm belief that such effects had been produced.

How can these diverse statements be reconciled within the framework of a genuinely critical science? In the interest of posterity we must see how.

RADIATION AND POSTERITY

Early attempts to arouse the public to the genetic dangers of radiation met with an opposition, the vigor of which was not to be explained by the purely intellectual issues involved. Men who insisted that atomic bombs endangered all mankind were openly accused of sympathy with the enemy. The reasons for these accusations are part of the history of post-World War II anti-intellectualism, but we will not go into them here. Disbelief in the genetic danger of radiation was not confined to uneducated people. Many medical men were also skeptical. As late as 1950, a much-revised medical manual, widely used by physicians, had this statement in it: "Many geneticists believe that there is danger of gene alteration in later generations if men and women who have been temporarily sterilized by radiation are allowed to have children. No concrete evidence to support this theory is yet available."

To a biologist this assertion is an astounding example of misplaced conservatism. What would we think of a medical manual that published this statement: "Many biologists believe that if a living man is dropped, without a parachute or other supporting device, from an airplane flying over rocky terrain at 42,000 feet, the man will be killed. No concrete evidence to support this theory is yet available." Such an assertion is true, in a narrow technical sense—there is no *concrete* evidence, if by that we imply a record of a particular event of this sort. Yet who could perform the experiment in good conscience, excusing himself from blame by saying that "no concrete evidence" was available to him beforehand? The point is, there is a whole fabric of evidence that supports us in the belief that a 42,000-foot drop to jagged rocks would be fatal, and we act confidently on the basis of this large body of general knowledge, without demanding the "concrete evidence" of a particular experiment. So it is also with the belief that radiation causes genetic damage in human beings. Here the lack of "concrete evidence" is not because the experiment of irradiating men and women has not been carried out, for it has—many times. The lack of evidence is due rather to the fact that, by their very nature, most genetic changes are very unlikely to be detected in less than three generations' time in human beings—and this only if first cousins marry. We have only recently become aware of the danger and begun to think we should keep the necessary records. There has not been time enough to carry out the necessary genetic tests. Unless we discover new and more sensitive methods of detection of genetic damage, it will be yet another fifty years or more before we have "concrete evidence" of radiation damage to the human germ plasm. In the meantime, we must make our decisions on the basis of experimental data from other animals and plants —and such data we have in great abundance, derived from the study of many scores of species. All the data substantiate the following important generalizations:

1. Mutation has been found to occur naturally in every species that

has been studied with adequate genetic techniques. The over-all rate of mutation varies from species to species, and, indeed, sometimes from race to race within a species.

2. High-energy radiation causes mutations in all species. No exception has ever been found.

3. It is practically unimportant whether a mutant allele is a "natural mutant" or an "artificial mutant," i.e., one induced by man.

4. Mutation is always a highly localized phenomenon within a cell. The mutation at each gene locus is independent of changes that may take place at other gene loci in other cells, in the same cell, or indeed, within the same chromosome. Gene mutation results when a particular chromosome is "hit" by a high-energy particle (quantum of radiation).

5. What particular mutation will occur when enough of a mutagenic agent is brought to bear on a cell is unpredictable, though (experience shows) some mutations are more probable than others.

6. Each gene is capable of existing in many different allelic forms. The mutation rate for each conceivable change (from one particular allele to another particular allele) is a constant.

7. There is, at present, no perceivable principle that determines what a particular mutation rate will be. . . .

8. The genetic effects of discontinuously administered irradiation seem to be strictly cumulative. That is, the genetic damage caused by, say, 50 roentgens of radiation is the same whether given all at once or subdivided into smaller doses administered over a period of time. (Damage to somatic tissues, i.e., nonreproductive tissues, is often not so strictly cumulative: repair processes may undo some of the damage between irradiation).

9. There is no known threshold below which damage does not occur. Half the dose, half the damage; one tenth the dose, one tenth the damage, and so on. We can hardly speak of a "safe" dosage; we can only hope to agree on a permissible one.

10. Mutability under radiation varies from species to species. Mice are about 15 times as sensitive as *Drosophila*. (We suspect that man is more like a mouse than he is like a fruit fly.)

11. Most new mutations are recessive to the "normal" or "wild" type from which they were derived.

12. Mutations with small phenotypic effects occur more commonly than those with large.

13. Finally, and most important: with very, very rare exceptions, most new mutations are harmful to the organism affected by them.

In the face of a great mass of highly consistent evidence, those who would deny the human danger of high-energy radiation can do so only by implying that man is not a part of nature. "But isn't man different from other animals?" some may say. Yes, man is different, if by "different" we mean that this remarkable animal is able to form elaborate intellectual concepts, to conceive of death and the future and to let his conceptions alter his instinctive reactions to present stimuli. But in his primitive corporeal manifestations he cannot usefully be distinguished from "the animals," i.e., the other animals. Shakespeare or Shylock, he has, like them, eyes, organs, dimensions and sense; he is warmed by summer and cooled by winter; and he is injured by disease and hurt by weapons. Among these weapons are those we call the mutagenic agents. By his intellect, man is able to do what no other animal can—to increase the activity of such agents; but, once loosed, mutagenic substances and emanations exert their effect impartially on all organisms, human or infra-human. The peculiar humanity of *Homo sapiens* is no direct shield against what we have the conceit to call his "inhuman" actions. We have no direct measure of the mutability of human germ plasm, but we have no reason to think that it is at all exceptional. The burden of proof lies on those who suggest that it is.

DIRECT PROOF OF DAMAGE

It should now be clear why the commission found no clear-cut evidence of genetic damage among the survivors of the atom blasts in Japan. Suppose that the (diploid) [1] genetic formula of a normal individual be represented thus:

$$AABBCCDDEE \ . \ . \ . \ .$$

Verifiable experience with other organisms tells us that the atomic radiation undoubtedly produced many gene mutations in the population, most of them recessive. Suppose that, after the bombing, the reproductive cells of a certain Mr. Kimura were altered so that he now produced some spermatozoa which had the following haploid [1] formula:

$$aBCDE$$

Suppose that Mrs. Kimura had had her reproductive cells altered, too. Since there are many gene loci—at least 10,000 in human beings—it is unlikely that Mrs. Kimura's genes would have been altered in the same way. We may represent her new type eggs as:

$$ABCDe$$

With sperm and egg of the types indicated, the zygote will be:

$$AaBBCCDDEe$$

1. See Figure 10–2, p. 551, for explanation of diploid and haploid. Ed.

Notice that it is homozygous for neither of the new recessive mutants; consequently, the child that it will develop into—the first generation after the bombing—will be "normal."

What about the second generation? It is very unlikely that this off-spring will happen to marry someone who contains either the mutant *a* or the mutant *e*, consequently the results of the bombing are very unlikely to show up in the second generation. (Brother-sister mating among the first generation offspring would have a reasonably good chance of pro-ducing some mutation homozygotes, but this is an uncommon type of reproduction in all human societies.) Only if some of the first cousins in the second generation marry is there a reasonably good chance (far less than fifty-fifty, however) of revealing in the third generation a mutant that was produced by the atomic irradiation more than fifty years earlier.

This is not a nice state of affairs, from a human point of view, and geneticists are naturally casting about for ways of proving and detecting genetic damage earlier.

IN PRAISE OF WASTE

Darwin changed our views of the origin of living things, but more important still, he changed our attitude toward waste. Before Darwin, the adaptedness of species was explained by William Paley as an example of "design in nature"—a design that existed in the mind of a Creator Who then fashioned nature in accordance with His blueprint; only so, said Paley, could such a marvelously adapted structure as the eye have been produced.

Not at all, said Darwin. It is not necessary that there exist in some mind the idea of a beautifully adapted machine in order that this machine may come into existence. It is enough if nature be permitted to try count-less experiments—"mutations" we now call them—among which a tiny percentage produces good results. Each such successful experiment is saved by natural selection and used as a base for further experimentation and natural selection. Mutation occurs at random and entails enormous waste, but natural selection acts like a ratchet to preserve each tiny ele-ment of progress; thus do nature's beautifully adapted machines come into being. There need be no blueprint for design to emerge; trial and error suffice. Something of this sort must have been meant by the poet William Blake who said, "To be an error and to be cast out is a part of God's design."

Design can emerge from blind waste. How old is this thought? Who can trace the earliest embryological stages of so tenuous an entity as an idea? Perhaps it is centuries old, but certainly its form was not unambiguously clear until Robert Malthus wrote his *Essay on Population* in 1798. This much-misunderstood work, yearly buried by liberal critics and yearly resurrected by its own vigor, has, entangled in its many errors, a correct view of stability achieved through waste—the Malthusian dynamic scheme of population. From the superabundant vitality of nature comes the ever-present threat of geometric increase, but this is opposed by the limitations set by the environment. The result is an equilibrium achieved through waste, an equilibrium that may, it is true, be subject to temporal shifts, but an equilibrium nonetheless. Forethought, planning and charity are either of secondary importance or are self-defeating in such a system.

This mode of thought met with immediate favor when it was put forward by Malthus, but within a very few years it was vigorously opposed by another idea of independent birth and apparently contradictory implications—the idea of cruelty, i.e., the idea that cruelty is something to be abhorred rather than enjoyed. Strange as it may seem, this idea is a rather young idea as far as the bulk of mankind is concerned. In the distant past, the gentle Jesus was a conspicuous exception among men. It is only within comparatively recent times that many Christians have become Christian.

The Christianization of Christians was made possible by a change in perspective. In the Middle Ages it was common for the population of a city to be lowered as much as 10 per cent in a single year by disease or famine; even a 25 per cent loss was not unknown. In a world so filled with suffering not caused by humans, it would seem to some rather out of perspective to complain of a little human fun—like the Spanish Inquisition, say. As suffering and death from seemingly divinely caused diseases decreased—as it did even before Pasteur and bacteriology—man's view of his own cruelties changed, perhaps because they loomed proportionately larger. Cruel fate was becoming reformed; cruel man now looked crueler. Tender-minded poets and novelists were determined that he, too, should reform, and quickly. . . .

Into this world of tender intentions burst Malthus, asserting that suffering was inevitable, simply because population had the capability of increasing more rapidly than the means of subsistence. A reasonable balance between population and subsistence—a decent scale of living for some—could be maintained only if others suffered from insufficient means of subsistence. Nor would it be a true solution for the haves to divide their means with the have-nots—this would merely encourage the production of more have-nots. Such a sentiment provoked a storm of protest from the literati, who were now making the cause of the poor and unfortunate their cause. The wealthy Percy Shelley saw a great social threat in "sophisms like those of Mr. Malthus, calculated to lull the oppressors of mankind into a security of everlasting triumph." The poet's friend William Hazlitt asserted that "Mr. Malthus' gospel is preached only to the poor."

This is not the place to examine Malthus' thesis—or rather, his theses, for there were several. We need only point out that the early decades of the nineteenth century saw an establishment of sharp lines of battle between—shall we say—humanitarians and analysts; it is difficult to name the factions without arousing prejudice. It must not be supposed that men like Malthus were inhumane; in his personal relations with family and friends, Malthus was the kindest and most considerate of men. But in his public statements he insisted on the primacy of analysis in the attack on social problems, whereas his opponents insisted on the humanitarian treatment of all existing people—particularly the poor and unfortunate—in the hope, or belief, that future generations would present no problem. The here and now is much more real than the there and tomorrow. The humanitarians won the minds of common men—who are, in the nature of things, the majority.

What Malthus was trying to get at in his bumbling way, and all-unconscious of what he was doing, was what we now call the impotence principles of science and logic. The trisection of an angle with ruler and compass alone is impossible—this is an impotence principle. So also is the principle of the conservation of matter and mass, and the finite velocity of the speed of light. Impotence principles tell us what cannot be done and for that reason are inacceptable to immature minds. Angle trisectors, circle squarers, and inventors of perpetual-motion machines we will always have with us. What these men fail to realize is that impotence principles are not only restrictive but also permissive. Only if some things are impossible can other things be. The second law of thermodynamics not only tells us to stop looking for a perpetual-motion machine but also tells us how to improve the machines already invented.

One of the impotence principles of biology is this—waste is inevitable. Waste, in the Darwinian scheme, not only produces progress but also conserves the advances already made. There is no heredity without its tax of mutation; most mutations are bad; their production and elimination are a kind of waste. The sentimentalist who seeks to eliminate the waste in a species by preserving all mutants and breeding equally of all genetic types ultimately brings about the extinction of the entire species. It is a throwing of good money after bad. It is the saving of pawns and losing the game. . . .

Another of the impotence principles of biology, and of sociology, is this—competition is inescapable. The form of competition and the participants may change; but it is always with us. A species that is not numerous competes principally against other species; as it increases in numbers, the situation changes. The "successful" species ends by becoming its own principal competitor. So it is with man, now. The world, in spite of comic-strip science, is a limited one. Man, freed of the population-controlling factors of predators and disease organisms, must—willy-nilly, like it or not—control his own numbers by competition with his own kind. By taking thought, he can elect the kind of competition he employs; but he cannot escape all kinds. This is not to imply that the election is a trivial matter. Surely there are few who would not prefer the endemic celibacy of the Irish to the ritual blood sacrifices of the Aztecs, who, at the dedication of the temple of Huitzilopochtli in 1486, slaughtered at least 20,000 victims—by the most conservative accounts—tearing the hearts out of the living bodies. There surely can be no serious question as to which behavior is preferable, but we should note that, though both practices have a religious "reason," both are, in the eyes of a biologist, competitive techniques associated with the threat of overpopulation, however unconscious of that threat the practitioners may be. The question is not whether competitive techniques shall be employed, but what techniques and by whom. . . .

The classical utopias, however much they vary, agree in two characteristics. The societies they sketch have a high degree of rigidity and finality; and they seek to eliminate all waste, which is variously conceived in terms of economic waste, human suffering or moral turpitude. The student of biological evolution cannot accept a utopia that embodies either of these features. Evolution is an unending process, in which waste plays an indispensable role. Until proof to the contrary is forthcoming, the evolutionist must assume that man is a part of nature. The biologist sees no end-state for man and his society, which must continue evolving until the day of his extinction. No one has conceived any substitute for the mechanism of evolution (whether biological or social) that does not necessarily involve variation and selection—that is to say, waste. Man, the slender reed that thinks, can alter the force and direction of natural forces somewhat, but only within limits. The wisdom of so doing is always questionable. Who is so wise as to descry the lineaments of man 1000 millenniums from now, using these visions as guides for consciously warping the course of human evolution? . . .

Mutation is a form of waste which, manage it though we will, we must in some sense accept. It is inevitable. It is the stuff from which are fashioned new adaptations to the world. In this realization we are brought back to an insight that is old, very old; much older than the theory of evolution. When we come to think of it, we realize that what we call charity owes its origin at least in part to a subconscious realization of the value of waste. Most interesting of early prescriptions for charity is the Jewish "law of the corner," which is given thus in Leviticus 19: 9–10: "And when ye reap the harvest of your land, thou shalt not wholly reap the corners of thy field, neither shalt thou gather the gleanings of thy harvest. And thou shalt not glean thy vineyard, neither shalt thou gather every grape of thy vineyard; thou shalt leave them for the poor and stranger. . . ." Such a directive sprang, no doubt, in part from a tender heart; but it may also have indicated an embryonic recognition of the danger of an unmodified competition in human affairs—a recognition that if competition were pure and unbridled, the more efficient man (the landowner) would starve out him who was less so (the poor and the stranger). Coupled with this was a surmise that perhaps complete efficiency might not always be best or right. . . .

Those who have painted pictures of an organized heaven have, implicitly or otherwise, appealed to the aesthetic sense in man to try to gain assent to their plans. We know now that a completely planned heaven is either impossible or unbearable. We know that it is not true that design can come only out of planning. Out of luxuriant waste, winnowed by selection, come designs more beautiful and in greater variety than ever man could plan. This is the lesson of nature that Darwin has spelled out for us. Man, now that he makes himself, cannot do better than to emulate nature's example in allowing for waste and encouraging novelty. There is a grandeur in this view of life as a complex of adjustive systems that produce adaptedness without foresight, design without planning and progress without dictation. From the simplest means, man, now master of his own fate, may evolve societies of a variety and novelty—yes, and even of beauty—that no man living can now foresee.

We soon cease to lament waste and death, and rather rejoice and exult in the imperishable, unspendable wealth of the universe, and faithfully watch and wait the reappearance of everything that melts and fades and dies about us, feeling sure that its next appearance will be better and more beautiful than the last.

John Muir

The Cruelty of Natural Selection *

by Linus Pauling (1958)

There is still the possibility of a genetic improvement in human beings. The world of today is different from that of a few hundred or a few thousand years ago. Some of the characters that were the best for life in the world as it was some time ago may not be the best now. Possibly some natural mutations will occur that will improve the human race, if some humane way of permitting the mutant variety to increase can be devised. Natural selection is a cruel way, and man has now outgrown it. The problem is not to be solved by increasing the mutation rate, and thus increasing the number of defective children born, but rather by finding some acceptable replacement for natural selection.

It is true that extraordinary advances have been made in plant and animal breeding. The reason for this is simple. In a breeding program a great many mutants may be produced (by the use of X-radiation, as described below). Almost all of them are harmful, but these mutant individuals are eliminated from the line. The mutant with the rare beneficial mutation—that is, beneficial by man's standard, though probably rarely, if ever, to the organism itself—is recognized by the person who is carrying on the breeding program, and a new variety of plant or animal is then obtained by breeding this mutant.

This is a special sort of selection—with man taking a hand in it.

Man is also taking a hand in the process of natural selection in human beings, but not in such a way as to improve the pool of human germ plasm. In earlier times the physically and mentally handicapped individual human beings were weeded out; they were not able to compete with their more fortunate brethren in having children. But with the development of modern man, with his strong feelings about humanity, the process is working the other way. In the modern world there is a greater and greater tendency for the handicapped individuals to be nurtured. As a result of this and also of medical progress, there is now a less effective process of weeding the bad genes out of the pool of human germ plasm than was operating even a few centuries ago.

There are many bad genes in the pool of human germ plasm. The number of bad genes is determined by the rate at which new ones are being formed and the rate at which they are being removed from the pool. A steady state has been set up, with these two rates equal to each other.

The rate at which the bad genes are being formed through mutation has been discussed . . . If some of the bad genes for diseases [like hemophilia] were not removed from the pool of human germ plasm, the number of children born with these diseases would increase with every generation, because of the new mutations. In fact, children who are born with hemophilia do not in general have offspring—the number of their offspring is only one-eighth of that for normal individuals. Consequently, most of the genes for hemophilia are not passed on to the next generation. This is the way in which the steady state is set up.

If something were to happen in the world that doubled the mutation rate for all genes, a new steady state would be set up in which the number of bad genes in the pool of human germ plasm would be twice as great as at the present time. Then there would be twice as many children born with hemophilia, twice as many with achondroplasia, twice as many defective in other ways determined by these bad genes.

If there were to be a great war fought with nuclear weapons the mutation rate for human beings might be doubled, might be tripled, might become ten times as great. There is even the possibility that such a war might not leave enough human beings alive for following generations to arise, or might cause such great changes in the pool of human germ plasm that the following generations would hardly be recognized as human beings.

Even the bomb tests are having an effect in increasing the mutation rate and consequently increasing the amount of human suffering.

The Problem of Fallout

The Scientists' Petition to the United Nations *

by Linus Pauling (1958)

At noon on Monday 15 January 1958 I placed in the hands of Mr. Dag Hammarskjold, Secretary-General of the United Nations, a petition from 9235 scientists, of many countries in the world.

This petition has the title "Petition to the United Nations Urging that an International Agreement to Stop the Testing of Nuclear Bombs be Made Now."

The petition consists of five paragraphs, as follows:

We, the scientists whose names are signed below, urge that an international agreement to stop the testing of nuclear bombs be made now.

Each nuclear bomb test spreads an added burden of radioactive elements over every part of the world. Each added amount of radiation causes damage to the health of human beings all over the world and causes damage to the pool of human germ plasm such as to lead to an increase in the number of seriously defective children that will be born in future generations.

So long as these weapons are in the hands of only three powers an agreement for their control is feasible. If testing continues, and the possession of these weapons spreads to additional governments, the danger of outbreak of a cataclysmic nuclear war through the reckless action of some irresponsible national leader will be greatly increased.

An international agreement to stop the testing of nuclear bombs now could serve as a first step toward a more general disarmament and the ultimate effective abolition of nuclear weapons, averting the possibility of a nuclear war that would be a catastrophe to all humanity.

We have in common with our fellow men a deep concern for the welfare of all human beings. As scientists we have knowledge of the dangers involved and therefore a special responsibility to make those dangers known. We deem it imperative that immediate action be taken to effect an international agreement to stop the testing of all nuclear weapons.

* From Linus Pauling, *No More War!*

NOBEL LAUREATES AMONG SIGNERS

NOBEL LAUREATES IN PHYSICS

Max Born
Germany

P. A. M. Dirac
Great Britain

W. Heisenberg
Germany

Tang-Dao Lee
(Resident in U.S.A.)
China

E. T. S. Walton
Ireland

C. F. Powell
Great Britain

C. V. Raman
India

C. N. Yang
(Resident in U.S.A.)
China

Hideki Yukawa
Japan

NOBEL LAUREATES IN CHEMISTRY

K. Alder
Germany

A. Butenandt
Germany

Otto Hahn
Germany

Leopold Ruzicka
Switzerland

N. N. Semenov
U.S.S.R.

R. L. M. Synge
Great Britain

Frederic Joliot-Curie
France

Richard Kuhn
Germany

Linus Pauling
U.S.A.

A. W. K. Tiselius
Sweden

Harold Urey
U.S.A.

Adolf Windaus
Germany

NOBEL LAUREATE IN LITERATURE

Bertrand Russell
Great Britain

NOBEL LAUREATES IN PEACE

Lord Boyd Orr
Great Britain

Albert Schweitzer
France

NOBEL LAUREATES IN PHYSIOLOGY AND MEDICINE

Jules Bordet Belgium	*W. P. Murphy* U.S.A.
Henry Dale Great Britain	*A. Szent-Györgyi* (Resident in U.S.A.) Hungary
Gerhard Domagk Germany	*Max Theiler* U.S.A.
Joseph Erlanger U.S.A.	*Hugo Theorell* Sweden
Hans Krebs Great Britain	*T. Reichstein* Switzerland
Otto Loewi U.S.A.	*G. H. Whipple* U.S.A.
Hermann Muller U.S.A.	

The Compelling Need for Nuclear Tests *
by Edward Teller and Albert Latter (1958)

Last month the U.N. received a petition signed by more than 9000 scientists urging an immediate halt to nuclear bomb tests. The petition said that the tests were endangering both the present population of the world and generations yet unborn and declared that an agreement to stop such testing is now feasible. Dr. Linus Pauling, the American scientist who presented the document to the U.N., said further that in his opinion the U.S. will never achieve one of the principal objectives of its nuclear tests: the production of a "clean" bomb—*i.e.*, one with little or no radio-activity. These are statements of tremendous importance. If true, they strongly support the position that we must stop nuclear tests at once.

But they are not true. The statements are at best half-truths, and they are misleading and dangerous. If acted upon, they could bring disaster to the free world. Sober consideration of the facts makes it perfectly

* Edward Teller and Albert Latter, "The Compelling Need for Nuclear Tests," *Life* Magazine, February 10, 1958. Reprinted by permission of S. G. Phillips, Inc. and the authors.

clear that we must continue testing nuclear weapons. Such tests do *not* seriously endanger either present or future generations. It is true that they might be halted by agreement—but there would be no way to prevent the Soviet Union, a notorious violator of agreements, from starting them up again in secret. And finally, American tests *are* leading to the development of a clean bomb.

Many people besides the scientists who signed the petition feel that tests should be discontinued. Since the people are the sovereign power in a democracy, it is of the greatest importance that they should be honestly and completely informed about all the relevant facts.

Unfortunately much of the discussion about continued nuclear experimentation has been carried out in a most emotional and confused manner. One argument is so fantastic that it deserves to be mentioned for that very reason: it has been claimed that nuclear explosions may change the axis of the earth. Of course nuclear explosions do produce such changes. But the cumulative effect of all past tests has been to shift the position of the North Pole by less than the diameter of an atom.

The argument about worldwide radioactive fallout is more serious. It is asserted that fallout is dangerous and that we are ignorant of the extent of the danger. But when we examine the facts we shall see that the danger is considerably less than the danger from other radiations to which we constantly expose ourselves without concern.

Every explosion of a conventional nuclear bomb fills the immediate vicinity with dust-carrying radioactive contamination. The heavier particles fall to earth in a short time and contaminate only the test area itself. But the remaining particles are carried aloft and some of them are transported all over the globe by high altitude winds. They fall back gradually, primarily in rain, depositing their radioactivity on the ground in every part of the world. This is the worldwide fallout that everybody is worried about. It contains two dangerous radioactive isotopes: Strontium-90, which in high doses could cause bone cancer and leukemia, and Cesium-137, which affects the reproductive organs. The big question is whether dangerous quantities of these two poisons are being absorbed by our bodies as a consequence of nuclear tests.

The dangers from big doses of radiation are well known. The intensity of radiation is usually measured in units called roentgens. Exposure to 1000 roentgens over one's whole body causes almost certain death in less than 30 days. Four or five hundred roentgens allow a 50-50 chance of survival. At less than 100 roentgens there is no danger of immediate death. And if the exposure is spread over a long period of time, bigger radiation doses than this can be tolerated.

THE SUBTLE DANGERS

Although 100 roentgens all at once, or several times this amount over a protracted period, will not cause sickness that can be directly blamed on the radiation, such a dose may have harmful biological consequences which are more subtle. A person who receives 100 roentgens does not necessarily contract bone cancer or leukemia. But there is strong evidence that his chance of contracting these diseases during his lifetime has been increased.

This sounds frightening until one considers the slight amount of radiation we are subjected to from worldwide fallout. When Strontium-90 falls to the earth it may be absorbed by growing plants. It reaches our bodies when we eat the plants or when we drink milk from cows which have grazed on radioactive grass. Since this isotope is concentrated in the bones, particularly in growing bones, the humans who absorb the greatest dosage of roentgens are young children—especially those in the northern part of the U.S. which is a region of maximum fallout. Adults who reached mature growth before the atomic testing started are now getting about 0.0003 roentgen a year in their bones from Strontium-90. Children who have grown up in an environment of Strontium-90 are absorbing a larger dosage, but it is still less than 0.002 roentgen a year (in addition, all of us receive a roughly equal amount from Cesium-137). At this rate the lifetime dosage for the average American comes to only a small fraction of one roentgen, although in rare cases it might be several times that amount.

If tests continue at the present rate, radiation levels might increase as much as fivefold. But even in this situation it is extremely unlikely that anyone would receive a lifetime dosage of as much as five roentgens from the worldwide fallout.

If radiation in this small amount actually does increase a person's chance of getting bone cancer or leukemia, the increase is so slight that it cannot be measured. Moreover, we have lived all our lives with radioactivity of even greater intensity, most of us without ever being aware of it (see Figure 10–6). We live on an earth which has radioactivity in its rocks and in its waters and which is continuously exposed to a rain of cosmic particles which produce effects on human beings identical to those from radioactive materials.

The average person living at sea level in the United States absorbs in his bones about 0.15 roentgen of radiation every year from natural sources. Of this amount, about 0.035 roentgen comes from cosmic rays. At higher altitudes the cosmic ray dosage increases. In Denver, at an

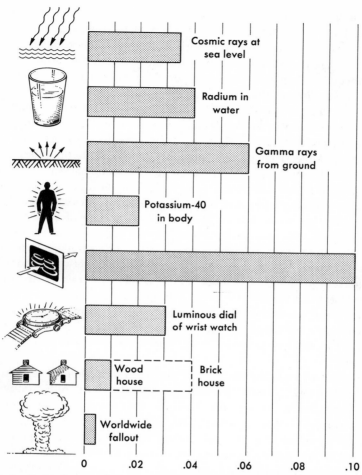

Figure 10–6. *Radiation danger to the average person from various sources is shown in chart in roentgens per year* (figures at bottom). *Wood house, for instance, gives off .01 roentgen, brick house* (dotted line), *.04. Present nuclear fallout is only .003.*

altitude of 5000 feet, the cosmic rays contribute 0.05 roentgen per year. The Strontium-90 radiation of about 0.002 roentgen per year from fallout is thus only about 5 per cent of the natural cosmic radiation. It is small even when compared with the variation of cosmic ray intensity between sea level and 5000 feet.

Is there a correlation between the frequency of leukemia or bone cancer and the intensity of natural radiation? Statistics for the year 1947 show that in Denver, where cosmic rays are relatively intense, the incidence of both diseases was actually lower than it was in the sea-level cities of San Francisco and New Orleans. For leukemia it was 6.4 per 100,000 in Denver, 6.9 in New Orleans and 10.3 in San Francisco. For bone cancer the incidence was 2.4 per 100,000 in Denver, 2.8 in New Orleans and 2.9 in San Francisco.

The only thing these statistics prove is that radiation in small doses need not necessarily be harmful—indeed, may conceivably be helpful. In either case the effects are so slight as to be virtually unnoticeable.

So far we have been considering only cosmic radiation, but human beings are subjected with no apparent ill effects to natural background radiation from many other sources as well. The radium deposited in our bones from drinking water has an average intensity of 0.04 roentgen per year and may go as high as 0.55—and this is a type of radiation more damaging than that emitted by Strontium-90. It has even been pointed out recently that brick contains enough radioactive materials to give a dosage of 0.04 roentgen per year. The difference between living in a brick house and living in a wood house could give rise to 10 times as much radiation as we are currently getting from fallout.

Human beings absorb radiation not only from natural sources but also from man-made sources. For example, a wrist watch with a luminous dial or X-rays for medical purposes subject us to much more radiation than the fallout.

To see fallout radiation in proper perspective it should be compared not only with other kinds of radiation but also with other dangers to health. Some estimates are, for example, that being 10 per cent overweight seems to reduce a person's life expectancy by 1.5 years, that the lifelong habit of smoking one package of cigarets a day cuts it by seven years, that living in the city instead of in the country reduces life expectancy by five years, and so on. On this statistical scale the reduction in life expectancy from worldwide fallout at present levels totals less than two days. Or, to put it another way, the worldwide fallout is as dangerous to human health as being one ounce overweight, or smoking one cigaret every two months.

Will the fallout danger increase as more nations develop and test atomic weapons? Although it is not easy to predict the future, some factors justify optimism. We are learning how to regulate the fallout by exploding bombs under proper surroundings. Development of clean bombs will greatly reduce the radioactivity produced. Deep underground tests will eliminate fallout altogether. Since fallout is a problem of concern to all the world's inhabitants, we may hope that every nation testing nuclear explosives will employ such safeguards. The rate at which U.S.

tests put radioactivity into the atmosphere has declined since 1954, and it is highly probable that this downward trend will continue.

Much of what we know about the aftereffects of nuclear explosions was learned following the famous hydrogen bomb tests of 1954. These tests became famous partly because they accidentally gave us our most harrowing experience with radioactive fallout. It is very improbable that an accident of this kind will ever occur again because we know more now than we did then about taking precautions. But in attempting to assess the degree of danger resulting from nuclear tests, we will find the information gathered after the Bikini explosion of March 1, 1954 invaluable.

Bikini lies at the northern rim of the Marshall Islands, with several inhabited islands to the east, west and south. For test purposes a wind from a general southerly direction was essential to blow the radioactive debris into the uninhabited sea to the north. On March 1 the wind was blowing to the northeast. That seemed perfectly safe and near dawn the bomb was exploded.

Almost immediately it became apparent that something had gone wrong. The wind had shifted and was blowing toward the east. In the hours that followed, radioactive dust fell on the naval vessels that were observing the shot from a position south and a little east of the atoll, and then on the islands of Ailinginae, Rongelap, Rongerik and Utirik. Unknown to anyone, the fallout also sifted down over a Japanese fishing boat, *The Fortunate Dragon*, that happened to be northeast of Bikini but was not noticed by patrolling aircraft.

On the naval vessels the radioactivity was dealt with quickly and effectively. The ships were washed down and moved out of the area until the fallout had ended. No one received a dangerous exposure. The only people on Rongerik were 28 American servicemen operating a weather station. They washed themselves, put on extra clothes and remained inside the shelter of their aluminum huts as much as possible during the danger period of fallout. They received a dosage of about 78 roentgens. The 18 Marshall Islanders on Ailinginae received 69 roentgens, and the 157 on Utirik received 14.

Elsewhere, however, the dosage was heavier. Worst hit were the 23 Japanese fishermen. It was not until two weeks after the explosion that the world—and the fishermen themselves—learned that they had been subjected to radioactivity. We do not know precisely what dosage the fishermen received, but the best estimate is about 200 roentgens. One of them has since died, presumably from complications associated with the exposure to radiation, although there is a possibility that his death resulted from a case of hepatitis unrelated to the radiation exposure. The other 22 men are in good health and back at work.

For scientific purposes the experience of the 64 native inhabitants of Rongelap is most significant, for our medical information about them is complete. Although they received about 175 roentgens, they narrowly escaped a much heavier dosage. They happened to be living on the southern part of their island. Ten miles to the north they would have received 400 roentgens, which would have given them only a 50-50 chance of survival. On the northern tip of the island, 30 miles away, the dosage would have been over 2000 roentgens, which would have meant certain death.

Ever since the incident the people of Rongelap have been living on another atoll where they have been kept under continuous medical surveillance. What happened to them is the best indication we have of the long-term effects of substantial radiation exposure.

In the first 24 hours after they were exposed to the fallout, some of the victims complained of nausea, fever and stomach-ache. But these symptoms abated promptly. There was also some complaint of itching skin and a burning sensation. These symptoms also lasted only a couple of days. Then followed a week or so of comfort and no complaint. After that, skin lesions and loss of hair began to occur. But at the end of six months lost hair had grown out again, unaltered in texture and color, and the skin lesions had healed. Everyone appeared healthy and normal with no apparent aftereffects.

There were four pregnancies among Rongelap women at the time of the exposure. One baby was born dead, but the other three were quite normal. There is no evidence that the stillbirth was due to radiation effects. The normal percentage of stillbirths among the Rongelapese is high and statistically one in four is not an unusual ratio.

The important fact is that today, more than three years after the accident, all of the Marshallese and American victims seem to be fully recovered from a dosage of radioactivity far greater than any humans are ever likely to be subjected to again from a bomb test. Although long-term effects are still being carefully watched for, no malignancies or cases of leukemia have shown up to date.

If fallout radiation from tests is relatively harmless to the individual compared with many risks which we habitually take and almost always ignore, what about the genetic danger to the race?

We transmit our properties to coming generations in a most curious and concentrated fashion. From the mother and the father a child inherits a number of chromosomes. Within these structures are the actual carriers of the properties, the genes. We are beginning to understand something about the nature of the genes. They seem to be big spiral molecules. They carry the master plan of our body and even of our character in a strange chemical code. The significant fact in this discussion is that any gene may suffer a mutation. That is, it may turn into a new chemical, carrying a new code and new properties.

A gene is an extremely finely and precisely constituted object. It must be so in order to carry all the racial past. A mutation due to chance will spoil this order in almost every instance. The great majority of mutations are detrimental because they produce characteristics not suited to the environment in which we live. Many are lethal.

Astonishingly, these random mutations, almost always harmful and never proceeding according to any plan, have nevertheless been responsible in the long run for all the many magnificent living creatures that nature has produced, including the human species. This may seem hard to believe. The biological thread that over the millennia has led from single cells to cell colonies, worms, fishes, vertebrates, mammals and human beings certainly does not seem to be the work of chance. Much less does it seem to be the result of a gamble, taking one chance of a small improvement against a thousand chances of deformity or death. Nevertheless it is just such a terrible game of chance, aided by natural selection, which has produced both the human body and in some manner also the human spirit.

Radiation is certainly disruptive. It does cause mutations. The less radiation, the smaller the chance of mutation. But the chance will always be there. A very great increase in the natural rate of mutations could indeed have terrifying effects.

We can be quite certain, however, that radiation from atomic tests will increase the chance of mutations by only a very small amount. Most such radiation comes from Cesium-137 which has been deposited in the ground or absorbed by the body. At present rates the tests inflict 0.001 or 0.002 roentgen per year from Cesium-137 on the human reproductive cells. This is equivalent to approximately 0.05 roentgen per generation. Over the same period background radiation—from cosmic rays or gamma and beta rays emitted by natural radioactive substances in or near our bodies —subjects the reproductive cells to a dosage of about five roentgens. Our best estimate is that 10 per cent of all natural mutations are due to this background radiation (the rest are caused by heat and chemicals). The atomic tests are therefore increasing the number of mutations by only about 0.1 per cent.

These man-made mutations seem even less significant when compared with the high degree of natural radiation endured without noticeable harm by the world's mountain dwellers.

The people of Tibet have been exposed for generation after generation to the intense cosmic radiation which bombards their plateau through a relatively thin layer of atmosphere. Compared with people who live in low countries, the Tibetans have been exposed over the centuries to a much greater additional intensity of radiation than is caused by atomic tests. Yet genetic differences have not been noticed in the humans of Tibet, or for that matter in any other living species there.

It has been repeated often that all genetic mutations due to radiation are harmful. There is every reason to believe that mutations due to radiation are not different in kind from mutations resulting from other causes. Should we then seriously believe that all mutations are harmful? That most of them are is admitted. To insist that all mutations are harmful, however, would be to deny the simplest facts of evolution.

The petition of the 9000 scientists placed great emphasis on fallout danger. But it also expressed the hope that halting the bomb tests "could serve as a first step toward a more general disarmament and the ultimate effective abolition of nuclear weapons, averting the possibility of a nuclear war that would be a catastrophe to all humanity."

It seems probable that the real root of the opposition to further tests —and not only among the petition-signers—is not so much the fear of fallout as it is this desire for disarmament and for peace.

There can be no doubt that the desire for peace is felt by all thinking and honest people. In the minds of most people it would be an important step in this direction if nuclear weapons tests were stopped by all nations. This belief is widely held, but it is not necessarily well founded.

It has been said that World War I was caused by an arms race. It might as justifiably be said that World War II was brought about by a disarmament race. In the 1920s and 1930s the peace-loving nations divested themselves of their military strength. When Germany adopted a program of rapid preparation for war, the rest of the world was caught unaware. By the time the danger was unmistakable, it was too late to avert a most cruel war, and almost too late to stop Hitler short of world conquest. Unfortunately disarmament is safe only when no one wants to impose his will upon his neighbors by force of arms.

In today's uneasy world no reasonable person will advocate unilateral disarmament. What people hope is that all sides will agree to reduce military power and thereby contribute to a more peaceful atmosphere. The elimination of tests has appeared possible and proper for two reasons. One is that tests are conspicuous, and therefore it is believed that we can check whether or not everyone has actually stopped testing. The second reason is that nuclear explosives already represent such terrifying power that further tests appear irrational. These arguments are simple and almost universally accepted. They are based on misconceptions.

A nuclear explosion is a violent event, but in the great expanses of our world such tests can be effectively hidden if appropriate care is taken to hide them. There can be no doubt that this is possible. The question is only how much it costs to hide a test of any given size.

If an agreement were made to discontinue the tests, the United States would surely abide by it. The social and political structure of our country excludes the possibility that many people would collaborate in breaking an international agreement. Whether the Soviet Union would keep such an agreement would depend on the ingenuity of the Russians, on their willingness to make the economic sacrifices required for expensive secret tests, and on their honesty. Of these three factors we can have a firm opinion about the first: the Russians are certainly ingenious enough to devise secret methods of testing. As to the other questions, each man is entitled to his own opinion. Past experience suggests that any international agreement to stop tests may well be followed immediately by secret and successful tests behind the Iron Curtain.

In a more general way we may ask the question, is it wise to make agreements which honesty will respect but dishonesty can circumvent? Shall we put a free, democratic government at a disadvantage compared with the absolute power of a dictatorship? Shall we introduce prohibition in a new form, just to give rise to bootlegging on a much greater scale? It is almost certain that in the competition between prohibition and bootlegging, the bootlegger will win.

THE PURPOSE OF NUCLEAR TESTING

All of these arguments, however, would become irrelevant if it were true that further testing would not accomplish any further desirable result. It has been said and often repeated that we now possess enough nuclear explosives to wreck the country of any enemy. What more do we need?

Our main purpose in further experimentation with nuclear bombs is not, of course, to make city-busters more horrible. It is to prepare to make defensive use of nuclear weapons. In particular we must be prepared to use nuclear weapons with proper discrimination in limited wars.

To understand what we are actually trying to do in our tests, we have to take a closer look at some military problems.

The proper role of nuclear weapons in a future war is not the killing of millions of civilians. It is rather to stop the armed forces of an aggressor. This is not easy to do because it requires not only nuclear weapons but very special kinds of nuclear weapons which are hard to develop and harder to perfect. But with proper experimentation and proper planning the defensive use of nuclear weapons is possible.

The idea of tactical nuclear weapons is not new. The possibility of using nuclear explosives in small wars has been frequently discussed. What kind of weapons do we need in order to fight these small wars and to defend the freedom of people wherever such defense becomes necessary? It has often been suggested that in small wars small weapons will be used, while big weapons are appropriate for big wars. Such a statement is much too simple and has no relation to reality. In every case the right kind of weapon is the one which performs the job of stopping the enemy's armed forces without inflicting unnecessary damage on innocent bystanders. For this purpose we need a great number of weapons which are adaptable to specific purposes, which are easy to transport and easy to deliver, and which do whatever job the situation may require.

For instance, a nuclear weapon may be carried by a fighter plane and used to shoot down an attacking bomber. Since the carrying capacity of the fighter plane is severely limited, the weapon used for this purpose must be both small and light. A major objective of the U.S. nuclear test program is to develop such purely defensive, highly mobile weapons.

The encounter between the fighter plane and the bomber may well take place in our own country over populated areas. What would happen then to the population underneath the explosion? Fortunately we know the answer. In a recent nuclear test in Nevada five Air Force officers and an intrepid civilian photographer demonstrated that under such circumstances there is complete safety for people on the ground. They did this by standing directly beneath the explosion at ground zero.

This important test took place only a short time ago—on July 19, 1957. An F-89 jet fighter plane flying at 19,000 feet above sea level delivered an air-to-air atomic rocket to a preassigned point in the sky. The ground zero men were 15,000 feet immediately below. They wore no helmets, no sunglasses and no protective clothing.

At the instant of the explosion the men looked up, saw the fireball and felt the heat. Then they waited for the shock wave to arrive—approximately 10 seconds. When the shock came, it was actually just a loud noise.

After the blast and heat waves had passed, the Air Force men stood their ground. One question still remained: would there be any fallout? They checked their radiation instruments and waited while the cloud drifted slowly away. There was no significant rise in the radiation level. The radioactivity, which normally condenses on dust partcles sucked up from the ground, did not find big enough particles because of the height of the explosion and was blown away harmlessly. The test had been a complete success. The effects of the explosion were utterly insignificant on the ground. But high in the air an enemy plane could have been demolished, even if the nuclear explosion had missed it by a considerable distance.

For nuclear weapons to be effective against armed invaders great numbers of them must be used. With present weapons such numbers will produce a considerable amount of radioactive contamination over a wide area, and this contamination will endanger the safety of friend and foe alike. In particular the radioactivity is likely to kill people in the very country whose liberty we are trying to defend. For this reason it is most important that we should be able to use nuclear weapons which cause the least possible contamination. In recent nuclear tests more and more attention has been paid to the development of such clean weapons, and most fortunately these efforts are well on the way toward success.

In order to produce nuclear weapons with minimum radioactivity we must continue our tests. The fallout from such tests is slight. But the danger from fallout in a nuclear war involving present weapons would be real and great (and as long as this danger exists, it may be added, we should protect ourselves from it by constructing shelters). If we stop testing now and if we should fail to develop to the fullest possible extent these clean weapons, we would unnecessarily kill a great number of noncombatants in any future war. Not to develop the explosives with the smallest possible radioactive fallout would, indeed, be completely inexcusable.

The only alternative to clean weapons is to avoid the use of nuclear weapons entirely. Since these weapons have been presented as purely evil instruments, most people hope that they will never be used and indeed that wars themselves will be avoided.

But in our conflict with the powerful Communist countries which strive for world domination, it may be too much to hope for uninterrupted peace. If we abandon our light and mobile weapons, we shall enable the Red bloc to take over one country after another, close to their borders, as opportunities arise. The free nations cannot maintain the massive armies which would be required to resist such piecemeal aggression. On the other hand, the flexible power of clean nuclear explosives would put us in a position where we could resist aggression in any part of the world, practically at a moment's notice.

The announced policy of our country is to maintain peace and stability in the world. By being patient and prepared, we are trying to arrive at a world order based on law and justice for all peoples. There is no doubt that this policy is supported by the overwhelming majority of Americans. Our armed forces need the greatest possible flexibility in order to give strength to this policy. We can possess such flexibility only if we have in our possession the strongest, best developed weapons—and the cleanest, so that they may be used for defense rather than for random destruction.

If we renounce nuclear weapons, we open the door to aggression. If we fail to develop clean explosives, we expose people to disaster from radioactive fallout in any serious military conflict. These are weighty arguments in favor of continued experimentation and development of nuclear weapons.

One more thing remains to be said. The spectacular developments of the last centuries, in science, in technology and in our everyday life, have been produced by a spirit of adventure, by a fearless exploration of the unknown. When we talk about nuclear tests, we have in mind not only military preparedness but also the execution of experiments which will give us more insight into the forces of nature. Such insight has led and will lead to new possibilities of controlling nature. There are many specific political and military reasons why such experiments should not be abandoned. There also exists this very general reason—the tradition of exploring the unknown. It is possible to follow this tradition without running any serious risk that radioactivity, carelessly dispersed, will interfere with human life.

The Facts about Fallout *

by Linus Pauling (1958)

DR. TELLER'S STATEMENTS

Dr. Edward Teller is an able and experienced scientist who was born and educated in Hungary and who came to the United States in 1935. During recent years he has become well known to the people of the United States and of other countries as "The Father of the H-Bomb." He has been called in by President Eisenhower to discuss nuclear weapons, and he himself has made many public statements about nuclear weapons, fallout, the education of scientists in the U.S.S.R. and the U.S., and other topics.

Dr. Teller's public statements about fallout and its biological effects may be misunderstood by some readers. The discussion that is given in the following pages may help the reader to discover what the truth is. . . .

As a simple example, I may quote the statement made by Dr. Teller that "The worldwide fallout is as dangerous to human health as being one ounce overweight."

* From Linus Pauling, *No More War!*

It would be hard to make a statement about fallout that is more easily misinterpreted than this one. What meaning does being one ounce overweight have? No scientist believes that being one ounce overweight causes a significant increase in the probability in having one's life cut short by leukemia or bone cancer or other disease—yet many scientists believe that fallout radioactivity increases the incidence of these diseases.

Dr. Teller's statement about being one ounce overweight is a ludicrous one, and it is a seriously misleading one, in that it gives the impression to the reader that the idea that fallout can shorten life expectancy is also ludicrous. . . .

The erroneous statements in the issue of *Life* Magazine for 10 February 1958 begin on the cover. Here, in large letters, is the statement "Dr. Teller refutes 9000 scientists." According to the dictionary, the word *refute* means "To disprove and overthrow by arguments or proofs; to prove to be false or erroneous." In fact Dr. Teller did not show that any single statement in the petition presented by 9235 scientists to the United Nations was false or erroneous. He did not disprove and overthrow, by any valid argument, evidence, or proof, any part of the petition.

Following the example of *Life* Magazine in its statement on the cover of their issue of 10 February 1958, I shall from now on speak of Dr. Teller, rather than both authors, in discussing the article and book by Drs. Teller and Latter.

The way in which Dr. Teller underestimates the fallout risks can be illustrated by his figures on radiation due to strontium-90. . . .

The best information that we now have about strontium-90 in the bones of man was published in the 7 February 1958 issue of the magazine *Science* by Dr. J. Laurence Kulp of the Lamont Geological Observatory of Columbia University and his colleagues Drs. W. R. Eckelmann and A. R. Schulert. Their results lead to the equilibrium level of 20 micro-microcuries of strontium-90 per gram of calcium, if testing is continued at the present rate. This corresponds to about 0.05 roentgen per year of radiation to the bones—not a five-fold increase, as Dr. Teller said, but a 25-fold increase over the present value for children, and a 167-fold increase over the present value for adults.

Dr. Teller's statement underestimates the future danger by a factor of 5, relative to children, or of 33, relative to adults.

Dr. Teller mentions that the people of Tibet have been exposed for generation after generation to a considerably larger amount of cosmic radiation than people who live at lower altitudes, and says "Yet genetic differences have not been noted in the humans of Tibet, or for that matter in any other living species there."

He surely knew, or should have known, that the increased amount of cosmic radiation in Tibet is such as to produce an estimated 15-per cent increase in the incidence of seriously defective children in Tibet. Instead of 2 per cent of the babies being born seriously defective because of bad genes, about 2.3 per cent might be expected in Tibet. And he surely knew, or should have known, that there exist no medical statistics whatever for Tibet to permit one to say whether or not there are somewhat more defective children born there than in the United States.

This paragraph about Tibet in Dr. Teller's article in *Life* Magazine cannot strictly be said to be incorrect. It is true that genetic differences that might be attributed to cosmic radiation have not been noticed in the humans of Tibet or other living species there; but it is also true that they have not been looked for. Thus the paragraph has to be described as seriously misleading.

In a television debate with Dr. Teller on 20 February 1958 I said to him that this argument was a red herring, designed to mislead the reader, and I asked him why he had included it in the *Life* article. He said that the argument had been included in order to "quiet excessive fears."

He also made a statement in the article and the book about the American servicemen and Marshallese islanders who had been exposed to fallout radioactivity after the Bikini explosion of 1 March 1954. . . . "The important fact is that today, more than three years after the accident, all of the Marshallese and American victims seem to be fully recovered from a dosage of radioactivity far greater than any humans are ever likely to be subjected to again from a bomb test. Although long-term effects are being carefully watched for, no malignancies or cases of leukemia have shown up to date."

But the probability of incidence of leukemia or bone cancer after exposure to radiation . . . is such that the exposure received by these 267 human beings would be expected to cause about one death by leukemia or bone cancer among them in 25 years. The fact that none of the American servicemen or Marshallese islanders has died of leukemia or bone cancer during three years has accordingly little value as evidence.

THE DENVER ARGUMENT

One argument that has been used by spokesmen for the Atomic Energy Commission to "allay the fears of the people" about the effects of fallout is an argument based on a comparison of the incidence of leukemia and bone cancer in Denver with that in San Francisco and New Orleans. . . .

The argument is, however, misleading. It has no significance upon the question whether or not fallout radiation causes leukemia and bone cancer, because the medical statistics at the present time are not good enough to detect the predicted difference, and because other factors may hide this effect. . . .

Nobody knows why there has been reported a larger incidence of bone cancer and leukemia in San Francisco than in Denver and New Orleans. It is possible that the medical statistics given in the table are so unreliable as to put the cities in the wrong order—the number of cases of bone cancer and leukemia in these cities in 1947 was so small that statistical fluctuations would cause each of the numbers in the table to be uncertain by one or two units, so that the differences cannot be considered to be very significant. Also, it is possible that the exposure to natural radioactivity—radium and potassium-40—is different in the different cities. It is not unlikely that the exposure to medical X-rays is significantly different in the different cities; it is with little doubt considerably larger in San Francisco than in the other two cities. It is probable that the average age of the people in Denver is less than that of the people in the other two cities, and the incidence of cancer increases with increasing age. And it may be that patients with these diseases are attracted to San Francisco and New Orleans by their medical facilities, and not to Denver. . . .

Dr. Teller and Dr. Latter say that the statistics *prove* that radiation in small doses need not necessarily be harmful, may conceivably be helpful. *The statistics do not prove this in any way—* . . . *these statistics do not prove anything.*

THE FABLE OF THE WRIST WATCH

Dr. Willard F. Libby, a distinguished scientist and member of the Atomic Energy Commision, in an article in *Science* (**122**, 57, 1955; also *The Nature of Radioactive Fallout and Its Effects on Man*, page 1460) wrote: "A wrist watch worn 24 hours per day that has a luminous dial assumed to have 1 microcurie of radium per watch—a figure perhaps slightly larger than the average—would give the central body, including the sex organs (at average distance of 1 foot), a dosage of about 0.040 roentgen per year."

Dr. Teller then wrote in his book and his *Life* Magazine article that a wrist watch with a luminous dial subjects us to much more radiation than we get from fallout. He amplified this statement in a chart . . . (Figures 10–6 and 10–7.)

Dr. Teller contends that the radiation danger to the average person is ten times as great from wrist watches as from fallout.

He overestimates the wrist watch effect greatly—I think that he has taken it to be about 100 times as great as it actually is for the average

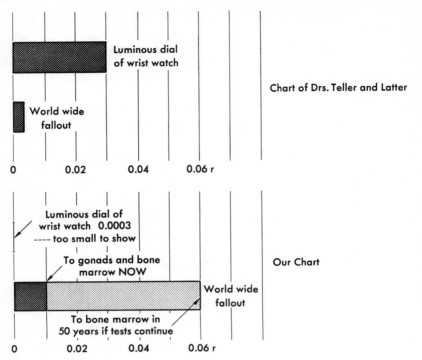

Figure 10–7.

person in the United States, and about 500 times as great as it actually is for the average person in the world.

Dr. Libby said that his 1 microcurie of radium might be a larger amount than that for the average wrist watch. The British Report of the Medical Research Council for presentation to Parliament (*The Nature of Radioactive Fallout and Its Effects on Man*, page 1593) says that measurements and calculations give one fifth of a microcurie of radium for the average wrist watch.

Dr. Libby's calculation was for a watch one foot from the gonads, 24 hours a day, throughout the life of the person. I think that 16 or 18 inches is a better distance, and that watches are often worn only a part of each day and during only a part of a lifetime. These two circumstances probably introduce a correction factor of ¼.

Moreover, only about 15 per cent of the people in the United States and Europe wear wrist watches with radium dials, and probably less than 3 per cent of the people in the world. This fact gives a correction factor of 0.15 or 0.03.

Dr. Teller cannot contend that his chart was to show the radiation exposure of those people wearing wrist watches, rather than the average person. First, the legend to his figure reads "Radiation danger to the average person." Second, he gives in the chart a representation of the value for medical X-rays which is the average value for all people in the United States, and not the much higher value for those who receive X-ray treatment.

The exposure of the gonads of the average person in the United States to wrist watch radioactivity is hence about $0.040 \times \frac{1}{5} \times \frac{1}{4} \times 0.15 = 0.0003$ roentgen per year. The exposure for the average person in the world is about 0.00006 roentgen per year.

The value given by Dr. Teller for radiation danger to the average person from luminous dials of wrist watches, 0.030 roentgen per year, is 100 times too large for the average person in the United States, and 500 times too large for the average person in the world! Compare our chart with the Teller-Latter chart (Figure 10–7).

Both in their book and in their article in *Life* Magazine Dr. Teller and Dr. Latter include the statement "Since the people are the sovereign power in a democracy, it is of the greatest importance that they should be honestly and completely informed about all the relevant facts." This statement seems to be out of place.

THE SAFE NUCLEAR BOMB

In his book and his *Life* Magazine article Dr. Teller shows a photograph of five intrepid Air Force officers standing unsheltered while a nuclear bomb explodes 19,000 feet directly above their heads. They experienced only a wave of warmth, a loud noise, and no significant rise in radioactivity.

Can we conclude from this that nuclear bombs are safe? No! Such a conclusion is not justified.

If the bomb had been exploded at 1900 feet, rather than 19,000 feet, the immediate radiation would have been 100 times as great, and the officers might not have been able to live through the experience. The Hiroshima bomb was detonated at an altitude of 2200 feet.

Dr. Teller does not say how big the bomb was. It was probably smaller than one kiloton. He does not say that the bombs that are ready for use in attack on the U.S. and the U.S.S.R. are 10,000 or 20,000 times more powerful. The officers could not stand unharmed under such a bomb.

One does not have to be an H-bomb scientist or to have secret information to know that Dr. Teller's miniscule bomb was a simple fission bomb, made of plutonium (possibly mixed with some uranium-235). It was a "dirty" bomb, releasing much radioactivity, in relation to its explosive energy. Yet Mr. Leonard Engel, in his review of the Teller-Latter book in *The New York Times Book Review* for 23 March 1958, was misled into describing this bomb as showing the progress that has been made in developing "clean" nuclear explosives!

MPD AND MPC

Amounts of radiation and of radioactive elements are often compared with the Maximum Permissible Dose (MPD) of radiation and the Maximum Permissible Concentration (MPC) of radioactive elements. The significance of these quantities is still uncertain, and there has been much misunderstanding of their meaning.

Beginning in 1928, the International Commission on Radiological Protection has set standards and procedures for protection from radiation and radioactive materials on an international basis. The same work has been done for the United States since 1929 by the National Committee on Radiation Protection and Measurement. From time to time recommendations are made by these organizations about the permissible doses for external radiation and internal radiation and for protection against high-energy radiation and radioactive elements in general.

The MPD and the MPC are not the amounts that are known to be safe, or to cause no harm whatever to human beings and to future generations. They are, instead, values that do not cause obvious harm. This fact is reflected in the history of the development of these standards of protection.

In 1925, when the International Commission on Radiological Units and Measurements was established by the First International Congress of Radiology, the MPD was set as an amount that caused a certain amount of erythema (redness of the skin), which is estimated to correspond to 50 to 100 roentgens per year. In 1934 the International Commission on Radiological Protection adopted the MPC as 0.2 roentgen per day, equal to 72 roentgens per year. In 1935, the National Committee on Radiological Protection adopted the value of 0.1 roentgen per day, equal to 36 roentgens per year. In 1947 the NCRP lowered the MPD to 0.3 roentgen per week (15 roentgens per year), and in 1957 it was lowered again to 0.1 roentgen per week (5 roentgens per year). The change from 0.3 roentgen per week to 0.1 roentgen per week for people exposed to radiation in the course of their professional work was adopted by the AEC in December 1957.

The present MPC is accordingly only one fourteenth of that adopted in 1934. . . .

The recommendation has been made that the values of the MPD and MPC should be smaller for large populations, such as the population of the world as a whole, than for industrial workers and other small populations. Suggested values are one-tenth to one-fiftieth of the values for small groups of people. The argument involved is that a dose of radiation or a concentration of radioactive element that seriously damages the health of one out of, say, one hundred recipients might be tolerated in a small group, of the order of hundreds in size, but that it should not be tolerated for the whole population of the United States or of the world, because it would lead to damage to millions or tens of millions of individual human beings. Similarly, a gonad dose that increases by some amount the mutation rate for a few human beings in the world would not seriously damage the pool of human germ plasm, but a gonad dose of, say, 50 roentgens for the entire population of the world would double the mutation rate, and, if continued, would double the number of seriously defective children born in future generations.

It is not justified to speak of the MPD or MPC as a safe amount of exposure, or an amount of exposure that does no damage. An example of the misunderstanding that has arisen is provided by an article by correspondent Gladwyn Hill of *The New York Times* (9 June 1957). In discussing some tests of small nuclear weapons at the Nevada Test Area, Mr. Hill said that the amount of exposure of people in that neighborhood to fallout radioactivity and to radiation from the tests was far less than the amount 50 roentgens which had been set by the Committee on Biological Effects of Atomic Radiation of the National Academy of Science-National Research Council as the amount that does no harm. This was an error in interpretation; the Committee did not describe 50 roentgens, nor 10 roentgens, as an amount that does no harm, but instead said that any additional radiation is undesirable, that genetic harm is proportional to the total dose.

The best course that we can follow is that recommended by the Committee: *keep the dose as low as you can.* . . .

NUCLEAR WAR AND THE HUMAN RACE

The genetic consequences of a nuclear war would be terribly serious —100 times or 1000 times as serious as the effects of the bomb tests that have been carried out.

We may estimate from the exposures of the gonads to fallout radiation from the bomb tests that the gonad exposure during the first thirty years of life of children and young people during the 30-year period following a standard nuclear war, with 5000 megatons of fission, would amount to somewhere between 10 roentgens and 50 roentgens. This is in the range of the estimates of the doubling dose of the mutation rate by radiation, and accordingly the mutation rate would be doubled for that generation. A smaller effect would be found in each succeeding generation, as the amount of radioactivity decreased.

The mutation rate for human beings all over the world would be increased by approximately ten-fold by the worldwide fallout from a still greater nuclear war, with 50,000 megatons of fission.

In addition, consideration must be given to the genetic effects of the local fallout in the countries where the nuclear bombs were exploded. With possible exposures of the magnitudes of thousands of roentgens, the genetic effects would be expected to be very great in these countries. Many people would be rendered sterile. Many would have seriously defective children. There would also be some populations, in regions far distant from the places where bomb tests were carried out, where the genetic effect was small, and there might be a great effort in the post-nuclear-war period for these populations to preserve the integrity of their pool of germ plasm and to remain isolated from the mutated populations in the surrounding regions.

The people in India, China, Africa, South America, and Australia would also be affected by the radiation from the worldwide fallout. For them the number of seriously defective children born might increase from its present value of 2 per cent to a considerably larger value, and in addition there would be a corresponding increase in the number of mutant genes producing smaller disabilities. Dr. H. J. Muller in his address "The Radiation Danger," published in the *Colorado Quarterly* for 1958, has pointed out that the total load of mutant genes in the population at the present time is such that about one person in five dies without progeny because of their effect, and hence if the load were to be increased five-fold there might be serious consequences.

There is a real possibility that a great nuclear war would change the nature of the pool of human germ plasm in such a way that the human species, as we know it, would not survive. This danger is a significant one for people living in every part of the world, but especially great for those in countries in which the nuclear war would be fought.

THE "CLEAN" BOMB

Ever since the possibility of making a hydrogen bomb was first discussed it has been recognized that nuclear bombs could be made with either a larger amount or a smaller amount of radioactive products.

The bomb of the Hiroshima type or the Nagasaki type produces a weight of radioactive fission products approximately equal to the weight of uranium-235 or plutonium-239 that has undergone fission. Also, a weight of radioactive fission products is produced approximately equal to that of the uranium that undergoes fission during the third stage of the detonation of a fission-fusion-fission superbomb, in addition to the products from the first fission stage. On the other hand, the fusion stage of a hydrogen bomb or a superbomb does not produce any very large quantity of radioactive products under ordinary conditions, except carbon-14.

A 20-megaton superbomb might produce the radioactive fission products corresponding to 10 megatons of fission, whereas a 20-megaton hydrogen bomb might produce radioactive materials corresponding in the main only to the 40 kilotons of fission involved in its first stage. For the same explosive power, the hydrogen bomb would have produced only 4 per cent as much radioactive material other than carbon-14 as the superbomb.

The superbomb is called a "dirty" bomb and the hydrogen bomb a "clean" bomb. This is the basis of the statement made by President Eisenhower that a 96-per cent clean bomb had been made.

There is, of course, the possibility that a bomb with still smaller ratio of radioactive products to explosive power can be constructed. Atomic bombs (fission bombs) with as small as 1 kiloton energy have been detonated. I do not know whether or not they contained a larger amount of fissionable material than the amount that underwent fission, but there is the possibility that the small amount of uranium-235 or plutonium-239 that would give 1 kiloton equivalent of explosive energy could be made to undergo essentially complete fission. If, then, a hydrogen bomb could be designed in such a way that this small amount of fissionable material would cause the fusion stage to take place, such a bomb, with total explosive power of 20 megatons, could be described as 99.9-per cent clean (except for its carbon-14).[1]

There are probably some serious technical difficulties involved in making a bomb with as little radioactivity as this, but there is a possibility that it can be done.

It is, on the other hand, unlikely that a bomb can be constructed in the near future that involves no fission whatever. Moreover, in order that there be no radioactivity, no materials could be used in the construction

---

1. Since this article was written it has been recognized that carbon-14 represents a very important biological hazard. It is formed when neutrons, which are produced in large numbers by *all* nuclear bombs, collide with nitrogen atoms in the atmosphere. Furthermore, the half-life of carbon-14 is very long (over 5000 years), so that its effect will be experienced by hundreds of generations. These facts make the concept of a "clean" bomb in the sense discussed here an impossibility. Ed.

of the bomb itself that could absorb neutrons to produce radioactivity isotopes, and no air could be around when it explodes.

In several speeches I have objected to the use of the expression the "clean" bomb. I have said that to call any weapon that can kill millions of people a "clean" bomb is to insult a noble word in the English language —the word clean. This comment, of course, has nothing to do with the radioactivity of the fission products; it is the expression of an objection to the immorality of war, and especially of nuclear war.

The argument has been used by President Eisenhower and by Dr. Teller that it is essential that the testing of nuclear weapons be continued in order that clean bombs be developed. For example, Drs. Teller and Latter in their article in *Life* Magazine said: "If we stop testing now and if we should fail to develop to the fullest possible extent these clean weapons, we would unnecessarily kill a great number of non-combatants in a future war. Not to develop the explosives with the smallest possible radioactive fallout would, indeed, be completely inexcusable."

I believe that the argument is fallacious. It seems to suggest that nuclear wars might be fought with non-radioactive weapons only.

Drs. Teller and Latter say that the fallout radioactivity might kill people in our own country or in the country whose liberty we are trying to defend and that we should for this reason be able to use nuclear weapons that cause the least possible contamination. They do not say that we should use nuclear weapons with little radioactivity in attacking the enemy country, and, in fact, we may be sure that in a nuclear war the weapons that would be used in attacking the enemy country, and that would be used against us, would be weapons with a large amount of radioactive fallout.

War is conducted in such a way as to produce the greatest damage to the enemy. A military leader who is given a choice between the principles of humanity and an effective defense of his nation always abandons the principles of humanity.

During the Second World War it was found that the saturation bombing of cities, doing damage to women and children and other non-combatants, was a far more effective way of waging war than the bombing of military objectives only, and the saturation way, despite its greater immorality, was adopted.

Far greater damage can be done to an enemy nation with the use of superbombs than can be done, for the same amount of effort, with the use of hydrogen bombs.

Let us, for example, assume that we have a stockpile of some thousands of 10-megaton hydrogen bombs. Each one may have, as part of its design, a tamper in the form of a metal shell surrounding the fusionable material. If this tamper, perhaps a one-thousand-pound metal shell, is replaced by a similar one-thousand-pound shell made of the metal uranium, the bomb is converted from a 10-megaton hydrogen bomb to a 20-megaton super-bomb. The cost of this conversion is practically zero—perhaps $15,000 for the uranium. For this small cost the bomb is changed into a superbomb with twice the explosive power and nearly twice the power of causing destruction and death through blast, fire, and immediate radiation effects. And, moreover, it is changed from a bomb with little radioactivity to a bomb with great radioactivity. The superbomb, detonated near the ground, can discharge as much as 80 per cent of its radioactive fission products into a radioactive local fallout that in large part descends within an hour or two over an area of 10,000 square miles near the point of explosion, with the possibility of killing through its radioactivity a large fraction of the people in this area of 10,000 square miles. This makes the weapon such a powerful one, in comparison with the 10-megaton hydrogen bomb, that no military leader would be willing to forego its use.

Moreover, there is little reason to expect that he would be dissuaded from using the weapon by the damage that the radioactivity would do to his own countrymen. Only 20 per cent of the fission products would go into the atmosphere, to descend later on, over a period of years, as worldwide fallout. A large fraction of the radioactive material would have decomposed before descending to the surface of the earth, and the effects of the remaining radioactive material may be described, as has been done so often by representatives of the AEC in discussing the tests, as being "negligible" or as being "small in comparison with many risks that we take in our everyday life."

There is no hope that a nuclear war will be fought with "clean" bombs. The "clean" bomb, in fact, may be a red herring which causes people to cease to worry about the perils of radioactivity. In the summer of 1957 it seemed to serve effectively as propaganda to stop, for a while, the growing concern about the horrors of nuclear weapons and nuclear war.

We might ask the question "Would it not be possible to achieve an international agreement to use only 'clean' bombs in future wars?" This is, however, not a sensible question. If such an international agreement could be reached, under which the great nations of the world would agree to limit themselves in a really serious way in waging war, it should be possible to reach international agreements about disputed questions without resorting to war at all.

If our nuclear future includes nuclear war, the world is lost.

Posing the Issue *

by Steven M. Spencer (1959)

The pervasive by-product of weapons testing now blankets the entire planet. It contaminates the air, the sea and the soil. It lies twice as thick over the Northern Hemisphere as the Southern, and is more heavily concentrated in the United States than anywhere else on the earth's surface. . . . (the greater concentration here and in other countries of similar latitude is due partly to the location of one of the two overhead cracks, which were discovered about fifteen years ago. They apparently girdle the earth over the North and South Temperate Zones—which happen to be the most populous. One is located at thirty to forty degrees north latitude—it is farther north in summer—and the other is at a similar distance south of the equator). . . .

Every living creature, man included, has in its body a few particles of radioactive strontium-90, some of which will remain for life.

Moreover, the fallout will get worse before it gets better, even if bomb tests are never resumed. The spring of 1959, contrary to some of the forecasts, was radioactively the "hottest" yet, due in large part to the Russian tests of last fall. Scientists estimate that the burden of accumulated bomb debris now floating in the stratosphere, seven to ten miles up, is so great that "drip-out" to the ground will actually increase for seven or eight years before it begins to taper off.

Upon these basic facts of fallout the experts are in fair agreement. But there is sharp and disturbing disagreement among them, and among Government officials, members of Congress and plain ordinary citizens, as to what the fallout figures mean in terms of hazard to the present and future populations of the world.

How concerned should we be, then, about the amounts of radioactivity in the air we breathe, the water we drink, the food we eat, the milk we give our babies and growing children? Is fallout partly responsible for the reported rise in leukemia? Is it also inducing other forms of cancer? Will it shorten our lives through subtle, nonspecific effects, as laboratory-applied radiation has shortened the lives of mice?

And what about the genetic effects? Are we now, without knowing it, sowing bad seed that will cause an increased number of physical and

* From Steven M. Spencer, "Fallout: The Silent Killer," *Saturday Evening Post,* August 29 and September 5, 1959. © by the Curtis Publishing Company in United States and Great Britain. Reprinted by permission.

mental defectives to be born to future generations? And finally, are the biological risks, no matter how small or large, worth taking as the cost of developing bigger, cheaper or more "discriminating" nuclear weapons?

Such questions do not lend themselves to quick, precise answers. No scientific issue in many years has so exasperatingly eluded all efforts to lay hands upon the truth. . . .

What it all boils down to is a question of human risk versus military risk. The United States is faced with the necessity of weighing a definite but as yet unmeasurable hazard against an uncertain benefit. The hazard is that continued nuclear testing—and perhaps even the testing we have already done—will create more physical and mental defectives within the world's future population, and possibly even some cancer or life-shortening in the present generations. The uncertain benefit is that testing will discourage Russia from attacking us.

In the meantime an elaborate program of world-wide sampling goes forward to keep track of the bomb debris already in the atmosphere and on the ground. And scores of research studies on biological effects of radiation are under way to see that human exposure to all radiation—bombs, nuclear reactors, isotopes, medical X rays and the natural background—is kept within reasonable limits. For all radiation is harmful to some degree, as the famous 1956 report of the National Academy of Sciences and National Research Council warned. . . .

Says Dr. James F. Crow, professor of genetics at the University of Wisconsin, a member of a special committee of the National Academy of Sciences: "No dose, however small, is free of all risk of mutation." In the light of this statement who can say when a "permissible" dose is "acceptable"? Is it morally right for anyone to "accept" the risk of damage to future generations? . . .

It must be recognized that the statements of . . . experts can only reflect their careful evaluation of evidence which isn't yet as good as they would like it to be. The vast global-sampling networks and the busy clicking of radiation counters have not yet given the final answers to all the questions bothering an uneasy world. Radioactive fallout is a silent killer which hides its poison among the more familiar causes of human illness and death and thus postpones positive identification. Its damage to our hereditary endowment, often called man's most priceless possession, may take generations to make itself felt. Therefore we may have to wait a half century or more before we can add up the total cost of our atomic arming. But there will be a cost in disease, deformity and early death for many yet unborn.

That is the reason the fallout controversy is important. It poses an issue the world's people and their governments cannot ignore if they have any regard for the future of man. They must weigh the facts and arguments carefully as they face the great decisions on atomic testing and arming versus a more sincere and wholehearted support of peace negotiations. For the result of a wrong decision made today probably can never be corrected.

Often in evolutionary processes a species must adapt to new conditions in order to survive. Today the atomic bomb has altered profoundly the nature of the world as we know it, and the human race consequently finds itself in a new habitat to which it must adapt its thinking.

During the war many persons fell out of the habit of doing their own thinking, for many had to do simply what they were told to do. Today lack of interest would be a great error, for there is much the average man can do about this danger.

This nation held a great debate concerning the menace of the Axis, and again today we need a great chain reaction of awareness and communication. Current proposals should be discussed in the light of the basic facts, in every newspaper, in schools, churches, in town meetings, in private conversations, and neighbor to neighbor. Merely reading about the bomb promotes knowledge in the mind, but only talk between men promotes feelings in the heart.

Albert Einstein
New York Times Magazine, June 23, 1946

Decisionmaking in the Nuclear Age *

by Hans J. Morgenthau (1962)

The event which occurred twenty years ago on Stagg Field of the University of Chicago has had three major consequences for our society: the expansion of our understanding of, and mastery over, nature; a radical change in the nature of warfare; and the atrophy both of democratic control over the government and of responsible government itself. The first chain reaction and what followed it have not so much created these three developments as accentuated them, greatly hastened their pace, and made at least some of their consequences obvious for all to see. The nuclear age is the—probably provisional—culmination of developments which moved slowly forward from the Renaissance to about the middle of the nineteenth century, accelerated their pace drastically during the following century, and under the impact of the second world war brought

* *Bulletin of the Atomic Scientists*, December, 1962. Reprinted by permission.

forth quantitative changes of such magnitude as to amount to a qualitative transformation of the political environment.

This is obvious—or at least ought to be—in the field of military technology. The H-bomb is in a sense nothing more than the quantitative extension of the principle which was first established by the machine gun more than a century ago: the ability of one combatant to eliminate through one action a multiplicity of enemies. Yet allowing for the simultaneous long-distance elimination of virtually whole populations has destroyed the traditional national relationship between violence as a means and the ends of foreign policy. The impossibility of adapting nuclear violence to the limited objectives of foreign policy has made nuclear war a suicidal absurdity.

The effects which the nuclear age has had upon the nature of modern government and its relations with the governed are less obvious but no less drastic than the military ones. Throughout the ages, the most effective check upon the powers of the government has been the possibility of popular revolution. It is a characteristic of the nuclear age that popular revolution is no longer possible. The impossibility of popular revolution is the result of technological changes which have put into the hands of governments a near monopoly of the most destructive instruments of violence and of the most effective means of communication and transportation.

It is not by accident that the rise of totalitarian government coincides with these technological changes. For these changes have made it possible for a traditional tyranny or autocracy to transform itself into a totalitarian regime. The central problem for a totalitarian government is to maintain control over the apparatus of the state. As long as the bureaucracy and the army remain loyal to the central government the people at large are impotent in the face of it. We are living in an age not of popular revolution but of *coups d' état*.

In countries which have maintained their democratic institutions, the enormous increase in the powers of the government goes hand in hand with the atrophy of democratic institutions. The great issues of state can no longer be understood, as they formerly were, by any knowledgeable man of average intelligence. That understanding requires a large degree of expert knowledge which is much more readily available to the government than to the individual citizen, part of which, because of its classified nature, is available only to the government or only to privileged sectors within it. Thus the government can speak in these matters with an authority unmatched by that of any individual or group outside it. Take as an instance last year's resumption of atmospheric nuclear tests. The reasons in favor of that resumption were first presented to the people in a cogent form at the moment the President announced the decision itself. There was in the nature of things no possibility for a meaningful popular discussion.

The reasons for this lack of popular participation in the great decisions of our age are two-fold. On the one hand, the issues with which these decisions deal are far removed from the life experiences of the man in the street. It is significant that the people at large became emotionally involved with the issue of atomic testing not on the basis of the merits of the case itself, but on the basis of what is really a side issue, that of fallout. For atomic fallout has a direct potential connection with the life of all of us and thus, while nobody really knows how important the danger of atomic fallout is to the health of the individual, the relation to our lives is direct and we react to it. But to the much more important issues of an unabated armaments race and the spread of nuclear weapons to an indefinite number of nations, the people at large are indifferent because the impact of these issues upon our lives is a matter of intellectual speculation, not of direct life experiences.

The other reason for the decline of popular participation in the great decisions of our age lies in what is generally regarded to be the technological complexity of the issues involved. Few laymen pretend to understand the technicalities of nuclear energy, such as the merits of underground testing versus atmospheric testing or the possibilities of detecting underground tests by techniques of inspection and control. Thus most of us have abdicated our personal judgment; we have left it to the scientists to decide.

This abdication on the part of the people as a whole vis-à-vis the government as a whole has been duplicated within the government. The belief in the technological complexity of the great political issues, intelligible only to a select few, has brought forth a shift of power within the government from the democratically responsible authorities to technological elites which are not subject to democratic control. To a certain extent at least, democratically responsible leadership has abdicated its responsibility to the leadership of technological elites, military and civilian, the guardians of the "arcana imperii." For the democratically responsible authorities have felt no more able to arrive at an independent judgment with regard to the great issues of the day, all of which to a greater or lesser degree have technological connotations, than did the people at large.

This has always been so in the relations between the civilian and military authorities. It has now also become true in the relations between the political and technical authorities. The Atomic Energy Commission, for instance, has become a kind of a state within the state. A few years ago, a very high official of our government told me that the Atomic Energy Commission would not tell him how many nuclear weapons we had. And recently, a former high official of the Atomic Energy Commission corroborated this experience from the other side by telling me that there are lots of things the State Department ought to know nothing about and which ought to remain a matter between the President and the director of the Central Intelligence Agency. There exists, then, a special secrecy within the general secrecy of the government which serves the purpose of protecting the monopolistic position of certain technological elites, of which the elite of the nuclear scientists is the most eminent and the most influential one.

What is the remedy for this dislocation of political power within the democratic state, brought about by the technological and, more particularly, the nuclear revolutions? The answer to that question is simple. It derives from the nature of the technological decision itself. There is a fundamental difference between a decision concerning the operations of a technological device *per se,* and a decision concerning the future use of a technological device in a political-military context. The factors going into the former are accessible only to the expert; the latter are a matter of conjecture based on technologically informed commonsense and, hence, accessible to all endowed with commonsense.

As concerns the great political decisions of the nuclear age, the technological expert does not know more than the man in the street or the politically responsible official. But he is made to pretend to have a monopoly of the answers because of the abdication of judgment on the part of the latter. And it is with his arcana as it was with those of old: they have to be guarded, in the words of the *Encyclopaedia Britannica,* as "essential points of the Mystery—which nevertheless everyone could come to know who desired to." Participants in our democratic processes can come to know the politically relevant secrets of the nuclear age if they regain confidence in their ability to judge for themselves on the basis of commonsense and if the scientific elites let them in on the secrets of their trade. It is then for the political authorities and, more particularly, for the President to present to the people ahead of the decision the alternative solutions to the great issues where scientific knowledge and political judgment meet.

Questions To Consider

If scientists decided that doubling the mutation rate would speed the evolution of man at the expense of producing millions of lethal mutations, would you be in favor of this course of action?

Would it be desirable to reduce the mutation rate if this should become possible?

Should man tamper at all with the balance of nature?

Do you agree with Muller that "it is by the standard of whether individuals are harmed, rather than whether the human race will be wiped out, that we should judge the propriety of everyday practices that may affect the human genetic constitution"?

Do you agree with Pauling that "Natural selection is a cruel way, and man has now outgrown it"?

What is the source of disagreement between Pauling and Teller? Is it a disagreement about the facts? About the interpretation of the facts? Or about the ethics involved in decisions based on these facts?

On the basis of our *present* scientific knowledge, what action do you think we should take about increasing the level of radiation throughout the world?

Suggestions for Further Reading

* Hardin, Garrett: *Nature and Man's Fate,* Mentor Books, The New American Library, 1959. A well-written presentation of the principles of heredity and the genetic influence on evolution. In the light of present knowledge of evolution, the author investigates the prospects for man's future. The selection beginning on p. 569 was taken from this book.

* Pauling, Linus: *No More War!,* Dodd, Mead and Company, 1962, enlarged edition. For the reader who is interested in further details of the argument between Pauling and Teller we recommend all of this book and the one by Teller and Latter.

* Schubert, Jack, and Ralph E. Lapp: *Radiation: What It Is and How It Affects You,* Compass Books, The Viking Press, 1957. Although not strictly up to date, this book contains valuable background information presented in language that can be understood by the student and layman.

* Teller, Edward, and Albert Latter: *Our Nuclear Future,* Criterion Publishers, 1958. The material that appears in the selection beginning on p. 582 is a condensation of some of the material from this book.

* Paperback edition

11

Is Science Destroyer or Creator?

Science has given man knowledge into the forces of nature and created new powers which can be used for good or for evil. Has man caused his own inevitable fall by eating of the tree of knowledge? Could he still return to the state of innocence by rejecting science? Or is it possible for him to rise to a higher level of adaptation, accepting the responsibility to understand and use the new knowledge for the good of all mankind?

Is Science Destroyer or Creator?

Introduction

THE THEME of a "forbidden knowledge" is deeply ingrained in our cultural heritage. It has appeared in religion, legend, and literature. The story of Adam and Eve, Pandora's Box, and Faustus are notable examples. During the Middle Ages the forbidden fruit was identified with the study of nature. In the earthly sphere, nature itself was considered to be imperfect and corrupt. It followed, therefore, that the investigation of the secrets of nature was a sinful pursuit, involving a compact with the devil and the death of the soul. Truth itself was to be found in an entirely different sphere, in religion and divine revelation rather than in the sphere of rational thought. Alchemists and astrologists were looked upon as practitioners of black magic and any belief in the natural virtue of man was considered heresy.

The scientific movement of the Renaissance brought about a profound change in this view of nature. In the end it resulted in the triumph of rationalism and the belief that God revealed himself through nature. The universe was God's handiwork and, therefore, to study it was a form of religious affirmation. One of the philosophers who was most influential in bringing about this change was Sir Francis Bacon. In *The Advancement of Learning* he discusses the medieval conception of natural philosophy and takes pains to elucidate "the ignorance and error" of this opinion. "It is not the knowledge of nature itself," he says, "but the vanity which it may cause in man which is the source of evil." He sets down three recommendations to avoid this evil, "the first, that we do not so place our felicity in knowledge, as we forget our mortality; the second, that we make application of our knowledge, to give ourselves repose and contentment, and not distaste or repining; the third, that we do not presume by the contemplation of nature to attain to the mysteries of God." [1]

Several of the authors of these selections feel that the emphasis on practical application expressed in Bacon's second recommendation has actually been responsible for some of the dangers that beset our scientific age: the rapid exploitation of practical advantage rather than the pursuit of knowledge for its own sake, and the lip service paid even by great theoretical scientists to these values. This materialistic emphasis, they maintain, has obscured the real aims of science and has contributed to the schism between scientists and intellectuals in other fields. It has also helped to create false images of science in the public mind. These images

1. See Francis Bacon selection, p. 621.

which Gerald Holton describes, are symptomatic of the rift between science and society.

It is interesting that three of the false images represent different aspects of a return to the medieval view of man's relationship to God and nature. One of these images is based on the view that knowledge leads man away from God, another views the scientist as the evil practitioner of black magic, and a third views man as being too corrupt to handle the new powers which science has uncovered. We may well ask whether a return to medieval concepts and a retreat from the rational approach will help solve the problems of the modern world.

Rejection of science and return to a simpler world represents one of the two solutions presented in these readings. The other can be summarized in the words of H. G. Wells, "Let us get wise as soon as possible." This course of action would involve an adaptation in our thinking to the new conditions of the scientific age. It would demand, according to Bronowski, that we put science and our social habits back in step by learning to understand *both;* and it would require a closer correlation between our moral code and the practical realities of human relations. It would imply a deeper respect for the pursuit of pure knowledge, Dubos insists. Finally, it would necessitate a recognition of the limitations of our own cleverness. This statement of Garrett Hardin's is reminiscent of Bacon's warning that vanity is the real source of the evils resulting from the knowledge of nature. The various aspects of this solution as presented by the different authors in these selections are complex and demanding. The final question we must ask is: Can we get wise soon enough?

Is Science the Forbidden Fruit?

The Garden of Eden *
Genesis

And the Lord God planted a garden eastward in Eden; and there he put the man whom he had formed.

And out of the ground made the Lord God to grow every tree that is pleasant to the sight, and good for food; the tree of life also in the midst of the garden, and the tree of knowledge of good and evil.

And a river went out of Eden to water the garden; and from thence it was parted, and became into four heads.

The name of the first is Pison: that is it which compasseth the whole land of Havilah, where there is gold;

And the gold of that land is good: there is bdellium and the onyx stone.

And the name of the second river is Gihon: the same is it that compasseth the whole land of Ethiopia.

And the name of the third river is Hiddekel: that is it which goeth toward the east of Assyria. And the fourth river is Euphrates.

And the Lord God took the man, and put him into the garden of Eden to dress it and to keep it.

And the Lord God commanded the man, saying, Of every tree of the garden thou mayest freely eat:

But of the tree of the knowledge of good and evil, thou shalt not eat of it: for in the day that thou eatest thereof thou shalt surely die.

And the Lord God said, It is not good that the man should be alone; I will make him an help meet for him.

And out of the ground the Lord God formed every beast of the field, and every fowl of the air; and brought them unto Adam to see what he would call them: and whatsoever Adam called every living creature, that was the name thereof.

And Adam gave names to all cattle, and to the fowl of the air, and to every beast of the field; but for Adam there was not found an help meet for him.

* From Genesis, 2. 8-25; 3, Authorized King James Version.

Figure 11-1. "The Expulsion from Paradise," Masaccio (1401-28), Florence, Brancacci Chapel. (Photograph courtesy of the Bettmann Archive.)

Figure 11–2. *Detail of Figure* 11–1.

And the Lord God caused a deep sleep to fall upon Adam, and he slept: and he took one of his ribs, and closed up the flesh instead thereof;

And the rib, which the Lord God had taken from man, made he a woman, and brought her unto the man.

And Adam said, This is now bone of my bones, and flesh of my flesh: she shall be called Woman, because she was taken out of Man.

Therefore shall a man leave his father and his mother, and shall cleave unto his wife: and they shall be one flesh.

And they were both naked, the man and his wife, and were not ashamed.

Now the serpent was more subtil than any beast of the field which the Lord God had made. And he said unto the woman, Yea, hath God said, Ye shall not eat of every tree of the garden?

And the woman said unto the serpent, We may eat of the fruit of the trees of the garden:

But of the fruit of the tree which is in the midst of the garden, God hath said, Ye shall not eat of it, neither shall ye touch it, lest ye die.

And the serpent said unto the woman, Ye shall not surely die:

For God doth know that in the day ye eat thereof, then your eyes shall be opened, and ye shall be as gods, knowing good and evil.

And when the woman saw that the tree was good for food, and that it was pleasant to the eyes, and a tree to be desired to make one wise, she took of the fruit thereof, and did eat, and gave also unto her husband with her; and he did eat.

And the eyes of them both were opened, and they knew that they were naked; and they sewed fig leaves together, and made themselves aprons.

And they heard the voice of the Lord God walking in the garden in the cool of the day: and Adam and his wife hid themselves from the presence of the Lord God amongst the trees of the garden.

And the Lord God called unto Adam and said unto him, Where art thou?

And he said, I heard thy voice in the garden, and I was afraid, because I was naked; and I hid myself.

And he said, Who told thee that thou wast naked? Hast thou eaten of the tree, whereof I commanded thee that thou shouldest not eat?

And the man said, The woman whom thou gavest to be with me, she gave me of the tree, and I did eat.

And the Lord God said unto the woman, What is this that thou hast done? And the woman said, The serpent beguiled me, and I did eat.

And the Lord God said unto the serpent, Because thou hast done this, thou art cursed above all cattle, and above every beast of the field; upon thy belly shalt thou go, and dust shalt thou eat all the days of thy life:

And I will put enmity between thee and the woman, and between thy seed and her seed; it shall bruise thy head, and thou shalt bruise his heel.

Unto the woman he said, I will greatly multiply thy sorrow and thy conception; in sorrow thou shalt bring forth children; and thy desire shall be to thy husband, and he shall rule over thee.

And unto Adam he said, Because thou has hearkened unto the voice of thy wife, and hast eaten of the tree, of which I commanded thee, saying, Thou shalt not eat of it: cursed is the ground for thy sake; in sorrow shalt thou eat of it all the days of thy life;

Thorns also and thistles shall it bring forth to thee; and thou shalt eat the herb of the field;

In the sweat of thy face shalt thou eat bread, till thou return unto the ground; for out of it wast thou taken: for dust thou art, and unto dust shalt thou return.

And Adam called his wife's name Eve; because she was the mother of all living.

Unto Adam also and to his wife did the Lord God make coats of skins, and clothed them.

And the Lord God said, Behold, the man is become as one of us, to know good and evil: and now, lest he put forth his hand, and take also of the tree of life, and eat, and live for ever:

Therefore the Lord God sent him forth from the garden of Eden, to till the ground from whence he was taken.

So he drove out the man; and he placed at the east of the garden of Eden Cherubims, and a flaming sword which turned every way, to keep the way of the tree of life.

The Advancement of Learning [*]

by Francis Bacon (1605)

I hear the . . . [divines] say, that knowledge is of those things which are to be accepted of with great limitation and caution: that the aspiring to overmuch knowledge was the original temptation and sin whereupon ensued the fall of man: that knowledge hath in it somewhat of the serpent, and therefore where it entereth into a man it makes him swell; "*Scientia inflat*": [1] that Salomon gives a censure, "That there is no end of making books, and that much reading is weariness of the flesh"; and again in another place, "That in spacious knowledge there is much contristation, and that he that increaseth knowledge increaseth anxiety": [2] that Saint Paul gives a caveat, "That we be not spoiled through vain philosophy": [3] that experience demonstrates how learned men have been arch-heretics, how learned times have been inclined to atheism, and how the contemplation of second causes doth derogate from our dependence upon God, who is the first cause.

To discover then the ignorance and error of this opinion, and the misunderstanding in the grounds thereof, it may well appear these men do not observe or consider that it was not the pure knowledge of nature and universality, a knowledge by the light whereof man did give names unto other creatures in Paradise, as they were brought before him, according unto their proprieties, which gave the occasion to the fall: but it was the proud knowledge of good and evil, with an intent in man to give law unto himself, and to depend no more upon God's commandments, which was the form of the temptation. Neither is it any quantity of knowledge, how great soever, that can make the mind of man to swell; for nothing can fill, much less extend the soul of man, but God and the contemplation of God; and therefore Salomon, speaking of the two principal senses of

[*] From Francis Bacon, *The Advancement of Learning*, First Book.
1. "Knowledge puffs up."
2. Eccles. 12. 12, and 1. 18.
3. I Cor. 8. 1.

inquisition, the eye and the ear, affirmeth that "the eye is never satisfied with seeing, nor the ear with hearing"; [4] and if there be no fulness, then is the continent greater than the content: so of knowledge itself, and the mind of man, whereto the senses are but reporters, he defineth likewise in these words, placed after that Kalendar or Ephemerides which he maketh of the diversities of times and seasons for all actions and purposes; and concludeth thus: "God hath made all things beautiful, or decent, in the true return of their seasons: Also he hath placed the world in man's heart, yet cannot man find out the work which God worketh from the beginning to the end": [5] declaring not obscurely, that God hath framed the mind of man as a mirror or glass, capable of the image of the universal world, and joyful to receive the impression thereof, as the eye joyeth to receive light; and not only delighted in beholding the variety of things and vicissitude of times, but raised also to find out and discern the ordinances and decrees, which throughout all those changes are infallibly observed. And although he doth insinuate that the supreme or summary law of nature, which he calleth "The work which God worketh from the beginning to the end," is not possible to be found out by man; yet that doth not derogate from the capacity of the mind, but may be referred to the impediments, as of shortness of life, ill conjunction of labours, ill tradition of knowledge over from hand to hand, and many other inconveniences, whereunto the condition of man is subject. For that nothing parcel of the world is denied to man's inquiry and invention, he doth in another place rule over, when he saith, "The spirit of man is as the lamp of God, wherewith he searcheth the inwardness of all secrets." If then such be the capacity and receipt of the mind of man, it is manifest that there is no danger at all in the proportion or quantity of knowledge, how large soever, lest it should make it swell or out-compass itself; no, but it is merely the quality of knowledge, which, be it in quantity more or less, if it be taken without the true corrective thereof, hath in it some nature of venom or malignity, and some effects of that venom, which is ventosity or swelling. This corrective spice, the mixture whereof maketh knowledge so sovereign, is charity, which the Apostle immediately addeth to the former clause: for so he saith, "*Knowledge bloweth up, but charity buildeth up*"; [6] not unlike unto that which he delivereth in another place: "If I spake," saith he, "with the tongues of men and angels, and had not charity, it were but as a tinkling cymbal"; not but that it is an excellent thing to speak with the tongues of men and angels, but because, if it be severed from charity, and not referred to the good of men and mankind,

4. Eccles. 1. 8.
5. Eccles. 3. 11.
6. I Cor. 8. 1.

it hath rather a sounding and unworthy glory, than a meriting and substantial virtue. And as for that censure of Salomon, concerning the excess of writing and reading books, and the anxiety of spirit which redoundeth from knowledge; and that admonition of Saint Paul, "That we be not seduced by vain philosophy"; let those places be rightly understood, and they do indeed excellently set forth the true bounds and limitations, whereby human knowledge is confined and circumscribed; and yet without any such contracting or coarctation, but that it may comprehend all the universal nature of things; for these limitations are three; the first, that we do not so place our felicity in knowledge, as we forget our mortality; the second, that we make application of our knowledge, to give ourselves repose and contentment, and not distaste or repining: the third, that we do not presume by the contemplation of nature to attain to the mysteries of God.

Figure 11–3. "Wages of Avarice," by Pieter Bruegel (1525–69). (The German National Museum, Nuremberg.)

The Proper Study of Mankind *

by Alexander Pope (1733)

Know then thyself, presume not God to scan;
The proper study of Mankind is Man.
Placed on this isthmus of a middle state,
A Being darkly wise, and rudely great:
With too much knowledge for the Sceptic side,
With too much weakness for the Stoic's pride,
He hangs between; in doubt to act, or rest;
In doubt to deem himself a God, or Beast;
In doubt his Mind or Body to prefer;
Born but to die, and reasoning but to err;
Alike in ignorance, his reason such,
Whether he thinks too little, or too much:
Chaos of Thought and Passion, all confused;
Still by himself abused, or disabused;
Created half to rise, and half to fall;
Great lord of all things, yet a prey to all;
Sole judge of Truth, in endless Error hurled:
The glory, jest, and riddle of the world!
   Go, wondrous creature! mount where Science guides,
Go, measure earth, weigh air, and state the tides;
Instruct the planets in what orbs to run,
Correct old Time, and regulate the Sun;
Go, soar with Plato to th'empyreal sphere,
To the first good, first perfect, and first fair;
Or tread the mazy round his followers trod,
And quitting sense call imitating God;
As Eastern priests in giddy circles run,
And turn their heads to imitate the Sun.
Go, teach Eternal Wisdom how to rule—
Then drop into thyself, and be a fool!
   Superior beings, when of late they saw
A mortal man unfold all Nature's law,
Admired such wisdom in an earthly shape,
And showed a NEWTON as we show an Ape.
   Could he, whose rules the rapid Comet bind,

* From Alexander Pope, *Essay on Man*, Epistle II.

Describe or fix one movement of his Mind?
Who saw its fires here rise, and there descend,
Explain his own beginning, or his end?
Alas, what wonder! Man's superior part
Unchecked may rise, and climb from art to art;
But when his own great work is but begun,
What Reason weaves, by Passion is undone.
Trace Science then, with Modesty thy guide;
First strip off all her equipage of Pride;
Deduct what is but Vanity, or Dress,
Or Learning's luxury, or Idleness;
Or tricks to show the stretch of human brain,
Mere curious pleasure, or ingenious pain;
Expunge the whole, or lop th'excrescent parts
Of all our Vices have created Arts;
Then see how little the remaining sum,
Which served the past, and must the times to come!

The Rejection of Science

Simplification *

by Joseph Wood Krutch (1953)

Man has, after all, survived up to now. . . . He was good enough to do so for many thousands of years. He survived his first struggles with animate and inanimate nature; he survived his diseases, his wars, his social systems, his religions, and a series of misconceptions which now seem to have been sometimes almost suicidal. What has made him in 1952 less fitted to survive than he was in 5000 B.C.?

There is, to be sure, one answer to that question currently familiar in one form or another. Reduced to its simplest terms, that answer is this: man's ingenuity has outrun his intelligence. He was good enough to survive in a simple, sparsely populated world, where he was neither powerful enough nor in sufficiently close contact with his neighbors to do them or himself fatal harm. He is not good enough to manage the more complicated and closely integrated world which he is, for the first time, powerful enough to destroy. He is, perhaps, no more prone to war than he used to be and no more inclined to commit other evil deeds. But a given amount of ill will or folly will go further than it used to. And what is so obviously true in connection with war is equally true in less spectacular affairs. The complexities of an industrial society make men more dependent on one another than they used to be, and the whole machinery of government is harder to handle. Wisdom and good will have either not increased at all or, in any event, have not kept pace with the necessity for them.

If we grant this familiar interpretation, then there are obviously at least a pair of alternatives to extinction. On the one hand we can say with [H. G.] Wells, "Let us get wise as soon as possible." On the other hand we could, of course, say with Thoreau, "Simplify."

If civilization is too complicated and there is no immediate prospect of our learning enough to manage it, we might suggest a reduction of that complexity. Instead of constantly seeking new sources of power, either in the oil of Arabia or in the interior of the atom, we might dispense with some of the sources we now have, and we might deliberately attempt to return to a political and social order which we would be capable of managing.

Our neighbors in different parts of the world were less a threat to us when we could not reach them and they could not reach us as readily as now—when, as a matter of fact, we could not even communicate with them, except after an interval of months. We would not need to be afraid of the Russians and they would not need to be afraid of us if we were as far away from each other as we used to be. In the thirteenth century, man was good enough at least to survive, and he would be good enough to survive now if things were as simple as they were then. We may think that we would hate to give up our "higher standard of living," but is that what we have really got—or is it only a higher standard of dying? What we ride toward at high speed may not be a more abundant life, but only a more spectacular death.

If you object that it would be as difficult to persuade mankind to simplify as it would be to make it wise, you may get from the enemies of complexity a grim answer. Events will not make man wise, but they may simplify him, willy-nilly. As a witticism current during the Second World War had it: "I don't know what will be the most important weapon in the next war, but I know what will be the most important weapon in the war after that—the bow and arrow." No one fought our most recent war for the purpose of "reducing the standard of living," but in all the countries involved, except the United States, it was reduced. After the next world war, or at latest by the time the next two or three are over, the reduction in complexity may be evident enough to the survivors. These wars might not, as Wells suggested, reduce man to the status of an extinct species, but they would very likely put him back into a new Dark Age, and he would probably be good enough to survive again in that environment, just as he was good enough to survive in it once before. A thousand years later, he might get another chance to try an industrial as opposed to an agricultural society. And if there is anything in the belief that he is getting better, no matter how slowly, then he might, by that time, be capable of making a go of it. If not, time is long. Back he would go again into something simple enough for him to be able to manage.

The Flame Deluge *
by Walter M. Miller, Jr. (1959)

It was said that God, in order to test mankind which had become swelled with pride as in the time of Noah, had commanded the wise men of that age, among them the Blessed Leibowitz, to devise great engines of war such as had never before been upon the Earth, weapons of such might that they contained the very fires of Hell, and that God had suffered these magi to place the weapons in the hands of princes, and to say to each prince: "Only because the enemies have such a thing have we devised this for thee, in order that they may know that thou hast it also, and fear to strike. See to it, m'Lord, that thou fearest them as much as they shall now fear thee, that none may unleash this dread thing which we have wrought."

But the princes, putting the words of their wise men to naught, thought each to himself: If I but strike quickly enough, and in secret, I shall destroy those others in their sleep, and there will be none to fight back; the earth shall be mine.

Such was the folly of princes, and there followed the Flame Deluge.

Within weeks—some said days—it was ended, after the first unleashing of the hell-fire. Cities had become puddles of glass, surrounded by vast acreages of broken stone. While nations had vanished from the earth, the lands littered with bodies, both men and cattle, and all manner of beasts, together with the birds of the air and all things that flew, all things that swam in the rivers, crept in the grass, or burrowed in holes; having sickened and perished, they covered the land, and yet where the demons of the Fallout covered the countryside, the bodies for a time would not decay, except in contact with fertile earth. The great clouds of wrath engulfed the forests and the fields, withering trees and causing the crops to die. There were great deserts where once life was, and in those places of the Earth where men still lived, all were sickened by the poisoned air, so that, while some escaped death, none was left untouched; and many died even in those lands where the weapons had not struck, because of the poisoned air.

In all parts of the world men fled from one place to other places, and there was a confusion of tongues. Much wrath was kindled against the princes and the servants of the princes and against the magi who had devised the weapons. Years passed, and yet the Earth was not cleansed. So it was clearly recorded in the Memorabilia.

From the confusion of tongues, the intermingling of the remnants of many nations, from fear, the hate was born. And the hate said;

Let us stone and disembowel and burn the ones who did this thing. Let us make a holocaust of those who wrought this crime, together with their hirelings and their wise men; burning, let them perish, and all their works, their names, and even their memories. Let us destroy them all, and teach our children that the world is new, that they may know nothing of the deeds that went before. Let us make a great simplification, and then the world shall begin again.

So it was that, after the Deluge, the Fallout, the plagues, the madness, the confusion of tongues, the rage, there began the bloodletting of the Simplification, when remnants of mankind had torn other remnants limb from limb, killing rulers, scientists, leaders, technicians, teachers, and whatever persons the leaders of the maddened mobs said deserved death for having helped to make the Earth what it had become. Nothing had been so hateful in the sight of these mobs as the man of learning, at first because they had served the princes, but then later because they refused to join in the bloodletting and tried to oppose the mobs, calling the crowds "bloodthirsty simpletons."

Joyfully the mobs accepted the name, took up the cry:

Simpletons! Yes, yes! I'm a simpleton! Are you a simpleton? We'll build a town and we'll name it Simple Town, because by then all the smart bastards that caused all this, they'll be dead! Simpleton! Let's go! This ought to show 'em! Anybody here not a simpleton? Get the bastard, if there is!

To escape the fury of the simpleton packs, such learned people as still survived fled to any sanctuary that offered itself. When Holy Church received them, she vested them in monks' robes and tried to hide them in such monasteries and convents as had survived and could be reoccupied, for the religious were less despised by the mob except when they openly defied it and accepted martyrdom. Sometimes such sanctuary was effective, but more often it was not. Monasteries were invaded, records and sacred books were burned, refugees were seized and summarily hanged or burned. The Simplification had ceased to have plan or purpose soon after it began, and became an insane frenzy of mass murder and destruction such as can occur only when the last traces of social order are gone. The madness was transmitted to the children, taught as they were— not merely to forget—but to hate, and surges of mob fury recurred sporadically even through the fourth generation after the Deluge. By then, the fury was directed not against the learned, for there were none, but against the merely literate.

The Schism Between Science and Society

Science, the Destroyer or Creator *

by J. J. Bronowski (1953)

We all know the story of the sorcerer's apprentice; or *Frankenstein* which Mary Shelley wrote in competition with her husband and Byron; or some other story of the same kind out of the macabre invention of the nineteenth century. In these stories, some one who has special powers over nature conjures or creates a stick or a machine to do his work for him; and then finds that he cannot take back the life he has given it. The mindless monster overwhelms him; and what began as an invention to do the housework ends by destroying the master with the house.

These stories have become the epitome of our own fears. We have been inventing machines at a growing pace now for about three hundred years. This is a short span even in our recorded history, and it is not a thousandth part of our history as men. In that short moment of time we have found a remarkable insight into the workings of nature. We have used it to make ourselves far more flexible in our adaptation to the outside world than any other animal has ever been. We can survive in climates which even germs find difficult. We can grow our own food and meat. We can travel overland and we can tunnel and swim and fly, all in the one body. More important than any of these, we have come nearest to the dream which Lamarck had, that animals might inherit the skills which their parents learnt. We have discovered the means to record our experience so that others may live it again.

The history of other animal species shows that the most successful in the struggle for survival have been those which were most adaptable to changes in their world. We have made ourselves by means of our tools beyond all measure more adaptable than any other species, living or extinct; and we continue to do so with gathering speed. Yet today we are afraid of our own shadow in the nine o'clock news; and we wonder whether we shall survive so over-specialised a creature as the Pekinese.

Everyone likes to blame his sense of defeat on someone else; and for

* From J. J. Bronowski, *The Commonsense of Science.*

some time scientists have been a favourite scapegoat. I want to look at their responsibility, and for that matter at everybody's, rather more closely. They do have a special responsibility; do not let us argue that out of existence; but it is a complicated one, and it is not the whole responsibility. For example, science obviously is not responsible for the readiness of people, who do not take their private quarrels beyond the stage of insult, to carry their public quarrels to the point of war. Many animals fight for their needs, and some for their mere greeds, to the point of death. Bucks fight for females, and birds fight for their territories. The fighting habits of man are odd because he displays them only in groups. But they were not supplied by scientists. On the contrary, science has helped to end several kinds of group murder, such as witch hunting and the taboos of the early nineteenth century against disinfecting hospitals.

Neither is science responsible for the existence of groups which believe themselves to be in competition: for the existence above all of nations. And the threat of war today is always a national threat. Some bone of contention and competition is identified with a national need: Fiume or the Polish corridor or the dignity of the Austrian Empire; and in the end nations are willing to organise and to invite the death of citizens on both sides in order to reach these collective aims. Science did not create the nations; on the contrary, it has helped to soften those strong national idiosyncrasies which it seems necessary to exploit if war is to be made with enthusiasm. And wars are not made by *any* traditional groups: they are made by highly organised societies, they are made by nations. Most of us have seen Yorkshiremen invade Old Trafford, and a bloody nose or two if the day was thirsty. But no Yorkshireman would have grown pale if he had been told that Lancashire had the atomic bomb.

The sense of doom in us today is not a fear of science; it is a fear of war. And the causes of war were not created by science; they do not differ in kind from the known causes of the War of Jenkin's Ear or the Wars of the Roses, which were carried on with only the most modest scientific aids. No, science has not invented war; but it has turned it into a very different thing. The people who distrust it are not wrong. The man in the pub who says "It'll wipe out the world," the woman in the queue who says "It isn't natural"—they do not express themselves very well; but what they are trying to say does make sense. Science has enlarged the mechanism of war, and it has distorted it. It has done this in at least two ways.

First, science has obviously multiplied the power of the warmakers. The weapons of the moment can kill more people more secretly and more unpleasantly than those of the past. This progress, as for want of another word I must call it—this progress has been going on for some time; and for some time it has been said, of each new weapon, that it is so destructive or so horrible that it will frighten people into their wits, and force the nations to give up war for lack of cannon fodder. This hope has never been fulfilled, and I know no one who takes refuge in it today. The acts of men and women are not dictated by such simple compulsions; and they themselves do not stand in any simple relation to the decisions of the nations which they compose. Grapeshot and TNT and gas have not helped to outlaw war; and I see no sign that the hydrogen bomb or a whiff of bacteria will be more successful in making men wise by compulsion.

Secondly, science at the same time has given the nations quite new occasions for falling out. I do not mean such simple objectives as someone else's uranium mine, or a Pacific Island which happens to be knee-deep in organic fertilizer. I do not even mean merely another nation's factories and her skilled population. These are all parts of the surplus above our simple needs which they themselves help to create and which gives our civilization its character. And war in our world battens on this surplus. This is the object of the greed of nations, and this also gives them the leisure to train and the means to arm for war. At bottom, we have remained individually too greedy to distribute our surplus, and collectively too stupid to pile it up in any more useful form than the traditional mountains of arms. Science can claim to have created the surplus in our societies, and we know from the working day and the working diet how greatly it has increased it in the last two hundred years. Science has created the surplus. Now put this year's budget beside the budget of 1750, anywhere in the world, and you will see what we are doing with it.

I myself think there is a third dimension which science has added to modern war. It has created war nerves and the war of nerves. I am not thinking about the technical conditions for a war of nerves: the camera man and the radio and the massed display of strength. I am thinking of the climate in which this stage lightning flickers and is made to seem real. The last twenty years have given us a frightening show of these mental states. There is a division in the mind of each of us, that has become plain, between the man and the brute; and the rift can be opened, the man submerged, with a cynical simplicity, with the meanest tools of envy and frustration, which in my boyhood would have been thought inconceivable in a civilised society. I shall come back to this cleavage in our minds, for it is much more than an item in a list of war crimes. But it is an item. It helps to create the conditions for disaster. And I think that science has contributed to it. Science; the fact that science is there, mysterious, powerful; the fact that most people are impressed by it but ignorant and helpless—all this seems to me to have contributed to the division in our minds. And scientists cannot escape the responsibility for this. They have enjoyed acting the mysterious stranger, the powerful voice without emotion, the expert and the god. They have failed to make themselves comfortable in the talk of people in the street; no one taught them the knack, of course, but they were not keen to learn. And now they find the distance which they enjoyed has turned to distrust, and the awe has turned to fear; and people who are by no means fools really believe that we should be better off without science.

These are the indictments which scientists cannot escape. Of course, they are often badly phrased, so that scientists can side-step them with generalities about the common responsibility, and who voted the credits for atomic research anyway; which are perfectly just, but not at all relevant. That is not the heart of the matter; and the people in queues and pubs are humbly groping for the heart. They are not good at saying things and they do not give model answers to interviewers. But when we say "We've forgotten what's right," when they say "We're not fit to handle such things," what is in their minds is perfectly true. Science and society are out of joint. Science has given to no one in particular a power which no one in particular knows how to use. Why do not scientists invent something sensible? Wives say it every time they stub their toe on the waste bin, and husbands say it whenever a fuse blows. Why is it the business of no one in particular to stop fitting science for death and to begin fitting it into our lives? We will agree that warlike science is no more than a by-product of a warlike society. Science has merely provided the means, for good or for bad; and society has seized it for bad. But what are we going to do about it?

The first thing to do, it seems to me, is to treat this as a scientific question: by which I mean as a practical and sensible question, which deserves a factual approach and a reasoned answer. Now that I have apologised on behalf of scientists, and this on a scale which some of them will certainly think too ample, let us cut out what usually happens to the argument at this point, the rush of recriminations. The scientists are conscious of their mistakes; and I do not want to discuss the mistakes of non-scientists—although they have made a great many—except those which we all must begin to make good.

I have said that a scientific answer must be practical as well as sensible. This really rules out at once the panaceas which also tend to run the argument into a blind alley at this stage; the panaceas which say summarily "Get rid of them." Naturally, it does not seem to me to be sensible to get rid of scientists; but in any case, it plainly is not practical. And whatever we do with our own scientists, it very plainly is not practical to get rid of the scientists of rival nations; because if there existed the conditions for agreement among nations on this far-reaching scheme, then the conditions for war would already have disappeared. If there existed the conditions for international agreement, say to suspend all scientific research, or to abandon warlike research, or in any other way to forgo science as an instrument of nationalism—if such agreements could be reached, then they would already be superfluous; because the conditions for war would already have disappeared. So, however we might sigh for Samuel Butler's panacea in *Erewhon,* simply to give up all machines, there is no point in talking about it. I believe it would be a disaster for mankind like the coming of the Dark Ages. But there is no point in arguing this. It just is not practical, nationally or internationally.

There are no panaceas at all; and we had better face that. There is nothing that we can do overnight, in a week or a month, which can straighten by a laying on of hands the ancient distortion of our society. Do not let us fancy that any one of us out of the blue will concoct that stirring letter to *The Times* which will change the black mood of history —and the instructions to diplomats. Putting scientists in the Cabinet will not do that, and women in the War Office will not, nor will bishops in the Privy Council. There are no panaceas. We are the heirs to a tradition which has left science and society out of step. The man in the street is right: we have never learnt to handle such things. Nothing will do but that we learn. But learning is not done in a year. Our ultimate survival is in our own hands. Our survival while we are learning is a much chancier thing. We had better be realistic about that.

Meanwhile we had better settle down to work for our ultimate survival; and we had better start now. We have seen that the diagnosis has turned out to be not very difficult. Science and our social habits are out of step. And the cure is no deeper either. We must learn to match them. And there is no way of learning this unless we learn to understand *both.*

Of the two, of course, the one which is strange is science. I have already blamed the scientist for that. He has been the monk of our age, timid, thwarted, anxious to be asked to help; and with a secret ambition to play the Grey Eminence. Through years of childhood poverty he dreamt of this. Scientific skill was a blue door beckoning to him, which would open into the society of dignitaries of state. But the private motives of scientists are not the trend of science. The trend of science is made by the needs of society: navigation before the eighteenth century, manufacture thereafter; and in our age I believe the liberation of personality. Whatever the part which scientists like to act, or for that matter which painters like to dress, science shares the aims of our society just as art does. The difficulties of understanding either are not fundamental; they are difficulties only of language. To grow familiar with the large ideas of science calls for patience and an effort of attention; . . .

For two hundred years, these ideas have been applied to technical needs; and they have made our world anew, triumphantly, from top to toe. Our shoes are tanned and stitched, our clothes are spun and dyed and woven, we are lighted and carried and doctored by means which were unknown to neat Mr. Pope at Twickenham in 1740. We may not think that is much to put against the eighty thousand dead in Hiroshima, or we may. We may not think it recompenses us for the absence of any Mr. Pope from Twickenham today; we may even hold it responsible. It is certainly not a spiritual achievement. But it has not yet tried to be. It has applied its ideas monotonously to shoe-leather and bicycle bells. And it has made a superb job of them. Compare its record in its own field with that of any other ideas of the same age: Burke's ideas of the imagination, or Bentham's on government, or Adam Smith on political economy. If any ideas have a claim to be called creative, because they have created something, then certainly it is the ideas of science.

We may think that all that science has created is comfort; and it certainly has done that—the very word "comfortable" in the modern sense dates from the Industrial Revolution. But have we always stopped to think what science has done not to our mode of living but to our life? We talk about research for death, the threat of war and the number of civilians who get killed. But have we always weighed this against the increase in our own life span? Let us do a small sum. The number of people killed in Great Britain in six years of war by German bombs, flying bombs, and V 2's was sixty thousand. They were an average lot of people, which means that on an average they lost half their expectation of life. Quite an easy long division shows that the effect of this in our population of fifty million people was to shorten the average span of life by less than one tenth of one per cent. This is considerably less than a fortnight. Put this on the debt side. And on the credit side, we know that in the last hundred years the average span of life in England has increased by twenty years. This is the price of science, take it or leave it—a fortnight for twenty years of life. And these twenty years have been created by applying to daily life, to clothing and bedding, to hygiene and infection, to birth and death, the simple ideas of science—the fundamental ideas . . . If any ideas have a claim to be called creative, because they have created life, it is the ideas of science. . . .

Science is a great many things, . . . but in the end they all return to this: science is the acceptance of what works and the rejection of what does not. That needs more courage than we might think.

It needs more courage than we have ever found when we have faced our worldly problems. This is how society has lost touch with science: because it has hesitated to judge itself by the same impersonal code of what works and what does not. We have clung to Adam Smith and Burke, or we have agitated for Plato or Aquinas, through wars and famine, through rising and falling birth-rates, and through libraries of learned argument. And in the end, our eyes have always wandered from the birth-rate to the argument: from the birth-rate to what we have wanted to believe. Here is the crux of what I have been saying. Here is our ultimate hope of saving ourselves from extinction. We must learn to understand that the content of all knowledge is empirical; that its test is whether it works; and we must learn to act on that understanding in the world as well as in the laboratory.

This is the message of science: our ideas must be realistic, flexible, unbigoted—they must be human, they must create their own authority. If any ideas have a claim to be called creative, because they have liberated that creative impulse, it is the ideas of science.

This is not only a material code. On the contrary, my hope is that it may heal the spiritual cleft which two wars have uncovered. I have seen in my lifetime an abyss open in the human mind: a gulf between the endeavour to be man, and the relish in being brute. The scientist has indeed had a hand in this, and every other specialist too, with his prim detachment and his oracular airs. But of course, the large strain which has opened this fault is social. We have made men live in two halves, a Sunday half and a workday half. We have ordered them to love their neighbour and to turn the other cheek, in a society which has constantly compelled them to shoulder their neighbour aside and to turn their backs. So we have created a savage sense of failure which, as we know now to our cost, can be tapped with an ease which is frightening; and which can thrust up, with explosive force, a symbol to repeat to an unhappy people its most degrading dream.

Can science heal that neurotic flaw in us? If science cannot, then nothing can. Let us stop pretending. There is no cure in high moral precepts. We have preached them too long to men who are forced to live how they can: *that* makes the strain which they have not been able to bear. We need an ethic which is moral *and* which works. It is often said that science has destroyed our values and put nothing in their place. What has really happened of course is that science has shown in harsh relief the division between our values and our world. We have not begun to let science get into our heads; where then was it supposed to create these values? We have used it as a machine without will, the conjured spirit to do the chores. I believe that science can create values: and will create them precisely as literature does, by looking into the human personality; by discovering what divides it and what cements it. That is how great writers have explored man, and this whether they themselves as men have been driven by the anguish in *Gulliver's Travels* or the sympathy in *Moll Flanders*.

The insight of science is not different from that of the arts. Science will create values, I believe, and discover virtues, when it looks into man; when it explores what makes him man and not an animal, and what makes his societies human and not animal packs.

I believe that we can reach this unity in our culture. . . . nations in their great ages have not been great in art or science, but in art and science. Rembrandt was the contemporary of Huygens and Spinoza. At that very time, Isaac Newton walked with Dryden and Christopher Wren. We know that ours is a remarkable age of science. It is for us to use it to broaden and to liberate our culture. These are the marks of science: that it is open for all to hear, and all are free to speak their minds in it. They are marks of the world at its best, and the human spirit at its most challenging.

The rapid progress true Science now makes occasions my regretting sometimes that I was born so soon. It is impossible to imagine the height to which may be carried, in a thousand years, the power of man over matter. O that *Moral* science were in as fair a way of improvement, that men would cease to be wolves to one another, and that human beings would at length learn what they now improperly call *humanity*.

Benjamin Franklin
In a letter to Joseph Priestley, 1780

The False Images of Science *
by Gerald Holton (1960)

Of the influences that shape man's actions, none is more powerful than the images we carry in our heads. Every subject is apt to invoke in our minds a specific image, made up of concrete information, misinformation, folklore, desire and prejudice. Thus, how people see themselves as a nation determines to a large extent how they will respond to any new challenge. The roles we play in our family life, particularly with respect to our children, depend greatly on what roles we assign ourselves in the society around us.

In the same way, our images of science vastly affect the relationship

* From Gerald Holton, "The False Images of Science," from the series "Adventures of the Mind," *Saturday Evening Post*, January 9, 1960. Reprinted by permission. This article is a briefer version of the essay "Modern Science and the Intellectual Tradition" published in *The Intellectuals*, edited by George B. de Huszar, Free Press of Glencoe, Illinois, 1960, pp. 180–91.

between science and society. Practically, these images determine the level and the sources of financial support, the quality and quantity of instruction offered, and the development of new scientists. The effects on professional morale and the goals scientists set for themselves—in short, on the scientists' image of their own work—are also considerable. But even more important is the role images play in deciding this urgent question: Can scientific activity be an integrated part of our culture, or will it be forced to develop independently?

Right or wrong, ideas are powerful. Therein lies the chief danger of false images. Like bad grammar, bad images become dominant when they gain wide currency, and so undermine communication among thoughtful people. It is high time, therefore, to consider the prevailing public images of the role of science, using the most straightforward language possible.

PURE THOUGHT AND PRACTICAL POWER

Each person's image of science is different from the next, but all are composed of seven main elements. The first goes back to Plato and portrays science as a tonic with double benefits—science as pure thought helps the mind find truth, and science as power provides the tools for effective action. The main flaw in this image is that it omits a third vital aspect. Pure science allows us to understand the physical world and, through its applications, allows us to control and change that world. But science also has a mythopoeic function; that is, it generates an important part of our symbolic vocabulary and provides some of the metaphysical bases and philosophical orientations of our ideology.

As a consequence, the methods of argument of science, its conceptions and its models, permeate first the intellectual life of the time, then the tenets and usages of everyday life. Our language of ideas, for example, owes a debt to the sciences of statics and hydraulics and the model of the solar system. These have furnished powerful analogies in many fields of study. Guiding ideas—such as conditions of equilibrium, centrifugal forces, conservation laws and the balance of energy or power, feedback, invariance or complementarity—enrich the general arsenal of imaginative tools of thought. All philosophies share with science the need to work with concepts such as space, time, quantity, matter, order, law, causality, verification, reality.

A sound image of science must, therefore, embrace this third function, in addition to those referring to pure understanding and to practical applications. However, more usually, only one of the three is recognized. For example, folklore sometimes depicts the life of the scientist as lonely, isolated, divorced from life and beneficent action in the larger sense.

ICONOCLASM

A second image of long standing is that of the scientist as iconoclast. Indeed, almost every major scientific advance, from the Copernican theory to the postulation of universal gravitation, from the discovery of the circulation of blood to the perfection of anesthesia and vaccination, has been interpreted as a blow against religion.

To some extent science was pushed into this position by the ancient but dangerous tendency of some philosophers to prove the existence of God by pointing to problems which science could not solve at the time. Newton himself, who was deeply interested in theology, wrote, "It is not to be conceived that mere mechanical causes could give birth to so many regular motions [in the solar system]. . . . This most beautiful system of the sun, planets and comets could only proceed from the counsel and dominion of an intelligent and powerful Being."

The same attitude governed thought concerning the earth's formation before the theory of geological evolution, the descent of man before the theory of biological evolution, and the origin of our galaxy before modern cosmology.

This aspect of the conflict between science and religion results largely from a misunderstanding of both science and religion. To base one's religious belief on an estimate of what science can *not* do is as foolhardy as it is blasphemous. The reverse, the deification of the discoveries of science, is equally precarious, for scientific knowledge continually grows, superseding its older formulations. The only secure foundation for religious belief, as all great religious leaders have taught, is neither the capacity nor the failure of man's imaginative mind, neither the powers nor the limits of his science—but faith.

Today political overtones make a wider understanding of this problem both more urgent and more difficult. "Religious propaganda," a recent dispatch in Iron Curtain countries advised, must be counteracted by "scientific atheistic propaganda" distributed by local societies "for the dissemination of political and scientific knowledge."

The iconoclastic image of science has, however, other components not ascribable to an elementary misunderstanding of its functions. For example, the historian Arnold Toynbee charges science and technology with usurping the place of Christianity as the main source of our new symbols. Neo-orthodox theologians call science the "self-estrangement" of man because it leads him into realms where no ultimate—that is, religious—concerns prevail.

But this image fails to recognize the multitude of influences that shape a culture—or a person. Neither to Christianity nor to science can one properly assign more than a limited part in the interplay between man's psychological and biological factors on one hand, and the opportunities and accidents of his history on the other. Moreover, to set science and religion at odds, to view them as nonintersecting paths, is to neglect the valuable possibilities of synthesis. As Alfred North Whitehead wrote in *Science and the Modern World,* these are "the two strongest general forces, apart from the mere impulses of the various senses, which influence man. . . . [On their relationship] depends the future course of history." Whitehead held that "the force of our religious intuitions, and the force of our impulse to accurate observation and deduction," are complementary rather than conflicting. The way many scientists and theologians state the issue today makes it seem as if we must choose between two normal and powerful drives. This is like forcing a child to choose between his father and his mother because they disagree on some matters.

ETHICAL PERVERSION

The next image of science sees it as a force which can invade, possess, pervert and destroy man. The stereotype is Anthime in André Gide's novel, *Lafcadio's Adventures,* the naturalist turned unbeliever. Anthime snarls at his niece who dares speak to him piously of religion, and retires angrily to his laboratory, where he weighs a group of starved rats, half of them partly blinded, the rest fully blinded, to find out which are dying faster.

In the current version, the soulless, evil scientist is the mad researcher of science fiction, or the nuclear destroyer—immoral if he develops the weapons he is asked to develop, traitorous if he refuses. According to this view, scientific morality is inherently negative. It causes the arts to languish, it blights culture and, when applied to human affairs, leads to regimentation and to the impoverishment of life. In short, science is the serpent seducing us into eating the fruit of the tree of knowledge—thereby dooming us.

The fear behind this attitude is genuine, but not confined to science. It is also directed against writers, artists, philosophers, theologians—in fact, against all thinkers and innovators. Plato condemned the work of Homer for conducing to impiety and immorality, and the same charge still greets many an original work. Society has always found it hard to deal with creativity, innovation and new knowledge. And since science assures a particularly rapid, and therefore particularly disturbing, turnover of ideas, it remains a prime target of suspicion.

Factors peculiar to our time intensify this suspicion. Progress in basic scientific knowledge, being confined to a minority of specialists, cannot by itself directly disturb society. But the discoveries of "pure" science now readily lend themselves to widespread exploitation through technology. Applications spread swiftly and widely. Thus we are in an inescapable dilemma—irresistibly tempted to reach for the fruits of science, yet deep inside aware that our biological and psychological metabolism may not be able to cope with this ever-increasing appetite.

Probably the dilemma can no longer be resolved, and this increases the anxiety and confusion concerning science. A current symptom is the popular identification of science with the technology of super-weapons. The missile is taking the place of the microscope as a symbol of modern science. All efforts to convince people that science itself can only give man knowledge about himself and his environment, and occasionally a choice of actions, have been unavailing. The scientist *as scientist* can take little credit or responsibility either for the facts he discovers—for he did not create them—or for the uses made of his discoveries, for he generally is neither permitted nor specially fitted to make these decisions. They are controlled by considerations of ethics, economics, or politics, and therefore shaped by the values, fears and historical circumstances of the whole society.

THE SORCERER'S APPRENTICE

The last two views held that man is inherently good and science evil. Now we come to an image based on the opposite assumption; it expresses the fear that man cannot be trusted with scientific knowledge. He has survived despite his wickedness only because he lacked sufficiently destructive weapons; now he can immolate his world. Science, indirectly responsible for this new power, is here considered ethically neutral. But, like the sorcerer's apprentice, man can neither understand this tool nor control it. Unavoidably he will bring upon himself catastrophe, partly through his natural sinfulness and partly through his lust for power, of which the pursuit of knowledge is a manifestation. The fear inspired by this image also motivates the repeated demand for a moratorium on the pursuit of science. The most famous formulation was that of the Bishop of Ripon at a meeting of the British Association for the Advancement of Science. We should all be better off, he contended, if every physical and chemical laboratory were closed for ten years, and the energy now directing them were turned to establishing the brotherhood of man.

This suggestion is based on two misunderstandings. First, science is not an occupation that one can pursue or change at short notice, like working on an assembly line. The creative scientist does not have a free choice of action. He does not advance toward his new knowledge; rather knowledge advances toward him and overwhelms him. Even a superficial glance at the work of a Kepler, a Darwin or a Pasteur shows that the driving power of creativity is as strong and as sacred for the scientist as for the artist.

Secondly, salvation cannot be considered a reward for ignorance. To survive and progress, man cannot know too much about his environment. The real price of new knowledge is the obligation knowledge imposes on all of us to assume responsibility for ourselves.

It may yet turn out, paradoxically, that science will help to compel us at last to curb the aggressions that in the past were condoned and even glorified. Organized warfare and genocide are practices as old as recorded history. The exploitation of science now has so sharpened the knife edge on which civilization has always balanced that the main antagonists themselves recognize the enormity of the threat. Never before have even the war lords on both sides openly expressed fear of war.

If man is inherently evil, Judgment Day is surely near. But if good exists in him, one can be more optimistic. The alternatives are so extreme and so obvious as to allow hope that the instinct of self-preservation will reinforce good sense and moral strength. Mankind has come to its *experimentum crucis*.

ECOLOGICAL DISASTER

A change in the average temperature of a pond or in the salinity of an ocean may cause a large number of plants and animals to die. One calls this a change in the ecological balance. The fifth prevalent image of science similarly holds that while neither science nor man may be inherently evil, the rise of science happened, as if by accident, to initiate an ecological change that now corrodes the only conceivable basis for a stable society. In the words of theologian Jacques Maritain, the "deadly disease" science set off in society is "the denial of eternal truth and absolute values."

How did this change come about? The main steps are usually presented in this way. Before modern science, man thought of himself as the ultimate purpose and the earth as the center of creation. Then science showed our planetary system to be heliocentric, and man toppled from his throne. Science replaced purposive creation with blind evolution, and discovered that such absolutes as space, time and certainty are meaningless. All a priori axioms, like those of Euclidean geometry, were discovered one by one to be convenient but arbitrary. Modern psychology and anthropology have led to an acceptance of cultural relativism. Truth itself seems to have dissolved into probabilistic and indeterministic statements.

The abandonment of absolutes, so goes the argument, has affected all areas of life, particularly ethical values. Drawing largely upon analogy with the sciences, liberal philosophers have become increasingly relativistic, denying either the necessity or the possibility of postulating immutable verities, and so have undermined the old foundations of moral and social authority. For though doubt and skepticism may be useful as stimulants to scientific investigation, society cannot thrive in an atmosphere of change for its own sake.

Worst of all, the argument concludes, though science cannot help us distinguish between good and evil, it nevertheless claims to be the only reliable guide for making decisions and solving problems of all kinds. Having destroyed absolute standards, it puts nothing in their place. In short, although science has exploded some fallacious traditional beliefs and increased our material comforts, it has also cut us adrift from our only secure moorings.

It should be noted in passing that most applications of scientific concepts outside science merely reveal ignorance about science. For example, relativism in nonscientific fields is based on farfetched analogies. As Crane Brinton put it in *The Shaping of the Modern Mind*, "For the general public, Einstein was not merely the tribal magician of our time; he was the man who stood for relativity; for the notion that things looked different to observers at different places at different times, that truth depends on the point of view of the seeker of truth, that a man moving at one rate of speed sees everything quite differently from a man moving at another rate, that, in short, there is no absolute Truth, but only relative truths."

This is precisely how the general public understands Einsteinian relativity. But physics did not find that everything is relative. On the contrary, relativity theory reformulated the laws of physics so that they would hold good for every observer, no matter how he moves or where he stands. Not everything depends on one's point of view; rather, the most valued truths are wholly independent of the point of view.

Ignorance of science is also the only excuse for adopting rapid changes within science as models for antitraditional attitudes outside science. In reality, no field of thought is more conservative than science; each change necessarily encompasses previous knowledge. Science grows like a tree, ring by ring. Einstein did not prove the work of Newton wrong; he provided a larger setting within which some contradictions and discontinuities of the older physics disappeared.

But the image of science as an ecological disaster can be subjected to a more severe critique. Regardless of science's part in the corrosion of absolute values, have those values really given us a safe anchor? A priori absolutes abound all over the globe in completely contradictory varieties.

Most of the horrors of history have been carried out under the banner of some absolutistic philosophy, from the Aztec mass sacrifices to the *auto da fé* of the Spanish Inquisition, from the massacre of the Huguenots to the Nazi gas chambers. It is at best an optical illusion which makes the fourteenth century look so serene and desirable to modern critics of the recent, "scientific" periods, just as the life of the "noble savage," so esteemed by eighteenth-century philosophers, has been exposed by modern anthropologists to be based largely on dread and misery.

If, therefore, some of the new philosophies, inspired rightly or wrongly by science, reject earlier bases of authority as faulty—as the founders of this nation did—if they point out that "absolutes" change and contradict one another, science cannot be blamed. The faults were there all the time.

In looking for a new and sounder basis on which to build a stable world, we shall find science indispensable. We can hope to match the resources and structure of society to the needs and potentialities of people only if we know more about the inner workings of man. Already science has much to say that is valuable and important about human relationships and problems. One must not be obsessed with the picture of bombs and missiles; from psychiatry to dietetics, from immunology to meteorology, from city planning to agricultural research, by far the largest part of our total scientific and technical effort today is concerned with man, his needs, relationships, health and comforts. Those who argue that the pursuit of science is necessarily the road to suicide have forgotten about this aspect of science. They do not believe, as I do, that man has been given his mind in order that he may find out where he is, what he is, and who he is.

SCIENTISM

The last four images implied a revulsion from science. We might describe the next one as addiction to science. Scientism divides all thought into two categories—up-to-date scientific knowledge, and nonsense. Some scientists subscribe to this view, but most of its adherents are outside the laboratories. Among the social studies, for example, there are some victims of the seductive idea that the mathematical sciences offer the only permissible models for successfully employing the mind.

A far more significant symptom of scientism is the growing identification of science with technology, to which I referred earlier. This trend is not difficult to understand. Nearly half of all the men and women trained as scientists are now working in industry or Government laboratories. Even in universities, applied research and development constitute about half of all scientific work. Of the huge sums spent annually on science and technology—about $10,000,000,000 this year in the United States—less than 8 per cent is devoted to really basic research.

Not long ago the typical scientist worked alone or with a few students and colleagues and built his own equipment with "love, string and sealing wax." Today he usually belongs to a group working under a contract with a sizable annual budget. In the research institute of one university more than 1500 scientists and technicians are grouped around a set of multi-million-dollar machines; the money comes from Government agencies whose ultimate aim is national defense.

Everywhere the overlapping interests of university science, industry and the military establishment have been merged in a way satisfactory to all three. Science has thereby become a large-scale operation with a potential for immediate and worldwide effects. It is not frivolous to call physics the liveliest political science today. If for some reason all physicists in the United States heeded a call for a moratorium, nobody would be more deeply disturbed than would the Congress and the State Department.

These are merely indications that we are passing through a revolutionary change in the nature of science. The effective cause was the perfection and dissemination of the methods of basic research by teams of specialists with widely different training and interests. The result is a splendid increase in scientific knowledge, but the side effects are analogous to those of sudden and rapid urbanization—a strain on communication facilities, the rise of an administrative bureaucracy, the depersonalization of some human relationships. To a large degree, all this is unavoidable. The new scientific revolution will justify itself by the flow of results and the material benefits that will no doubt follow. The danger, the point where scientism enters, is that the fascination with the *mechanism* of scientific research may change society and the scientist himself.

The new science requires a new kind of scientist. The unorthodox, withdrawn individualist, on whom most great scientific advances have depended in the past, does not fit well into the new system. We must keep a special place for him and protect him—if only to symbolize our commitment to science itself rather than to the new machinery. Society, on the other hand, will also have to hold out against the seductive urge of scientism to adopt generally the pattern of organization of the new science; this pattern can only be justified by the quality of creative results in a specialized profession.

MAGIC

Few nonscientists would be likely to suspect a hoax if it were suddenly announced that a stable chemical element lighter than hydrogen had been synthesized, or that the United States had beaten Russia in a secret race to establish a manned observation platform at the surface of the sun. Apparently anything can happen these days; science has no inherent limitations. Thus, the seventh image depicts science as magic, the scientist as a wizard. Depending on our orientation, we tend either to fear him or to accept his opinions about everything.

Like the other false images of science, this one is partly an educational problem. All our voracious consumption of technical devices, all our talk about science, and all the money spent on engineering developments cannot hide that most of us are content to remain completely ignorant of science. In a recent nationwide survey, nearly 40 per cent of those who had attended college confessed they took not a single course in physical or biological science. Those who did devoted generally less than 10 per cent of their courses to these sciences. Moreover, in science class they miss all too often the kind of teacher who can impart to the average student a wider appreciation of both the inherent powers and the inherent limitations of science, who can show how to distinguish challenging from trivial problems, how to detect the inconspicuous hind leg of the solution by which to drag it forth.

THE ROOT OF THE FAILURE

To expose the falsity of the current images of science is not enough, any more than is treating symptoms rather than the disease itself. The inadequate scientific education the general student receives at all levels helps to explain the distortions, but only in part. When we try to understand why people hold these views and why they are satisfied with too little knowledge about science, we discover that the major share of the blame does not lie with the ordinary citizen. In this matter he is only taking his cue from the intellectuals—the writers, scholars, lawyers, politicians, scientists and all others who deal professionally in ideas. Among the scientists themselves, busy wtih exciting work, the majority feel no strong responsibility for taking part in the necessary educational efforts; many have forgotten that, especially at a time of rapid expansion of knowledge, they have an extra obligation to the general public, if only because it must foot the bill and furnish the next crop of young scientists.

Among the rest of the intellectuals the case is worse. The wrong images, which they share with the common man, prevail because they are anchored in two kinds of ignorance. One kind is basic and factual— what biology says about life, what chemistry and physics say about matter, what astronomy says about the structure of our galaxy. The nonscientist realizes that the old common-sense ways of understanding nature have become obsolete. The ground trembles under his feet; gone are the simple interpretations of solidity, permanence, reality; he flounders among four-dimensional continua, probability amplitudes, undecidable identities, indeterminacies. About the basic concepts of modern science that define the physical part of reality, he knows only that he cannot grasp them and never will.

On the second level of ignorance, the contemporary intellectual fails to understand how the different sciences fit together with one another and with the humanities as different aspects of one cosmos. He has left behind those great syntheses which once comprised our intellectual and moral home—the cosmic view of the book of Genesis, Homer, Dante, Milton, Goethe—and now finds himself blindfolded in a maze without exit. The brutal fact is that, by losing contact with even the elementary facts of modern science, our intellectuals, for the first time in history, are losing their hold on understanding the world. Of all the evils arising from the separation of culture and scientific knowledge, this bewilderment and homelessness is the most terrifying.

Indeed, it is amazing to me that the intellectuals have not attacked science, the source of the apparent threats to their common-sense sanity, much more fiercely, that the dissociation has not produced an even graver cultural psychosis. This, I am convinced, is likely to occur, for there is at present no mechanism at work in our society for dealing effectively with the situation.

What remedies suggest themselves? At the least, science must again be made a natural part of every intelligent man's common literacy—not because science is more important than other fields, but because it is an important part of the whole jigsaw puzzle of knowledge. This would require sound, thorough work at every level of education—for example, a good part of a person's college work, as used to be the rule in good colleges fifty years ago. It would demand imaginative new curricula, strengthened standards of achievement, more recognition of excellence whether exhibited by instructors or by students. Adult education, including the presentation of the factual and cultural aspects of science through mass media, is another obvious measure meriting the support and participation of our best minds.

Here and there, to be sure, some efforts are being made in the right direction, but the total is pitifully small. Virtually nobody has been courageous enough to face the magnitude of the problem squarely, so large is the range and amount of knowledge needed before one can "know science" in any real sense. The converse need—namely, the humanistic education of scientists—is also urgent; but at least in principle it can be served with existing methods of instruction. The tools of humanistic study are still in touch with our sensibilities. This, unhappily, is no longer so in science.

Every great age has been shaped by intellectuals such as Jefferson and Franklin, who would have been horrified by the idea of cultivated men and women turning their backs on science. That tradition has been broken. Few intellectuals are now equipped to act as informed mediators. And meanwhile science advances faster and faster every day, widening the rift between science and culture.

To restore them to some kind of reciprocal contact within the concerns of most men—to bring science into an orbit about us instead of letting it escape from the field of our common culture—that is the great challenge before intellectuals today. And nothing better illustrates the urgency and difficulty of this task than the false images prevailing about science.

Science and Human Welfare * (1960)
American Association for the Advancement of Science

Four years ago, the report of the A.A.A.S. Interim Committee on the Social Aspects of Science stated: "We are now in the midst of a new and unprecedented scientific revolution which promises to bring about profound changes in the condition of human life. The forces and processes now coming under human control are beginning to match in size and intensity those of nature itself, and our total environment is now subject to human influence. In this situation it becomes imperative to determine that these new powers shall be used for the maximum human good, for, if the benefits to be derived from them are great, the possibility of harm is correspondingly serious." . . .

Now, as in 1956, our premises are these:

1. We are witnessing an unprecedented growth in the scale and intensity of scientific work.

2. This growth has been stimulated by an intense demand for the practical products of research, especially for military and industrial use.

3. The public interest in, and understanding of, science is not commensurate with the importance that science has attained in our social structure. It cannot be said that society provides good conditions for the proper growth of science.

4. For reasons such as those just cited, science is experiencing a

* From a report prepared by the American Association for the Advancement of Science, Committee on Science in the Promotion of Human Welfare. Reprinted by permission of the A.A.A.S. from *Science*, July 8, 1960.

period of rapid but rather unbalanced growth. Basic research, which is the ultimate source of the practical results so much in demand, is poorly supported and, in the view of some observers, lacks vigor and quality.

5. The growth of science and the great enhancement of the degree of control which we now exert over nature have given rise to new social practices, of great scope and influence, which make use of new scientific knowledge. While this advance of science has greatly improved the condition of human life, it has also generated new hazards of unprecedented magnitude.

Since 1956 this general pattern has taken on some new features which concern us at this time.

1. The conscious exploitation of science for military advantage continues at an accelerating rate. But in recent years this process has merged with another, equally important trend: science is being pressed into the service of international politics. Scientific accomplishment per se has become an accepted—and at present dominant—factor of prestige among nations. The philosophy of "getting ahead of the Russians" (or Americans), which once referred only to military matters, now includes scientific achievements as well. This rivalry has strongly motivated the recent intensification of government support for scientific research.

2. The rapid emergence of political independence among the "underdeveloped" nations of the world, and their natural desire to exploit modern technology, has added to the importance of international exchange of scientific knowledge and personnel. Perhaps one reason for the rivalry for scientific pre-eminence among the more advanced nations is the expectation of political advantage from this exchange.

3. Certain recent scientific advances add directly to the ease with which our knowledge of nature can be applied to the control of human beings and of social organization. Development of new psychotomimetic drugs and psychological techniques have suggested, to some, effective means for controlling the behavior of social groups. Progress in the science of cybernetics and the development of automation techniques result in new capabilities for direct control of social and economic processes.

4. Despite some recent effort toward improvement, there is no reason to alter the earlier conclusion that our present social environment does not favor the development of an understanding of science, or of science's aims and needs. The increasingly spectacular practical achievements of science have only accentuated misconceptions about the relative significance, for the growth of science, of practical results and the advancement of basic knowledge. To many people physical science means nuclear energy and rockets. The public is sometimes led to expect

that biological and medical research will conquer every human ailment—will overcome death. There is a tendency to equate scientific progress with a sum of money and a number of people. There is insufficient appreciation of the significance of basic research, or of the conditions in which it can flourish. . . .

The military and political advantages, to a nation, of scientific progress within its own borders are self-evident. Yet, it is a truism—but nevertheless a vital one—that nature is the same everywhere, and that the study of nature is an activity of the whole human race. Any effort to divide science into fragments which are delimited by national boundaries, and dominated by a local social philosophy, will inevitably restrict the free discovery and communication of new knowledge that is the substance of scientific progress. A "nationalistic" science is an anachronism which cannot long continue without damage to science and eventually to the nation.

What, then, is the scientist's responsibility to his own nation's scientific effort? Clearly, we need to understand that what science contributes to the national purpose is measured by what it adds to the sum of human knowledge; science serves the nation by serving humanity.

A further examination of the effects of the present social uses of science on life inside the house of science itself leads to even more disturbing conclusions. There is some evidence that the integrity of science is beginning to erode under the abrasive pressure of its close partnership with economic, social, and political affairs.

In recent controversies about fallout and the detection of nuclear explosions, partisanship on the part of some scientists for a particular political approach to the problem has been so intense in some instances as to cloud—at least in the public mind—the identity between science and an objective regard for the facts.

The grim international competition for "supremacy" in scientific accomplishment also endangers the integrity of science. Unseemly claims of priority may be encouraged. Premature reports of new scientific discoveries, which will occur to some extent in any circumstances, may be permitted to acquire a semblance of credibility.

An illustration—as yet unrealized—is the matter of "the creation of life." Some scientists believe that the properties of life are inherent in the chemistry of nucleic acid, and would regard the artificial synthesis of a reproducible nucleic acid or nucleoprotein molecule—which may occur in the reasonably near future—as the "creation" of life. Other scientists would disagree with this interpretation because they believe that nucleic acid, nucleoprotein, or anything less than a living cell is not "life," for the reason that it is not a self-sufficient replicative agent.

Under ordinary circumstances this difference of opinion would be occasionally debated among scientists and finally resolved when the weight of evidence on one side or the other became sufficiently strong, or when a new and more acceptable idea emerged. However, in the present circumstances this matter may take another course. There is some evidence that a claimed "creation of life" based on the test-tube synthesis of an infectious molecule might be regarded by a government as a scientific accomplishment of great political importance—a kind of "biological Sputnik." In this case, scientists may be hard pressed to persuade government officials—and perhaps even some of their colleagues—that the discovery should be given an interpretation which is less dramatic but more in keeping with the divided scientific opinion of its significance.

It is evident that the accelerating progress of science has evoked a number of serious problems that affect both the social order and the internal situation of our scientific establishment. Having become a major instrument in political affairs, science is inseparably bound up with many troublesome questions of public policy. That science is valued more for these uses than for its fundamental purpose—the free inquiry into nature —leads to pressures which have begun to threaten the integrity of science itself. . . .

The scientific community should accept the obligation to determine how new advances in our understanding and control of natural forces are likely to affect human welfare, to call these matters to public attention, and to provide for the public and its social and political agencies the objective statements of the facts and of the consequences of alternative policies that are required as the basis for informed decisions on the relative merits of proposed courses of action.

At what point in the social process should the scientific community enter as an agency of information? One view is that, since most social decisions are executed by government, the scientist's function is to inform and advise government departments and officials. The goverment does, of course, need such advice, and a number of useful methods of providing it have been evolved. In these instances, scientists serve only by invitation. Inevitably, the general content of the information that is provided and the tenor of the advice that is offered are to some degree conditioned by the particular interests of the requesting agency, which determines what questions are asked and who is given an opportunity to answer them.

Such a relationship does not wholly fulfill the scientist's social role, as we see it. In dealing with social issues, the scientific community must demonstrate its responsibility and its inherent regard for truth and objectivity and must zealously preserve the freedom of thought and communication that is essential to the pursuit of these goals. Accordingly, we believe that the scientific community ought to assume, on its own initiative, an *independent* and *active* informative role, whether or not other social agencies see any immediate advantage in hearing what the scientist has to say.

We believe, also, that what scientists have to say about the social implications of science should be addressed directly to the general public. Our traditional preference for democratic procedures requires that the citizen be sufficiently informed to decide for himself what is to be done about the issues that scientific progress has thrust upon us. Furthermore, our command over natural forces—for example, the destructive potential of nuclear war—is now so great as to create social and moral questions of such great moment that no social agency ought to intervene between the issue and the public.

In sum, we conclude that the scientific community should, on its own initiative, assume an obligation to call to public attention those issues of public policy which relate to science, and to provide for the general public the facts and estimates of the effects of alternative policies which

Figure 11–4. A tragedy of innocence. Unaware of their peril, these technicians engaged in purifying radium are leaning, without protection, over open dishes of radium salts. They are unknowingly getting dangerous doses of radiation which, after a continued exposure over many years, will cause irreparable damage. Similar exposure by radium watch-dial painters during World War I caused at least 40 deaths. (Radioactivity Center, Massachusetts Institute of Technology. Reprinted by permission.)

the citizen must have if he is to participate intelligently in the solution of these problems. A citizenry thus informed is, we believe, the chief assurance that science will be devoted to the promotion of human welfare.

Dehumanization of the Scientist *

by René Dubos (1961)

That "science will find a way out" is a dangerous illusion because it serves as an excuse for intellectual laziness and apathy. I shall try to show that this attitude, which corresponds in reality to a deterioration of public interest in the intellectual aspects of science, originates in part from a change of ideals among the scientists themselves.

Until Bacon's time the motivation of scientists was either plain curiosity or the philosophical urge to understand the world; the practical problems of life were hardly ever mentioned as a justification for their efforts. This does not mean that practical matters did not orient and influence somewhat the activities of scientists. It is obvious that in the past as today what scientists did was necessarily conditioned by the techniques at their disposal and by the preoccupations of their times. But the enormous gap that existed until 1800 beween the large amount of theoretical knowledge and the paucity of applications derived from it bears witness to the fact that very few of the ancient scientists focused their efforts on practical issues. One example must suffice to illustrate how profoundly the Industrial Revolution changed in this regard the professional outlook of the scientific community.

William Thompson (Lord Kelvin) had proved himself a most gifted theoretical investigator during the early part of his life. Before the age of thirty-three he had published studies which constituted the foundation of thermodynamics, provided Maxwell with the mathematical clues to the electromagnetic theory of light and led Hertz to the discovery of radio oscillations. But instead of pursuing the large theoretical implications of his discoveries, Thompson soon shifted his efforts to technological developments and became the first great scientist to organize a laboratory devoted to industrial research. The change in scientific ideals that he symbolizes constitutes one of the most important characteristics of the nineteenth century. It has had such far-ranging consequences that we must consider in greater detail the forces involved in the conflict between

* From René Dubos, *Dreams of Reason,* Columbia University Press, New York and London. Copyright 1961 by Columbia University Press. Reprinted by permission.

the philosophy that "the true scientist has elected to know, not to do" and the other attitude, more common today, that the true role of science is to be, in I. Bernard Cohen's words, the "servant of man." . . .

Today, in our social structure, technological science is a commodity much in demand, and for this reason educational techniques are being developed for the assembly-line production of the human skills required to manufacture gadgets, products, and cures. Wherever this has been attempted with sufficient vigor, the results have been according to anticipation—most men can become effective technologists if adequately trained. Obviously, man finds it easy to behave as *homo faber* whether his function is to produce pineapples, antibiotics, automobiles, or guided missiles. But *homo sapiens* has never been produced on a large scale, and it is his genesis which is the real puzzle. . . .

It is often claimed that Pasteur's scientific activities originated from a concern with practical problems—for example, that his studies on fermentation had their basis in attempts to improve the quality of French wines and beer, or that his interest in infectious processes developed from efforts to save the production of silkworms in France. Nothing could be further from the truth. In reality . . . Pasteur began his scientific life as a purely theoretical investigator and he was already a famous scientist when he began to work on practical problems. From 1847 to 1857 his dominating scientific interests were problems of no apparent practical significance but with large theoretical implications: the relation of molecular structure to optical activity, and the bearing of stereoisomerism on the origin of life; a few years later he became engrossed in other abstract thoughts concerning the biochemical unity of life. As time went on, however, he yielded more and more to the social pressures of his environment, and he spent the largest part of his productive life working on practical problems of fermentation and disease. He became increasingly involved in using science as an instrument of economic conquest rather than as a technique for understanding the universe. Repeatedly he expressed gratification at seeing that his labor would help man to gain mastery over the physical world and to improve human life. "To him who devotes his life to science," Pasteur wrote, "nothing can give more happiness than increasing the number of discoveries, but his cup of joy is full when the results of his studies immediately find practical applications."

There can be no doubt, in my opinion, that Pasteur was aware that his involvement in practical problems had interfered with the pursuit of his deeper scientific interests. He tried to justify his partial neglect of theoretical studies by the statement, "There are not two sciences. There is only science and the applications of science and these two activities are

Figure 11–5. Most portraits of Pasteur, either in youth or in old age, reveal the contemplative aspect of his personality, his concern with large theoretical problems of science. Here he is shown in another mood, dictating to his wife during his practical studies on silkworm diseases in the South of France. The violent controversies in which he was then engaged are reflected in the tenseness of his facial expression. (Photograph courtesy of René Dubos.)

linked as the fruit is to the tree." Yet, despite these brave words and irrespective of his immense success and popular acclaim, it is certain that he often regretted the choice that had been imposed on him by the *Zeitgeist*. Time and time again he stated that he had been "enchained" by an inescapable forward-moving logic that had led him from the study of crystals to the problems of fermentation and then of contagious diseases. He came to believe that it was only through accidental circumstances that he had become involved in practical problems—important, of course, but not so deeply significant as those he had visualized early in life. Yet the desire of his early days to work on crystallography and on the nature of life apparently remained with him as a haunting dream. Pasteur's grandson, Professor L. Pasteur Vallery-Radot, has recently told a moving story which reveals the pathetic intensity of this inner conflict during Pasteur's later years.

I see again that face, that appeared to be carved from a block of granite—that high and large forehead, those grayish-green eyes, with such a deep and kind look. . . .

He seemed to me serious and sad. He was probably sad because of all the things he had dreamed of but not realized.

I remember one evening, at the Pasteur Institute. He was writing quietly at his desk, his head bent on his right hand, in a familiar pose. I was at the corner of the table, not moving or speaking. I had been taught to respect his silences. He stood up and, feeling the need to express his thoughts to the nearest person, even a child, he told me: "Ah! my boy, I wish I had a new life before me! With how much joy I should like to undertake again my studies on crystals!" To have given up his research on crystals was the eternal sorrow of his life.

Many modern scientists suffer from the schizophrenic attitude illustrated by . . . Pasteur. Fortunately, one particular aspect of science helps to minimize the inner conflicts generated by this attitude—namely, the fact, already mentioned and universally recognized, that it is often difficult to dissociate the theoretical from the practical aspects of science. Nevertheless, the conflicts are not entirely resolved by this interdependence of theory and practice. The uneasiness of scientists on this score is revealed by the fact that, whereas among themselves they claim that their primary interest is in the conceptual rather than the applied aspects of science, in public they justify basic research by asserting that it always leads to "useful" results, meaning by this the development of processes and products that can be converted into wealth or power. In a symposium on "basic research" recently held in New York, only one of the very distinguished participants dared take the position that the search for knowledge per se is an activity sufficient unto itself, one which does not need further justification.

Like Pasteur, other scientists seem to be afraid to admit in public—or do not really believe—that detached intellectual curiosity and desire to understand the universe are proper goals of scientific activity, whether or not "useful" results will ever follow. Yet, despite Francis Bacon's claim that "Knowledge, that tendeth but to satisfaction is but as a courtesan . . . ," the attempt to justify science only by its worldly products is fraught with dangers. Not only does it compromise the intellectual honesty of the scientific community for reasons that need not be discussed here; in my opinion, it also helps to foster among lay people a fundamental skepticism about and even contempt for science itself.

To be scornful of the ultimate intellectual and moral value of natural sciences is, of course, a very ancient attitude. Socrates' skepticism, as expressed in Plato's dialogues, has its counterpart in the talk about the bankruptcy of science that was widespread in literary and philosophical circles at the beginning of the present century. Until recently, however, the attitude of the skeptics was not one of hostility but rather one of impatience and disappointment at the fact that, despite oft repeated promises, science had not yet solved for man the riddle of his nature and his destiny. Far more dangerous, it seems to me, are the expressions of contempt for science as an intellectual discipline, and for scientists as individuals, that have appeared repeatedly during the past few decades. Along with admiration for and awe at the power of science, there exists among the lay public, as pointed out by Margaret Mead, a curious mistrust of the scientist himself, as if he were something scarcely normal and human. This modern attitude toward the scientist is not far removed from that of primitives toward the shaman or medicine man, an individual regarded as essential to the group but one who is feared and often hated.

As typical of the hostile attitude toward science and scientists, I shall consider two books published respectively in 1913 and 1930: *The Tragic Sense of Life*, by Miguel de Unamuno, and *The Revolt of the Masses*, by José Ortega y Gasset. Both books have been translated into several languages and are still widely read and quoted; they have spread far and wide the doctrine of the bankruptcy of science. Although they deal with different themes, I shall consider them together since they have in common several aspects of the antiscience movement.

Unamuno and Ortega recognize, of course, the contributions made by science to human safety and comfort. But while they appreciate the merits of aspirin and motor cars, they are very little impressed by the kind of intellectual process involved in the technology that has produced these conveniences. Most scientific thinking, according to them, corresponds to a mechanical performance of a rather low order. Just as ancient societies used slaves for the affairs of everyday life, so modern societies produce and use scientific technicians for the same end. Consciously or unconsciously, Unamuno and Ortega have accepted to the letter Bacon's claim that the scientific method is so mechanical and foolproof as to be readily and effectively handled by small minds. They seem to have taken to heart his statement that "brutes by their natural instinct have produced many discoveries, whereas men by discussion and the conclusions of reason have given birth to few or none." As an extension of Bacon's aphorism, it seems worth while to quote at some length from the several pages in *The Revolt of the Masses* that Ortega devotes to the low intellectual caliber of scientists and their discoveries.

The actual scientific man is the prototype of the mass-man. Not by chance, not through the individual failings of each particular man of science, but because science itself . . . automatically converts him into mass-man, makes of him a primitive, a modern barbarian. Experimental science has progressed thanks in great part to the work of men astoundingly mediocre, and even less than mediocre. That is to say, modern science . . . finds a place for the intellectually commonplace man and allows him to work therein with success. The reason of this lies in what is at the same time the great advantage and the gravest peril of the new science, and of the civilization directed and represented by it, namely, mechanisation. A fair amount of the things that have to be done in physics or in biology is mechanical work of the mind which can be done by anyone, or almost anyone. . . . The work is done . . . as with a machine, and in order to obtain quite abundant results it is not even necessary to have rigorous notions of their meaning and foundation. The specialist . . . is not learned, for he is formally ignorant of all that does not enter into his speciality; but neither is he ignorant, because he is "a scientist," and "knows" very well his own tiny portion of the universe. We shall have to say that he is a learned *ignoramus*. Anyone who wishes can observe the stupidity of thought, judgment, and action shown today in politics, art, religion, and the general problems of life and the world by the "men of science."

Scientists having become so mechanical and unconcerned with philosophical and truly intellectual problems, it is not surprising that, in Unamuno's words, "Science does not satisfy the needs of our heart and our will." Not only does it not deal with the problems of the real man "of flesh and bone," but it "turns against those who refuse to submit to its orthodoxy the weapons of ridicule and contempt."

Thus, according to Unamuno and Ortega, the modern scientist is thoroughly dehumanized, with no horizon beyond his specialized techniques, no awareness of distant human goals. Science fails to deal with the problems that are the real concerns of mankind; and, furthermore, it stultifies all higher aspirations by fostering and satisfying the mass aspects of human nature. Lest there be an illusion that the antiscience movement is peculiar to Latin countries, I shall conclude this discussion with remarks originating from the Anglo-Saxon world. In *The Human Situation,* W. Macneile Dixon asserted that "Science is the view of life where everything human is excluded from the prospect. It is of intention inhuman, supposing, strange as it may seem, that the further we travel from ourselves the nearer we approach the truth, the further from our deepest sympathies, from all we care for, the nearer are we to reality, the stony heart of the scientific universe." As pointed out by Kenneth E. Boulding in *The Image,* many are those all over the world who believe that: "Science might also be defined as the process of substituting unimportant questions which can be answered for important questions which cannot."

The contempt for science and the scientist illustrated by Unamuno's and Ortega's writings reflects an attitude now fairly widespread. To account for it, scientists are inclined to assume that the public does not have the training or the ability required to appreciate the intellectual beauty and the higher morality of science. But it might be worth while to consider the possibility that the antiscience movement has its origin in the behavior of the scientists themselves—in their own failure to convey to the public the nobler aspects of the scientific heritage, and in misleading assertions which create antagonism. It seems to me, for example, that some scientists have a tendency to derive a kind of unjustified intellectual haughtiness from their familiarity with experimental techniques of which the chief intellectual merit is that they happen to permit the solution of practical problems. These scientists exhibit pride of intellect in speaking of the scientific method as if it were something esoteric, superhuman in its power and precision, whereas it is in reality a very human activity supplemented by a few specialized techniques. Instead of bragging about the purely professional aspects of a "scientific method" that they really cannot define, should not scientists emphasize more than they do the spiritual, creative, and almost artistic aspects of all great scientific advances?

Scientists defend basic research in public by asserting that it cannot fail eventually to yield practical results, but they rarely advertise that knowledge per se is also a precious fruit of science. There is truth, of course, in Benjamin Farrington's statement that "man makes his mental history in the process of conquering the world," but only partial truth. Science, like philosophy, has long been pursued for its own sake, or, rather, for the sake of intellectual satisfaction and increased understanding. Long before science could be justified by its industrial uses Ptolemy experienced the kind of intellectual intoxication that only knowledge can provide. "I know that I am mortal, a creature of a day; but when I search into the multitudinous revolving spirals of the stars, my feet no longer rest on the earth, but, standing by Zeus himself, I take my fill of ambrosia, the food of the gods." In a similar mood Kepler exclaimed, "Eighteen months ago the first dawn rose for me, three months ago the bright day, and a few days ago the full sun of a most wonderful vision." And at the end of his life Pasteur spoke lovingly of "the charm of our studies, the enchantment of science."

It would be interesting to know the reasons which have made such very great scientists as . . . Pasteur emphasize the practical worth of their studies and leave unexpressed their loftier intellectual goals. The most obvious interpretation of this attitude is that it was dictated by the wish to gain public approval. But there is no evidence that the public of their time would not have recognized and respected a purely intellectual scientific motivation. In fact, it seems to me that in all situations where the public has exhibited any interest in science, it has been just as eager to learn of the philosophical aspects as of the practical applications. . . .

Nothing could illustrate better the change that occurred in the focus of the scientific community during the Industrial Revolution than the sudden and complete disappearance of the term "natural philosophy." The schism between science and philosophy was the result of two forces which operated almost simultaneously. One was the recognition that knowledge could be used for creating wealth and power; the other was the rapid accumulation of new and unexpected facts which engendered a sense of humility before the complexity of nature and rendered scientists shy of extrapolating from factual knowledge into speculative thoughts. Then humility evolved into scorn for speculation, and today the statement "This is not science, this is philosophy" rules out of scientific discussion any statement that goes a step beyond established fact.

Yet it is apparent that today, as in the past, many scientists—among them some of the most brilliant and most effective—are eager to escape from the austere discipline of factual knowledge and to experience again the intoxication of philosophical thought. They may distrust Plato, but, like him, they seem to regard philosophy as the "dear delight." Witness the flurry of speculative books published by scientists as soon as some discovery enlarges the scope of their knowledge. The theory of evolution has been used by biologists as a platform to erect or justify religious, political, and economic philosophies. Familiarity with modern theoretical physics seems to warrant opinions not only on the structure of matter and its relation to energy, but also on the nature of life, the existence of free will, or the symbolism of language.

This return to scientific philosophy negates, it seems to me, the fears so commonly expressed that scientists are becoming a class apart from the rest of society by developing a culture without contact with the rest of human life. . . .

A while ago I used the names of Miguel de Unamuno and Ortega y Gasset to represent the movement which is often called antiscience. This was unfair to these authors because they are, in truth, the voice of humanity begging scientists to remember that man does not live by bread alone. They express also the fear of seeing science identified exclusively with power and technology at a time when it is beginning to reach populations which have never known it under any other guise. It should not be forgotten that in the Western World science was part of culture for several centuries before coming to be used extensively for practical ends. Even today this cultural heritage still conditions to a certain extent the manner in which science is pursued and employed in the countries of Western civilization. In contrast, science is being introduced in the underdeveloped parts of the world not as a cultural pursuit, but merely as a powerful and convenient tool—at best to be used for the production of material wealth, at worst for destructive purposes. For these reasons it seems to me that scientists and science writers betray a public trust when they neglect to emphasize the disinterested aspects of knowledge and are satisfied instead with claiming that all scientific discoveries eventually prove of practical use. On the one hand, there is no evidence that this is true. On the other hand, this attitude ignores the fact that today, as in the past, men starve for understanding almost as much as for food. In the long run the exclusive appeal to practical values may well endanger the future of science and its very existence.

It is obvious, of course, that during recent decades science has improved the lot of man on earth, even more successfully than Francis Bacon had anticipated. It is equally true, however, that for many centuries before the modern era, science had enriched mankind with a wealth of understanding at least as valuable as material riches. Scientists, like other men, win esteem and contribute to happiness more effectively by the exercise of wisdom than by the practice of power. And it is good for them to remember that, long before they had achieved technological mastery over nature and thus become servants of society, their functions as high priests of pure knowledge had given them ancient titles of nobility which they must continue to honor.

Is Knowledge a Good in Itself?

The Value of Science *

by Henri Poincaré (1907)

The search for truth should be the goal of our activities; it is the sole
end worthy of them. Doubtless we should first bend our efforts to assuage
human suffering, but why? Not to suffer is a negative ideal more surely
attained by the annihilation of the world. If we wish more and more to
free man from material cares, it is that he may be able to employ the
liberty obtained in the study and contemplation of truth.

But sometimes truth frightens us. And in fact we know that it is sometimes deceptive, that it is a phantom never showing itself for a moment
except to ceaselessly flee, that it must be pursued further and ever further
without ever being attained. Yet to work one must stop, as some Greek,
Aristotle or another, has said. We also know how cruel the truth often
is, and we wonder whether illusion is not more consoling, yea, even more
bracing, for illusion it is which gives confidence. When it shall have
vanished, will hope remain and shall we have the courage to achieve?
Thus would not the horse harnessed to his treadmill refuse to go, were
his eyes not bandaged? And then to seek truth it is necessary to be independent, wholly independent. If, on the contrary, we wish to act, to be
strong, we should be united. This is why many of us fear truth; we consider it a cause of weakness. Yet truth should not be feared, for it alone
is beautiful.

When I speak here of truth, assuredly I refer first to scientific truth; but
I also mean moral truth, of which what we call justice is only one aspect.
It may seem that I am misusing words, that I combine thus under the
same name two things having nothing in common; that scientific truth,
which is demonstrated, can in no way be likened to moral truth, which
is felt. And yet I can not separate them, and whosoever loves the one
can not help loving the other. To find the one, as well as to find the

* From Henri Poincaré, *The Value of Science*, translated by G. B. Halstead, 1907.
Reprinted from *Moments of Discovery*, edited by George Schwartz and Philip W.
Bishop, Basic Books, Inc., New York. Copyright 1958 by Basic Books, Inc. Reprinted
by permission.

other, it is necessary to free the soul completely from prejudice and from passion; it is necessary to attain absolute sincerity. These two sorts of truth when discovered give the same joy; each when perceived beams with the same splendor, so that we must see it or close our eyes. Lastly, both attract us and flee from us; they are never fixed: when we think to have reached them, we find that we have still to advance, and he who pursues them is condemned never to know repose. It must be added that those who fear the one will also fear the other; for they are the ones who in everything are concerned above all with consequences. In a word, I liken the two truths, because the same reasons make us love them and because the same reasons make us fear them.

If we ought not to fear moral truth, still less should we dread scientific truth. In the first place it can not conflict with ethics. Ethics and science have their own domains, which touch but do not interpenetrate. The one shows us to what goal we should aspire, the other, given the goal, teaches us how to attain it. So they can never conflict since they can never meet. There can no more be immoral science than there can be scientific morals.

But if science is feared, it is above all because it can not give us happiness. Of course it can not. We may even ask whether the beast does not suffer less than man. But can we regret that earthly paradise where man brute-like was really immortal in knowing not that he must die? When we have tasted the apple, no suffering can make us forget its savor. We always come back to it. Could it be otherwise? As well ask if one who has seen and is blind will not long for the light. Man, then, can not be happy through science, but today he can much less be happy without it.

The Search for Truth *

by Garrett Hardin (1959)

A harmful truth is better than a useful lie, as Thomas Mann has said. Why better? Surely we do not desire harm? No: but the history of science—indeed, the history of all creative thought—shows that time after time a new truth, which has at first appeared dangerous and ugly, has in the end proved to be both useful and beautiful. Some argue that we would have been better off had we never left the garden of Eden. Perhaps; but once we have discovered a new truth, our two options are to acknowledge the truth or to repress our knowledge of it. Psychology has shown clearly enough the evils of repression. We must acknowledge the

* From Garrett Hardin, *Nature and Man's Fate.*

truth and go ahead to explore its implications. To do so is an act of faith in science, faith in the future, faith in the essential goodness of truth.

. . . We are terribly clever people, we moderns: we bend Nature to our will in countless ways. We move mountains, and make caves, fly at speeds no other organism can achieve and tap the power of the atom. We are terribly clever. The essentially religious feeling of subserviency to a power greater than ourselves comes hard to us clever people. But by our intelligence we are now beginning to make out the limits to our cleverness, the impotence principles that say what can and cannot be. In an operational sense, we are experiencing a return to a religious orientation toward the world.

That this orientation was lost for a while was perhaps—at least from a certain point of view—good for man. Man refused to accept the world as it is, and out of this *impiety* came technological science. No world of thoroughly pious men could have achieved what we have achieved. In spite of all that may be said—and much truly said—about the perils of eating of the tree of knowledge, we do not honestly regret that we did so, whatever the final outcome. It has been a wonderful adventure, this science of ours, and we would not have even suspected its magnificence had we not impiously refused to accept the world as it appeared to be. By so doing we have plunged beneath the appearance, ultimately (we believe) to discover the real. Impiety, coupled with honesty, will lead us finally to a new and defensible piety.

Questions To Consider

Is scientific knowledge the forbidden fruit?

Do you think that it would be possible to reject science and return to a simple society? If it were possible would you be in favor of this solution?

Is the schism between science and society a symptom of the unconscious rejection of science by society?

Is the emphasis on technology and practical results rather than pure research one of the reasons for the rejection of science by our intellectuals?

Does society try to exploit too quickly the practical applications that result from pure research?

Can we be sure that "science will find a way out"?

Is there any way that science can help mankind adapt to the new powers which it has created?

Suggestions for Further Reading

* Bronowski, J. J.: *Science and Human Values.* Torchbooks, Harper & Row, 1959. The author relates creative science to creative art and shows how important human values grow out of the true scientific spirit fostered by the desire for understanding and respect for the truth.

Dubos, René: *Dreams of Reason,* Columbia University Press, 1961. A stimulating and thought-provoking series of lectures on some of the fallacies and dangers of our scientific civilization. The Dubos selection beginning on p. 653 came from this collection.

* Price, Derek J.: *Science Since Babylon,* Yale University Press, 1962. A series of lectures in which the author covers five areas of scientific crises (e.g., the crossover from pure thought to technology), the solutions of which led to the scientific age. He then discusses certain threatening "diseases" of science (e.g., overspecialization) which demand a high degree of social responsibility.

* Russell, Bertrand: *The Future of Science,* Wisdom Library, Philosophical Library, Inc., 1959. Russell examines the dangers which he feels are inherent in the conflict between the progress of science and human nature, science and the increased intensity of organization and national rivalry, and the probable outcome of an increasingly scientific civilization. The conclusions are controversial, as Russell questions whether science is a blessing or a curse.

* Whitehead, Alfred North: *Science and the Modern World,* Mentor Books, The New American Library, 1948. This famous work examines the relationship between science and philosophy throughout the last three centuries and discusses the impact of science on modern thought.

* Paperback edition.

ASHFORD, Theodore A., was born in Greece, February 27, 1908. He taught chemistry for many years at the University of Chicago. There he developed several courses in physical science covering physics, chemistry, astronomy, geology, meteorology, and mathematics. Concurrently he was, as a member of the examinations staff of the U. S. Armed Forces Institute, responsible for constructing the comprehensive tests used by the USAFI. Since 1947 he has been chairman of the examinations committee of the division of chemical education of the American Chemical Society. The committee designs and publishes national standardized tests for chemistry courses. Dr. Ashford is now professor of chemistry and director of the Institute for the Teaching of Chemistry at St. Louis University.

ASIMOV, Isaac, was born in Russia in 1920. He was educated at Columbia University (Ph.D. in 1948) and is an associate professor of biochemistry at Boston University School of Medicine. To date he has an impressive record of more than thirty successful books and is considered one of today's most imaginative interpreters of scientific subjects. He lives in West Newton, Massachusetts.

BACON, Francis (1561–1626), was an English philosopher and essayist whose career led him into a most difficult position in the famous dispute between Elizabeth I and Essex. Although Essex was his patron and although Elizabeth had repeatedly overlooked Bacon for political office, he served as the Queen's counsel in the trial of the rebels of 1601 and was instrumental in securing Essex's conviction for treason.

His efforts in the case brought him ill feeling on the part of the public and did not advance him in favor with the Queen. It was not until fifteen years after the coronation of James I that Bacon was appointed Lord Chancellor of England.

A year after he had completed his *Novum Organum* he was tried for taking bribes and accused of corrupt dealings in chancery suits. He was convicted, fined, and imprisoned. A general pardon was granted by the King, and Bacon was released after four days in the Tower. Although he admitted taking bribes, he denied they had ever influenced his decisions.

He did the major portion of his most important work after retirement from public life, including the *History of Henry VII* and the *History of Life and Death*.

BERGSON, Henri (1859–1941), was born in Paris. He taught philosophy at Clermont-Ferrand, obtained his doctorate from the University of Paris in 1889, and from 1900 taught philosophy at the Collège de France. He was elected to the French Academy, and in 1927 was awarded a Nobel Prize for his books on philosophy. In 1940 he refused the Vichy government's offer to exempt him from the anti-Semitic decrees. He resigned his honorary chair at the Collège de France. Eighty-one years old and feeble, he rose from a sick bed and stood in line, supported by his valet and nurse, for the required registration. The effort may have hastened his death on January 4, 1941.

BRONOWSKI, Jacob, is well known for his work in two fields often thought incompatible: mathematics and literature. He was born in Poland in 1908 and educated as a mathematician, earning his Ph.D. from the University of Cambridge in 1933. He was senior lecturer in mathematics at University College until 1942, when he left that post to do wartime research. In 1953 he came to the United States as a visiting professor at the Massachusetts Institute of Technology. Besides this scientific career, he has made a considerable reputation as a radio dramatist and won the Italia Prize for the best dramatic work broadcast in Europe during the 1950–51 season. His combined scientific and literary abilities have made him important to the modern movement of scientific humanism in England.

COATES, Robert M., was born April 6, 1897, in New Haven, Connecticut. He was graduated from Yale in 1916 and lived in France from 1921 to 1926. He has worked as editor for the *New Yorker*—as book and art critic—and also published a number of books. Coates lives in Old Chatham, New York.

COMPTON, Arthur Holly (1892–1954), was born in Wooster, Ohio. He was graduated from Wooster College and received his Ph.D. from Princeton. He also studied at the University of Cambridge. In 1927 he was awarded a Nobel Prize for his discovery of the wave-length change of scattered X rays (known as the Compton effect). He served as professor of physics and department head at Washington University in St. Louis, and became chancellor there in 1945. Later he went to the University of Chicago where he was head of the department of physics and dean of the physical sciences. It was at the Metallurgical Laboratory there that the first atomic chain reaction was achieved.

CONANT, James Bryant, was awarded his Ph.D. by Harvard University in 1916. During World War I he spent a year in the research division of the chemical warfare service and then returned to Harvard to teach. Becoming widely recognized as a brilliant organic chemist, he advanced to the rank of professor, and in 1933 was made president of Harvard.

During World War II he was instrumental in organizing American scientists for the war effort and participated in the development of the atomic bomb. At the end of the war he became senior adviser to the National Science Foundation and to the Atomic Energy Commission. In 1953 he was named the United States High Commissioner for Western Germany and in 1955 ambassador. When he returned to the United States in 1957, he again pursued his interest in education and completed a study on the comprehensive high school, which has been of considerable value both to the general public and to educators.

CURIE, Marie Sklodowska (1867–1934), was born in Warsaw, Poland, and came to Paris to study science. In 1895 she met and married Pierre Curie, who was a professor at the Paris School of Physics and Chemistry. They had two daughters, Eva and Irène. In 1903 Marie and Pierre Curie shared a Nobel Prize for the discovery of the radioactive elements polonium and radium. Pierre was killed in a traffic accident in 1906. Marie succeeded him as professor of general physics at the Sorbonne and later received another Nobel Prize for her further work on radium and its compounds. She became director of the research department of the Radium Institute of the University of Paris and organized radiological service in the hospitals during World War I. One of the Curie daughters, Irène, shared a Nobel Prize in chemistry (1935) with her husband Frédéric Joliot for the production of artificially radioactive substances.

DALTON, John (1766–1844), was a color-blind school teacher, son of a poor Westmoreland hand-loom weaver. At the age of twelve he started to teach in the village school, and when only nineteen he was made principal of a Quaker boarding school. His color-blindness spurred him to investigate and write on this phenomenon, which has since been called "Daltonism." He kept a meteorological diary and was familiar enough with electricity to assert correctly in 1793 that the aurora borealis was electrical in origin. A crude experimenter, Dalton relied a good deal on the facts reported by others, but he had the gift of synthesis which enabled him to relate the experimental facts on combining ratios of the elements to the theory that matter was composed of atoms.

DANTZIG, Tobias, was born in Russia in 1884, came to the United States in 1910, and received his Ph.D. in mathematics from Indiana University in 1916. He has taught at Indiana University, Columbia University, and at the University of Maryland, where he is now professor emeritus. In addition to *Number, the Language of Science,* Dr. Dantzig has also published *Aspects of Science* (1937) and *The Story of Geometry* (1940).

DUBOS, René, was born in Saint-Brice, France, in 1901. He was educated at the Collège Chaptal and Institut National Agronomique in Paris. In 1924, after a few years with the International Institute of Agriculture in Rome, he went to Rutgers University, where he was awarded his Ph.D. in 1927. Since that time, except for the period 1942–44, when he was George Fabyan professor of comparative pathology and professor of tropical medicine at Harvard University Medical School, Dr. Dubos has been associated with the Rockefeller Institute, where he did pioneer work in the field of antibiotics. In 1951 he was elected president of the Harvey Society and the Society of American Bacteriologists. In addition to his scientific achievements and honors, Dr. Dubos is the author of eight books. Since 1946 he has been editor of the *Journal of Experimental Medicine.*

EINSTEIN, Albert, was born in Ulm, Germany, in 1879. He was educated in Germany and in Switzerland. After receiving his Ph.D. from the University of Zurich, he tried, in vain, for a position with a university and finally took a job with the patent office in Berne. His job left him with much time for his own work, and in 1905 he published four important papers. It was in the areas of physics dealt with in these papers that he was to do most of his important work: the special theory of relativity, the establishment of the mass energy equivalence, the theory of Brownian motion, and the photon theory of light.

In 1921 he was awarded a Nobel Prize for his photoelectric law and his work in theoretical physics. He emigrated to the United States in 1933 and joined the Institute for Advanced Study at Princeton. He became a United States citizen in 1940.

By the time of Einstein's death in 1955, the science of physics had been vastly changed. The general theory of relativity, which demonstrates that the laws of physics are the laws of geometry in four dimensions and that these laws are determined by the distribution of matter and energy in the universe, is one of the most beautiful and profound constructions ever conceived by the mind of man.

EISELEY, Loren, was born in Lincoln, Nebraska, in 1907. Having received his A.B. from the University of Nebraska, he completed graduate work in anthropology at the University of Pennsylvania. He returned to the Midwest for his first academic job, at the University of Kansas. He later became head of the department of sociology and anthropology at Oberlin College in Ohio. In 1947 he returned to the University of Pennsylvania to head the department of anthropology. Since 1948 he has been curator of Early Man in the University Museum. Dr. Eiseley has lectured at a number of universities and has published many books and articles. He is past president of the American Institute of Human Paleontology.

For a number of years he was active in the search for early postglacial man in the western United States; he has worked in the high plains, mountains, and deserts bordering the Rocky Mountains from Canada into Mexico.

EVANS, Earl A. Jr., was born in Baltimore in 1910 and educated at Johns Hopkins and Columbia. In 1942 he won the Eli Lilly prize of the American Chemical Society for the early use of a radioactive isotope in biological experiments. After wartime work on malaria, he served as chief scientific officer to the United States Embassy in London. He is chairman of the biochemistry department at the University of Chicago and has for the past fourteen years been engaged in research on virus growth. In addition to his research and teaching duties, he has served the State Department in various advisory capacities.

GAMOW, George, was born in Odessa, Russia, in 1904. He studied nuclear physics at the University of Leningrad and received his Ph.D. there in 1928. In 1934 he came to the United States as a professor of physics at George Washington University where he was for over twenty years. Since 1956 he has been at the University of Colorado. During this time his interest moved from the atomic nucleus to astrophysics, to the theory of the expanding universe, and later to the fundamental problems of biology, including molecular genetics and the synthesis of proteins. He has written frequently for the British magazine *Discovery* and for *Scientific American*.

HALDANE, John Scott (1860–1936), was born in Edinburgh. He was a member of a distinguished family of biologists, grandnephew of Richard Burdon Haldane, and father of John Burdon Sanderson Haldane. He conducted extensive researches into mining and industrial diseases caused by poor ventilation. Elected a fellow of New College, Oxford, he also served as a director of a mining laboratory at Birmingham, and was the author of several books on scientific subjects.

HARDIN, Garrett, was born in Dallas in 1915. He received his Sc.B. from the University of Chicago and his Ph.D. in biology from Stanford in 1941. From 1942 to 1946 he was a staff member of the division of plant biology at Carnegie Institute. After several years of teaching at Stanford he went to the University of California, where he is now professor of biology. In addition to teaching, Dr. Hardin has been engaged in microbiological research on algae and protozoa, photosynthesis, and antibiotics.

HECHT, Selig (1892–1947), was born in Glogow, Austria, and was brought to the United States in 1898. He received his B.S. from the College of the City of New York, and his Ph.D. from Harvard in 1917. He was a research fellow at Liverpool, Harvard, Naples, and Cambridge (England). In 1926 he became professor of biophysics at Columbia University and was involved in research in the physics of vision. He lectured widely and served on many committees concerned with the problems of vision and light perception. He edited the *Columbia Biological Series, Monographs on Experimental Biology,* and the *Biological Bulletin.* Not only was he a great scholar in his field, but also deeply concerned about the impact of atomic energy on the fate of mankind.

HEISENBERG, Werner Karl, born in Würzburg, Germany, in 1901, was educated at Munich and Göttingen. From 1922 to 1927 he worked with Niels Bohr in Copenhagen. Here he formulated the uncertainty principle in 1925. During the 1930's he collaborated with a fellow German, Max Born, to develop a new mathematical theory that bridged the gap between wave and particle theories. He was professor of physics at Leipzig from 1927 to 1941, when he left to direct Germany's uranium committee. After the German defeat, he took over the chair of physics at the University of Göttingen and became director of the Max Planck Institute. Winner of a Nobel Prize in 1932, and foreign-member of the Royal Society since 1955, Werner Heisenberg is one of the greatest and most influential physicists of our time.

HOLDEN, Alan, was born in New York City in 1904 and attended high school in Montclair, New Jersey. Mr. Holden broadened his early scientific interest at Harvard—from which he was graduated in 1925—by studying physics and mathematics. He joined the Bell Telephone Laboratories, working first as a commercial methods investigator and later as a writer of instructions for accounting practices. He became an editor of technical articles published by scientists at the laboratories, and for a time, as an avocation, he and Mrs. Holden hand-set, printed, bound, and published books under the name of "The Cassowary Press."

Since 1935 he has been on the research staff of Bell Telephone Laboratories. For several years he conducted a search for artificial crystals with useful applications in electronic equipment, and during World War II he helped develop methods for producing large crystals, the heart of sonar equipment used to detect submarines. Since the war he has turned his attention to spectroscopic studies and microwave frequencies.

HOLTON, Gerald, was born in Berlin in 1922 of Austrian parents. He received his B.A. and M.A. from Wesleyan University and his Ph.D. from Harvard in 1948. He has held teaching positions at Wesleyan, Brown, and Harvard where he is now professor of physics, pursuing experimental research on the properties of materials under high pressures. He teaches and writes in the fields of physics, and in the history and philosophy of science. He was, at one time, editor in chief of *Daedalus, the Journal of the American Academy of Arts and Sciences*. In 1961 he received the distinguished service citation of the American Association of Physics Teachers.

HUXLEY, Julian, was born in London in 1887, the grandson of Thomas H. Huxley, an eminent biologist. Julian was educated at Eton and Oxford. He has taught at Rice Institute in Houston, Texas, at Oxford, and at the University of London. He has made many lecture tours in America and for three years served as director general of UNESCO. Among the many honors he has received are the Huxley Memorial Lecture and Medal of the Royal Anthropological Institute and the Darwin Medal of the Royal Society. His countless publications are well known for their imaginative scope, wisdom, and responsibility. He was knighted in 1958.

INFELD, Leopold, was born in Cracow, Poland, in 1898 and received his Ph.D. from the University of Cracow in 1921. He was a lecturer at the University of Lvov in Poland from 1929 to 1934, and a fellow of the Rockefeller Foundation at Cambridge, England, from 1934 to 1935. In 1936 he joined the Institute for Advanced Study at Princeton, and after spending two years there he became a professor of applied mathematics at the University of Toronto. In 1950 he returned to Poland to the University of Warsaw. His books include *Quest: The Evolution of a Scientist*, which was awarded the Annisfield Prize in 1941, and *Albert Einstein, His Work and Its Influence on Our World*.

JEANS, Sir James Hopwood (1877–1946), was a classical mathematician and physicist widely known for his popular books on astronomy. He was born in London and educated at Cambridge and became university lecturer in applied mathematics at Cambridge and later professor of applied mathematics at Princeton University. He had marked success with applied mathematics in the fields of physics and astronomy especially. He wrote papers on many aspects of radiation, on the formation of binary stars, spiral nebulae, giant and dwarf stars, the source of stellar energy, and the evolution and radiation of gaseous stars. He was knighted in 1938 and awarded the Order of Merit in 1939.

KRUTCH, Joseph Wood, was born in Knoxville, Tennessee, in 1893. He took his A.B. at the University of Tennessee, and his M.A. and Ph.D. at Columbia, where he became Brander Matthews Professor of Dramatic Literature. One of America's distinguished naturalists, he has been equally well known as a teacher, drama and literary critic, biographer, editor and journalist, and public speaker. Now retired, he lives in Tucson, Arizona.

LATTER, Albert L., received his Ph.D. in nuclear physics at the University of California at Los Angeles in 1952. A member of the U.S. Scientific Delegation to the test ban negotiations in Geneva, he is now head of the physics department at the Rand Corporation in Santa Monica, California. He is also a member of the U.S. Air Force Scientific Advisory Board as well as numerous other government committees.

LEEUWENHOEK, Antony Van (1632–1723), was once a shopkeeper and petty official of the picturesque city of Delft in Holland. Grinding his own lenses and constructing his own jealously guarded microscopes, this keen-sighted, infinitely curious, amateur naturalist was the first human being to see —in rain water and on the "scum from the teeth"—the little living creatures we now call microbes, bacteria, or germs. His microscopic adventures were inde-fatigably recorded (filling four quarto volumes) in rambling letters to the Royal Society of London, which unanimously elected him to membership in 1680. He repaid the honor by bequeathing the Society twenty-six microscopes. Almost everything that Leeuwenhoek saw with his microscopes was new to the world of science. Especially significant were what he saw (1) in a tadpole's tail—the tiny capillary blood vessels, also seen by the Italian physiologist Malpighi (1628–94), which solved the final mystery of the circulation of the blood; and (2) in human semen—spermatozoa, the male element.

LUCRETIUS (*c*. 99–55 B.C.), was a Roman poet, a contemporary of Cicero and Julius Caesar. He was an Epicurean, and his famous poem *De rerum natura* is, for the most part, an exposition of the views of the Greek philosophers Democ-ritus (460–370 B.C.) and Epicurus (341–270 B.C.). This poem helped to bring the Greek atomic theories to the scholars of the Middle Ages and was thus in-strumental in its later acceptance as a scientific theory.

MASON, Brian, was born in New Zealand in 1917, and studied geology and chemistry at the University of New Zealand, which awarded him an M.Sc. in 1938. In 1939 he resigned his job as a geologist for an oil company and went to Norway in order to improve his skiing. While there he enrolled at the Uni-versity of Oslo and came under the influence of the geochemist Victor Moritz Goldschmidt, who introduced him to the subject of meteorites and their geo-chemical significance. After the German invasion of Norway in 1940, Mason escaped to Sweden, where he continued his studies at the University of Stock-holm, receiving a Ph.D. in mineralogy in 1943. He spent the following year as a scientific liaison officer for the New Zealand Government, was senior lecturer in geology at the University of New Zealand, and from 1947 to 1953 was asso-ciate professor of mineralogy at the University of Indiana. In 1953 he took his present job of curator of physical geology and mineralogy at the American Museum of Natural History. He is also professor of mineralogy at Columbia University.

MENDEL, Gregor Johann (1822–1884), was born into a peasant family in a village in Austrian Silesia, now Czechoslovakia. He attended high school at Troppau and the Philosophical Institute at Olmütz, and entered the Augustinian monastery at Brünn. He later attended the University of Vienna for four terms and returned to teach in the Brünn "Modern School." In the monastery garden at Brünn, he conducted his famous experiments on plants. In 1868 he was elected abbot of the monastery.

MENDELÉEFF, Dmitri Ivanovich (1834–1907), was born in Siberia, the youngest of seventeen children. His widowed mother moved to St. Petersburg so that Dmitri could have a scientific education. There he was admitted to the Pedagogical Institute, a school for the training of high school teachers and graduated at the head of his class. He taught science in the Crimea and at St. Petersburg for a few years, then went abroad to study at Paris and Heidelberg. Before he was thirty-two, he wrote a textbook on organic chemistry which won him the Domidoff Prize, earned his doctorate in chemistry, and was appointed full professor at the University of St. Petersburg. In 1869 he read before the Russian Chemical Society his paper *On the Relation of the Properties to the Atomic Weights of the Elements,* which quickly brought him world-wide fame. Commissioned by the Russian government to study the coal, oil, and naphtha resources, he developed methods of commercial distillation which saved Russia vast sums of money. One day, to photograph a solar eclipse, he shot into the air in a balloon, "flew on a bubble and pierced the sky," thus pioneering his country's interest in the conquest of space.

MILLER, Walter M. Jr., grew up in the southern United States and began his first year of college while the blitzkrieg rumbled across Poland and France. He enlisted in the Army Air Corps a month after Pearl Harbor and spent most of World War II as a radio operator and gunner. He participated in fifty-five combat sorties over Italy and the Balkans. After his discharge from the Air Corps, he entered the University of Texas to study electrical engineering, but an automobile accident put him in the hospital—and on the way to becoming a writer. While convalescing, he wrote his first short story, which was published in 1950 in the *American Mercury.* Thereafter, he combined his interests in art and engineering by writing science-fiction. Mr. Miller now lives in Florida.

MOORE, Ruth, was born in St. Louis, Missouri, and received her A.B. and A.M. from Washington University there. She has worked as a reporter on the St. Louis *Star-Times,* as Washington reporter for the *Chicago Sun,* and as assistant editor of the *Kiplinger Magazine.* She is now in Chicago on the *Sun-Times,* where science feature stories are one of her specialties. She has become well known as a popular science writer, having published four books on science for the layman. Her interest in housing and urban renewal has made her a specialist on these questions. In May 1960 she received the first individual award given by the American Association of Planning Officials for her 1959 series on urban renewal in seven major cities.

MORGENTHAU, Hans Joachim, was born in Coburg, Germany, in 1904. He attended the universities of Berlin, Frankfurt, and Munich and the Graduate Institute for International Studies in Geneva. Leaving Germany in 1932, just before the coming of Hitler, he taught in Switzerland and Spain before emigrating to the United States in 1937. He became a naturalized citizen in 1943. Since 1961 Morgenthau has been professor of political science and modern history at the University of Chicago; in 1963 he was made the Albert A. Michelson Distinguished Service professor. He has also served as visiting professor to a number of universities and as lecturer to colleges of the armed forces.

For almost two decades Morgenthau has been a powerful voice in the affairs of the nation. As a professor, consultant to the Departments of State and Defense, adviser to Presidents Truman, Eisenhower, and Kennedy, as well as a prolific writer of books and articles, he has contributed penetrating insights into some of the more perplexing problems facing the world.

MORRISON, Philip, was born in Somerville, New Jersey, in 1915, was graduated from the Carnegie Institute of Technology in 1936, then studied theoretical physics under J. Robert Oppenheimer at the University of California, where he received his doctorate in 1940. When World War II broke out, Morrison left a lectureship at the University of Illinois to join the Metallurgical Laboratory of the University of Chicago, and later became a group leader at the Los Alamos laboratory of the Manhattan District. Morrison joined the Cornell faculty in 1946, where he has done pioneer work applying physical theory in a number of fields, including microbiology.

MULLER, H. J., was born in New York City in 1890 and was educated at Columbia University, where he took a Ph.D. in zoology in 1916. From 1915 to 1936 he taught biology first at the Rice Institute, then at the University of Texas. In the years 1933–37 he worked at the Institute of Genetics in Moscow as senior geneticist, but he later became a fierce foe of the Soviet system. After spending some years at the University of Edinburgh and at Amherst College, he joined Indiana University in 1945. Professor Muller discovered that the rate of mutation could be accelerated by X rays. This discovery, which he made in 1927, won him the Nobel Prize in physiology and medicine for 1946.

MURCHIE, Guy, was already working his way around the world on the day of his Harvard commencement in 1929. In the years since, he has been a school teacher, pilot, lecturer, newspaperman, illustrator, photographer, aerial navigator, war correspondent, building contractor, founder and director of a children's camp in New Hampshire, and author of books on science for the layman.

OPARIN, Alexander I., was born in Russia in 1894. He graduated in natural science in 1917, and specialized in biological chemistry at the Academy of Bakh until 1929, when he became chairman of plant biochemistry at Moscow University. He helped to organize the Institute of Biochemistry, U.S.S.R. Academy of Sciences, and served as secretary for the department and corresponding member of the Academy. Since 1946 he has been professor and director of biological science at the U.S.S.R. Academy of Sciences. He has also been a member of the Soviet Committee for Soviet Peace, the World Peace Council, and vice president of the World Federation of Scientists. Professor Oparin is the author of several authoritative books and has received many awards for his distinguished contributions to biochemistry.

OVENDEN, Michael William, was born in 1927. He was educated at London University and did his graduate work at Cambridge and London. He was elected secretary of the British Astronomical Association in 1946 and became president of the group in 1951. He is now a lecturer on the staff of the astronomy department at the University of Glasgow. His books include *Looking at the Stars, Artificial Satellites,* and *Life in the Universe.*

PAULING, Linus, was born in 1901 in Portland, Oregon. He received his Ph.D. from the California Institute of Technology in 1925, and in the years 1937–58 he was chairman of the division of chemistry and chemical engineering, and director of the Gates and Crellin Laboratories of Chemistry, at the Institute. In 1947 he received the Royal Society's Davy medal; in 1948, the Presidential Medal for Merit, for outstanding services to the United States from 1940 to 1946; and in 1954 he was awarded the highest honor of all, the Nobel Prize in chemistry, for his research into the nature of the chemical bond. His remarkable contributions to scientific knowledge span chemistry, geology, biology, and medicine.

POINCARÉ, Henri (1854–1912), was generally considered to be one of the greatest mathematicians and original thinkers of his day. He was educated at the École Polytechnique and the École des Mines and taught in Caen and Paris. From his first work in pure mathematics he went on to develop new mathematical techniques, and he founded the study of topological dynamics. In a paper on the dynamics of the electron published in 1906 he arrived at many of the results of the special theory of relativity independently of Einstein.

His writings in philosophy are just as interesting and original, and perhaps as important, as his work in mathematics. His mastery of French prose provided him with a wide and various audience for his work, and he produced more than thirty books and five hundred papers during his career.

POPE, Alexander (1688–1744), was born in London, the son of a linen-draper. He did not receive much formal education, but undermined his health by overstudy and developed a physical deformity as the result of a severe illness at the age of twelve. In 1709 he began publishing poetry and soon enjoyed a wide reputation as the result of such brilliant works as *Essay on Criticism* and *The Rape of the Lock.* In 1717, when his father died, he moved to Twickenham with his mother and his villa there became a meeting place for many prominent figures, both political and literary. During the next twenty-seven years he published many works of witty and satiric poetry.

RABINOWITCH, Eugene, was born in St. Petersburg, Russia, in 1901. He was educated in Berlin and in 1926 became an assistant at the Kaiser Wilhelm Institute for Physics and Chemistry. In 1933 he went to Denmark to the Royal Academy of Science and the next year to London. He is now professor of biophysics at the University of Illinois and also edits the *Bulletin of the Atomic Scientists.* As a physicist his main interest has been in reaction kinetics; as a private person his main interest is public affairs.

ROMER, Alfred, was born in Pleasantville, New York, in 1906 and educated at Williams College (B.A., 1928) and the California Institute of Technology (Ph.D., 1935). He returned to Williams as an assistant in chemistry. Dr. Romer has contributed to *Isis* and the *American Journal of Physics.* For the last ten years he has been teaching at St. Lawrence University in Canton, New York.

SCHRÖDINGER, Erwin (1887–1961), was born in Vienna. He was educated at the university there and later became professor of physics at Stuttgart, Breslau, Zurich, and finally, in 1928, at Berlin. From there he went to Dublin to become a professor at the Institute for Advanced Studies. Most of his work is highly mathematical in character and has dealt with the physics of the atom. He extended De Broglie's theory of wave mechanics and applied it to the problem of atomic structure. In 1933 he won a Nobel Prize for physics for his contribution to the new science of wave mechanics.

SIMPSON, George Gaylord, was born in Chicago in 1902. He was graduated from Yale in 1923 and received his Ph.D. three years later. He was long associated with the American Museum of Natural History, New York, leaving there to become Alexander Agassiz professor of vertebrate paleontology at the Museum of Comparative Zoology at Harvard. He is a member of the National

Academy of Sciences, American Philosophical Society, American Academy of Arts and Science, Society of Vertebrate Paleontology, and many others. He is the author of more than 350 articles and several books.

SINNOTT, Edmund W., was born at Cambridge, Massachusetts, in 1888. Educated at Harvard, he taught botany there, at the Connecticut Agricultural College, and at Columbia, before becoming a member of the faculty at Yale. Now emeritus, he was Sterling Professor of Botany, director of the Sheffield Scientific School, and dean of the graduate school. He was also president of the American Association for the Advancement of Science, the Botanical Society of America, and the American Society of Naturalists. In addition to numerous papers in scholarly journals, he is the author of *The Biology of the Spirit, Botany Principles and Problems; Cell and Psyche; Two Roads to Truth;* and *Plant Morphogenesis.*

SPENCER, Steven M., graduated from the University of Pennsylvania and was a Nieman Fellow at Harvard in 1939, specializing in medical and science studies. He later became science editor of the *Philadelphia Evening Bulletin* and for several years was a science writer on the public relations staff of the DuPont Company. In 1945 he joined *The Saturday Evening Post*, where he is now senior editor in charge of science coverage. In this capacity he has covered a number of science and medical assignments at home and abroad, including the Atoms-for-Peace conference in Geneva (1958). Mr. Spencer has published several books and won a number of awards for science writing, among them the George Westinghouse-American Association for the Advancement of Science prize for distinguished science writing in magazines (1947).

TELLER, Edward, was born in Budapest in 1908, graduated in chemical engineering at Karlsruhe, studied theoretical physics at Munich, Göttingen, and under Niels Bohr at Copenhagen. He left Germany in 1933, lectured in London and Washington (1935), and contributed profoundly to the modern explanation of solar energy, anticipating thereby the theory behind thermonuclear explosions. He worked on the atomic bomb project (1941–46), taught at the University of Chicago, and later joined Oppenheimer's theoretical study group at Berkeley, California. After Russia's first atomic test (1949), he was one of the architects of Truman's crash program to build and test (1952) the world's first hydrogen bomb. In 1952 he was placed in charge of the newly established nuclear laboratories at Livermore. Among the other honors he has received are the Albert Einstein award (1958) and the Research Institute of America Living History award (1960).

WALD, George, was born in New York in 1906. He was graduated from New York University in 1927, and then did graduate work in zoology at Columbia University under Selig Hecht. After receiving his Ph.D. in 1932, he traveled to Germany on a National Research Council fellowship. While studying in Otto Warburg's laboratory at the Kaiser Wilhelm Institute in Berlin, Wald made his first notable contribution to knowledge of the eye—his discovery of vitamin A in the retina. After another year of post-doctoral study at the University of Chicago, he went to Harvard, where he is now professor of biology and a well-known authority on the chemistry of vision.

WEISSKOPF, Victor F., was born in Vienna in 1908. During the early years of his career, he worked successively with the great physicists Heisenberg, Schrödinger, and Pauli, and with Niels Bohr at the Bohr Institute in Copenhagen. In 1937 he came to the United States and joined the faculty of the University of Rochester, where he remained until 1943, when he became associated with the Manhattan Project at Los Alamos. In 1946 he joined the faculty at the Massachusetts Institute of Technology as a professor of physics.

In 1960 Weisskopf was president of the American Physical Society, and is now a member of the National Academy of Sciences, the French Academy of Sciences, and the Federation of American Scientists. In 1956 he received the Max Planck medal of the German Physical Society, in recognition of his work in theoretical physics. He was appointed in 1961 to a two-year post as director-general of CERN, the fourteen-nation European organization for nuclear research in Geneva.

WELLS, Herbert George (1866–1946), was born in Bromley, Kent, of lower middle-class parents. After winning a scholarship to the Royal College of Science, he received his B.S. from London University in 1888. He became a teacher and wrote a biology textbook, but tuberculosis forced him to abandon his work and leave London for a period of convalescence. Upon his return, he began his career as novelist and journalist.

A prolific writer, he produced science-fiction, realistic novels, and novels designed primarily as vehicles for his political beliefs, which were Socialist but anti-Marxist. In addition to his fiction, Wells also worked on two compendiums of knowledge, *The Outline of History* and *The Science of Life*, the second written in collaboration with his son G. P. Wells and Julian Huxley.

WEYL, Hermann (1885–1955), was born in Elmshorn, Germany, and was educated at the universities of Munich and Göttingen. At the latter institution he received his doctorate and held his first teaching post in mathematics. From 1913 to 1930 he was professor of mathematics at the Zürich Technische Hochschule (with a year off, 1928–29, to serve as research professor in mathematical physics at Princeton); from 1930 to 1933 he held a chair at Göttingen; in 1933 he joined the Institute for Advanced Study, Princeton, retiring in 1952. He died in Zurich.

The researches and writings of this distinguished man span a wide field of mathematics, theoretical physics, and philosophy. He was a member of the National Academy of Sciences and was awarded one of the rare foreign fellowships of the Royal Society.

GLOSSARY

Following is a glossary of terms which appear in the text and which may be unfamiliar to the reader. Definitions of these terms are included for easy reference, and in some cases supplementary information is also given. Cross references in the glossary are indicated by italics in those cases where the cross reference may throw additional light on the term being defined. Page numbers refer the reader to material in the body of the text that further explains the term.

A

A-bomb (short for atom bomb) See *fission bomb*. See also pages 170–71, 185.

absolute zero (−273.16°C.) The lowest possible temperature, since at that temperature all thermal, molecular motion ceases. See page 410.

absorption spectrum A spectrum containing dark bands on a colored background produced by white light which has been passed through a cool gas. The dark bands represent the *wave lengths* absorbed by the gas. See Figure 3-10, pages 96–7, and pages 116–17.

acid A substance which produces hydrogen *ions* (*protons*) in solution. Acids corrode metals, releasing hydrogen as a by-product.

acquired characteristic A characteristic acquired by an individual from his environment or training, not from his genes. See pages 343–4.

adenine See *purines*. See also page 485.

albuminous Refers to *proteins* having properties similar to those of egg white, i.e., being soluble in water and coagulating when heated. See page 311.

alleles or **allelomorphs** Contrasting pairs of characters, such as smooth or wrinkled, or the contrasting *genes* which produce them are known as alleles or allelomorphs. See page 436.

alpha particle Helium nucleus, a close combination of two *neutrons* and two *protons* and therefore positively charged. See page 91.

alpha rays (α-rays) Streams of fast-moving *alpha particles*. See page 85.

amino acid An organic compound whose molecule contains an amine group (nitrogen and two hydrogens) and an acid group (a carbon, two oxygens, and a hydrogen) separated by a single carbon atom. Amino acids are the building blocks of protein molecules. See page 317.

amoeba A simple, one-celled animal, consisting of a mass of protoplasm, which moves by changing shape. See page 330.

anode The positive electrode of a battery or vacuum tube, or that electrode in a circuit to which *electrons* flow. See *electrode* and Figure 3-1, page 72.

anther The tiny sac containing pollen on the end of the *stamen*.

anti-lambda A subatomic particle. See page 258.

679

anti-matter   See *anti-particles*.

anti-neutrino   A particle similar to the *neutrino* but opposite in spin.

anti-neutron   A particle similar to the neutron but having an opposite spin. (In other words, it is oppositely affected by a magnetic field.) See page 252.

anti-particles   Particles which have an opposite charge and spin to the particles named, being similar in other respects. See pages 251–2.

anti-proton   A particle equal in weight to the proton but negatively charged and having an opposite spin. See page 251.

aperiodic crystal   A solid whose molecules form a single non-repeating pattern. See page 434.

artificial radioactivity   Radioactive disintegration of artificially made elements. See *radioactivity*.

asexual reproduction   The process whereby a single organism produces an exact replica of itself. See page 347.

atomic energy   *Energy* binding the constituent particles of the atom together, which is released when the atom disintegrates or is split apart. Can also be applied to energy released in any nuclear reaction. See pages 156–7.

atomic nucleus   The positively charged center of an atom. It has a diameter which is roughly only one ten-thousandth the diameter of the whole atom, but contains nearly all of its mass. See pages 88, 89, 91.

atomic number   The number that designates the position of an element in the sequence of the *periodic table*, starting with hydrogen as number one. See page 45.

atomic volume   The volume of space occupied by an element as a solid in an amount of grams equal to its *atomic weight*. See page 44.

atomic weight   Comparative weight of an atom of a particular element, taking the weight of an oxygen atom to be 16. See page 38.

autogeneration   Spontaneous generation of life from inorganic substances. See page 301.

B

beta ray   A stream of *electrons* traveling close to the speed of light. Beta rays are emitted by radioactive substances and are capable of penetrating matter very deeply. See page 85.

binary fission   The process in which a single individual reproduces by splitting into two halves. See page 347.

binding energy   The *energy* required to break up an *atomic nucleus* into its constituent particles. This corresponds to the energy emitted in the formation of the nucleus. See page 155.

biochemistry   The chemistry of living organisms. See page 290.

bond, valency bond   The capacity of an atom to hold (combine with) a hydrogen atom or its equivalent. See page 50.

Brownian motion   The erratic movements of small particles suspended in a medium, caused by the irregular bombardment of molecules of the surrounding medium. See pages 409–10.

C

calcined air   Air that has been heated to a high temperature. See page 294.

calorie   The heat energy necessary to raise the temperature of 1 gram of water 1 degree Centigrade.

carbohydrate   Organic substance containing carbon, hydrogen, and oxygen.

The hydrogen and oxygen are usually in a proportion of 2 to 1, as in water. Carbohydrates include *sugars*, gums, starches, and *cellulose*. See page 310.

catalysis   The action of a *catalyst*. See page 477.

catalyst   A chemical whose presence increases the speed of a chemical reaction, but which is not changed in the reaction. See page 477.

cathode   The negative electrode of a battery or vacuum tube—that electrode in a circuit from which electrons issue. See *electrode* and Figures 2-14 and 2-15, pages 52, 53.

cell   A unit of living matter. In plants, the living matter is contained in tiny compartments, or cells, made of *cellulose*. See page 355.

cell nucleus   An approximately spherical body in the center of a cell, containing mechanisms which control reproduction and *metabolism* in the cell.

cellulose   A *carbohydrate* making up the greater part of the *cell* walls of plants. See page 310.

centrifugal force   The apparent outward force acting on a body rotating in a circle.

chain reaction   A reaction in which one of the agents necessary to the reaction is itself produced by the reaction so as to cause like reactions. In the neutron-fission chain reaction, a *neutron* plus a fissionable atom causes a *fission* resulting in a number of neutrons that in turn cause other fissions. See pages 165–6.

chemical change   A change in a substance due to an increase, decrease, or rearrangement of atoms within its *molecules*. See page 219.

chemical compound   A combination of two or more *elements* in a definite proportion by weight, making a pure homogeneous substance having distinctive properties different from its constitutive elements. See page 24.

chlorophyll   A green pigment contained in all green plants. It enables the plant to utilize the energy from sunlight to build up *sugars, lipids,* and *proteins.* See *photosynthesis.* See also page 516.

chromosomes   Threadlike structures contained in the *nucleus* of a *cell,* which duplicate themselves when the cell reproduces and which govern the characteristics of the cell. See page 377.

cloud chamber, or **Wilson cloud chamber** after its inventor   It is represented schematically in the figure below. Its operation is based on the fact that fast-moving charged particles, such as *alpha particles,* produce on their way through the air, or through any other gas, a certain distortion in the atoms situated along their route. With their strong electric fields, these projectiles tear off one *electron* or more from the atoms of gas that happen to be in their way, leaving behind a large number of ionized atoms. This state of affairs does not last very long, for very soon after the passage of the projectile the ionized atoms will catch back their electrons, returning to the normal state. But if the gas in which such ionization takes place is saturated with water vapor, tiny droplets will be formed on each of the *ions*—it is a property of water vapor that it tends to accumulate on ions, dust particles, and so on—producing a thin band of fog along the track of the projectile. In other words, the track of any charged particle moving through a gas thus becomes visible in the same way as does the track of a sky-writing airplane. From the technical point of view, the cloud chamber is a very simple apparatus, consisting essentially of a metallic cylinder (A) with a glass cover (B) containing a piston (C), which can be moved up and down by an arrangement not shown in the picture. The space between the glass cover and the surface of the piston is filled with ordinary atmospheric air (or any other gas, if so desired) containing a considerable amount of water vapor. If the piston is abruptly pulled down immediately after some atomic projectiles have entered the chamber through the window (*E*), the air above the piston will cool and the water vapor will begin to precipitate, in the form of thin bands of fog, along the track of the projectiles. These bands of fog, being illumined by a strong light through a side window (*D*), will stand out clearly against the blackened surface of the piston and can be observed visually or photographed by the camera (*F*), which is operated automatically by the action of the piston. This simple arrangement, one of the most valuable bits of equipment in modern physics, permits us to obtain beautiful photographs of the results of nuclear bombardment.

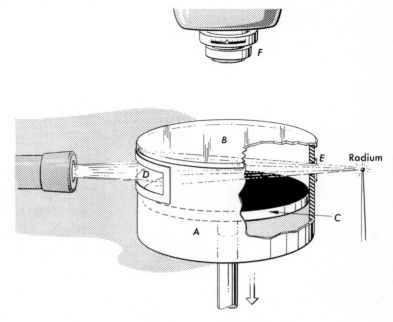

The scheme of Wilson's cloud chamber.

combining weights   The proportion by weight in which specific *elements* combine to make a *chemical compound*. See page 27.

conjugation   A process in which nuclear material is exchanged between two one-celled animals. See page 349.

conservation of matter   The law that matter cannot be created or destroyed in any chemical reaction: the weight of the reactants is equal to the weight of the products. See page 26.

control experiment   An exact duplication of the conditions of an actual experiment, excepting the one condition whose effects the experiment is trying to discover. See pages 286–7.

cosmozoa theory   The theory that germs of life arrived on earth from interstellar spaces. See page 303.

critical mass   The mass of a minimum assembly of fissionable material needed to maintain a *chain reaction*. See pages 171–2.

crossing over In *chromosomes* the reassortment of traits normally appearing together. The reassortment is due to a realignment of the *genes* within the chromosomes during reproduction. See page 384 and Figure 7-11, page 385.

crystal A solid substance whose *molecules* are arranged in a regular, geometric pattern. See pages 222–6.

Directions for growing an alum crystal:

Buy ½ pound of alum (available in most drugstores). Add 4 ounces of alum to 19 ounces of water. Warm the mixture in a porcelain or stainless steel pan and stir until the solution is clear. Set about one ounce aside in a small uncovered glass to evaporate and form a seed crystal. Pour the rest of the solution into a Mason jar and cover. Shake the Mason jar several times a day. After two days pour off the liquid, leaving any sediment or crystals in the bottom. Add one more ounce of alum, heat and stir as before. When solution is clear, pour into clean Mason jar. Suspend a seed crystal by a thread from a piece of cardboard cut to fit on top of the jar. Be sure your hands are clean and do not touch the seed crystal any more than necessary. The crystal should hang about one inch from the bottom of the jar. Screw the top back on and place the jar in a location where the temperature remains relatively constant (around 65°– 75°F.) and where the jar will not be disturbed.

crystallography The study of the geometric form of *crystals*. See page 240.

cytochromes *Enzymes* which *catalyze* the release of hydrogen atoms from certain organic molecules so that they may combine with oxygen to form water.

cytosine See *pyrimidines*. See page 485.

D

deoxyribose A *sugar* contained in the *nucleotides* of certain *nucleic acids*. It is similar to *ribose* but the two occur in different types of nucleic acid. See page 484.

deuterium An *isotope* of hydrogen, having a *neutron* and a *proton* in its nucleus, and therefore an atomic weight of 2 and a charge of 1. See page 147.

dextrorotatory Substances rotating the plane of vibration of *polarized light* to the right when the observer is looking against the oncoming light. See Figure 5-25, page 241, and page 244.

diffraction When a beam of light passes through an aperture or past the edge of an opaque obstacle and is allowed to fall upon a screen, patterns of light and dark bands (with monochromatic light) or colored bands (with white light) are observed near the edges of the beam, and extend into the geometrical shadow. This phenomenon, which is a particular case of interference, is due to the wave nature of light, and is known as diffraction. The phenomenon is common to all *wave* motions. See Figure 3-13, page 104, and Figure 3-15A, page 105.

diffusion The process whereby the *molecules* of one substance mix freely and randomly with those of another due to their random *thermal motions*. The process of diffusion moves more molecules from regions of higher concentration to those of lower concentration, until an even distribution is attained. See page 417. For diffusion technique for separation of *isotopes*, see page 144.

diploid A cell having two paired sets of *chromosomes*. See Figure 10-2, page 551.

divalent Having a *valence* of two. See *monovalent*.

DNA (**deoxyribosenucleic acid**) *Nucleic acids* whose *nucleotides* all contain deoxyribose. Present only in the nuclei of cells, the DNA *molecule* has recently been identified with the *gene*. See page 485.

dominant trait or **gene**   A trait which masks a related and opposite trait when the *genes* for both traits are present in the *chromosome* of the individual. See page 360.

E

electric current   A stream of moving *electrons*. See Figure 2-14, page 52. A moving electric charge produces a magnetic field around it. See *electromagnetic theory*.

electricity, static   A collection of *electrons* which are not moving produces electrostatic forces due to the accumulation of charge. There are not associated magnetic fields as in the case of current electricity. See page 51.

electrodes   The terminal, conducting plates of a "gap" in an electrical circuit. This "gap" may be an electrolyte in *electrolysis* or a vacuum in an electric arc or vacuum tube. The positive electrode is the *anode*. The negative one is the *cathode*. See Figure 3-1, page 72.

electrolysis   Chemical decomposition of certain substances by an *electric current* passed through the substance in a dissolved or molten state. Such substances are *ionized* into electrically charged atoms or groups of atoms, and when an electric current is passed through them by means of conducting *electrodes,* the "ions" move toward the oppositely charged electrodes. There they give up their electric charges, become uncharged atoms or groups, and are either liberated or deposited at the electrode, or react chemically with the solvent, or each other, according to their chemical nature. See page 31.

electromagnetic radiation   *Waves* consisting of electric and magnetic *fields* (*of force*) at right angles to each other traveling through a vacuum at the speed of light (approximately 186,000 miles per second). Electromagnetic waves are known as radio waves, infrared (heat) rays, light waves, *ultraviolet* rays, *X rays, gamma rays*—cited in order of increasing *frequency* of vibration.

electromagnetic theory   The discovery that a changing electric *field* (*of force*) produces a magnetic field and a changing magnetic field produces an electric field suggested the possibility that this process might be self-perpetuating. The process propagates in space—a varying electric field at one point produces a magnetic field which increases in the process of being created and which in turn produces an electric field a little farther off, and so on.

electrometer   A device which measures the amount of electric charge on a body.

Pierre Curie's electrometer   With this apparatus Marie Curie measured the intensity of rays given off by uranium ores and pitchblende. The device at the right, a form of ion-collector, consisted of two insulated plates, on the lower one of which was spread the ray-giving material. The meter proper, center and left, had eight quarter-circle metal plates arranged on insulating rods to form four quadrants. Between the upper and lower sets of quarter-circle plates swung a thin aluminum needle, suspended on a fine wire in a glass chimney and free to rotate. At the end of the wire below the needle was a small mirror, which rotated as the needle swung. Light reflected from the mirror showed the extent of the rotation. A high-voltage battery charged the lower insulated plate in the device at the right. Rays from the material on the lower insulated plate permitted flow of current to the upper plate, which was connected to one pair of quadrants in the meter. The aluminum needle was charged through the wire from another source, and as it was attracted or repelled by the charged quadrants, it swung sideways. The amount it swung was measured by movement of light reflected from the mirror.

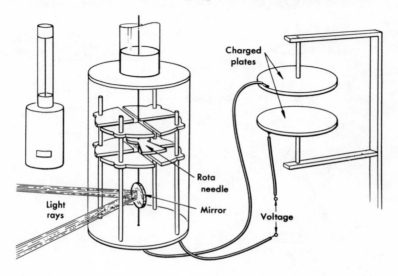

Charged
plates

Rota
needle

Light
rays

Mirror

Voltage

electron One of the fundamental particles of nature. It has a mass of 9.1×10^{-28} grams and a negative charge of 4.8×10^{-10} electrostatic units. See page 53.

electron miscroscope An instrument of greater resolving power and far greater magnification than an optical microscope. The magnifying power of a microscope is limited by the fact that objects cannot be distinguished unless they are somewhat larger than the waves of electromagnetic radiation reflected from them. Light waves are too long to distinguish very small objects. (ILL.,p.686)

electron volt The *energy* acquired by an *electron* when accelerated across a potential difference of one volt. See page 100.

electron waves *Electromagnetic waves* of very high *frequency* which are associated with *electrons*. See pages 105–6.

element A distinct, natural, elementary substance which is irreducible to any other elementary substance or substances by chemical means. See page 23. For information on individual elements, see Figure 2-13, page 48.

emission spectrum The characteristic pattern produced when light from a substance which has been heated to glowing is passed through a prism or grating. An emission spectrum contains sharp bright lines, characteristic of the substance. See page 79 and Figure 3-3, page 80.

energy The capacity for doing work. There are many different forms of energy: potential, kinetic, electrical, heat, chemical, atomic, and radiant. Energy is a conserved quantity: it cannot be created or destroyed, but it may be exchanged among various bodies or converted from one form to another. Kinetic energy (the energy of a body in motion) is equal to $\frac{1}{2}mv^2$ where m is the *mass* of the body and v is the velocity. See page 75.

energy levels *Electrons* in an atom can occupy only certain particular orbits, each orbit containing electrons of a particular energy. The energy associated with these orbits of the atom are termed energy levels. See pages 101, 109–11, 438.

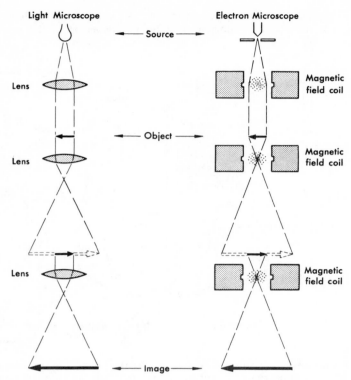

*Comparison of the principles of the conventional optical miscroscope
and the electron microscope.*

entropy A measure of the degree of disorder of a system. All physical
processes which depend on the irregular motion of *molecules* go in the direction
of increasing entropy, in which the random motion is more evenly distributed
among the greatest possible number of molecules. See page 425.

enzymes Organic *catalysts* produced by living organisms to speed *chemical
changes*. See page 479.

erg The work done by a force of one dyne acting through a distance of one
centimeter. See page 153.

evaporation The process of a liquid changing to a gas by the dissociation
of the *molecules* at the surface of the liquid from the main body of the liquid.
This takes place by virtue of their thermal *energy*. See page 220. For evaporation technique for separation of *isotopes*, see page 143.

evolution The process by which the hereditary characteristics of living things
are modified over a long period of time, resulting in new species which are
better adapted to their environment. See page 342.

extrapolation The method by which data of a restricted range may be
projected to establish inferences about data lying outside that range. See
page 456.

F

fatty acid The product of a reaction between a *lipid* and an *acid*. Fatty acids have the general form $R \cdot COOH$, where R is a radical of carbon and hydrogen. See page 313.

ferment A substance producing *fermentation* (formerly used to designate an *enzyme*). See page 479.

fermentation The process whereby certain minute organisms convert *sugar* to alcohol and carbon dioxide by *enzyme* action. See page 478.

fields of force A concept created to explain the action at a distance of electricity and magnetism. The field is assumed to be a property of space itself which is in a state of tension in the neighborhood of an electric charge or *magnetic pole*. This tension acts on certain objects within this region of space. The tension of a magnetic field "pushes" an iron filing toward the magnet. The tension of a field around a positive electric charge "pushes" a negative charge toward it. A changing electric field produces a magnetic field and vice versa. See *electromagnetic theory*.

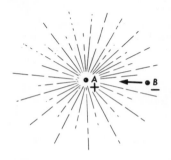

Electric field around a positive charge A. *A state of tension is created in the space around* A. *The negative charge* B *is forced toward* A.

fission bomb Bomb containing uranium or *plutonium,* whose nuclei can be split with *neutrons,* releasing enormous amounts of *energy*. Also called *A-bomb*. See pages 170–71, 185.

flagellated cell (Flagellates) A *cell* which has several long whiplike extensions (flagella) to propel it through the medium in which it occurs. See page 349.

fluorescent Having the property of absorbing light of one *wave length* and re-emitting it as another wave length. See page 72.

fractionation The process of separating a mixture of several similar substances into its component parts.

frame of reference A system of lines or planes used for defining position and direction.

frequency The number of *waves* passing a given point every second. See page 107.

fructose ($C_6H_{12}O_6$) fruit *sugar*. See pages 312, 316.

fusion, nuclear If the reader reflects on the "binding-energy" curve of the elements given on page 156, he will immediately see another possibility for obtaining nuclear energy on a large scale. The binding energy is greatest for the elements of intermediate atomic weight. Just as it is possible to obtain large amounts of energy by breaking down heavy nuclei into intermediate elements, it should be possible to obtain even greater amounts of energy by fusing very light nuclei into the heavier nuclei of the intermediate range.

The most obvious reaction is the fusion of four atoms of ordinary hydrogen to form a helium atom.

$$4H \rightarrow He + energy$$

or, what amounts to the same thing, the fusion of four protons and two electrons to form a helium nucleus. From the binding energy of the respective particles or from the difference in mass, the total energy produced is 25.7 Mev for every alpha particle produced. This corresponds to 660 billion calories for every 4 grams of hydrogen reacting. It may be of interest that as early as 1917 this reaction was suspected to be responsible for the prodigious sources of energy that the sun and the stars squander by radiating it into space.

For this reaction to take place, however, the protons must collide at very high speeds in order to overcome their mutual repulsions . . . to attain such speeds by thermal motion, temperatures of several hundred-million degrees are necessary. Even in the interior of the sun, the temperature is not that high. It is estimated to be only about 20 million degrees. Consequently other mechanisms had to be postulated to explain the source of energy of the sun and the stars. For this problem—the release of nuclear energy by fusion on the earth—other reactions must be investigated, that may proceed at much lower temperatures.

Of particular interests are the reactions of the nuclei of the two heavier isotopes of hydrogen, deuterium and tritium. The lighter of the two is the deuteron, $_1H^2$, containing a proton and a neutron. The heavier is the triton, $_1H^3$, containing one proton and two neutrons. Related to these two is another light particle, the nucleus of helium-3, $_2He^3$, containing two protons and one neutron.

Proton, P $\oplus$ $_1H^1$

Deuteron, D $\oplus\bigcirc$ $_1H^2$

Triton, T $\overset{\oplus}{\underset{\bigcirc\bigcirc}{}}$ $_1H^3$

Helium-3 $\oplus\oplus$ $_2He^3$
nucleus $\bigcirc$

Particles important in nuclear fusion.

When a deuteron at high speed collides with another deuteron, at first the two combine to form a nucleus of helium-4. Under these conditions this nucleus is unstable and immediately breaks up. It may break up in either of two ways:

$$\bigcirc\!\!\oplus \;+\; \bigcirc\!\!\oplus \;\longrightarrow\; \left[\,\right] \;\longrightarrow\; \;+\; \bigcirc \;+\; 3.25\ \text{Mev}$$

or it may break up into a tritium nucleus, and a proton, releasing 4 Mev of energy:

$$\bigcirc\!\!\oplus \;+\; \bigcirc\!\!\oplus \;\longrightarrow\; \left[\,\right] \;\longrightarrow\; \;+\; \oplus \;+\; 4.0\ \text{Mev}$$

The net result of this encounter is that one deuteron grabs either a proton or a neutron from the other. In either case the amount of energy is roughly the same, and it is very large.

One of the encouraging aspects of this reaction is that the deuterons react with one another at much lower speeds than do the protons. . . . at 100 million degrees enough deuterons move sufficiently fast to make the reaction quite appreciable. The temperatures necessary are still high, but not quite so high. Our search is proceeding in the right direction. Apparently the presence of the neutron makes the deuteron more reactive than the proton.

As might be suspected the reaction of a deuteron with a triton takes place at still lower temperatures. In this reaction, the two nuclei fuse to form the unstable, helium-5 nucleus, which immediately breaks up into a helium-4 (stable under these conditions) and a neutron releasing 17.6 Mev.

$$\bigcirc\!\!\oplus \;+\; \;\longrightarrow\; \left[\,\right] \;\longrightarrow\; \;+\; \bigcirc \;+\; 17.6\ \text{Mev}$$

This reaction not only takes place at much lower temperatures but releases about five times the amount of energy.

Equally promising is the reaction between a deuteron and a helium-3 nucleus. In this reaction an unstable lithium-5 nucleus is first formed, which then breaks up into a stable helium-4 nucleus and a proton releasing 18.3 Mev.

$$\bigcirc\!\!\oplus \;+\; \;\longrightarrow\; \left[\,\right] \;\longrightarrow\; \;+\; \oplus \;+\; 18.3\ \text{Mev}$$

This reaction releases an even greater amount of energy and, as expected, takes place at lower temperatures.

The reader no doubt suspects by this time that the reaction between two tritons should take place at still lower temperatures and, in fact, it does. The tritons, containing two neutrons each, fuse at relatively lower speeds, to form an unstable helium-6 nucleus, which then explodes to form a helium-4 nucleus and two neutrons. This reaction not only takes place at the lowest temperature of the previous reactions so far considered, but releases the greatest amount of energy per encounter. However, of the materials available, on the earth, only deuterium is relatively abundant. It exists in all the natural waters to the extent of about 1 part in 6000. Tritium is far too rare (1 part in a million) to be of practical consequence. Helium-3 is even less abundant on the earth. If these materials are to be used for fusion energy, they must be manufactured artificially as in the case of plutonium.

(From Theodore A. Ashford, *From Atoms to Stars,* © 1960 by Holt, Rinehart and Winston, Inc. Reprinted by permission.)

fusion bomb   Up to 1945 the fusion reactions were of theoretical interest only. The highest temperature attained by man for a sustained length of time was the temperature of the electric arc, about 5000° Centigrade.

The first successful detonation of the uranium atomic bomb near Los Alamos, however, changed this picture suddenly and dramatically. The temperature inside the exploding bomb was estimated at 70 to 100 million degrees in the initial stages. This temperature is four or five times higher than the temperature at the very center of the sun. Even though the temperature drops rapidly as the fireball expands, it remains at many million degrees for some time. Moreover, before the fireball begins to cool, it has attained a volume of several cubic feet. Here we have a good-sized furnace of unbelievable hotness in which fusion reactions may take place.

It occurred to Enrico Fermi, J. R. Oppenheimer, Edward Teller, and others that fusion reactions may be initiated and sustained in the interior of the fireball. If any of the heavy isotopes of hydrogen are present in the fireball, they would fuse, giving off their own energy. The energy given off would, in turn, tend to raise the temperature of the fireball or at least delay its cooling until more hydrogen materials are ignited. Ultimately, of course, the cooling by expansion will take the upper hand, but by that time the energy released would be many times that of the atomic bomb alone. The reader no doubt recognizes in this description the essential idea of the hydrogen bomb.

The exact design of the hydrogen bomb is a military secret, but its essential features are not hard to figure out. To begin with, an ordinary atomic bomb is assembled, consisting of, say, two subcritical pieces of U-235 or Pu-239. Surrounding the two subcritical pieces and filling all free space around, there are packed the light isotopes which can fuse at the temperatures about to develop. In all probability, the fusible material is deuterium, which is readily available in quantity. Most probably, too, the deuterium is in liquid or solid form, for it is desirable to have it as compact as possible. It may very well be in the form of heavy water but it is more likely to be lithium deuteride, LiD_2, which is a solid. There is an additional reason for this. The lithium itself can react with neutrons to form the easily fusible tritium and thus generate additional reagent.

From the description of the bomb and its operation it is obvious that it is not possible to have a "baby" hydrogen bomb. The thermonuclear bomb cannot

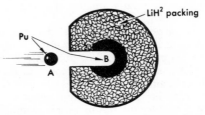

The hydrogen bomb (diagrammatic). A subcritical mass of plutonium (B) is surrounded by a packing of lithium deuteride. For detonation, an additional mass of plutonium (A) is shot into (B).

be smaller than one atomic bomb. In a real sense the atomic bomb is the *fuse* that sets off the fusion reaction. On the other hand, there seems to be no upper limit to the size of the hydrogen bomb. With very compact fusible materials, and of the right type, hydrogen bombs of almost any size may be made.

G

galactose A *sugar* ($C_6H_{12}O_6$). See pages 313, 316.

gametes Reproductive *cells* or germ cells which unite with another to produce a new individual. The cell which is formed by the union of two gametes (usually male and female) is called the *zygote*. See page 350.

gamma ray A high-*energy electromagnetic wave* of very short *wave length*. See page 85.

Geissler tube A partially evacuated tube through which a stream of *electrons* passes, causing the gas in the tube to glow. See Figure 2-14, page 52.

gene A particular part of a *chromosome* which governs the development of a specific trait in an individual. The gene is regarded as the unit of heredity. See page 373.

genotype The hereditary structure of the organism. See also *phenotype*.

germ plasm Reproductive *cells*. See page 352.

glucose ($C_6H_{12}O_6$) grape *sugar*. Occurs in most fruits. See pages 312, 316.

glycine White, sweet-tasting, crystalline substance contained in *proteins*. An *amino acid*. See page 314.

glycogen A starch found in animal liver. See page 313.

gravitational mass See *mass*.

gravity The mutual force of attraction between any two pieces of matter in the universe. The magnitude of the force is given by Newton's Law: $F = \dfrac{GMm}{r^2}$, where M and m are the two *masses*, r the distance between them, and G the gravitational constant.

guanine See *purines*. See also page 485.

H

H-bomb See *fusion bomb*.

haploid A *cell* having only one complete set of *chromosomes* (half the usual number). See Figure 10-2, page 551.

heat motion (thermal motion) The irregular, random motions of *molecules* in a substance. See page 409.

heavy water Water *molecules* containing *deuterium* instead of hydrogen. See page 147.

Heitler-London theory A theory explaining the nature of chemical *bonds* in terms of the *quantum theory*. See page 437.

hemoglobin A *protein* contained in the red blood *cells* of animals. It combines with oxygen in the lungs and gives it up to body cells. See page 517.

heterogenesis The spontaneous formation of life from non-living matter. See page 290.

heterozygous An individual is said to be heterozygous with respect to a particular trait when he has inherited dissimilar *genes* from his two parents with respect to that trait. See page 553.

homozygous An individual is said to be homozygous with respect to a particular trait if he has inherited similar *genes* for this trait from both parents. See page 553.

hydrogen bomb   See *fusion bomb.*
hydrogen bond   A very weak *bond* in which two groups of atoms are linked by a hydrogen atom belonging to one of the groups. See page 498.

I

inert gases   See *noble gases.*
inertia   The resistance of matter to a change of motion either in amount or in direction.
inertial mass   See *mass.* See also page 154.
inorganic chemistry   The chemistry of compounds (see *chemical compounds*) which do not contain carbon atoms in their *molecules.* See page 288.
interpolation   The method of inferring previously unknown facts from known facts when the former lie within the range over which the known data are valid.
invariant   An expression involving the coefficients of an algebraic function that remain constant when a transformation, such as translation or rotation of coordinate axes, is made. See page 261.
ion   An atom or group of atoms which has temporarily lost or gained *electrons* and thus acquired a charge (either positive or negative).
ionization   The formation of *ions.* See also *thermal ionization.*
isomeric molecule   A *molecule* with several *isomers.* See page 439.
isomers   *Molecules* having the same combination of atoms but differing in structural arrangement, and hence in certain properties. See page 315. For *optically active* isomers, see page 242.
isotopes   *Elements* that have the same *atomic number* and chemical properties, but differ in *atomic weight.* See page 139.

K

K-meson   Subatomic particle. See page 258.
kilowatt-hour   The work done or *energy* delivered when a power source of 1000 watts operates for one hour.
kinetic theory of gases   Explanation of the behavior of gases on the assumption that gases consist of widely dispersed *molecules* in rapid, random motion. According to the theory, the pressure a gas exerts on the walls of its container is due to the average number of collisions which the molecules make with the walls. The diffusion of gases is also due to their random motion (see *diffusion*) and the temperature of a gas is simply a measure of the average speed of the molecules. See page 33.

L

lactose   ($C_{12}H_{22}O_6$) milk *sugar.* A gritty sugar, less sweet than cane sugar. See page 313.
Lamarckism   The belief that *acquired characteristics* are inherited. See page 344.
lattice pile   A structure of interspaced graphite and uranium blocks, used in nuclear reactors. See page 176.
leucine   A white, tasteless, crystalline substance contained in *proteins.* An *amino acid.* See page 314.
levorotatory   Substances rotating the plane of vibration of *polarized light* to the left when the observer is looking against the oncoming light. See Figure 5-25, page 241, and page 244.

lipids Fats and oils, a group of *organic* compounds composed of carbon, hydrogen, and oxygen but distinguished from *carbohydrates* by having a higher percentage of carbon and a lower percentage of oxygen. See page 311.

M

magnetic pole Any free magnet tends to align itself in a north-south direction in the earth's magnetic *field* (*of force*). The end pointing north is the north pole and the end pointing south is the south pole. Unlike poles attract and like poles repel each other. The force of attraction or repulsion varies inversely as the square of the distance between them. See page 52.

mass There are two principal ways of describing and measuring mass. We will discuss each separately and then the relationship between them. Inertial mass is the constant m in the equation $F = ma$. It is the physical measure of the resistance of any body to a change of motion and can be measured by finding the acceleration produced by a known force acting on the body in question (if the speeds are small compared to the speed of light). Except at very high speeds, inertial mass is believed to be an unchangeable property of matter, having the same value anywhere in the universe. Gravitational mass is a measure of the amount of matter acted upon by a gravitational field and is proportional to the weight of the object in question. It should be borne in mind, however, that the weight (which is the force of attraction of the earth on a given mass) varies with location, depending on the position from the center of the earth, just as the acceleration of gravity, g, also varies in the same proportion. The relationship becomes clear if we substitute weight W for Force and g for acceleration in the equation $F = ma$, which then becomes $W = mg$. W and g both vary, depending on the position, but m remains constant. If the proper units are chosen, gravitational mass equals inertial mass and is assumed to remain constant everywhere in the universe except at speeds approaching the speed of light. See page 6.

meiosis The process whereby *chromosome* pairs undergo nuclear division as the germ *cell* matures.

meson A subatomic particle of intermediate *mass*. A mu-meson (muon) is about 200 times the mass of an *electron;* the pi-meson (pion) is about 270 times the mass of an electron. Mesons can be either positively or negatively charged. See page 256.

metabolism The interchange of matter between a living thing and its environment, including the chemical processes by which the living thing uses and assimilates the matter. See pages 448, 473.

meteorite A solid body from outer space. A meteorite is termed a "shooting star" when it burns up on entering the earth's atmosphere. Consists of various materials, often metallic iron. See pages 321 ff.

microscope A device for magnifying very small objects. The compound microscope consists of an objective lens LM and an eyepiece L'M'. The objective lens forms a magnified, but inverted image A'B' of an object placed just outside its focus and the eyepiece lens further magnifies this image (see A"B"). See page 354. (ILLUS., p. 694)

microsomes Small particulates in the cytoplasm, containing *ribosomes* where *protein* is synthesized. See page 504 and Figure 9-13, pages 508–9.

microtome An instrument used for cutting thin sections of material for viewing under the *microscope*.

mitochondria Small, specialized bodies in a *cell* which contain certain *enzymes* necessary for the cell's *metabolism*. See page 480.

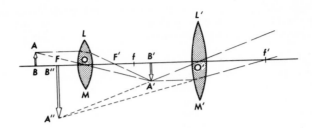

mitosis   Nuclear *cell* division in which resulting *nuclei* have the same numbers and kinds of *chromosomes* as the original cell. See Figure 7-7, page 379.

moderator   A material used in a nuclear reactor to slow down fast-moving *neutrons*. See page 171.

molecule   The smallest individual unit of a *chemical compound* having the properties of the compound. See page 24.

monovalent   The capacity of an atom to share one *electron* when chemically *bonded* with another atom. *Divalent* and trivalent refer to the capacity for sharing two and three electrons, respectively. See page 50.

MPC (maximum permissible concentration of radiation)   Standard set by National Committee on Radiation Protection and Measurement. See page 600.

MPD (maximum permissible dose of radiation)   Standard set by National Committee on Radiation Protection and Measurement. See page 600.

multiple fission   The process in which a single individual reproduces by splitting into many smaller, identical individuals.

mu-meson   See *meson.*

mutation   A distinct trait which appears in an individual without having been inherited, but which is passed on to that individual's offspring. Change in molecular structure of a *gene.* See page 373.

N

natural selection   The process whereby living things that are best adapted to survival gradually supplant those that are not as well adapted. See page 392.

Neo-Lamarckism   The theory that *acquired characteristics* and certain involuntary responses to environment are inherited. See page 344.

neptunium (symbol **Np**)   The artificially produced *element* following uranium in the *periodic table,* having an *atomic number* of 93. See page 168.

neutrino   A *mass*less, neutral particle postulated theoretically to explain *energy* deficits in atomic reactions. Later its existence was verified. See page 255.

neutron   An uncharged particle having a slightly greater *mass* than the *proton.* A constituent of all *atomic nuclei* except the hydrogen nucleus (which contains one proton). Since a neutron is uncharged it can pass readily through matter. See page 149.

Newton's Laws of Motion   Three laws which form the basis of classical mechanics: 1. Every body continues in its state of rest or uniform motion in a straight line except insofar as it is compelled by external forces to change that state. 2. Rate of change of momentum is proportional to the applied force and takes place in the direction in which the force acts. 3. To every action there is always an equal and opposite reaction.

noble gases The inert gases, so-called because their outer *electron* shells are naturally complete, and hence they are chemically inactive. See page 41.

nuclear fusion See *fusion, nuclear*.

nucleic acid A substance fundamental to living *cells*. It contains carbon, hydrogen, oxygen, nitrogen, and phosphorus. There are two types of nucleic acid differentiated by the *carbohydrate* present—*DNA* (deoxyribose) and *RNA* (ribose). The former is found only in the *nucleus* of normal cells. See page 484.

nucleon A particle occurring in the *nucleus* (i.e., a *proton* or a *neutron*).

nucleoprotein A *nucleic acid* combined with a *protein*. See page 484.

nucleotides The building blocks of *nucleic acids*. See page 484.

nucleus See *atomic nucleus* or *cell nucleus*.

O

optical activity The property possessed by certain substances of rotating the plane of vibration of *polarized light* when the light is passed through the substance. See page 240 and Figure 5-25, page 241.

organic chemistry Originally, the study of substances produced only by living things. Now defined as the chemistry of those *compounds* containing carbon atoms in their *molecules*. See page 288.

organized ferment Old-fashioned term denoting a *ferment* which cannot act in the absence of living *cells*, a distinction subsequently disproved. See page 479.

orthogenesis A theory of *evolution* which postulates that the evolution of living things is directed by certain unknown forces.

ozone A form of oxygen containing three atoms to the *molecule*. It is formed in ordinary air by an electric discharge, such as lightning or cosmic rays. See page 319.

P

packing factor The *packing loss* of an atom divided by the number of *nucleons* in its *nucleus*. See page 155.

packing loss The difference between the *mass* of a *nucleus* and the mass of its components taken separately. See page 155.

paleontology A science that deals with the life of past geological periods. It is based on the study of fossil remains of plants and animals.

panspermia theory The theory that living spores are transferred from one celestial body to another by the action of light rays. See page 305.

paper chromatography A process which separates a mixture of similar *compounds* by the difference in the rates at which they are adsorbed by a piece of filter paper. See paper 496.

parity A symmetry property of the *wave* function by which *quantum mechanics* describes the wave characteristics of a particle and represents its position in space. The parity is even if the wave function is unchanged by reflection, and odd if the wave function is changed only in sign. The principle of the conservation of parity says that in an isolated system parity never changes its value. For overthrow of this principle, see pages 264–5.

parthenogenesis Reproduction by the development of unfertilized eggs. See page 351.

peptide chain A string of *amino acids* as in a *protein molecule*. See page 475.

periodic crystal A solid whose *molecules* are arranged in a regular, repetitive, geometric pattern. See page 434.

periodic table   An arrangement of the elements in order of their atomic number. See pages 39–44.

phenotype   The appearance, structure, and functional state of an organism at any given moment constitutes its phenotype. The phenotype results from the interaction of the environment on the *genotype* (the hereditary structure of the organism).

photoelectric effect   The emission of *electrons* by a substance being irradiated with light. See Figure 3-20, page 115.

photon   A packet or *quantum* of *electromagnetic energy*. The energy of a photon is $h\nu$, where h is *Planck's constant* and ν is the *frequency* associated with the photon. See page 114.

photosynthesis   The process by which green plants (containing *chlorophyll*) convert carbon dioxide and water to *carbohydrates* and oxygen in the presence of sunlight. $6\ CO_2 + 6\ H_2O \rightarrow C_6H_{12}O_6 + 6\ O_2$. See page 517.

physical change   Any change in a substance which does not involve a change in its chemical composition. See pages 218–19.

pi-meson   See meson.

pitchblende   Ore containing uranium oxide and small amounts of another radioactive element, radium. See pages 76–7.

Planck's constant.   A very small constant that is denoted by the letter h and expressed in units of action ($h = 6.624 \times 10^{-27}$ erg sec.). When multiplied by the *frequency* of radiation ν, it gives the quantity of *energy* ($= h\nu$) contained in one *quantum*. See page 109.

plasma   A condition of matter in which a large proportion of the atoms are split into free *electrons* and positive *ions*. See pages 102–3.

plutonium (symbol **Pu**)   The element following *neptunium* in the *periodic table*, having an *atomic number* of 94. See page 169.

polarimeter   Instrument for measuring the rotation of the plane of vibration of *polarized light* by substances which are *optically active*. See page 244.

polarized light   Light which has had certain components of its *wave* vibrations filtered out by being passed through or reflected from appropriate materials. See Figure 5-25, page 241.

pollen   The "male" reproductive cells of flowers. The *ovule* is the female reproductive cell. Pollen is transferred from one plant to another by wind or insects.

positron   An elementary particle having the same *mass* as an *electron* and a positive charge. See page 151.

precipitation   The process by which a substance in solution separates out in the form of small particles. See page 78.

probability   The likelihood that some particular form of event might occur. This likelihood is expressed in numerical form by the numbers between 0 and 1, a probability of 1 being certain that some event would occur and the probability 0 being certain that the event would not occur. The probability 0.5 means an equal likelihood that the event would or would not occur. This number is obtained by evaluating the ratio R/N, R being the number of elements in the set of events to take place and N being the total possibilities. For example, what is the probability of picking a spade from a deck of cards? The total possibilities are 52 of which 13 are spades, therefore the probability is 13/52 or 0.25. See pages 418–23.

protein   A class of *organic* compounds with very large *molecules*, containing carbon, hydrogen, oxygen, and nitrogen invariably, sometimes also sulphur and phosphorus. Proteins are used to build body tissue. See page 311.

proton Positively charged particle, having a *mass* approximately 1840 times greater than that of the *electron* (i.e., 1.00757 atomic mass units) and charge numerically equal but opposite in sign to that of the electron. Constituent of all *atomic nuclei.*

protoplasm A name given to the material of which all living things are made. Consists of several different types of organic compounds: *carbohydrates, lipids, proteins.* See page 312.

protozoa A one-celled animal, having the power to ingest food, excrete waste, move, and reproduce.

purines A type of *organic* compound found in certain *nucleotides.* They contain nitrogen and have a double ring of atoms in their molecular structure. The two purines found in *nucleic acid* are adenine and guanine. See page 485.

pyrimidines A type of *organic* compound found in certain *nucleotides.* They contain nitrogen and have a single ring of atoms in their molecular structure. The types of pyrimidines found in *nucleic acid* are cytosine, thymine, and uracil. See page 485.

Q

quantum A discrete quantity of radiation (also called a *photon*). A quantum has a particle-like behavior, and an *energy* equal to hv, where h is *Planck's constant* and v is the *frequency* of the radiation. See page 109.

quantum theory A general physical theory which followed Planck's introduction of discontinuity into atomic physics. Quantum mechanics (also called wave mechanics) is a later more mathematical expression of this theory. See pages 108–12, 437.

R

radioactive isotopes *Isotopes* of an *element* which are unstable and decay by emitting a particle or *gamma ray* from the *nucleus.* Radioactive isotopes of the heavier elements occur naturally; radioactive isotopes of almost every element can be made artificially. See pages 160–62.

radioactivity The spontaneous disintegration of unstable *atomic nuclei* to give more stable product nuclei, accompanied by the emission of charged particles and *electromagnetic energy,* e.g., *alpha* or *beta particles* and *gamma rays.*

radon One of the inert (*noble*) *gases.* It is produced when radium disintegrates. See page 138.

recessive trait A trait which is "masked" in an individual if the *gene* for the corresponding *dominant trait* is also present. See page 360.

refraction When a ray of light travels obliquely from one medium to another, it is bent or "refracted" at the surface separating the two media. This bending is due to the difference in *wave* velocity in the two media.

ribose A *sugar* contained in the *nucleotides* of certain *nucleic acids.* See page 484.

ribosomes Very small particles found in the cytoplasm of all *cells* and in the *nuclei* of some cells. They are about the size of the smallest *viruses* and are made up of roughly equal portions of *RNA* and *protein.* The RNA is believed to act as a template for the formation of the *proteins* peculiar to that particular cell.

RNA (ribosenucleic acid)   *Nucleic acids* whose *nucleotides* all contain *ribose*. Present in both the *nuclei* and the cytoplasm of *cells*. See page 485.

Roentgen unit   A measure of the quantity of absorbed radiation as defined by the amount of *ionization* produced. One roentgen will produce *ions* carrying one electrostatic unit of electricity in one cubic centimeter of dry air.

S

side-chain   A group of atoms in a large *molecule* which can be replaced by another similar group without altering the rest of the molecule. Side-chains are very important in determining the nature of an *organic* compound. See page 317.

solid   See *states of matter*.

soma   All of an organism except the *germ-plasm*. See page 352.

specific gravity   The ratio of the density of a substance to the density of water at 4°C. (Density is the *mass* of a sample divided by its volume.)

spectrum   The characteristic pattern produced when light is passed through a prism or grating, separating the different *wave lengths*. See *emission* and *absorption spectra*. See also pages 79–80.

spin   Subatomic particles spin on their own axes like tops, and hence produce a magnetic *field* (*of force*). See page 252.

stability   Resistance to a change of state or position. See pages 154–5.

stamen   The male organ of the flower. It consists of a tiny filament with a sac on the end of it containing the *pollen*.

states of matter   Solid, liquid, and gas. The difference between these three states is due to the amount of *heat motion* possessed by the *molecules*. When the heat motion is high as in a gas it overcomes the attractive forces between the molecules. When it is low as in a solid the molecules are bound together, vibrating about fixed positions. See page 217.

statistical behavior   Mathematical laws predicting the outcome of a large number of completely random events. The example of the drunkard's walk given on pages 414–15 can be used to illustrate the principles underlying these calculations.

stereoisomerism   Refers to *isomers* whose *molecules* are mirror images of each other. See pages 249–50.

stigma   A sticky or hairy protrusion from the center of the flower, which collects *pollen* on its surface from the air or from insects.

strange particle   A particle which breaks down as a result of a *weak interaction*. See pages 256–60.

strong interaction   A nuclear interaction which takes place in a very short time, showing that a very strong force must be acting. See page 258.

structural formula   A chemical formula for a *molecule* showing the spatial arrangement of the atoms within the molecule. See page 315.

sucrose (cane sugar)   Has molecules that are made of one *glucose* unit and one *fructose*. See page 312.

sugar   Any sweet, soluble *carbohydrate*. See page 310.

symmetry class   A property of a *crystal* defined by the total series of symmetry operations which may be performed on it without changing its form. See page 233.

T

thermal ionization   The process whereby high speed *molecules* in a very hot substance collide and knock *electrons* off each other, causing free electrons and positively charged *ions*. See page 413.

thermal motion   See *heat motion*.

thermal neutrons   *Neutrons* moving at approximately the speed of the ordinary thermal motions of gas *molecules* at room temperatures. See page 163.

thermonuclear reaction   A nuclear reaction which takes place only at extremely high temperatures. See page 202.

threshold energy   The amount of *energy* which must be supplied to a *molecule* or atom to produce a transition between two different energy states. See page 102.

thymine   See *pyrimidines*. See also page 485.

transuranic elements   *Elements* of *atomic number* greater than 92 (uranium). See pages 163, 168–9.

tritium   An *isotope* of hydrogen, of *atomic weight* 3, having a *nucleus* of 1 *proton* and 2 *neutrons*.

trivalent   See *monovalent*.

tyrosine   White crystalline substance contained in *proteins*. An *amino acid*. See page 314.

U

ultraviolet light   Invisible *electromagnetic radiation* of very short *wave length* ($10^{-5} - 10^{-7}$ cm.).

unorganized ferment   Old-fashioned term designating a *ferment* which will act independently of living *cells*. Known as *enzyme* today. See page 479.

uracil   See *pyrimidines*. See also page 486.

V

valence   The combining power of an atom (the number of *bonds* it can provide). See page 50.

vapor pressure   If a liquid or solid substance is confined in an enclosed space the pressure created by the *molecules* which *evaporate* from the surface will reach a maximum. The vapor is then saturated and its pressure is the saturated vapor pressure of the substance at that temperature.

velocity of light 3×10^{10} cm./sec., usually designated by the letter *c*. See page 153.

viability   The ability to live.

virus   An ultramicroscopic agent of disease. Viruses are thought to be *molecules* of *nucleic acid* with a *protein* shell. See page 488.

vitalism   The theory that living things and *organic* substances were created on principles which were different from the principles which regulate *inorganic* matter. It postulated the presence of a "vital force." See page 289.

W

wave   The propagation of a periodic disturbance carrying *energy*. At any point along the path of a wave motion, a periodic displacement or vibration about a mean position takes place. This may take the form of a displacement of air *molecules* (e.g., sound waves in air), of water molecules (waves on water), a displacement of elements of a string or wire, displacement of electric and magnetic vectors, etc. The locus of these displacements at any instant is called the wave. *Wave length* is the distance in convenient units from crest to crest or from any one place on a wave to the same place on the next wave. The amplitude is the maximum departure from the equilibrium value. Waves in which the vibration or displacement takes place in the direction of propagation of the waves are called longitudinal waves. Sound is an example of longitudinal wave motion. Waves in which the vibration or displacement takes place in a plane at right angles to the direction of propagation are called transverse waves, e.g., *electromagnetic* waves. See pages 106–8.

wave length   See *wave.*

weak interaction   A class of nuclear interactions which take a longer time to occur than *strong interactions.* See page 258.

Wilson cloud chamber   See *cloud chamber.*

X Y Z

X rays   *Electromagnetic waves* of very short *wave length* ($10^{-7} - 10^{-10}$ cm.). Produced when a beam of *electrons* strike a material object. See pages 71–3.

yeast   A type of one-celled plant, capable of causing *fermentation* in *carbohydrates.* See page 294.

zygote   A *cell* formed by the union of two sex cells or *gametes.* See page 553.

INDEX

NOTE: A page number followed by *n* indicates that reference is to a footnote on indicated page.